D1480679

A partial list of other volumes in the
Viking Portable Library
appears at the end of the book.

THE PORTABLE RING LARDNER

THE PORTABLE
RING LARDNER

EDITED AND
WITH AN INTRODUCTION
BY GILBERT SELDES

NEW YORK 1946
THE VIKING PRESS

CONTENTS

MISCELLANEOUS

PARODIES AND "PLAYS"

EDITOR'S INTRODUCTION

RING LARDNER is generally known as an American humorist who wrote in slang about baseball. It would be hard to pack any more misleading ideas into a single statement, especially since every word of it is true. Ring Lardner did write about baseball, among other things; he used slang, although his major contribution to the American language lies elsewhere; and he was a humorist, in the sense that Dean Swift and Mark Twain were humorists: people are amused when they read *A Connecticut Yankee* and *Gulliver's Travels*, as they are when they read Lardner. But it is not true that these writers were clowns and the word "humorist" in our time takes in the clowns as well. Lardner's best work is in the field of satiric comedy and sometimes the satire, sometimes the comedy, is uppermost. I think you are not likely to read more than a page or two of the selections in this book without a smile or a laugh; I also think it unlikely that the smile or the laugh will not be followed by a peculiar, and highly rewarding, human activity: a thought. And that accompaniment of thought is what makes the difference between, let us say, a gag writer and a comic spirit.

I have mentioned Swift and Mark Twain, but I do not mean to force a comparison. There are times in reading Lardner when you feel his total sympathy with Swift's terrible verdict on humanity—that we are the most odious little race of vermin that ever inhabited the planet; you feel his sympathy with the half-hidden sardonic side of Mark Twain's temperament. He takes less pleasure in the accidents of human behavior than Twain did and is not so thoughtful as Swift; but like both of these, Lardner has the habit of catching human beings when they think no one is looking at them; and he touches them with tiny drops of acid to see what they do and how they react. Unlike Swift, but like Mark Twain, Lardner made his living by the exercise of his talent and was caught in a run of quantity production such as a man of the eighteenth century would not have understood or undertaken.

The proprietary worship of Mark Twain has preserved for us hundreds of occasionally funny pieces; and when Lardner was at the peak of his reputation (or saleability) he too was over-collected in book form. The long run is usually hardest on writers who work for the next issue; and both Twain and Lardner are improved by severe culling. This book does not contain all of Lardner worth reading; it omits a great deal. It omits much that Lardner wrote as a syndicated writer with a quota of words to deliver every week. I think no one will regret the omission; but I should add that I found among these occasional pieces many more to reprint here than I thought I would. It was only when he had nothing to say that Lardner became negligible; and that didn't happen often.

As to baseball: Ring Lardner made his first bid for great popularity with those letters of a busher which are now famous as *You Know Me Al.* Newspapermen in Chicago will tell you how Lardner was urged and egged and finally challenged into writing his first story; they tell you—and it may be only part of the myth—that he wrote the first letter over night and was astounded at the vast check he got for it from the *Saturday Evening Post.* He knew baseball as a reporter; and here, too, the story is that he got into reporting by accident, having been hired instead of his brother. But Ring's stuff was good and presently he reached all the high points for a Midwestern sports writer; he was running a column, "In the Wake of the News" on the *Chicago Tribune* when his first story appeared. (Incidentally, I went through many issues of the column and found a few things of interest, but nothing essential. It is not represented in this collection.)

To understand what Lardner accomplished by his baseball stories, you have to recall what "the national game" was when he began to write. Today the business is highly organized; an ex-Senator has succeeded a judge as its czar; and the skeptical observer may feel that the sentimentality about the Brooklyn Dodgers is as carefully synthesized as any other form of jingoism. But the game is popular. Children in Wisconsin villages or in the remote fastness of Vermont will quarrel about the merits of big league teams they have never seen; and men from Arkansas and Idaho, as well as men from the great baseball cities, rose from their foxholes in Sicily or Bataan to ask for the box scores when, according to good moralists, they should have demanded the Four Freedoms.

In 1910, when Lardner began to write about baseball, it was popular, with a less synthetic appeal. It was still in its romantic era, on the threshold of glorification. In the East we still heard of Rube Waddell waving the entire outfield to the bench as he prepared to strike out the last three men; heroic figures like Christy Mathewson had their pictures on cards in boxes of cigarettes; for the Midwest in time there were Tinker and Evers and Chance; the South weighed in with the graceful stylist Cobb and we Pittsburghers swore by Honus Wagner; and all of these were more than great players, they were

MEN, almost legendary in their qualities. There were debates on the possibility of pitching a curve and on the ethics of the spitball; and presently the baseball writers invaded the magazines with the story of the game as strategy, intricate, requiring not only a master plan, but a directing genius prompt to alter the plan at a moment's hazard. It was the time of big things generally and baseball was only following the procession, puffing itself up as everything else was being puffed.

Into this parade stepped Ring Lardner with the pin-prick report that baseball players were ignorant and childish and stupid and not a little mean-spirited. (He was doing a bit of debunking ten years before anyone had heard the word; and he was doing it intelligently, without rancor.)

It was a notable thing that in all Lardner's baseball stories the only decent human beings are the actual managers and owners and players called by their real names and protected by the laws of libel; the created characters are, with almost no exceptions, knaves and fools. Between the time of *You Know Me Al* and Lardner's second baseball series, *Lose with a Smile*, the great baseball scandal broke out. Enough members of the White Sox accepted bribes to throw the 1919 World Series to the Cincinnati Reds. People who had read Lardner's stories intelligently were not so shocked as those who considered them merely as humorous stories in slang; but everybody recognized as pure Lardner the sentimental phrase that came out of the muck: "I did it for the wife and kiddies." To protect the business, a baseball czar was appointed on the assumption that one could cure the ills of democracy by an appeal to Caesar. But for a long time baseball, as a gambler's paradise, took the sweetness from the sandlots. Heroic publicity and maybe a faster ball were used to bring the game back. In 1932, when Lardner reverted to his first theme, his heart was not engaged. He was no longer amused, and the book may be funny, but it is not amusing. It is melancholy.

In the meantime Lardner had begun to write about theatrical managers, salesmen, policemen, bridge-players, nurses, prize fighters, suburbanites, tin-can tourists, flappers, and practical jokers. His report on these is no more flattering than his verdict on ball-players. And that points to a significant thing—that Lardner was always writing about human beings; they happened at first to be ball-players because he knew the diamond and the bull-pen and the bench; but his stories are always about human beings who suffer pride and avarice and love and folly and ambition—as you find them wherever simple people are gathered together, not necessarily in the sight of God.

It was probably inevitable, though not particularly fortunate that Lardner should take Jack Keefe, the busher, into the army and overseas. With secondhand experience of training camps and only a civilian visit to the front, Lardner let his stories degenerate into a series of far-fetched practical jokes. In *Treat 'Em Rough*, the ex-busher is made to believe that his bunkmates are criminals; in *The Real Dope*, he accepts as genuine a letter signed "Black Jack Pershing, Folies Bergère, Paris, France." Perhaps one cannot be enthusiastic nowadays over humorous anecdotes about the First World War; I have not taken the trouble to reread other, and more famous, books of the same kind; but my memory tells me that few of them had the prime merit of creating character through the written word, at which Lardner never fails; his war stories are negligible chiefly because he had no personal report to make, so he used the character he had created as if he were a lay figure, and surrounded him with others out of the common stockpile; and, to keep his stories going, he inflated his small bubbles of fancy until they exploded damply in your face.

As this touches on Lardner's one major fault, we might as well look at it for a moment and be done with it. The habit of carrying a theme farther than it's worth is a mark of nearly all early humorous writing in America, especially that part of it influenced by the westward movement; it is a form of exaggeration (in Bill Nye, Artemus Ward, and Mark Twain); and it runs side by side with a laconic understatement which has become standard in our day. Lardner can be devastatingly brief, exposing a folly in a line and a whole society in a paragraph; and he can also bound all over the field in high spirits; both are good. But when you feel that he is filling space, you are so aware of the effort he is making, that the total effect is tiresome. In the thirty-five stories which were collected under the title of *Round Up* there are at least a dozen anecdotes spread thin. One of them, included in this book, is "Alibi Ike," a highly entertaining series of variations on a small theme which gave, I think, a name to a character as real, and nearly as round, as Babbitt. The story of the man who alibi'd himself even when he was good, is amusing and corresponds to something in our normal experience; I know a dozen Alibi Ikes. But all the story has to say is said before you have read a thousand words; the other three thousand are superfluous. Another story, "Liberty Hall," is about the over-solicitous hostess; "Zone of Quiet" is about the nurse who talks too much; "Mr. and Mrs. Fix-It" is all that the name implies. Not one of these fails to bring a character to life; not one is without its humor and intelligence; not one I don't wish I could have written myself. But when you compare them with the masterpieces, you are at once aware of the difference. "Champion" is, on the surface, a series of brutalities; you have the theme in the first two sentences: "Midge Kelly scored his first knockout when he was seventeen. The knockee was his brother Connie, three years his junior and a cripple." There follows item after item in the harsh catalogue of Midge Kelly's cruelty; but the items are woven together, one rises out of the other, each is a picture taken from a different angle; it isn't until the end that you know all you need to know about Midge Kelly. So also the character of the old man who describes "The Golden Honeymoon" is created with loving kindness and power, almost as soon as he is launched into his story; but it is not complete until the journey is done.

Lardner was observant and creative; he was not exceptionally inventive. This isn't a serious defect in a great writer; in Lardner's case the lack of invention wouldn't have mattered at all if he had been free to end his stories when their breath of life was spent. He couldn't; he had to give them artificial respiration because there is a sort of unwritten law that a magazine story, especially in "the slicks" ought to fill a certain amount of space. It may be to provide reading matter (next to advertising in the back pages) or it may be that readers need that much time to establish any sort of relation to the characters in the story. In any case, Lardner wrote stories of conventional length; it was a good length for his masterpieces; in the others he keeps shooting long after the bull's eye has been hit.

The same thing is true of many of Lardner's Sunday newspaper pieces. It was not so much that the space allotted to him was too much; it was that Sunday happened every week while something to be funny about happened irregularly. So there were unfunny days or long and labored attempts to eke out the genuine shrewd and sardonic comments of a gifted observer, with puns and exaggerations. But when Lardner went to work on a special job, and when his first inspiration was right, he was incomparable. You will find in this book five newspaper columns about—or let us say "supposed to be about"—a World Series. They were written in the short hours between the end of the game and the morning paper's deadline; they all use the same theme, without abusing it; and they are high-spirited, ingenious, and, to be bold about it, funny. Lardner was sent to cover political conventions, the Lipton Cup race, the Disarmament Conference, and various battles of the century. Toward the end of his life (at Doctor's Hospital and in the Western desert) he wrote the first (and the best) sustained critical reviews of broadcasting. Some of these are reprinted here; after fourteen years or so, they are still valid; and anyone who has written about popular entertainment knows how exceptional this is. In these special articles, with the pressures removed, Lardner seemed to set himself the strictest standards; free from the restrictions of time and space, he worked under the laws of his own integrity; I think he took vast satisfaction in doing them.

On this business of the writer's integrity, something needs to be said.

The position of the writer in the United States is an odd one. He is both a businessman and an artist; he has to be, because he has a living to make; his only patron is the public, acting through editors and publishing houses. Yet it is considered unfortunate, or downright treasonable, if the writer writes for money. This feeling is shared by writers themselves; they frequently denounce their ill-gotten gains and threaten to write something for themselves alone; sometimes they even carry out their threats. (Perhaps one of the most famous of these works, written to be unpopular, written after the author had felt the lash and the bitter bread of commercial success, is *Main Street,* which Sinclair Lewis intended to be a sort of American *Madame Bovary;* and the story is told that, as its sales mounted, his opinion of the work went down, lower and lower, until it almost arrived at a judicious estimate of the book's real worth.)

Now the fact is that a number of writers get a deal of money for doing the work they most want to do; and some of this work is first rate and some is not. I suspect that Edgar Rice Burroughs got as much pleasure out of the *Tarzan* series as did Robert Sherwood out of *Idiot's Delight.* There are artists who can turn out commercially acceptable stuff at two or more levels—pulps and slicks; slicks and art magazines, and so on. And there are some who stop doing good work, after it has begun to give them a decent living, to do poor work which pays them more. Perhaps the most disastrous effect of popularity on a writer is that he is encouraged to stick to the form, or formula, which first caught the public fancy. He is rather like a star in the movies who cannot break out of an established character for fear of "losing her audience." The writer in such a case is asked not to grow; not even to grow old. But the only way to stop growth is to die; and some writers do this, while they continue to write.

My feeling about Lardner is that he was destined to great—but not the greatest—popularity by his choice of subject matter and by his miraculous use of the language; out of both he drew so much comedy that his readers either did not catch, or did not mind, the strong current of sardonic misanthropy on which his stories float. (It is recorded that one popular magazine rejected "The Golden Honeymoon," another printed it. The first may have felt that "it isn't a story" or the editor may have had misgivings about Lardner's less than filial handling of the sacred theme of old age. The second editor, in any case, took a chance on his readers' indifference.) I do not feel that external pressure deterred Lardner from writing bitter stories outside the vein which came naturally to him, a comic vein. When a theme came to him, he cast it in the form he liked to handle; just as Chaplin, when the theme of the machine came to him, cast it in the comic terms of *Modern Times*, and not as a grim fable.

No one would have asked Theodore Dreiser to write like Lardner; but even good friends of Lardner's felt that he might have been "more important" if he hadn't stuck to his comic vein. I think that the way he told his stories corresponded to the way his mind worked; given a theme, he could not handle it otherwise. But when there was no theme, Lardner fell back on automatic writing. If he had never been a creative artist, no one would have reproached him. He suffered from coming too close to the top level of creativeness and, at the same time, being so copious and indifferent a potboiler. In dealing with him we have to separate the professional man of letters from the inspired creator.

I said above that one of Lardner's books was melancholy, and implied that all of his humorous work has shadows as well as lights. But you cannot forget the other side of the coin. Even the most savage of Lardner's stories (such as "Champion", "The Love Nest" and the story of Conrad Green's day) are extremely funny, too. And, to make the point again, some of Lardner's journalism, which is funny in the great tradition of exaggerated American humor, has a bitter aftertaste which doesn't in any way spoil your first innocent delight. This is so true that many people remember only the fun. They think of *You Know Me Al* as positively romantic about baseball. They have forgotten how stingy the characters are, how acutely aware of the price of a glass of beer, a suit of "cloths," or a wedding feast; and how the busher exposes himself as a liar, a coward, a defeated small-town Don Juan. All that Lardner loves in him is his abysmal folly, his invincible ignorance about himself; to that he is almost tender; to all the other faults, unrelenting.

We aren't aware of this perhaps because we are accustomed to the kind of bludgeoning our serious novelists give their characters. It is common form in writing about certain authors to take a crack at Sinclair Lewis, so I will try not to be ungenerous. I hear in Lewis a yawp of joy when he sees the head of Babbitt bloody with the theatrical gore his author has spilled over him. I do not hear this in Lardner because Lardner has never "set up" his characters for slaughter. He neither jeers at them nor crows over them. In "Haircut" and "Champion" his compassionate indignation is of a high emotional order; but he has gone so deeply into the characters of the bully and the practical joker that they become human—and terrible because they are human. Lardner does not have to gloat.

We are now talking about the solid foundations of Lardner's fame—the dozen or so short stories and the series called *The Big Town*. The latter is, to my mind, a much neglected work, and I am glad of the chance to put it into a book with better known pieces. It was written in 1920-21, and could hardly have been influenced by *Main Street*. It has the same disabused observation, without Lewis's romanticism. The book is, in fact, a direct descendant of the busher letters; it is cast in the same mold, but the characters are more varied, the emotions are somewhat deeper, the satire is more genial and more active, both. Some critics (among them Ring's close friend Scott Fitzgerald) have said that Lardner failed to grow beyond the baseball diamond. Fitzgerald, for instance, wrote:

During those years, when most men of promise achieve an adult education . . . Ring moved in the company of a few dozen illiterates playing a boy's game . . . This material, the observation of it under such circumstances, was the text of Ring's schooling during the most formative period of the mind. A writer can spin on about his adventures after thirty . . . but the criteria by which these adventures are weighed and valued are irrevocably settled at the age of twenty-five. However deeply Ring might cut into it, his cake had exactly the diameter of Frank Chance's diamond.

He kept on recording but he no longer projected . . .

I would say that even when he wrote about left-handed pitchers, Lardner was writing about humanity at large; and in *The Big Town,* the field of reference is wider; the appreciation of human character is more generous; the creation of a whole fraction of society is more powerfully and completely done.

About the short stories, I don't feel that anything need be said. No pointers to their excellence is required. Being of Lardner's generation, I read them when they appeared in magazines; and again in book form. Making the selections for this book, I read them all over again, and then for my own pleasure, read most of them a second and third time. Their surface is attractive; their depths clear. They have the power of life in them.

Instead of analyzing the stories, I want to say something about Lardner's language. My recollection is that H. L. Mencken was the first to recognize in Lardner a true artist in the American language and did not make the error of reducing that language to slang. It is quite true that in a hundred pages of the baseball stories you will find dozens of current expressions which you can call slang; and Lardner either invented or gave currency to terms like "World Serious" and "Alibi Ike." But his great gift is in another field. He wrote a language which corresponded to the way his people thought and he used the words he heard them speak, spelling them as the speakers imagined they should be spelled. A lot of his work is in the form of letters, diaries, and stories in the first person, all of which gave him a chance to use direct discourse; and it is interesting to note that Lardner always wanted to write plays (*June Moon* was based on the story "Some Like Them Cold"; and *Elmer the Great* and *The Bull Pen*, a sketch in one of the Ziegfeld Follies, were a sort of essence of the baseball group); the way people spoke was to him a complete revelation of what they were; he used conversation as a dramatist uses it, to let you into the secrets of the heart.

His ear, as everyone knows, was sensitive and his memory was accurate. You never say, "People don't talk that way" when you read Lardner; people do talk that way because people *are* that way. I do not know whether anyone ever wrote the word "he-ll" like that before Lardner's characters began it; but I know that the way it is written represents confusion in the person's mind, and so helps to create a character for us. I do know that many people are as painstaking about their times of arrival and departure as all Lardner's travelers are (and he burlesqued his own fascination with the subject in "The Young Immigrunts"). One of the lasting memories of an unmemorable army career is listening for hours to an argument about street car lines: whether a certain car turned at 23rd Street or 25th Street; a constant experience which no one escapes is the endless road-talk of motorists. These are the things Lardner's people talk about. And if the phrases they use are not exactly repeated today, it is because we have different roads and cars; the rhythm of speech is still precisely the same.

Rhythm is the key word here. It is the tune to which we sing our daily speech. Everyone who has learned a foreign tongue knows that speaking French or Italian or Russian is something more than pronouncing the right words. A moment comes when you are "speaking like a native" and that is the moment when you fall into the rhythm of the language. Countries more compact and unified than our own have a single basic rhythm, with minor variations; the United States has three or four distinct patterns, in which the tempo and the beat and accent differ; but they are connected and the difference between them will probably disappear as movies and network radio tend to impose a single standard (varied only by exaggerated dialects).

The stories of Ring Lardner, and a great many of the sundry pieces he wrote in character, are written in the dominant Midwestern American rhythm, with ventures into shorter, harder cadences of the Atlantic seaboard for contrast. Within this general pattern, all of his major characters have their individual modes: the flapper is of the same breed as the caddy; the theatrical promoter is brother to the baseball manager; you recognize each one as a separate person because you hear the sound of his voice. In part you hear it because of the way each person pronounces the words (in Lardner's astonishingly accurate phonetic spelling); but more often you hear the words spoken because the way they are written sets up the correct rhythm in your mind. The characters impose the style; and that is one of the two ways in which a dialogue becomes effective. The other, equally good, occurs when the style creates the characters for you. Read Ernest Hemingway's "Fifty Grand" and Lardner's "Champion" for brilliant examples of these two methods.

Ring Lardner played an important part in one of the interesting developments of the 1920's, which you might call the delayed recognition of American popular art. I do not know whether I was the first professional critic to consider Lardner's work as a notable contribution to our literature; I am sure Mencken preceded me in regard to Lardner's use of the American language. But when I wrote an article in *Vanity Fair* analyzing his qualities as a satirist and paying tribute to his literary talents, he sent me a note of thanks, adding that some of the things I wrote were over his head, but the boys who understood them assured him they were favorable. This was, of course, written in character; I was not an obscure writer. But it was an indication of the gap between the "serious" critic and the "popular" writer, better known as the highbrow and the lowbrow. In character, Lardner had to pretend that the gap was not to be crossed; actually he had made the crossing himself, and with ease.

The same thing had happened to Mark Twain; the pedants had belittled him, he was a humorist, a writer of boys' books; and presently he was recognized as one of the glories of our literature. The same thing happened to popular artists in other fields, especially music. The great tradition was that whatever is popular cannot be good, and it was a holdover from the days of limited education and limited editions. Our writers were accepting the system of mass distribution; but our critics had not, in Malraux's phrase, come to terms with the printing press. As for radio and the movies, the best people were content to leave them in the hands of vulgar people, complaining all the time that the results were vulgar.

I was one of a small number of critics who, in the 1920's found more satisfaction in popular entertainment than in most of the serious work America was producing. This is not an unusual event. In the 1890's in England there were enthusiasts for vaudeville who were tired of the well-made plays of Pinero; in Germany a few years later, there was a whole movement, in which painters and poets and critics combined to destroy the stodgy and praise all that was light and high-spirited; in France, I am told, the separation between the popular and the worthy in the arts was never so wide. It was odd that in the United States, when our revues and newspaper writing and songs and dancing were all expressing the rude energies released by the war, our critics should still have felt that the American spirit must express itself in the terms of the European play, the British novel, and the Beaux Arts easel painting. Only our architecture was permitted, without criticism, to soar freely; and the reason was that building had not only become big business; it had come under the influence of men who knew the capacities of structural steel. A few banks insisted on looking like the Pantheon; but the skyscraper and the good, small house were recognized as specific creations of our own.

When it was suggested that Chaplin and Kern and Berlin and Herriman and Lardner were interesting to the adult intelligence, two distinct lines of hostility developed. One was that "everyone always knew it"—which was true with one exception, the critics. The other was that these "naive" artists would be spoiled by analysis and praise. You will find in this book a story called "Rhythm"; I have put it in although I do not think it is a very good story, because the point of view is interesting and because I suspect that Spencer Deal is myself. On the defensive, I hasten to say that there is no record of any composer having lost his popular touch because of a yearning for the praise of the intellectuals. The ones we praised, in those days, were beyond the reach of our influence: Kern and Donaldson and Berlin—and Gershwin. I think that Gershwin was encouraged to write *Porgy and Bess* by influences outside Tin-Pan Alley; but the first instigation to go beyond half a dozen songs for a musical comedy came to Gershwin from Paul Whiteman, when he commissioned the *Rhapsody in Blue;* and Whiteman himself never fell for the blandishments of the blue stocking. He had never been a priest of hot jazz; his band was a well-functioning, smoothly oiled machine; he hit a precise level of popular appreciation and he stayed with it for a generation.

I have testimony to prove that some half a dozen popular artists were gratified at the discovery that some-one could distinguish between them and the less talented people in their lines. For the point about criticism of the popular arts is the same as it is in the great arts: to discover what an artist means, to distinguish the good from the less good. There were other short-story writers who used slang and sports; they were as popular as Lardner, but they were insignificant; and we who cared for popular entertainment cared as little for them as we cared for the music of "Yes, We Have No Bananas"; we saw no virtue in popularity without talent, which is the demagoguery of the arts.

In Lardner we had our most effective instance of the popular writer who had genius. Fitzgerald had removed himself from the field when he wrote *The Great Gatsby;* Sinclair Lewis was trying to be the American Flaubert; Hemingway was yet to come. Lardner, writing of common things in the common tongue, was unmistakably creating something new and powerful. When the editors of a club gave him their accolade, he had been finally accepted.

By that time, according to Fitzgerald, he was no longer having any fun in his work. That isn't the happiest

expression of the truth, for a writer may have little fun
and still have profound satisfaction in the practice of his
calling. Lardner seems to have lost the feeling that his
work meant anything. One of the familiar explanations
was that he no longer cared to be pigeon-holed as a
humorous writer about sports. It doesn't explain. Lardner
was well aware of the esteem in which he was held by
the good writers and the good critics of his day; but it is
quite possible that he did not respect them and their
judgment too highly. He was a skeptical man. Read what
he wrote; note how doubtful he is of all those things on
which human beings pride themselves, how fame and
riches and love are whittled down; it is not hard to believe that the writer of this dark commentary on human
affairs was a little doubtful of the reality of fame.

Of his friends, I knew only those in the theater and
in his own profession; I know he had others, but I do
not remember having heard him speak sentimentally
about any sports figure; perhaps because he knew my
ignorance and relative indifference in these matters. He
was devoted to half a dozen people whom I knew; and
I know ten times as many who were devoted to him, to
whom he was a singularly endearing man. He was certainly not easy to know; his silences were long, but
friendly; he was the least aggressive man I have ever
known, the one who did least to attract attention to himself. Yet you never felt that he was making himself
distant or difficult; quite the reverse, you felt his liking.
Whatever dark thoughts he had were for himself. If he
was, as Bolitho said, one of the great American pessimists, if he disliked humanity as a whole and had little
hope for it, he was, like many misanthropes, possessed of
an exceptional power to make himself loved. And I think
that this power, which was the essential thing in Lard-

ner, was strong enough to carry over into everything he
wrote; the millions who read what he wrote felt that
they knew him. And liked him. Because one of the irre-
pressible, and attractive, things about the human race is
that we embrace our detractors. Perhaps in self-defense,
as the only way we can bear what they say about us.

GILBERT SELDES

BIOGRAPHICAL NOTE

Ring Lardner's given name in full was Ringgold Wilmer; he was born in Niles, Michigan, March 6, 1885. He died in New York September 25, 1933.

He graduated from high school in Niles and was hoping to take "football and dentistry" at the University of Michigan; instead he went to the Armour Institute in Chicago, to study mechanical engineering; his report on his career is that he passed in rhetoric and out of Armour after one semester.

He knocked about, doing odd jobs—freight agent, bookkeeper, etc.—and then began work as a newspaperman. In 1907 he went to the Chicago *Inter-Ocean* and was taken from that paper by the Chicago *Examiner*, which sent him south with the White Sox, for training camp stories. In 1913 he ran "In the Wake of the News," a column of original comment and letters, on the Chicago *Tribune*. The next year he wrote the first of the busher stories.

He wrote for the Bell Syndicate for many years and among other things worked on a strip cartoon derived from his baseball stories. Many newspapers published his weekly articles and his special assignments were always featured in metropolitan papers. His first critical recognition came around 1923; in 1924 a collection of his stories, under the title, *How to Write Short Stories*, with zany introductions and his own stories appended as samples, was generally taken as the first proof of his serious talent.

June Moon was written with George S. Kaufman, a play worked out from the story, "Some Like Them Cold," and it was a success; *Elmer* the *Great*, written with George M. Cohan, was derived from the baseball stories; and Lardner wrote some sketches for revues. Scott Fitzgerald reports that Lardner had a great ambition to write songs; most of the verses he wrote are parodies of popular Tin-Pan Alley stuff, but a few fugitive lines, remembered by friends, indicate that he might have satisfied his ambition and added a fresh accent to popular music if ho had persisted.

A biographical encyclopedia says that Lardner was first known for his humorous and slangy genre sketches of the sporting world, his baseball players and Broadway hangers-on being depicted with fidelity and kindness. Later, according to the same sources, his work was grouped with that of Edgar Lee Masters and such stories as Sherwood Anderson's *Winesburg, Ohio.* This may turn out to be the accepted critical estimate; for a somewhat dissenting opinion, the reader is referred back to the Introduction to this volume.

G. S.

NOVELS

YOU KNOW ME AL

Preface

THE WRITER has been asked frequently, or perhaps not very often after all, two vital questions regarding the letters published in this book: (1) Are they actual letters or copies of actual letters? and (2) Who is the original of Jack Keefe?

The first question seemed highly complimentary until you thought it over and realized that no one with good sense could have asked it. Some of the letters run as long as a thousand words and there is only one person in the world who writes letters of that length. She is a sister-in-law of mine living in Indianapolis, and when she sits down to write a letter, she holds nothing back. But she is a Phi Beta and incapable of the mistakes in spelling and grammar that unfortunately have crept into this volume.

As for the other question, I have heretofore declined to reply to it, as a reply would have stopped the boys and girls from guessing, and their guesses have given me many a thrill. But now there are no ball players left whom they haven't guessed, from Noah to Bucky Harris, and I may as well give the correct answer. The original of Jack Keefe is not a ball player at all, but Jane Addams of Hull House, a former Follies girl.

An introduction to this book was written by Will Rogers, but the Scribner boys threw it out on the ground that it was better than the book. However, there was one remark of Mr. Rogers, which I think should be preserved. Referring to me, he wrote: "He is undoubtedly the biggest—" The rest of the sentence is so blurred as to be indecipherable.

The writer wishes to acknowledge his indebtedness to Mayo brothers, Ringling brothers, Smith brothers, Rath brothers, the Dolly sisters, and former President Buchanan for their aid in instructing him in the technical terms of baseball, such as "bat," "ball," "pitcher," "foul," "sleeping car," and "sore arm."

R. W. L.

March, 1925.

1. A Busher's Letters Home

Terre Haute, Indiana, September 6

FRIEND AL: Well, Al old pal I suppose you seen in the paper where I been sold to the White Sox. Believe me Al it comes as a surprise to me and I bet it did to all you good old pals down home. You could of knocked me over with a feather when the old man come up to me and says Jack I've sold you to the Chicago Americans.

I didn't have no idea that anything like that was coming off. For five minutes I was just dum and couldn't say a word.

He says We aren't getting what you are worth but I want you to go up to that big league and show those birds that there is a Central League on the map. He says Go and pitch the ball you been pitching down here and there won't be nothing to it. He says All you need is the nerve and Walsh or no one else won't have nothing on you.

So I says I would do the best I could and I thanked him for the treatment I got in Terre Haute. They always was good to me here and though I did more than my share I always felt that my work was appresiated. We are finishing second and I done most of it. I can't help but be proud of my first year's record in professional baseball and you know I am not boasting when I say that Al.

Well Al it will seem funny to be up there in the big show when I never was really in a big city before. But I guess I seen enough of life not to be scared of the high buildings eh Al?

I will just give them what I got and if they don't like it they can send me back to the old Central and I will be perfectly satisfied.

I didn't know anybody was looking me over, but one of the boys told me that Jack Doyle the White Sox scout was down here looking at me when Grand Rapids was here. I beat them twice in that serious. You know Grand Rapids never had a chance with me when I was right. I shut them out in the first game and they got one run in the second on account of Flynn misjuging that fly ball. Anyway Doyle liked my work and he wired Comiskey to buy me. Comiskey come back with an offer and they excepted it. I don't know how much they got but anyway I am sold to the big league and believe me Al I will make good.

Well Al I will be home in a few days and we will have some of the good old times. Regards to all the boys and tell them I am still their pal and not all swelled up over this big league business.   Your pal,   JACK.

Chicago, Illinois, December 14

OLD PAL: Well Al I have not got much to tell you. As you know Comiskey wrote me that if I was up in Chi this month to drop in and see him. So I got here Thursday morning and went to his office in the afternoon. His office is out to the ball park and believe me its some park and some office.

I went in and asked for Comiskey and a young fellow says He is not here now but can I do anything for you? I told him who I am and says I had an engagement to see Comiskey. He says The boss is out of town hunting and did I have to see him personally?

I says I wanted to see about signing a contract. He told me I could sign as well with him as Comiskey and he took me into another office. He says What salary did you think you ought to get? and I says I wouldn't think of playing ball in the big league for less than three thousand dollars per annum. He laughed and says You don't want much. You better stick round town till the boss comes back. So here I am and it is costing me a dollar a day to stay at the hotel on Cottage Grove Avenue and that don't include my meals.

I generally eat at some of the cafes round the hotel but I had supper downtown last night and it cost me fifty-five cents. If Comiskey don't come back soon I won't have no more money left.

Speaking of money I won't sign no contract unless I get the salary you and I talked of, three thousand dollars. You know what I was getting in Terre Haute, a hundred and fifty a month, and I know it's going to cost me a lot more to live here. I made inquiries round here and find I can get board and room for eight dollar a week but I will be out of town half the time and will have to pay for my room when I am away or look up a new one when I come back. Then I will have to

buy cloths to wear on the road in places like New York.
When Comiskey comes back I will name him three
thousand dollars as my lowest figure and I guess he
will come through when he sees I am in ernest. I heard
that Walsh was getting twice as much as that.

The papers says Comiskey will be back here sometime to-morrow. He has been hunting with the president of the league so he ought to feel pretty good. But
I don't care how he feels. I am going to get a contract
for three thousand and if he don't want to give it to me
he can do the other thing. You know me Al.

Yours truly,   JACK.

Chicago, Illinois, December 16

DEAR FRIEND AL: Well I will be home in a couple of
days now but I wanted to write you and let you know
how I come out with Comiskey. I signed my contract
yesterday afternoon. He is a great old fellow Al and no
wonder everybody likes him. He says Young man will
you have a drink? But I was to smart and wouldn't take
nothing. He says You was with Terre Haute? I says
Yes I was. He says Doyle tells me you were pretty wild.
I says Oh no I got good control. He says Well do you
want to sign? I says Yes if I get my figure. He asks
What is my figure and I says three thousand dollars per
annum. He says Don't you want the office furniture
too? Then he says I thought you was a young ball-
player and I didn't know you wanted to buy my park.

We kidded each other back and forth like that a
while and then he says You better go out and get the
air and come back when you feel better. I says I feel
O. K. now and I want to sign a contract because I have
got to get back to Bedford. Then he calls the secretary
and tells him to make out my contract. He give it to

me and it calls for two hundred and fifty a month. He
says You know we always have a city serious here in
the fall where a fellow picks up a good bunch of money.
I hadn't thought of that so I signed up. My yearly
salary will be fifteen hundred dollars besides what the
city serious brings me. And that is only for the first
year. I will demand three thousand or four thousand
dollars next year.

I would of started home on the evening train but I
ordered a suit of cloths from a tailor over on Cottage
Grove and it won't be done till to-morrow. It's going
to cost me twenty bucks but it ought to last a long time.
Regards to Frank and the bunch.   Your pal,   JACK.

Paso Robles, California, March 2

OLD PAL AL: Well Al we been in this little berg now a
couple of days and its bright and warm all the time just
like June. Seems funny to have it so warm this early in
March but I guess this California climate is all they said
about it and then some.

It would take me a week to tell you about our trip
out here. We came on a Special Train De Lukes and it
was some train. Every place we stopped there was
crowds down to the station to see us go through and
all the people looked me over like I was a actor or something. I guess my hight and shoulders attracted their
attention. Well Al we finally got to Oakland which is
across part of the ocean from Frisco. We will be back
there later on for practice games.

We stayed in Oakland a few hours and then took a
train for here. It was another night in a sleeper and believe me I was tired of sleepers before we got here. I
have road one night at a time but this was four straight

nights. You know Al I am not built right for a sleeping car birth.

The hotel here is a great big place and got good eats. We got in at breakfast time and I made a B line for the dining room. Kid Gleason who is a kind of asst. manager to Callahan come in and sat down with me. He says Leave something for the rest of the boys because they will be just as hungry as you. He says Ain't you afraid you will cut your throat with that knife. He says There ain't no extra charge for using the forks. He says You shouldn't ought to eat so much because you're over-weight now. I says You may think I am fat, but it's all solid bone and muscle. He says Yes I suppose it's all solid bone from the neck up. I guess he thought I would get sore but I will let them kid me now because they will take off their hats to me when they see me work.

Manager Callahan called us all to his room after break-fast and give us a lecture. He says there would be no work for us the first day but that we must all take a long walk over the hills. He also says we must not take the training trip as a joke. Then the colored trainer give us our suits and I went to my room and tried mine on. I ain't a bad looking guy in the White Sox uniform Al. I will have my picture taken and send you boys some.

My roommate is Allen a lefthander from the Coast League. He don't look nothing like a pitcher but you can't never tell about them dam left handers. Well I didn't go on the long walk because I was tired out. Walsh stayed at the hotel too and when he seen me he says Why didn't you go with the bunch? I says I was too tired. He says Well when Callahan comes back you better keep out of sight or tell him you are sick. I says I don't care nothing for Callahan. He says No but Callahan is crazy about you. He says You better obey orders and you will git along better. I guess Walsh thinks I am some rube.

When the bunch come back Callahan never said a word to me but Gleason come up and says Where was you? I told him I was too tired to go walking. He says Well I will borrow a wheel-barrow some place and push you round. He says Do you sit down when you pitch? I let him kid me because he has not saw my stuff yet.

Next morning half the bunch mostly vetrans went to the ball park which isn't no better than the one we got at home. Most of them was vetrans as I say but I was in the bunch. That makes things look pretty good for me don't it Al? We tossed the ball round and hit fungos and run round and then Callahan asks Scott and Russell and I to warm up easy and pitch a few to the batters. It was warm and I felt pretty good so I warmed up pretty good. Scott pitched to them first and kept laying them right over with nothing on them. I don't believe a man gets any batting practice that way. So I went in and after I lobbed a few over I cut loose my fast one. Lord was to bat and he ducked out of the way and then throwed his bat to the bench. Callahan says What's the matter Harry? Lord says I forgot to pay up my life insurance. He says I ain't ready for Walter Johnson's July stuff.

Well Al I will make them think I am Walter Johnson before I get through with them. But Callahan come out to me and says What are you trying to do kill somebody? He says Save your smoke because you're going to need it later on. He says Go easy with the boys at first or I won't have no batters. But he was laughing and I guess he was pleased to see the stuff I had.

There is a dance in the hotel to-night and I am up in my room writing this in my underwear while I get my suit pressed. I got it all mussed up coming out here. I don't know what shoes to wear. I asked Gleason and he says Wear your baseball shoes and if any of the girls gets fresh with you spike them. I guess he was kidding me.

Write and tell me all the news about home.

Yours truly,   JACK.

Paso Robles, California, March 7

FRIEND AL: I showed them something out there to-day Al. We had a game between two teams. One team was made up of most of the regulars and the other was made up of recruts. I pitched three innings for the recruts and shut the old birds out. I held them to one hit and that was a ground ball that the recrut shortstop Johnson ought to of ate up. I struck Collins out and he is one of the best batters in the bunch. I used my fast ball most of the while but showed them a few spitters and they missed them a foot. I guess I must of got Walsh's goat with my spitter because him and I walked back to the hotel together and he talked like he was kind of jealous. He says You will have to learn to cover up your spitter. He says I could stand a mile away and tell when you was going to throw it. He says Some of these days I will learn you how to cover it up. I guess Al I know how to cover it up all right without Walsh learning me.

I always sit at the same table in the dining room along with Gleason and Collins and Bodie and Fournier and Allen the young lefthander I told you about. I feel sorry for him because he never says a word. To-night at supper Bodie says How did I look to-day Kid? Gleason says Just like you always do in the spring. You

looked like a cow. Gleason seems to have the whole
bunch scared of him and they let him say anything he
wants to. I let him kid me to but I ain't scared of him.
Collins then says to me You got some fast ball there
boy. I says I was not as fast to-day as I am when I am
right. He says Well then I don't want to hit against you
when you are right. Then Gleason says to Collins Cut
that stuff out. Then he says to me Don't believe what
he tells you boy. If the pitchers in this league weren't
no faster than you I would still be playing ball and I
would be the best hitter in the country.

After supper Gleason went out on the porch with
me. He says Boy you have got a little stuff but you have
got a lot to learn. He says You field your position like
a wash woman and you don't hold the runners up. He
says When Chase was on second base to-day he got
such a lead on you that the little catcher couldn't of
shot him out at third with a rifle. I says They all thought
I fielded my position all right in the Central League.
He says Well if you think you do it all right you better
go back to the Central League where you are appresiated. I says You can't send me back there because you
could not get wavers. He says Who would claim you?
I says St. Louis and Boston and New York.

You know Al what Smith told me this winter. Gleason
says Well if you're not willing to learn St. Louis and
Boston and New York can have you and the first time
you pitch against us we will steal fifty bases. Then he
quit kidding and asked me to go to the field with him
early to-morrow morning and he would learn me some
things. I don't think he can learn me nothing but I promised I would go with him.

There is a little blonde kid in the hotel here who
took a shine to me at the dance the other night but I
am going to leave the skirts alone. She is real society

and a swell dresser and she wants my picture. Regards to all the boys.   Your friend,   JACK.

P. S. The boys thought they would be smart to-night and put something over on me. A boy brought me a telegram and I opened it and it said You are sold to Jackson in the Cotton States League. For just a minute they had me going but then I happened to think that Jackson is in Michigan and there's no Cotton States League round there.

Paso Robles, California, March 9

DEAR FRIEND AL: You have no doubt read the good news in the papers before this reaches you. I have been picked to go to Frisco with the first team. We play practice games up there about two weeks while the second club plays in Los Angeles. Poor Allen had to go with the second club. There's two other recrut pitchers with our part of the team but my name was first on the list so it looks like I had made good. I knowed they would like my stuff when they seen it. We leave here to-night. You got the first team's address so you will know where to send my mail. Callahan goes with us and Gleason goes with the second club. Him and I have got to be pretty good pals and I wish he was going with us even if he don't let me eat like I want to. He told me this morning to remember all he had learned me and to keep working hard. He didn't learn me nothing I didn't know before but I let him think so.

The little blonde don't like to see me leave here. She lives in Detroit and I may see her when I go there. She wants me to write but I guess I better not give her no encouragement.

Well Al I will write you a long letter from Frisco.
        Yours truly,   JACK.

Oakland, California, March 19

DEAR OLD PAL: They have gave me plenty of work here
all right. I have pitched four times but have not went
over five innings yet. I worked against Oakland two
times and against Frisco two times and only three runs
have been scored off me. They should only ought to
of had one but Bodie misjuged a easy fly ball in Frisco
and Weaver made a wild peg in Oakland that let in a
run. I am not using much but my fast ball but I have
got a world of speed and they can't foul me when I
am right. I whiffed eight men in five innings in Frisco
yesterday and could of did better than that if I had of
cut loose.

Manager Callahan is a funny guy and I don't understand him sometimes. I can't figure out if he is kidding
or in ernest. We road back to Oakland on the ferry
together after yesterday's game and he says Don't you
never throw a slow ball? I says I don't need no slow ball
with my spitter and my fast one. He says No of course
you don't need it but if I was you I would get one of
the boys to learn it to me. He says And you better watch
the way the boys fields their positions and holds up the
runners. He says To see you work a man might think
they had a rule in the Central League forbidding a
pitcher from leaving the box or looking toward first base.

I told him the Central didn't have no rule like that.
He says And I noticed you taking your wind up when
What's His Name was on second base there to-day. I
says Yes I got more stuff when I wind up. He says Of
course you have but if you wind up like that with Cobb
on base he will steal your watch and chain. I says Maybe
Cobb can't get on base when I work against him. He
says That's right and maybe San Francisco Bay is made
of grapejuice. Then he walks away from me.

He give one of the youngsters a awful bawling out for something he done in the game at supper last night. If he ever talks to me like he done to him I will take a punch at him. You know me Al.

I come over to Frisco last night with some of the boys and we took in the sights. Frisco is some live town Al. We went all through China Town and the Barbers' Coast. Seen lots of swell dames but they was all painted up. They have beer out here that they call steam beer. I had a few glasses of it and it made me logey. A glass of that Terre Haute beer would go pretty good right now.

We leave here for Los Angeles in a few days and I will write you from there. This is some country Al and I would love to play ball round here.

Your Pal, JACK.

P. S.—I got a letter from the little blonde and I suppose I got to answer it.

Los Angeles, California, March 26

FRIEND AL: Only four more days of sunny California and then we start back East. We got exhibition games in Yuma and El Paso, Texas, and Oklahoma City and then we stop over in St. Joe, Missouri, for three days before we go home. You know Al we open the season in Cleveland and we won't be in Chi no more than just passing through. We don't play there till April eighteenth and I guess I will work in that serious all right against Detroit. Then I will be glad to have you and the boys come up and watch me as you suggested in your last letter.

I got another letter from the little blonde. She has went back to Detroit but she give me her address and telephone number and believe me Al I am going to look her up when we get there the twenty-ninth of April.

She is a stenographer and was out here with her uncle and aunt.

I had a run in with Kelly last night and it looked like I would have to take a wallop at him but the other boys separated us. He is a bush outfielder from the New England League. We was playing poker. You know the boys plays poker a good deal but this was the first time I got in. I was having pretty good luck and was about four bucks to the good and I was thinking of quitting because I was tired and sleepy. Then Kelly opened the pot for fifty cents and I stayed. I had three sevens. No one else stayed. Kelly stood pat and I drawed two cards. And I catched my fourth seven. He bet fifty cents but I felt pretty safe even if he did have a pat hand. So I called him. I took the money and told them I was through.

Lord and some of the boys laughed but Kelly got nasty and begun to pan me for quitting and for the way I played. I says Well I won the pot didn't I? He says Yes and he called me something. I says I got a notion to take a punch at you.

He says Oh you have have you? And I come back at him. I says Yes I have have I? I would of busted his jaw if they hadn't stopped me. You know me Al.

I worked here two times once against Los Angeles and once against Venice. I went the full nine innings both times and Venice beat me four to two. I could of beat them easy with any kind of support. I walked a couple of guys in the forth and Chase drops a throw and Collins lets a fly ball get away from him. At that I would of shut them out if I had wanted to cut loose. After the game Callahan says You didn't look so good in there to-day. I says I didn't cut loose. He says Well you been working pretty near three weeks now and you ought to be in shape to cut loose. I says Oh I am in shape all right. He says Well don't work no harder than you have to or you might get hurt and then the league would blow up. I don't know if he was kidding me or not but I guess he thinks pretty well of me because he works me lots oftener than Walsh or Scott or Benz.

I will try to write you from Yuma, Texas, but we don't stay there only a day and I may not have time for a long letter.   Yours truly,   JACK.

Yuma, Arizona, April 1

DEAR OLD AL: Just a line to let you know we are on our way back East. This place is in Arizona and it sure is sandy. They haven't got no regular ball club here and we play a pick-up team this afternoon. Callahan told me I would have to work. He says I am using you because we want to get through early and I know you can beat them quick. That is the first time he has said anything like that and I guess he is wiseing up that I got the goods.

We was talking about the Athaletics this morning and Callahan says None of you fellows pitch right to Baker. I was talking to Lord and Scott afterward and I say to Scott How do you pitch to Baker? He says I use my fadeaway. I says How do you throw it? He says Just like you throw a fast ball to anybody else. I says Why do you call it a fadeaway then? He says Because when I throw it to Baker it fades away over the fence.

This place is full of Indians and I wish you could see them Al. They don't look nothing like the Indians we seen in that show last summer.   Your old pal,   JACK.

FRIEND AL: Coming out of Amarillo last night I and
Lord and Weaver was sitting at a table in the dining
car with a old lady. None of us were talking to her but
she looked me over pretty careful and seemed to kind
of like my looks. Finally she says Are you boys with
some football club? Lord nor Weaver didn't say nothing
so I thought it was up to me and I says No mam this
is the Chicago White Sox Ball Club. She says I knew
you were athaletes. I says Yes I guess you could spot
us for athaletes. She says Yes indeed and specially you.
You certainly look healthy. I says You ought to see me
stripped. I didn't see nothing funny about that but I
thought Lord and Weaver would die laughing. Lord
had to get up and leave the table and he told everybody
what I said.

All the boys wanted me to play poker on the way here
but I told them I didn't feel good. I know enough to
quit when I am ahead Al. Callahan and I sat down to
breakfast all alone this morning. He says Boy why don't
you get to work? I says What do you mean? Ain't I
working? He says You ain't improving none. You have
got the stuff to make a good pitcher but you don't go
after bunts and you don't cover first base and you don't
watch the baserunners. He made me kind of sore talking that way and I says Oh I guess I can get along all
right.

He says Well I am going to put it up to you. I am
going to start you over in St. Joe day after to-morrow
and I want you to show me something. I want you to
cut loose with all you've got and I want you to get round
the infield a little and show them you aren't tied in that
box. I says Oh I can field my position if I want to. He
says Well you better want to or I will have to ship you
back to the sticks. Then he got up and left. He didn't

scare me none Al. They won't ship me to no sticks after the way I showed on this trip and even if they did they couldn't get no wavers on me.

Some of the boys have begun to call me Four Sevens but it don't bother me none.   Yours truly,   JACK.

St. Joe, Missouri, April 7

FRIEND AL: It rained yesterday so I worked to-day instead and St. Joe done well to get three hits. They couldn't of scored if we had played all week. I give a couple of passes but I catched a guy flatfooted off of first base and I come up with a couple of bunts and throwed guys out. When the game was over Callahan says That's the way I like to see you work. You looked better to-day than you looked on the whole trip. Just once you wound up with a man on but otherwise you was all O. K. So I guess my job is cinched Al and I won't have to go to New York or St. Louis. I would rather be in Chi anyway because it is near home. I wouldn't care though if they traded me to Detroit. I hear from Violet right along and she says she can't hardly wait till I come to Detroit. She says she is strong for the Tigers but she will pull for me when I work against them. She is nuts over me and I guess she has saw lots of guys to.

I sent her a stickpin from Oklahoma City but I can't spend no more dough on her till after our first payday the fifteenth of the month. I had thirty bucks on me when I left home and I only got about ten left including the five spot I won in the poker game. I have to tip the waiters about thirty cents a day and I seen about twenty picture shows on the coast besides getting my cloths pressed a couple of times.

We leave here to-morrow night and arrive in Chi the next morning. The second club joins us there and then that night we go to Cleveland to open up. I asked one of the reporters if he knowed who was going to pitch the opening game and he says it would be Scott or Walsh but I guess he don't know much about it.

These reporters travel all round the country with the team all season and send in telegrams about the game every night. I ain't seen no Chi papers so I don't know what they been saying about me. But I should worry eh Al? Some of them are pretty nice fellows and some of them got the swell head. They hang round with the old fellows and play poker most of the time.

Will write you from Cleveland. You will see in the paper if I pitch the opening game.

Your old pal,   JACK.

Cleveland, Ohio, April 10

OLD FRIEND AL: Well Al we are all set to open the season this afternoon. I have just ate breakfast and I am sitting in the lobby of the hotel. I eat at a little lunch counter about a block from here and I saved seventy cents on breakfast. You see Al they give us a dollar a meal and if we don't want to spend that much all right. Our rooms at the hotel are paid for.

The Cleveland papers says Walsh or Scott will work for us this afternoon. I asked Callahan if there was any chance of me getting into the first game and he says I hope not. I don't know what he meant but he may surprise these reporters and let me pitch. I will beat them Al. Lajoie and Jackson is supposed to be great batters but the bigger they are the harder they fall.

The second team joined us yesterday in Chi and we practiced a little. Poor Allen was left in Chi last night with four others of the recrut pitchers. Looks pretty good for me eh Al? I only seen Gleason for a few minutes on the train last night. He says, Well you ain't took off much weight. You're hog fat. I says Oh I ain't fat. I didn't need to take off no weight. He says One good thing about it the club don't have to engage no birth for you because you spend all your time in the dining car. We kidded along like that a while and then the trainer rubbed my arm and I went to bed. Well Al I just got time to have my suit pressed before noon.

Yours truly, JACK.

Cleveland, Ohio, April 11

FRIEND AL: Well Al I suppose you know by this time that I did not pitch and that we got licked. Scott was in there and he didn't have nothing. When they had us beat four to one in the eighth inning Callahan told me to go out and warm up and he put a batter in for Scott in our ninth. But Cleveland didn't have to play their ninth so I got no chance to work. But it looks like he means to start me in one of the games here. We got three more to play. Maybe I will pitch this afternoon. I got a postcard from Violet. She says Beat them Naps. I will give them a battle Al if I get a chance.

Glad to hear you boys have fixed it up to come to Chi during the Detroit serious. I will ask Callahan when he is going to pitch me and let you know. Thanks Al for the papers. Your friend, JACK.

St. Louis, Missouri, April 15

FRIEND AL: Well Al I guess I showed them. I only worked one inning but I guess them Browns is glad I wasn't in there no longer than that. They had us beat seven to one in the sixth and Callahan pulls Benz out. I honestly felt sorry for him but he didn't have nothing, not a thing. They was hitting him so hard I thought they would score a hundred runs. A righthander named Bumgardner was pitching for them and he didn't look to have nothing either but we ain't got much of a batting team Al. I could hit better than some of them regulars. Anyway Callahan called Benz to the bench and sent for me. I was down in the corner warming up with Kuhn. I wasn't warmed up good but you know I got the nerve Al and I run right out there like I meant business. There was a man on second and nobody out when I come in. I didn't know who was up there but I found out afterward it was Shotten. He's the centerfielder. I was cold and I walked him. Then I got warmed up good and I made Johnston look like a boob. I give him three fast balls and he let two of them go by and missed the other one. I would of handed him a spitter but Schalk kept signing for fast ones and he knows more about them batters than me. Anyway I whiffed Johnston. Then up come Williams and I tried to make him hit at a couple of bad ones. I was in the hole with two balls and nothing and come right across the heart with my fast one. I wish you could of saw the hop on it. Williams hit it right straight up and Lord was camped under it. Then up come Pratt the best hitter on their club. You know what I done to him don't you Al? I give him one spitter and another he didn't strike at that was a ball. Then I come back with two fast ones and Mister Pratt was a dead baby. And you notice they didn't steal no bases neither.

In our half of the seventh inning Weaver and Schalk got on and I was going up there with a stick when Callahan calls me back and sends Easterly up. I don't know what kind of managing you call that. I hit good on the training trip and he must of knew they had no chance to score off me in the innings they had left while they were liable to murder his other pitchers. I come back to the bench pretty hot and I says You're making a mistake. He says If Comiskey had wanted you to manage this team he would of hired you.

Then Easterly pops out and I says Now I guess you're sorry you didn't let me hit. That sent him right up in the air and he bawled me awful. Honest Al I would of cracked him right in the jaw if we hadn't been right out where everybody could of saw us. Well he sent Cicotte in to finish and they didn't score no more and we didn't neither.

I road down in the car with Gleason. He says Boy you shouldn't ought to talk like that to Cal. Some day he will lose his temper and bust you one. I says He won't never bust me. I says He didn't have no right to talk like that to me. Gleason says I suppose you think he's going to laugh and smile when we lost four out of the first five games. He says Wait till to-night and then go up to him and let him know you are sorry you sassed him. I says I didn't sass him and ain't sorry.

So after supper I seen Callahan sitting in the lobby and I went over and sit down by him. I says When are you going to let me work? He says I wouldn't never let you work only my pitchers are all shot to pieces. Then I told him about you boys coming up from Bedford to watch me during the Detroit serious and he says Well I will start you in the second game against Detroit. He says But I wouldn't if I had any pitchers. He says A girl could get out there and pitch better than some of them have been doing.

So you see Al I am going to pitch on the nineteenth. I hope you guys can be up there and I will show you something. I know I can beat them Tigers and I will have to do it even if they are Violet's team.

I notice that New York and Boston got trimmed today so I suppose they wish Comiskey would ask for waivers on me. No chance Al.   Your old pal,   JACK.

P. S.—We play eleven games in Chi and then go to Detroit. So I will see the little girl on the twenty-ninth.

Oh you Violet.

Chicago, Illinois, April 19

DEAR OLD PAL: Well Al it's just as well you couldn't come. They beat me and I am writing you this so as you will know the truth about the game and not get a bum steer from what you read in the papers.

I had a sore arm when I was warming up and Callahan should never ought to of sent me in there. And Schalk kept signing for my fast ball and I kept giving it to him because I thought he ought to know something about the batters. Weaver and Lord and all of them kept kicking them round the infield and Collins and Bodie couldn't catch nothing.

Callahan ought never to of left me in there when he seen how sore my arm was. Why, I couldn't of threw hard enough to break a pain of glass my arm was so sore.

They sure did run wild on the bases. Cobb stole four and Bush and Crawford and Veach about two apiece. Schalk didn't even make a peg half the time. I guess he was trying to throw me down.

The score was sixteen to two when Callahan finally took me out in the eighth and I don't know how many more they got. I kept telling him to take me out when I seen how bad I was but he wouldn't do it. They started bunting in the fifth and Lord and Chase just stood there and didn't give me no help at all.

I was all O. K. till I had the first two men out in the first inning. Then Crawford come up. I wanted to give him a spitter but Schalk signs me for the fast one and I give it to him. The ball didn't hop much and Crawford happened to catch it just right. At that Collins ought to of catched the ball. Crawford made three bases and up come Cobb. It was the first time I ever seen him. He hollered at me right off the reel. He says You better walk me you busher. I says I will walk you back to the bench. Schalk signs for a spitter and I gives it to him and Cobb misses it.

Then instead of signing for another one Schalk asks for a fast one and I shook my head no but he signed for it again and yells Put something on it. So I throwed a fast one and Cobb hits it right over second base. I don't know what Weaver was doing but he never made a move for the ball. Crawford scored and Cobb was on first base. First thing I knowed he had stole second while I held the ball. Callahan yells Wake up out there and I says Why don't your catcher tell me when they are going to steal. Schalk says Get in there and pitch and shut your mouth. Then I got mad and walked Veach and Moriarty but before I walked Moriarty Cobb and Veach pulled a double steal on Schalk. Gainor lifts a fly and Lord drops it and two more come in. Then Stanage walks and I whiffs their pitcher.

I come in to the bench and Callahan says Are your friends from Bedford up here? I was pretty sore and I says Why don't you get a catcher? He says We don't need no catcher when you're pitching because you can't get nothing past their bats. Then he says You better leave your uniform in here when you go out next inning or Cobb will steal it off your back. I says My arm is sore. He says Use your other one and you'll do just as good.

Gleason says Who do you want to warm up? Callahan says Nobody. He says Cobb is going to lead the league in batting and basestealing anyway so we might as well give him a good start. I was mad enough to punch his jaw but the boys winked at me not to do nothing.

Well I got some support in the next inning and nobody got on. Between innings I says Well I guess I look better now don't I? Callahan says Yes but you wouldn't look so good if Collins hadn't jumped up on the fence and catched that one off Crawford. That's all the encouragement I got Al.

Cobb come up again to start the third and when Schalk signs me for a fast one I shakes my head. Then Schalk says All right pitch anything you want to. I pitched a spitter and Cobb bunts it right at me. I would of threw him out a block but I stubbed my toe in a rough place and fell down. This is the roughest ground I ever seen Al. Veach bunts and for a wonder Lord throws him out. Cobb goes to second and honest Al I forgot all about him being there and first thing I knowed he had stole third. Then Moriarty hits a fly ball to Bodie and Cobb scores though Bodie ought to of threw him out twenty feet.

They batted all round in the forth inning and scored four or five more. Crawford got the luckiest three-base hit I ever see. He popped one way up in the air and the wind blowed it against the fence. The wind is something fierce here Al. At that Collins ought to of got under it.

I was looking at the bench all the time expecting Callahan to call me in but he kept hollering Go on and pitch. Your friends wants to see you pitch.

Well Al I don't know how they got the rest of their runs but they had more luck than any team I ever seen. And all the time Jennings was on the coaching line yelling like a Indian. Some day Al I'm going to punch his jaw.

After Veach had hit one in the eight Callahan calls me to the bench and says You're through for the day. I says It's about time you found out my arm was sore.

He says I ain't worrying about your arm but I'm afraid some of our outfielders will run their legs off and some of them poor infielders will get killed. He says The reporters just sent me a message saying they had run out of paper. Then he says I wish some of the other clubs had pitchers like you so we could hit once in a while. He says Go in the clubhouse and get your arm rubbed off. That's the only way I can get Jennings sore he says.

Well Al that's about all there was to it. It will take two or three stamps to send this but I want you to know the truth about it. The way my arm was I ought never to of went in there.   Yours truly,   JACK.

Chicago, Illinois, April 25

FRIEND AL: Just a line to let you know I am still on earth. My arm feels pretty good again and I guess maybe I will work at Detroit. Violet writes that she can't hardly wait to see me. Looks like I got a regular girl now Al. We go up there the twenty-ninth and maybe I won't be glad to see her. I hope she will be out to the game the day I pitch. I will pitch the way I want to next time and them Tigers won't have such a picnic.

I suppose you seen what the Chicago reporters said about that game. I will punch a couple of their jaws when I see them.   Your pal,   JACK.

Chicago, Illinois, April 29

DEAR OLD AL: Well Al it's all over. The club went to Detroit last night and I didn't go along. Callahan told me to report to Comiskey this morning and I went up to the office at ten o'clock. He give me my pay to date and broke the news. I am sold to Frisco.

I asked him how they got wavers on me and he says

Oh there was no trouble about that because they all heard how you tamed the Tigers. Then he patted me on the back and says Go out there and work hard boy and maybe you'll get another chance some day. I was kind of choked up so I walked out of the office.

I ain't had no fair deal Al and I ain't going to no Frisco. I will quit the game first and take that job Charley offered me at the billiard hall.

I expect to be in Bedford in a couple of days. I have got to pack up first and settle with my landlady about my room here which I engaged for all season thinking I would be treated square. I am going to rest and lay round home a while and try to forget this rotten game. Tell the boys about it Al and tell them I never would of got let out if I hadn't worked with a sore arm.

I feel sorry for that little girl up in Detroit Al. She expected me there today.   Your old pal,   JACK.

P. S. I suppose you seen where that lucky lefthander Allen shut out Cleveland with two hits yesterday. The lucky stiff.

II. The Busher Comes Back

San Francisco, California, May 13

FRIEND AL: I suppose you and the rest of the boys in Bedford will be supprised to learn that I am out here, because I remember telling you when I was sold to San Francisco by the White Sox that not under no circumstances would I report here. I was pretty mad when Comiskey give me my release, because I didn't think I had been given a fair show by Callahan. I don't think so yet Al and I never will but Bill Sullivan the old White Sox catcher talked to me and told me not to pull no boner by refuseing to go where they sent me. He says You're only hurting yourself. He says You must remember that this was your first time up in the big show and very few men no matter how much stuff they got can expect to make good right off the reel. He says All you need is experience and pitching out in the Coast League will be just the thing for you.

So I went in and asked Comiskey for my transportation and he says That's right Boy go out there and work hard and maybe I will want you back. I told him I hoped so but I don't hope nothing of the kind Al. I am going to see if I can't get Detroit to buy me, because I would rather live in Detroit than anywheres else. The little girl who got stuck on me this spring lives there. I guess I told you about her Al. Her name is Violet and she is some queen. And then if I got with the Tigers I wouldn't never have to pitch against Cobb and Crawford, though I believe I could show both of them up if I was right. They ain't got much of a ball club here and hardly any good pitchers outside of me. But I don't care.

I will win some games if they give me any support and I will get back in the big league and show them birds something. You know me, Al. Your pal, JACK.

Los Angeles, California, May 20

AL: Well old pal I don't suppose you can find much news of this league in the papers at home so you may not know that I have been standing this league on their heads. I pitched against Oakland up home and shut them out with two hits. I made them look like suckers Al. They hadn't never saw no speed like mine and they was scared to death the minute I cut loose. I could of pitched

the last six innings with my foot and trimmed them they
was so scared.

Well we come down here for a serious and I worked
the second game. They got four hits and one run, and
I just give them the one run. Their shortstop Johnson
was on the training trip with the White Sox and of
course I knowed him pretty well. So I eased up in the
last inning and let him hit one. If I had of wanted to let
myself out he couldn't of hit me with a board. So I am
going along good and Howard our manager says he is
going to use me regular. He's a pretty nice manager
and not a bit sarkastic like some of them big leaguers.
I am fielding my position good and watching the baserunners to. Thank goodness Al they ain't no Cobbs in
this league and a man ain't scared of haveing his uniform
stole off his back.

But listen Al I don't want to be bought by Detroit
no more. It is all off between Violet and I. She wasn't
the sort of girl I suspected. She is just like them all Al.
No heart. I wrote her a letter from Chicago telling her I
was sold to San Francisco and she wrote back a postcard saying something about not haveing no time to
waste on bushers. What do you know about that Al?
Calling me a busher. I will show them. She wasn't no
good Al and I figure I am well rid of her. Good riddance
is rubbish as they say.

I will let you know how I get along and if I hear anything about being sold or drafted.

Yours truly,   Jack.

San Francisco, California, July 20

FRIEND AL: You will forgive me for not writeing to you
oftener when you hear the news I got for you. Old pal
I am engaged to be married. Her name is Hazel Carney

and she is some queen, Al—a great big stropping girl that must weigh one hundred and sixty lbs. She is out to every game and she got stuck on me from watching me work.

Then she writes a note to me and makes a date and I meet her down on Market Street one night. We go to a nickel show together and have some time. Since then we been together pretty near every evening except when I was away on the road.

Night before last she asked me if I was married and I tells her No and she says a big handsome man like I ought not to have no trouble finding a wife. I tells her I ain't never looked for one and she says Well you wouldn't have to look very far. I asked her if she was married and she said No but she wouldn't mind it. She likes her beer pretty well and her and I had several and I guess I was feeling pretty good. Anyway I guess I asked her if she wouldn't marry me and she says it was O. K. I ain't a bit sorry Al because she is some doll and will make them all sit up back home. She wanted to get married right away but I said No wait till the season is over and maybe I will have more dough. She asked me what I was getting and I told her two hundred dollars a month. She says she didn't think I was getting enough and I don't neither but I will get the money when I get up in the big show again.

Anyway we are going to get married this fall and then I will bring her home and show her to you. She wants to live in Chi or New York but I guess she will like Bedford O. K. when she gets acquainted.

I have made good here all right Al. Up to a week ago Sunday I had won eleven straight. I have lost a couple since then, but one day I wasn't feeling good and the other time they kicked it away behind me.

I had a run in with Howard after Portland had beat

me. He says Keep on running round with that skirt and you won't never win another game.

He says Go to bed nights and keep in shape or I will take your money. I told him to mind his own business and then he walked away from me. I guess he was scared I was going to smash him. No manager ain't going to bluff me Al. So I went to bed early last night and didn't keep my date with the kid. She was pretty sore about it but business before pleasure Al. Don't tell the boys nothing about me being engaged. I want to surprise them.   Your pal,   JACK.

Sacramento, California, August 16

FRIEND AL: Well Al I got the surprise of my life last night. Howard called me up after I got to my room and tells me I am going back to the White Sox. Come to find out, when they sold me out here they kept a option on me and yesterday they exercised it. He told me I would have to report at once. So I packed up as quick as I could and then went down to say good-by to the kid. She was all broke up and wanted to go along with me but I told her I didn't have enough dough to get married. She said she would come anyway and we could get married in Chi but I told her she better wait. She cried all over my sleeve. She sure is gone on me Al and I couldn't help feeling sorry for her but I promised to send for her in October and then everything will be all O. K. She asked me how much I was going to get in the big league and I told her I would get a lot more money than out here because I wouldn't play if I didn't. You know me Al.

I come over here to Sacramento with the club this morning and I am leaving to-night for Chi. I will get there next Tuesday and I guess Callahan will work me right away because he must of seen his mistake in letting me go by now. I will show them Al.

I looked up the skedule and I seen where we play in Detroit the fifth and sixth of September. I hope they will let me pitch there Al. Violet goes to the games and I will make her sorry she give me that kind of treatment. And I will make them Tigers sorry they kidded me last spring. I ain't afraid of Cobb or none of them now, Al.

Your pal,   JACK.

Chicago, Illinois, August 27

AL: Well old pal I guess I busted in right. Did you notice what I done to them Athaletics, the best ball club in the country? I bet Violet wishes she hadn't called me no busher.

I got here last Tuesday and set up in the stand and watched the game that afternoon. Washington was playing here and Johnson pitched. I was anxious to watch him because I had heard so much about him. Honest Al he ain't as fast as me. He shut them out, but they never was much of a hitting club. I went to the clubhouse after the game and shook hands with the bunch. Kid Gleason the assistant manager seemed pretty glad to see me and he says Well have you learned something? I says Yes I guess I have. He says Did you see the game this afternoon? I says I had and he asked me what I thought of Johnson. I says I don't think so much of him. He says Well I guess you ain't learned nothing then. He says What was the matter with Johnson's work? I says He ain't got nothing but a fast ball. Then he says Yes and Rockefeller ain't got nothing but a hundred million bucks.

Well I asked Callahan if he was going to give me a chance to work and he says he was. But I sat on the bench a couple of days and he didn't ask me to do nothing. Finally I asked him why not and he says I am saving you to work against a good club, the Athletics. Well the Athletics come and I guess you know by this time what I done to them. And I had to work against Bender at that but I ain't afraid of none of them now Al.

Baker didn't hit one hard all afternoon and I didn't have no trouble with Collins neither. I let them down with five blows all though the papers give them seven. Them reporters here don't no more about scoreing than some old woman. They give Barry a hit on a fly ball that Bodie ought to of eat up, only he stumbled or something and they handed Oldring a two base hit on a ball that Weaver had to duck to get out of the way from. But I don't care nothing about reporters. I beat them Athaletics and beat them good, five to one. Gleason slapped me on the back after the game and says Well you learned something after all. Rub some arnicky on your head to keep the swelling down and you may be a real pitcher yet. I says I ain't got no swell head. He says No. If I hated myself like you do I would be a moveing picture actor.

Well I asked Callahan would he let me pitch up to Detroit and he says Sure. He says Do you want to get revenge on them? I says, Yes I did. He says Well you have certainly got some comeing. He says I never seen no man get worse treatment than them Tigers give you last spring. I says Well they won't do it this time because I will know how to pitch to them. He says How are you going to pitch to Cobb? I says I am going to feed him on my slow one. He says Well Cobb had ought to make a good meal off of that. Then we quit jokeing and he says You have improved a hole lot and I am going to work you right along regular and if you can stand the gaff I may be able to use you in the city serious. You know Al the White Sox plays a city serious every fall with the Cubs and the players makes quite a lot of money. The winners gets about eight hundred dollars a peace and the losers about five hundred. We will be the winners if I have anything to say about it.

I am tickled to death at the chance of working in Detroit and I can't hardly wait till we get there. Watch my smoke Al. Your pal, JACK.

P. S. I am going over to Allen's flat to play cards a while to-night. Allen is the left-hander that was on the training trip with us. He ain't got a thing, Al, and I don't see how he gets by. He is married and his wife's sister is visiting them. She wants to meet me but it won't do her much good. I seen her out to the game today and she ain't much for looks.

Detroit, Mich., September 6

FRIEND AL: I got a hole lot to write but I ain't got much time because we are going over to Cleveland on the boat at ten p.m. I made them Tigers like it Al just like I said I would. And what do you think, Al, Violet called me up after the game and wanted to see me but I will tell you about the game first.

They got one hit off of me and Cobb made it a scratch single that he beat out. If he hadn't of been so dam fast I would of had a no hit game. At that Weaver could of threw him out if he had of started after the ball in time. Crawford didn't get nothing like a hit and I whiffed him once. I give two walks both of them to Bush but he is such a little guy that you can't pitch to him.

When I was warming up before the game Callahan was standing beside me and pretty soon Jennings come over. Jennings says You ain't going to pitch that bird are you? And Callahan said Yes he was. Then Jennings says I wish you wouldn't because my boys is all tired out and can't run the bases. Callahan says They won't get no chance to-day. No, says Jennings I suppose not. I suppose he will walk them all and they won't have to run. Callahan says He won't give no bases on balls, he says. But you better tell your gang that he is liable to bean them and they better stay away from the plate. Jennings says He won't never hurt my boys by beaning them. Then I cut in. Nor you neither, I says. Callahan laughs at that so I guess I must of pulled a pretty good one. Jennings didn't have no comeback so he walks away.

Then Cobb come over and asked if I was going to work. Callahan told him Yes. Cobb says How many innings? Callahan says All the way. Then Cobb says Be a good fellow Cal and take him out early. I am lame and can't run. I butts in then and said Don't worry, Cobb. You won't have to run because we have got a catcher who can hold them third strikes. Callahan laughed again and says to me You sure did learn something out on that Coast.

Well I walked Bush right off the real and they all begun to holler on the Detroit bench There he goes again. Vitt come up and Jennings yells Leave your bat in the bag Osker. He can't get them over. But I got them over for that bird all O. K. and he pops out trying to bunt. And then I whiffed Crawford. He starts off with a foul that had me scared for a minute because it was pretty close to the foul line and it went clear out of the park. But he missed a spitter a foot and then I supprised them Al. I give him a slow ball and I honestly had to laugh to see him lunge for it. I bet he must of strained himself. He throwed his bat way like he was mad and I guess he was. Cobb came prancing up like he always does and yells Give me that slow one Boy. So I says All right. But I fooled him. Instead of giveing him a slow one like I said I was going I handed him a spitter. He hit it all right but it was a line drive right in Chase's hands. He says Pretty lucky Boy but I will get you next time. I come right back at him. I says Yes you will.

Well Al I had them going like that all through. About the sixth inning Callahan yells from the bench to Jennings What do you think of him now? And Jennings didn't say nothing. What could he of said?

Cobb makes their one hit in the eighth. He never would of made it if Schalk had of let me throw him spitters instead of fast ones. At that Weaver ought to of threw him out. Anyway they didn't score and we made a monkey out of Dubuque, or whatever his name is.

Well Al I got back to the hotel and snuck down the street a ways and had a couple of beers before supper. So I come to the supper table late and Walsh tells me they had been several phone calls for me. I go down to the desk and they tell me to call up a certain number. So I called up and they charged me a nickel for it. A girl's voice answers the phone and I says Was they some one there that wanted to talk to Jack Keefe? She says You bet they is. She says Don't you know me, Jack? This is Violet. Well, you could of knocked me down with a peace of bread. I says What do you want? She says Why I want to see you. I says Well you can't see me. She says Why what's the matter, Jack? What have I did that you should be sore at me? I says I guess you know all right. You called me a busher. She says Why I didn't do nothing of the kind. I says Yes you did on that postcard. She says I didn't write you no postcard.

Then we argued along for a while and she swore up and down that she didn't write me no postcard or call me no busher. I says Well then why didn't you write me a letter when I was in Frisco? She says she had lost my address. Well Al I don't know if she was telling me the truth or not but may be she didn't write that post-card after all. She was crying over the telephone so I says Well it is too late for I and you to get together because I am engaged to be married. Then she screamed and I hang up the receiver. She must of called back two or three times because they was calling my name round the hotel but I wouldn't go near the phone. You know me Al.

Well when I hang up and went back to finish my supper the dining room was locked. So I had to go out and buy myself a sandwich. They soaked me fifteen cents for a sandwich and a cup of coffee so with the nickel for the phone I am out twenty cents altogether for nothing. But then I would of had to tip the waiter in the hotel a dime.

Well Al I must close and catch the boat. I expect a letter from Hazel in Cleveland and maybe Violet will write to me too. She is stuck on me all right Al. I can see that. And I don't believe she could of wrote that post-card after all. Yours truly, JACK.

Boston, Massachusetts, September 12

OLD PAL: Well Al I got a letter from Hazel in Cleveland and she is comeing to Chi in October for the city serious. She asked me to send her a hundred dollars for her fare and to buy some cloths with. I sent her thirty dollars for the fare and told her she could wait till she got to Chi to buy her cloths. She said she would give me the money back as soon as she seen me but she is a little short now because one of her girl friends borrowed fifty off of her. I guess she must be pretty softhearted Al. I hope you and Bertha can come up for the wedding because I would like to have you stand up with me.

I all so got a letter from Violet and they was blots all

over it like she had been crying. She swore she did not write that postcard and said she would die if I didn't believe her. She wants to know who the lucky girl is who I am engaged to be married to. I believe her Al when she says she did not write that postcard but it is too late now. I will let you know the date of my wedding as soon as I find out.

I guess you seen what I done in Cleveland and here. Allen was going awful bad in Cleveland and I relieved him in the eighth when we had a lead of two runs. I put them out in one-two-three order in the eighth but had hard work in the ninth due to rotten support. I walked Johnston and Chapman and Turner sacrificed them ahead. Jackson come up then and I had two strikes on him. I could of whiffed him but Schalk makes me give him a fast one when I wanted to give him a slow one. He hit it to Berger and Johnston ought to of been threw out at the plate but Berger fumbles and then has to make the play at first base. He got Jackson all O. K. but they was only one run behind then and Chapman was on third base. Lajoie was up next and Callahan sends out word for me to walk him. I thought that was rotten manageing because Lajoie or no one else can hit me when I want to cut loose. So after I give him two bad balls I tried to slip over a strike on him but the lucky stiff hit it on a line to Weaver. Anyway the game was over and I felt pretty good. But Callahan don't appresiate good work Al. He give me a call in the club-house and said if I ever disobeyed his orders again he would suspend me without no pay and lick me too. Honest Al it was all I could do to keep from wrapping his jaw but Gleason winks at me not to do nothing.

I worked the second game here and give them three hits two of which was bunts that Lord ought to of eat up. I got better support in Frisco than I been getting

here Al. But I don't care. The Boston bunch couldn't of
hit me with a shovvel and we beat them two to nothing.
I worked against Wood at that. They call him Smoky
Joe and they say he has got a lot of speed.

Boston is some town, Al, and I wish you and Bertha
could come here sometime. I went down to the wharf
this morning and seen them unload the fish. They must
of been a million of them but I didn't have time to count
them. Every one of them was five or six times as big as a
blue gill.

Violet asked me what would be my address in New
York City so I am dropping her a postcard to let her
know all though I don't know what good it will do her. I
certainly won't start no correspondents with her now that
I am engaged to be married.   Yours truly,   JACK.

New York, New York, September 16

FRIEND AL: I opened the serious here and beat them
easy but I know you must of saw about it in the Chi
papers. At that they don't give me no fair show in the
Chi papers. One of the boys bought one here and I seen
in it where I was lucky to win that game in Cleveland
If I knowed which one of them reporters wrote that I
would punch his jaw.

Al I told you Boston was some town but this is the
real one. I never seen nothing like it and I been going
some since we got here. I walked down Broadway the
Main Street last night and I run into a couple of the
ball players and they took me to what they call the
Garden but it ain't like the gardens at home because
this one is indoors. We sat down to a table and had
several drinks. Pretty soon one of the boys asked me if i
was broke and I says No, why? He says You better
get some lubricateing oil and loosen up. I don't know

what he meant but pretty soon when we had had a lot of drinks the waiter brings a check and hands it to me. It was for one dollar. I says Oh I ain't paying for all of them. The waiter says This is just for that last drink.

I thought the other boys would make a holler but they didn't say nothing. So I give him a dollar bill and even then he didn't act satisfied so I asked him what he was waiting for and he said Oh nothing, kind of sassy. I was going to bust him but the boys give me the sign to shut up and not to say nothing. I excused myself pretty soon because I wanted to get some air. I give my check for my hat to a boy and he brought my hat and I started going and he says Haven't you forgot something? I guess he must of thought I was wearing a overcoat.

Then I went down the Main Street again and some man stopped me and asked me did I want to go to the show. He said he had a ticket. I asked him what show and he said the Follies. I never heard of it but I told him I would go if he had a ticket to spare. He says I will spare you this one for three dollars. I says You must take me for some boob. He says No I wouldn't insult no boob. So I walks on but if he had of insulted me I would of busted him.

I went back to the hotel then and run into Kid Gleason. He asked me to take a walk with him so out I go again. We went to the corner and he bought me a beer. He don't drink nothing but pop himself. The two drinks was only ten cents so I says This is the place for me. He says Where have you been? and I told him about paying one dollar for three drinks. He says I see I will have to take charge of you. Don't go round with them ball players no more. When you want to go out and see the sights come to me and I will stear you. So to-night he is going to stear me. I will write to you from Philadelphia.

Your pal,   JACK.

FRIEND AL: They won't be no game here to-day because it is raining. We all been loafing round the hotel all day and I am glad of it because I got all tired out over in New York City. I and Kid Gleason went round together the last couple of nights over there and he wouldn't let me spend no money. I seen a lot of girls that I would of like to of got acquainted with but he wouldn't even let me answer them when they spoke to me. We run in to a couple of peaches last night and they had us spotted too. One of them says I'll bet you're a couple of ball players. But Kid says You lose your bet. I am a bellhop and the big rube with me is nothing but a pitcher.

One of them says What are you trying to do kid somebody? He says Go home and get some soap and remove your disguise from your face. I didn't think he ought to talk like that to them and I called him about it and said maybe they was lonesome and it wouldn't hurt none if we treated them to a soda or something. But he says Lonesome. If I don't get you away from here they will steal everything you got. They won't even leave you your fast ball. So we left them and he took me to a picture show. It was some California pictures and they made me think of Hazel so when I got back to the hotel I sent her three postcards.

Gleason made me go to my room at ten oclock both nights but I was pretty tired anyway because he had walked me all over town. I guess we must of saw twenty shows. He says I would take you to the grand opera only it would be throwing money away because we can hear Ed Walsh for nothing. Walsh has got some voice Al a loud high tenor.

To-morrow is Sunday and we have a double header Monday on account of the rain to-day. I thought sure I would get another chance to beat the Athaletics and

I asked Callahan if he was going to pitch me here but he said he thought he would save me to work against Johnson in Washington. So you see Al he must figure I am about the best he has got. I'll beat him Al if they get a couple of runs behind me.   Yours truly,   JACK.

P. S. They was a letter here from Violet and it pretty near made me feel like crying. I wish they was two of me so both them girls could be happy.

Washington, D. C., September 22

DEAR OLD AL: Well Al here I am in the capital of the United States. We got in last night and I been walking round town all morning. But I didn't tire myself out because I am going to pitch against Johnson this afternoon.

This is the prettiest town I ever seen but I believe they is more colored people here than they is in Evansville or Chi. I seen the White House and the Monumunt. They say that Bill Sullivan and Gabby St. once catched a baseball that was threw off of the top of the Monumunt but I bet they couldn't catch it if I throwed it.

I was in to breakfast this morning with Gleason and Bodie and Weaver and Fournier. Gleason says I'm surprised that you ain't sick in bed to-day. I says Why?

He says Most of our pitchers gets sick when Cal tells them they are going to work against Johnson. He says Here's these other fellows all feeling pretty sick this morning and they ain't even pitchers. All they have to do is hit against him but it looks like as if Cal would have to send substitutes in for them. Bodie is complaining of a sore arm which he must of strained drawing to two card flushes. Fournier and Weaver have strained their legs doing the tango dance. Nothing could cure them except to hear that big Walter had got throwed out of his machine and wouldn't be able to pitch against us in this serious.

I says I feel O. K. and I ain't afraid to pitch against Johnson and I ain't afraid to hit against him neither. Then Weaver says Have you ever saw him work? Yes, I says, I seen him in Chi. Then Weaver says Well if you have saw him work and ain't afraid to hit against him I'll bet you would go down to Wall Street and holler Hurrah for Roosevelt. I says No I wouldn't do that but I ain't afraid of no pitcher and what is more if you get me a couple of runs I'll beat him. Then Fournier says Oh we will get you a couple of runs all right. He says That's just as easy as catching whales with a angleworm.

Well Al I must close and go in and get some lunch. My arm feels great and they will have to go some to beat me Johnson or no Johnson.   Your pal,   JACK.

Washington, D. C., September 22

FRIEND AL: Well I guess you know by this time that they didn't get no two runs for me, only one, but I beat him just the same. I beat him one to nothing and Callahan was so pleased that he give me a ticket to the theater. I just got back from there and it is pretty late and I already have wrote you one letter to-day but I am going to sit up and tell you about it.

It was cloudy before the game started and when I was warming up I made the remark to Callahan that the dark day ought to make my speed good. He says Yes and of course it will handicap Johnson.

While Washington was takeing their practice their two coachers Schaefer and Altrock got out on the infield and cut up and I pretty near busted laughing at them. They certainly is funny Al. Callahan asked me what was I laughing at and I told him and he says That's the first time I ever seen a pitcher laugh when he was going to work against Johnson. He says Griffith is a pretty good fellow to give us something to laugh at before he shoots that guy at us.

I warmed up good and told Schalk not to ask me for my spitter much because my fast one looked faster than I ever seen it. He says It won't make much difference what you pitch to-day. I says Oh, yes, it will because Callahan thinks enough of me to work me against Johnson and I want to show him he didn't make no mistake. Then Gleason says No he didn't make no mistake. Wasting Cicotte or Scotty would of been a mistake in this game.

Well, Johnson whiffs Weaver and Chase and makes Lord pop out in the first inning. I walked their first guy but I didn't give Milan nothing to bunt and finally he flied out. And then I whiffed the next two. On the bench Callahan says That's the way, boy. Keep that up and we got a chance.

Johnson had fanned four of us when I come up with two out in the third inning and he whiffed me to. I fouled one though that if I had ever got a good hold of I would of knocked out of the park. In the first seven innings we didn't have a hit off of him. They had got five or six lucky ones off of me and I had walked two or three, but I cut loose with all I had when they was men on and they couldn't do nothing with me. The only reason I walked so many was because my fast one was jumping so. Honest Al it was so fast that Evans the umpire couldn't see it half the time and he called a lot of balls that was right over the heart.

Well I come up in the eighth with two out and the score still nothing and nothing. I had whiffed the second time as well as the first but it was account of Evans missing one on me. The eighth started with Shanks muffing a fly ball off of Bodie. It was way out by the fence so he got two bases on it and he went to third while they was throwing Berger out. Then Schalk whiffed.

Callahan says Go up and try to meet one Jack. It might as well be you as anybody else. But your old pal didn't whiff this time Al. He gets two strikes on me with fast ones and then I passed up two bad ones. I took my healthy at the next one and slapped it over first base. I guess I could of made two bases on it but I didn't want to tire myself out. Anyway Bodie scored and I had them beat. And my hit was the only one we got off of him so I guess he is a pretty good pitcher after all Al.

They filled up the bases on me with one out in the ninth but it was pretty dark then and I made McBride and their catcher look like suckers with my speed.

I felt so good after the game that I drunk one of them pink cocktails. I don't know what their name is. And then I sent a postcard to poor little Violet. I don't care nothing about her but it don't hurt me none to try and cheer her up once in a while. We leave here Thursday night for home and they had ought to be two or three letters there for me from Hazel because I haven't heard from her lately. She must of lost my road addresses.

Your pal,	JACK.

P. S. I forgot to tell you what Callahan said after the game. He said I was a real pitcher now and he is going to use me in the city serious. If he does Al we will beat them Cubs sure.

Chicago, Illinois, September 27

FRIEND AL: They wasn't no letter here at all from Hazel and I guess she must of been sick. Or maybe she didn't think it was worth while writeing as long as she is comeing next week.

I want to ask you to do me a favor Al and that is to see if you can find me a house down there. I will want to move in with Mrs. Keefe, don't that sound funny Al? sometime in the week of October twelfth. Old man Cutting's house or that yellow house across from you would be O. K. I would rather have the yellow one so as to be near you. Find out how much rent they want Al and if it is not no more than twelve dollars a month get it for me. We will buy our furniture here in Chi when Hazel comes.

We have a couple of days off now Al and then we play St. Louis two games here. Then Detroit comes to finish the season the third and fourth of October.

Your pal, JACK.

Chicago, Illinois, October 3

DEAR OLD AL: Thanks Al for getting the house. The one-year lease is O. K. You and Bertha and me and Hazel can have all sorts of good times together. I guess the walk needs repairs but I can fix that up when I come. We can stay at the hotel when we first get there.

I wish you could of came up for the city serious Al but anyway I want you and Bertha to be sure and come up for our wedding. I will let you know the date as soon as Hazel gets here.

The serious starts Tuesday and this town is wild over it. The Cubs finished second in their league and we was fifth in ours but that don't scare me none. We would of finished right on top if I had of been here all season.

Callahan pitched one of the bushers against Detroit this afternoon and they beat him bad. Callahan is save-ing up Scott and Allen and Russell and Cicotte and I for the big show. Walsh isn't in no shape and neither is Benz. It looks like I would have a good deal to do because most of them others can't work no more than once in four days and Allen ain't no good at all.

We have a day to rest after to-morrow's game with the Tigers and then we go at them Cubs.

Your pal,   JACK.

P. S. I have got it figured that Hazel is fixing to surprise me by dropping in on me because I haven't heard nothing yet.

Chicago, Illinois, October 7

FRIEND AL: Well Al you know by this time that they beat me to-day and tied up the serious. But I have still got plenty of time Al and I will get them before it is over. My arm wasn't feeling good Al and my fast ball didn't hop like it had ought to. But it was the rotten support I got that beat me. That lucky stiff Zimmerman was the only guy that got a real hit off of me and he must of shut his eyes and throwed his bat because the ball he hit was a foot over his head. And if they hadn't been makeing all them errors behind me they wouldn't of been nobody on bases when Zimmerman got that lucky scratch. The serious now stands one and one Al and it is a cinch we will beat them even if they are a bunch of lucky stiffs. They has been great big crowds at both games and it looks like as if we should ought to get over eight hundred dollars a peace if we win and we will win sure because I will beat them three straight if necessary.

But Al I have got bigger news than that for you and I am the happyest man in the world. I told you I had not heard from Hazel for a long time. To-night when I got back to my room they was a letter waiting for me from her.

Al she is married. Maybe you don't know why that

makes me happy but I will tell you. She is married to Kid Levy the middle weight. I guess my thirty dollars is gone because in her letter she called me a cheap skate and she inclosed one one-cent stamp and two twos and said she was paying me for the glass of beer I once bought her. I bought her more than that Al but I won't make no holler. She all so said not for me to never come near her or her husband would bust my jaw. I ain't afraid of him or no one else Al but they ain't no danger of me ever bothering them. She was no good and I was sorry the minute I agreed to marry her.

But I was going to tell you why I am happy or maybe you can guess. Now I can make Violet my wife and she's got Hazel beat forty ways. She ain't nowheres near as big as Hazel but she's classier Al and she will make me a good wife. She ain't never asked me for no money.

I wrote her a letter the minute I got the good news and told her to come on over here at once at my expense. We will be married right after the serious is over and I want you and Bertha to be sure and stand up with us. I will wire you at my own expence the exact date.

It all seems like a dream now about Violet and I haveing our misunderstanding Al and I don't see how I ever could of accused her of sending me that postcard. You and Bertha will be just as crazy about her as I am when you see her Al. Just think Al I will be married inside of a week and to the only girl I ever could of been happy with instead of the woman I never really cared for except as a passing fancy. My happyness would be complete Al if I had not of let that woman steal thirty dollars off of me. Your happy pal, JACK.

P. S. Hazel probibly would of insisted on us takeing a trip to Niagara falls or somewheres but I know Violet will be perfectly satisfied if I take her right down to Bedford. Oh you little yellow house.

FRIEND AL: Well Al we have got them beat three games
to one now and will wind up the serious to-morrow sure.
Callahan sent me in to save poor Allen yesterday and I
stopped them dead. But I don't care now Al. I have lost
all interest in the game and I don't care if Callahan
pitches me to-morrow or not. My heart is just about
broke Al and I wouldn't be able to do myself justice feeling the way I do.

I have lost Violet Al and just when I was figureing on
being the happyest man in the world. We will get the
big money but it won't do me no good. They can keep
my share because I won't have no little girl to spend
it on.

Her answer to my letter was waiting for me at home
to-night. She is engaged to be married to Joe Hill the
big lefthander Jennings got from Providence. Honest Al
I don't see how he gets by. He ain't got no more curve
ball than a rabbit and his fast one floats up there like a
big balloon. He beat us the last game of the regular season here but it was because Callahan had a lot of bushers
in the game.

I wish I had knew then that he was stealing my girl
and I would of made Callahan pitch me against him.
And when he come up to bat I would of beaned him.
But I don't suppose you could hurt him by hitting him
in the head. The big stiff. Their wedding ain't going to
come off till next summer and by that time he will be
pitching in the Southwestern Texas League for about
fifty dollars a month.

Violet wrote that she wished me all the luck and happyness in the world but it is too late for me to be happy
Al and I don't care what kind of luck I have now.

Al you will have to get rid of that lease for me. Fix it
up the best way you can. Tell the old man I have

changed my plans. I don't know just yet what I will do but maybe I will go to Australia with Mike Donlin's team. If I do I won't care if the boat goes down or not. I don't believe I will even come back to Bedford this winter. It would drive me wild to go past that little house every day and think how happy I might of been.

Maybe I will pitch to-morrow Al and if I do the serious will be over to-morrow night. I can beat them Cubs if I get any kind of decent support. But I don't care now Al.   Yours truly,   JACK.

Chicago, Illinois, October 12

AL: Your letter received. If the old man won't call it off I guess I will have to try and rent the house to some one else. Do you know of any couple that wants one Al? It looks like I would have to come down there myself and fix things up someway. He is just mean enough to stick me with the house on my hands when I won't have no use for it.

They beat us the day before yesterday as you probibly know and it rained yesterday and to-day. The papers says it will be all O. K. to-morrow and Callahan tells me I am going to work. The Cub pitchers was all shot to peaces and the bad weather is just nuts for them because it will give Cheney a good rest. But I will beat him Al if they don't kick it away behind me.

I must close because I promised Allen the little left-hander that I would come over to his flat and play cards a while to-night and I must wash up and change my collar. Allen's wife's sister is visiting them again and I would give anything not to have to go over there. I am through with girls and don't want nothing to do with them.

I guess it is maybe a good thing it rained to-day because I dreamt about Violet last night and went out and got a couple of high balls before breakfast this morning. I hadn't never drank nothing before breakfast before and it made me kind of sick. But I am all O. K. now.

Your pal,   JACK.

Chicago, Illinois, October 13

DEAR OLD AL: The serious is all over Al. We are the champions and I done it. I may be home the day after to-morrow or I may not come for a couple of days. I want to see Comiskey before I leave and fix up about my contract for next year. I won't sign for no less than five thousand and if he hands me a contract for less than that I will leave the White Sox flat on their back. I have got over fourteen hundred dollars now Al with the city serious money which was $814.30 and I don't have to worry.

Them reporters will have to give me a square deal this time Al. I had everything and the Cubs done well to score a run. I whiffed Zimmerman three times. Some of the boys say he ain't no hitter but he is a hitter and a good one Al only he could not touch the stuff I got. The umps give them their run because in the fourth inning I had Leach flatfooted off of second base and Weaver tagged him O. K. but the umps wouldn't call it. Then Schulte the lucky stiff happened to get a hold of one and pulled it past first base. I guess Chase must of been asleep. Anyway they scored but I don't care because we piled up six runs on Cheney and I drove in one of them myself with one of the prettiest singles you ever see. It was a spitter and I hit it like a shot. If I had hit it square it would of went out of the park.

Comiskey ought to feel pretty good about me winning and I guess he will give me a contract for anything I want. He will have to or I will go to the Federal League.

We are all invited to a show to-night and I am going with Allen and his wife and her sister Florence. She is O. K. Al and I guess she thinks the same about me. She must because she was out to the game to-day and seen me hand it to them. She maybe ain't as pretty as Violet and Hazel but as they say beauty isn't only so deep.

Well Al tell the boys I will be with them soon. I have gave up the idea of going to Australia because I would have to buy a evening full-dress suit and they tell me they cost pretty near fifty dollars. Yours truly, Jack.

Chicago, Illinois, October 14

FRIEND AL: Never mind about that lease. I want the house after all Al and I have got the suprise of your life for you.

When I come home to Bedford I will bring my wife with me. I and Florence fixed things all up after the show last night and we are going to be married to-morrow morning. I am a busy man to-day Al because I have got to get the license and look round for furniture. And I have also got to buy some new cloths but they are haveing a sale on Cottage Grove Avenue at Clark's store and I know one of the clerks there.

I am the happyest man in the world Al. You and Bertha and I and Florence will have all kinds of good times together this winter because I know Bertha and Florence will like each other. Florence looks something like Bertha at that. I am glad I didn't get tied up with Violet or Hazel even if they was a little bit prettier than Florence.

Florence knows a lot about baseball for a girl and you would be suprised to hear her talk. She says I am the best pitcher in the league and she has saw them all. She

all so says I am the best looking ball player she ever
seen but you know how girls will kid a guy Al. You will
like her O. K. I fell for her the first time I seen her.

Your old pal,   JACK.

P. S. I signed up for next year. Comiskey slapped me
on the back when I went in to see him and told me I
would be a star next year if I took good care of myself.
I guess I am a star without waiting for next year Al. My
contract calls for twenty-eight hundred a year which is
a thousand more than I was getting. And it is pretty
near a cinch that I will be in on the World Serious money
next season.

P. S. I certainly am relieved about that lease. It would
of been fierce to of had that place on my hands all winter and not getting any use out of it. Everything is all
O. K. now. Oh you little yellow house.

III. The Busher's Honeymoon

Chicago, Illinois, October 17

FRIEND AL: Well Al it looks as if I would not be writeing so much to you now that I am a married man. Yes Al
I and Florrie was married the day before yesterday just
like I told you we was going to be and Al I am the happyest man in the world though I have spent $30 in the
last 3 days incluseive. You was wise Al to get married in
Bedford where not nothing is nearly half so dear. My
expenses was as follows:

License	$ 2.00
Preist	3.50
Haircut and shave	.35
Shine	.05

Carfair	.45
New suit	14.50
Show tickets	3.00
Flowers	.50
Candy	.30
Hotel	4.50
Tobacco both kinds	.25

You see Al it costs a hole lot of money to get married here. The sum of what I have wrote down is $29.40 but as I told you I have spent $30 and I do not know what I have did with that other $0.60. My new brother-in-law Allen told me I should ought to give the preist $5 and I thought it should be about $2 the same as the license so I split the difference and give him $3.50. I never seen him before and probily won't never see him again so why should I give him anything at all when it is his business to marry couples? But I like to do the right thing. You know me Al.

I thought we would be in Bedford by this time but Florrie wants to stay here a few more days because she says she wants to be with her sister. Allen and his wife is thinking about takeing a flat for the winter instead of going down to Waco Texas where they live. I don't see no sense in that when it costs so much to live here but it is none of my business if they want to throw their money away. But I am glad I got a wife with some sense though she kicked because I did not get no room with a bath which would cost me $2 a day instead of $1.50. I says I guess the clubhouse is still open yet and if I want a bath I can go over there and take the shower. She says Yes and I suppose I can go and jump in the lake. But she would not do that Al because the lake here is cold at this time of the year.

When I told you about my expenses I did not include

in it the meals because we would be eating them if I was getting married or not getting married only I have to pay for six meals a day now instead of three and I didn't used to eat no lunch in the playing season except once in a while when I knowed I was not going to work that afternoon. I had a meal ticket which had not quite ran out over to a resturunt on Indiana Ave and we eat there for the first day except at night when I took Allen and his wife to the show with us and then he took us to a chop suye resturunt. I guess you have not never had no chop suye Al and I am here to tell you you have not missed nothing but when Allen was going to buy the supper what could I say? I could not say nothing.

Well yesterday and to-day we been eating at a resturunt on Cottage Grove Ave near the hotel and at the resturunt on Indiana that I had the meal ticket at only I do not like to buy no new meal ticket when I am not going to be round here no more than a few days. Well Al I guess the meals has cost me all together about $1.50 and I have eat very little myself. Florrie always wants desert ice cream or something and that runs up into money faster than regular stuff like stake and ham and eggs.

Well Al Florrie says it is time for me to keep my promise and take her to the moveing pictures which is $0.20 more because the one she likes round here costs a dime apeace. So I must close for this time and will see you soon.   Your pal,   JACK.

Chicago, Illinois, October 22

AL: Just a note Al to tell you why I have not yet came to Bedford yet where I expected I would be long before this time. Allen and his wife have took a furnished flat for the winter and Allen's wife wants Florrie to stay

here untill they get settled. Meentime it is costing me a
hole lot of money at the hotel and for meals besides I
am paying $10 a month rent for the house you got for
me and what good am I getting out of it? But Florrie
wants to help her sister and what can I say? Though I
did make her promise she would not stay no longer
than next Saturday at least. So I guess Al we will be,
home on the evening train Saturday and then may be I
can save some money.

I know Al that you and Bertha will like Florrie when
you get acquainted with her spesially Bertha though
Florrie dresses pretty swell and spends a hole lot of time
fusing with her face and her hair.

She says to me to-night Who are you writing to and
I told her Al Blanchard who I have told you about a
good many times. She says I bet you are writeing to some
girl and acted like as though she was kind of jealous. So
I thought I would tease her a little and I says I don't
know no girls except you and Violet and Hazel. Who is
Violet and Hazel? she says. I kind of laughed and says
Oh I guess I better not tell you and then she says I guess
you will tell me. That made me kind of mad because no
girl can't tell me what to do. She says Are you going to
tell me? and I says No.

Then she says If you don't tell me I will go over to
Marie's that is her sister Allen's wife and stay all night.
I says Go on and she went downstairs but I guess she
probily went to get a soda because she has some money
of her own that I give her. This was about two hours
ago and she is probily down in the hotel lobby now trying to scare me by makeing me believe she has went to
her sister's. But she can't fool me Al and I am now going
out to mail this letter and get a beer. I won't never tell
her about Violet and Hazel if she is going to act like that.

Yours truly,   JACK.

Chicago, Illinois, October 24

FRIEND AL: I guess I told you Al that we would be home Saturday evening. I have changed my mind. Allen and his wife has a spair bedroom and wants us to come there and stay a week or two. It won't cost nothing except they will probily want to go out to the moveing pictures nights and we will probily have to go along with them and I am a man Al that wants to pay his share and not be cheap.

I and Florrie had our first quarrle the other night. I guess I told you the start of it but I don't remember. I made some crack about Violet and Hazel just to tease Florrie and she wanted to know who they was and I would not tell her. So she gets sore and goes over to Marie's to stay all night. I was just kidding Al and was willing to tell her about them two poor girls whatever she wanted to know except that I don't like to brag about girls being stuck on me. So I goes over to Marie's after her and tells her all about them except that I turned them down cold at the last minute to marry her because I did not want her to get all swelled up. She made me sware that I did not never care nothing about them and that was easy because it was the truth. So she come back to the hotel with me just like I knowed she would when I ordered her to.

They must not be no mistake about who is the boss in my house. Some men lets their wife run all over them but I am not that kind. You know me Al.

I must get busy and pack my suitcase if I am going to move over to Allen's. I sent three collars and a shirt to the laundrey this morning so even if we go over there to-night I will have to take another trip back this way in a day or two. I won't mind Al because they sell my kind of beer down to the corner and I never seen it sold nowheres else in Chi. You know the kind it is, eh Al? I wish I was lifting a few with you to-night.

Your pal,   JACK.

Chicago, Illinois, October 28

DEAR OLD AL: Florrie and Marie has went downtown shopping because Florrie thinks she has got to have a new dress though she has got two changes of cloths now and I don't know what she can do with another one. I hope she don't find none to suit her though it would not hurt none if she got something for next spring at a reduckshon. I guess she must think I am Charles A. Comiskey or somebody. Allen has went to a colledge football game. One of the reporters give him a pass. I don't see nothing in football except a lot of scrapping between little slobs that I could lick the whole bunch of them so I did not care to go. The reporter is one of the guys that travled round with our club all summer. He called up and said he hadn't only the one pass but he was not hurting my feelings none because I would not go to no rotten football game if they payed me.

The flat across the hall from this here one is for rent furnished. They want $40 a month for it and I guess they think they must be lots of suckers running round loose. Marie was talking about it and says Why don't you and Florrie take it and then we can be right together all winter long and have some big times? Florrie says It would be all right with me. What about it Jack? I says What do you think I am? I don't have to live in no high price flat when I got a home in Bedford where they ain't no people trying to hold everybody up all the time. So they did not say no more about it when they seen I was in ernest. Nobody cannot tell me where I

am going to live sister-in-law or no sister-in-law. If I
was to rent the rotten old flat I would be paying $50 a
month rent includeing the house down in Bedford. Fine
chance Al.

Well Al I am lonesome and thirsty so more later.

Your pal,   JACK.

Chicago, Illinois, November 2

FRIEND AL: Well Al I got some big news for you. I am
not comeing to Bedford this winter after all except to
make a visit which I guess will be round Xmas. I changed
my mind about that flat across the hall from the Allens
and decided to take it after all. The people who was in
it and owns the furniture says they would let us have it
till the 1 of May if we would pay $42.50 a month which
is only $2.50 a month more than they would of let us
have it for for a short time. So you see we got a bargain
because it is all furnished and everything and we won't
have to blow no money on furniture besides the club
goes to California the middle of Febuery so Florrie
would not have no place to stay while I am away.

The Allens only subleased their flat from some other
people till the 2 of Febuery and when I and Allen goes
West Marie can come over and stay with Florrie so you
see it is best all round. If we should of boughten furniture it would cost us in the neighborhood of $100 even
without no piano and they is a piano in this here flat
which makes it nice because Florrie plays pretty good
with one hand and we can have lots of good times at
home without it costing us nothing except just the bear
liveing expenses. I consider myself lucky to of found out
about this before it was too late and somebody else had
of gotten the tip.

Now Al old pal I want to ask a great favor of you Al.

I all ready have payed one month rent $10 on the house in Bedford and I want you to see the old man and see if he won't call off that lease. Why should I be paying $10 a month rent down there and $42.50 up here when the house down there is not no good to me because I am liveing up here all winter? See Al? Tell him I will gladly give him another month rent to call off the lease but don't tell him that if you don't have to. I want to be fare with him.

If you will do this favor for me, Al, I won't never forget it. Give my kindest to Bertha and tell her I am sorry I and Florrie won't see her right away but you see how it is Al. Yours, JACK.

Chicago, Illinois, November 30

FRIEND AL: I have not wrote for a long time have I Al but I have been very busy. They was not enough furniture in the flat and we have been buying some more. They was enough for some people maybe but I and Florrie is the kind that won't have nothing but the best. The furniture them people had in the liveing room was oak but they had a bookcase bilt in in the flat that was mohoggeny and Florrie would not stand for no joke combination like that so she moved the oak chairs and table in to the spair bedroom and we went downtown to buy some mohoggeny. But it costs too much Al and we was feeling pretty bad about it when we seen some Sir Cashion walnut that was prettier even than the mohoggeny and not near so expensive. It is not no real Sir Cashion walnut but it is just as good and we got it reasonable. Then we got some mission chairs for the dining room because the old ones was just straw and was no good and we got a big lether couch for $9 that somebody can sleep on if we get to much company.

I hope you and Bertha can come up for the holidays and see how comfertible we are fixed. That is all the new furniture we have boughten but Florrie set her heart on some old Rose drapes and a red table lamp that is the biggest you ever seen Al and I did not have the heart to say no. The hole thing cost me in the neighbor-hood of $110 which is very little for what we got and then it will always be ourn even when we move away from this flat though we will have to leave the furniture that belongs to the other people but their part of it is not no good anyway.

I guess I told you Al how much money I had when the season ended. It was $1400 all told includeing the city serious money. Well Al I got in the neighborhood of $800 left because I give $200 to Florrie to send down to Texas to her other sister who had a bad egg for a hus-band that managed a club in the Texas Oklahoma League and this was the money she had to pay to get the divorce. I am glad Al that I was lucky enough to marry happy and get a good girl for my wife that has got some sense and besides if I have got $800 left I should not worry as they say.   Your pal,   JACK.

Chicago, Illinois, December 7

DEAR OLD AL: No I was in ernest Al when I says that I wanted you and Bertha to come up here for the holi-days. I know I told you that I might come to Bedford for the holidays but that is all off. I have gave up the idea of comeing to Bedford for the holidays and I want you to be sure and come up here for the holidays and I will show you a good time. I would love to have Bertha come to and she can come if she wants to only Florrie don't know if she would have a good time or not and thinks maybe she would rather stay in Bedford and you came alone. But be sure and have Bertha come if she wants to come but maybe she would not injoy it. You know best Al.

I don't think the old man give me no square deal on that lease but if he wants to stick me all right. I am grateful to you Al for trying to fix it up but maybe you could of did better if you had of went at it in a different way. I am not finding no fault with my old pal though. Don't think that. When I have a pal I am the man to stick to him threw thick and thin. If tho old man is going to hold me to that lease I guess I will have to stand it and I guess I won't starv to death for no $10 a month because I am going to get $2800 next year besides the city serious money and maybe we will get into the World Serious too. I know we will if Callahan will pitch me every 3d day like I wanted him to last season. But if you had of approached the old man in a different way maybe you could of fixed it up. I wish you would try it again Al if it is not no trouble.

We had Allen and his wife here for thanksgiveing dinner and the dinner cost me better than $5. I thought we had enough to eat to last a week but about six o'clock at night Florrie and Marie said they was hungry and we went downtown and had dinner all over again and I payed for it and it cost me $5 more. Allen was all ready to pay for it when Florrie said No this day's treat is on us so I had to pay for it but I don't see why she did not wait and let me do the talking. I was going to pay for it any way.

Be sure and come and visit us for the holidays Al and of coarse if Bertha wants to come bring her along. We will be glad to see you both. I won't never go back on a friend and pal. You know me Al. Your old pal,   JACK.

Chicago, Illinois, December 20

FRIEND AL: I don't see what can be the matter with Bertha because you know Al we would not care how she dressed and would not make no kick if she come up here in a night gown. She did not have no license to say we was to swell for her because we did not never think of nothing like that. I wish you would talk to her again Al and tell her she need not get sore on me and that both her and you is welcome at my house any time I ask you to come. See if you can't make her change her mind Al because I feel like as if she must of took offense at something I may of wrote you. I am sorry you and her are not comeing but I suppose you know best. Only we was getting all ready for you and Florrie said only the other day that she wished the holidays was over but that was before she knowed you was not comeing. I hope you can come Al.

Well Al I guess there is not no use talking to the old man no more. You have did the best you could but I wish I could of came down there and talked to him. I will pay him his rotten old $10 a month and the next time I come to Bedford and meet him on the street I will bust his jaw. I know he is a old man Al but I don't like to see nobody get the best of me and I am sorry I ever asked him to let me off. Some of them old skinflints has no heart Al but why should I fight with a old man over chicken feed like $10? Florrie says a star pitcher like I should not ought never to scrap about little things and I guess she is right Al so I will pay the old man his $10 a month if I have to.

Florrie says she is jealous of me writeing to you so much and she says she would like to meet this great old pal of mine. I would like to have her meet you to Al and I would like to have you change your mind and come and visit us and I am sorry you can't come Al.

Yours truly,   JACK.

Chicago, Illinois, December 27

OLD PAL: I guess all these lefthanders is alike though I thought this Allen had some sense. I thought he was different from the most and was not no rummy but they are all alike Al and they are all lucky that somebody don't hit them over the head with a ax and kill them but I guess at that you could not hurt no lefthanders by hitting them over the head. We was all down on State St. the day before Xmas and the girls was all tired out and ready to go home but Allen says No I guess we better stick down a while because now the crowds is out and it will be fun to watch them. So we walked up and down State St. about a hour longer and finally we come in front of a big jewlry store window and in it was a swell dimond ring that was marked $100. It was a ladies' ring so Marie says to Allen Why don't you buy that for me? And Allen says Do you really want it? And she says she did.

So we tells the girls to wait and we goes over to a salloon where Allen has got a friend and gets a check cashed and we come back and he bought the ring. Then Flortie looks like as though she was getting all ready to cry and I asked her what was the matter and she says I had not boughten her no ring not even when we was engaged. So I and Allen goes back to the salloon and I gets a check cashed and we come back and bought another ring but I did not think the ring Allen had boughten was worth no $100 so I gets one for $75. Now Al you know I am not makeing no kick on spending a little money for a present for my own wife but I had allready boughten her a rist watch for $15 and a rist watch was just what she had wanted. I was willing to give her the ring if she had not of wanted the rist watch more than the ring but when I give her the ring I kept the rist watch and did not tell her nothing about it.

Well I come downtown alone the day after Xmas and they would not take the rist watch back in the store where I got it. So I am going to give it to her for a New Year's present and I guess that will make Allen feel like a dirty doose. But I guess you cannot hurt no lefthander's feelings at that. They are all alike. But Allen has not got nothing but a dinky curve ball and a fast ball that looks like my slow one. If Comiskey was not good hearted he would of sold him long ago.

I sent you and Bertha a cut glass dish Al which was the best I could get for the money and it was pretty high pricet at that. We was glad to get the pretty pincushions from you and Bertha and Florrie says to tell you that we are well supplied with pincushions now because the ones you sent makes a even half dozen. Thanks Al for remembering us and thank Bertha too though I guess you paid for them.   Your pal,   JACK.

Chicago, Illinois, Januery 3

OLD PAL: Al I been pretty sick ever since New Year's eve. We had a table at 1 of the swell resturunts downtown and I never seen so much wine drank in my life. I would rather of had beer but they would not sell us none so I found out that they was a certain kind that you can get for $1 a bottle and it is just as good as the kind that has got all them fancy names but this lefthander starts ordering some other kind about 11 oclock and it was $5 a bottle and the girls both says they liked it better. I could not see a hole lot of difference myself and I would of gave $0.20 for a big stine of my kind of beer. You know me Al. Well Al you know they is not nobody than can drink more than your old pal and I was all O. K. at one oclock but I seen the girls was getting kind of sleepy so I says we better go home.

Then Marie says Oh, shut up and don't be no quiter. I says You better shut up yourself and not be telling me to shut up, and she says What will you do if I don't shut up? And I says I would bust her in the jaw. But you know Al I would not think of busting no girl. Then Florrie says You better not start nothing because you had to much to drink or you would not be talking about busting girls in the jaw. Then I says I don't care if it is a girl I bust or a lefthander. I did not mean nothing at all Al but Marie says I had insulted Allen and he gets up and slaps my face. Well Al I am not going to stand that from nobody not even if he is my brother-in-law and a lefthander that has not got enough speed to brake a pain of glass.

So I give him a good beating and the waiters butts in and puts us all out for fighting and I and Florrie comes home in a taxi and Allen and his wife don't get in till about 5 oclock so I guess she must of had to of took him to a doctor to get fixed up. I been in bed ever since till just this morning kind of sick to my stumach. I guess I must of eat something that did not agree with me. Allen come over after breakfast this morning and asked me was I all right so I guess he is not sore over the beating I give him or else he wants to make friends because he has saw that I am a bad guy to monkey with.

Florrie tells me a little while ago that she paid the hole bill at the resturunt with my money because Allen was broke so you see what kind of a cheap skate he is Al and some day I am going to bust his jaw. She won't tell me how much the bill was and I won't ask her to no more because we had a good time outside of the fight and what do I care if we spent a little money?

Yours truly,   JACK.

Chicago, Illinois, Januery 20

FRIEND AL: Allen and his wife have gave up the flat across the hall from us and come over to live with us because we got a spair bedroom and why should they not have the bennifit of it? But it is pretty hard for the girls to have to cook and do the work when they is four of us so I have a hired girl who does it all for $7 a week. It is great stuff Al because now we can go round as we please and don't have to wait for no dishes to be washed or nothing. We generally almost always has dinner downtown in the evening so it is pretty soft for the girl too. She don't generally have no more than one meal to get because we generally run round downtown till late and don't get up till about noon.

That sounds funny don't it Al, when I used to get up at 5 every morning down home. Well Al I can tell you something else that may sound funny and that is that I lost my taste for beer. I don't seem to care for it no more and I found I can stand allmost as many drinks of other stuff as I could of beer. I guess Al they is not nobody ever lived can drink more and stand up better under it than me. I make the girls and Allen quit every night.

I only got just time to write you this short note because Florrie and Marie is giving a big party to-night and I and Allen have got to beat it out of the house and stay out of the way till they get things ready. It is Marie's berthday and she says she is 22 but say Al if she is 22 Kid Gleason is 30. Well Al the girls says we must blow so I will run out and mail this letter.

Yours truly,   JACK.

Chicago, Illinois, Januery 31

AL: Allen is going to take Marie with him on the training trip to California and of course Florrie has been at

me to take her along. I told her postivly that she can't
go. I can't afford no stunt like that but still I am up
against it to know what to do with her while we are on
the trip because Marie won't be here to stay with her.
I don't like to leave her here all alone but they is nothing
to it Al I can't afford to take her along. She says I don't
see why you can't take me if Allen takes Marie. And I
says That stuff is all O. K. for Allen because him and
Marie has been grafting off of us all winter. And then she
gets mad and tells me I should not ought to say her
sister was no grafter. I did not mean nothing like that
Al but you don't never know when a woman is going to
take offense.

If our furniture was down in Bedford everything
would be all O. K. because I could leave her there and
I would feel all O. K. because I would know that you
and Bertha would see that she was getting along O. K.
But they would not be no sense in sending her down to
a house that has not no furniture in it. I wish I knowed
somewheres where she could visit Al. I would be willing
to pay her bord even.

Well Al enough for this time.   Your old pal,   JACK.

Chicago, Illinois, Febuery 4

FRIEND AL: You are a real old pal Al and I certainly
am greatful to you for the invatation. I have not told
Florrie about it yet but I am sure she will be tickled to
death and it is certainly kind of you old pal. I did not
never dream of nothing like that. I note what you say
Al about not excepting no bord but I think it would be
better and I would feel better if you would take something say about $2 a week.

I know Bertha will like Florrie and that they will get
along O. K. together because Florrie can learn her how

to make her cloths look good and fix her hair and fix up her face. I feel like as if you had took a big load off of me Al and I won't never forget it.

If you don't think I should pay no bord for Florrie all right. Suit yourself about that old pal.

We are leaveing here the 20 of Febuery and if you don't mind I will bring Florrie down to you about the 18. I would like to see the old bunch again and spesially you and Bertha.   Yours,   JACK.

P. S. We will only be away till April 14 and that is just a nice visit. I wish we did not have no flat on our hands.

Chicago, Illinois, Febuery 9

OLD PAL: I want to thank you for asking Florrie to come down there and visit you Al but I find she can't get away. I did not know she had no engagements but she says she may go down to her folks in Texas and she don't want to say that she will come to visit you when it is so indefanate. So thank you just the same Al and thank Bertha too.

Florrie is still at me to take her along to California but honest Al I can't do it. I am right down to my last $50 and I have not payed no rent for this month. I owe the hired girl 2 weeks' salery and both I and Florrie needs some new cloths.

Florrie has just came in since I started writeing this letter and we have been talking some more about California and she says maybe if I would ask Comiskey he would take her along as the club's guest. I had not never thought of that Al and maybe he would because he is a pretty good scout and I guess I will go and see him about it. The league has its skedule meeting here tomorrow and may be I can see him down to the hotel where

they meet at. I am so worried Al that I can't write no
more but I will tell you how I come out with Comiskey.

                              Your pal,   JACK.

FRIEND AL: I am up against it right Al and I don't know
where I am going to head in at. I went down to the
hotel where the league was holding its skedule meeting
at and I seen Comiskey and got some money off of the
club but I owe all the money I got off of them and I am
still wondering what to do about Florrie.

Comiskey was busy in the meeting when I went down
there and they was not no chance to see him for a while
so I and Allen and some of the boys hung round and
had a few drinks and fanned. This here Joe Hill the
busher that Detroit has got that Violet is hooked up to
was round the hotel. I don't know what for but I felt
like busting his jaw only the boys told me I had better
not do nothing because I might kill him and any way he
probily won't be in the league much longer. Well finally
Comiskey got threw the meeting and I seen him and he
says Hello young man what can I do for you? And I says
I would like to get $100 advance money. He says Have
you been takeing care of yourself down in Bedford? And
I told him I had been liveing here all winter and it did
not seem to make no hit with him though I don't see
what business it is of hisn where I live.

So I says I had been takeing good care of myself.
And I have Al. You know that. So he says I should come
to the ball park the next day which is to-day and he
would have the secretary take care of me but I says I
could not wait and so he give me $100 out of his pocket
and says he would have it charged against my salary. I

was just going to brace him about the California trip when he got away and went back to the meeting.

Well Al I hung round with the bunch waiting for him to get threw again and we had some more drinks and finally Comiskey was threw again and I braced him in the lobby and asked him if it was all right to take my wife along to California. He says Sure they would be glad to have her along. And then I says Would the club pay her fair? He says I guess you must of spent that $100 buying some nerve. He says Have you not got no sisters that would like to go along to? He says Does your wife insist on the drawing room or will she take a lower birth? He says Is my special train good enough for her?

Then he turns away from me and I guess some of the boys must of heard the stuff he pulled because they was laughing when he went away but I did not see nothing to laugh at. But I guess he ment that I would have to pay her fair if she goes along and that is out of the question Al. I am up against it and I don't know where I am going to head in at.   Your pal,   JACK.

Chicago, Illinois, Febuery 12

DEAR OLD AL: I guess everything will be all O. K. now at least I am hopeing it will. When I told Florrie about how I come out with Comiskey she bawled her head off and I thought for a while I was going to have to call a doctor or something but pretty soon she cut it out and we sat there a while without saying nothing. Then she says If you could get your salery razed a couple of hundred dollars a year would you borrow the money ahead somewheres and take me along to California? I says Yes I would if I could get a couple hundred dollars more salery but how could I do that when I had signed a contract for $2800 last fall allready? She says Don't you think you are worth more than $2800? And I says Yes of coarse I was worth more than $2800. She says Well if you will go and talk the right way to Comiskey I believe he will give you $3000 but you must be sure you go at it the right way and don't go and ball it all up.

Well we argude about it a while because I don't want to hold nobody up Al but finally I says I would. It would not be holding nobody up anyway because I am worth $3000 to the club if I am worth a nichol. The papers is all saying that the club has got a good chance to win the pennant this year and talking about the pitching staff and I guess they would not be no pitching staff much if it was not for I and one or two others—about one other I guess.

So it looks like as if everything will be all O. K. now Al. I am going to the office over to the park to see him the first thing in the morning and I am pretty sure that I will get what I am after because if I do not he will see that I am going to quit and then he will see what he is up against and not let me get away.

I will let you know how I come out.

Your pal,   JACK.

Chicago, Illinois, Febuery 14

FRIEND AL: Al old pal I have got a big supprise for you. I am going to the Federal League. I had a run in with Comiskey yesterday and I guess I told him a thing or 2. I guess he would of been glad to sign me at my own figure before I got threw but I was so mad I would not give him no chance to offer me another contract.

I got out to the park at 9 oclock yesterday morning and it was a hour before he showed up and then he kept me waiting another hour so I was pretty sore when I finally went in to see him. He says Well young man what can I do for you? I says I come to see about my contract. He says Do you want to sign up for next year all ready? I says No I am talking about this year. He says I thought I and you talked business last fall. And I says Yes but now I think I am worth more money and I want to sign a contract for $3000. He says If you behave yourself and work good this year I will see that you are took care of. But I says That won't do because I have got to be sure I am going to get $3000.

Then he says I am not sure you are going to get anything. I says What do you mean? And he says I have gave you a very fare contract and if you don't want to live up to it that is your own business. So I give him a awful call Al and told him I would jump to the Federal League. He says Oh, I would not do that if I was you. They are haveing a hard enough time as it is. So I says something back to him and he did not say nothing to me and I beat it out of the office.

I have not told Florrie about the Federal League business yet as I am going to give her a big supprise. I bet they will take her along with me on the training trip and pay her fair but even if they don't I should not worry because I will make them give me a contract for $4000 a year and then I can afford to take her with me on all the trips.

I will go down and see Tinker to-morrow morning and I will write you to-morrow night Al how much salery they are going to give me. But I won't sign for no less than $4000. You know me Al.   Yours,   JACK.

Chicago, Illinois, Febuery 15

OLD PAL: It is pretty near midnight Al but I been to bed a couple of times and I can't get no sleep. I am worried to death Al and I don't know where I am going to head in at. Maybe I will go out and buy a gun Al and end it all and I guess it would be better for everybody. But I cannot do that Al because I have not got the money to buy a gun with.

I went down to see Tinker about signing up with the Federal League and he was busy in the office when I come in. Pretty soon Buck Perry the pitcher that was with Boston last year come out and seen me and as Tinker was still busy we went out and had a drink together. Buck shows me a contract for $5000 a year and Tinker had allso gave him a $500 bonus. So pretty soon I went up to the office and pretty soon Tinker seen me and called me into his private office and asked what did I want. I says I was ready to jump for $4000 and a bonus. He says I thought you was signed up with the White Sox. I says Yes I was but I was not satisfied. He says That does not make no difference to me if you are satisfied or not. You ought to of came to me before you signed a contract. I says I did not know enough but I know better now. He says Well it is to late now. We cannot have nothing to do with you because you have went and signed a contract with the White Sox. I argude with him a while and asked him to come out and have a drink so we could talk it over but he said he was busy so they was nothing for me to do but blow.

So I am not going to the Federal League Al and I will not go with the White Sox because I have got a raw deal. Comiskey will be sorry for what he done when his team starts the season and is up against it for good pitchers and then he will probily be willing to give me anything I ask for but that don't do me no good now Al. I am way in debt and no chance to get no money from nobody. I wish I had of stayed with Terre Haute Al and never saw this league.   Your pal,   JACK.

Chicago, Illinois, Febuery 17

FRIEND AL: Al don't never let anybody tell you that these here lefthanders is right. This Allen my own brother-in-law who married sisters has been grafting and spongeing on me all winter Al. Look what he done to me now Al. You know how hard I been up against it for money and I know he has got plenty of it because I seen it on him. Well Al I was scared to tell Florrie I was cleaned out and so I went to Allen yesterday and says I had to have $100 right away because I owed the rent and owed the hired girl's salery and could not even pay no grocery bill. And he says No he could not let me have none because he has got to save all his money to take his wife on the trip to California. And here he has been liveing on me all winter and maybe I could of took my wife to California if I had not of spent all my money takeing care of this no good lefthander and his wife. And Al honest he has not got a thing and ought not to be in the league. He gets by with a dinky curve ball and has not got no more smoke than a rabbit or something.

Well Al I felt like busting him in the jaw but then I thought No I might kill him and then I would have Marie and Florrie both to take care of and God knows one of them is enough besides paying his funeral expenses. So I walked away from him without takeing a crack at him and went into the other room where Florrie and Marie was at. I says to Marie I says Marie I wish you would go in the other room a minute because I want to talk to Florrie. So Marie beats it into the other room and then I tells Florrie all about what Comiskey and the Federal League done to me. She bawled something awful and then she says I was no good and she wished she had not never married me. I says I wisht it too and then she says Do you mean that and starts to cry.

I told her I was sorry I says that because they is not

no use fusing with girls Al specially when they is your wife. She says No California trip for me and then she says What are you going to do? And I says I did not know. She says Well if I was a man I would do something. So then I got mad and I says I will do something. So I went down to the corner salloon and started in to get good and drunk but I could not do it Al because I did not have the money.

Well old pal I am going to ask you a big favor and it is this I want you to send me $100 Al for just a few days till I can get on my feet. I do not know when I can pay it back Al but I guess you know the money is good and I know you have got it. Who would not have it when they live in Bedford? And besides I let you take $20 in June 4 years ago Al and you give it back but I would not have said nothing to you if you had of kept it. Let me hear from you right away old pal.

Yours truly,   JACK.

Chicago, Illinois, Febuery 19

AL: I am certainly greatful to you Al for the $100 which come just a little while ago. I will pay the rent with it and part of the grocery bill and I guess the hired girl will have to wait a while for hern but she is sure to get it because I don't never forget my debts. I have changed my mind about the White Sox and I am going to go on the trip and take Florrie along because I don't think it would not be right to leave her here alone in Chi when her sister and all of us is going.

I am going over to the ball park and up in the office pretty soon to see about it. I will tell Comiskey I changed my mind and he will be glad to get me back because the club has not got no chance to finish nowheres without me. But I won't go on no trip or give the club my services without them giveing me some more advance money so as I can take Florrie along with me because Al I would not go without her.

Maybe Comiskey will make my salery $3000 like I wanted him to when he sees I am willing to be a good fellow and go along with him and when he knows that the Federal League would of gladly gave me $4000 if I had not of signed no contract with the White Sox.

I think I will ask him for $200 advance money Al and if I get it may be I can send part of your $100 back to you but I know you cannot be in no hurry Al though you says you wanted it back as soon as possible. You could not be very hard up Al because it don't cost near so much to live in Bedford as it does up here.

Anyway I will let you know how I come out with Comiskey and I will write you as soon as I get out to Paso Robles if I don't get no time to write you before I leave.   Your pal,   JACK.

P. S. I have took good care of myself all winter Al and I guess I ought to have a great season.

P. S. Florrie is tickled to death about going along and her and I will have some time together out there on the Coast if I can get some money somewheres.

Chicago, Illinois, Febuery 21

FRIEND AL: I have not got the heart to write this letter to you Al. I am up here in my $42.50 a month flat and the club has went to California and Florrie has went too. I am flat broke Al and all I am asking you is to send me enough money to pay my fair to Bedford and they and all their leagues can go to hell Al.

I was out to the ball park early yesterday morning and some of the boys was there allready fanning and kidding each other. They tried to kid me to when I come in but I guess I give them as good as they give me. I was not in no mind for kidding Al because I was there on business and I wanted to see Comiskey and get it done with.

Well the secretary come in finally and I went up to him and says I wanted to see Comiskey right away. He says The boss was busy and what did I want to see him about and I says I wanted to get some advance money because I was going to take my wife on the trip. He says This would be a fine time to be telling us about it even if you was going on the trip.

And I says What do you mean? And he says You are not going on no trip with us because we have got wavers on you and you are sold to Milwaukee.

Honest Al I thought he was kidding at first and I was waiting for him to laugh but he did not laugh and finally I says What do you mean? And he says Cannot you understand no English? You are sold to Milwaukee. Then I says I want to see the boss. He says It won't do you no good to see the boss and he is to busy to see you. I says I want to get some money. And he says You cannot get no money from this club and all you get is your fair to Milwaukee. I says I am not going to no Milwaukee anyway and he says I should not worry about that. Suit yourself.

Well Al I told some of the boys about it and they was pretty sore and says I ought to bust the secretary in the jaw and I was going to do it when I thought No I better not because he is a little guy and I might kill him.

I looked all over for Kid Gleason but he was not nowheres round and they told me he would not get into town till late in the afternoon. If I could of saw him Al he would of fixed me all up. I asked 3 or 4 of the boys for some money but they says they was all broke.

But I have not told you the worst of it yet Al. When

I come back to the flat Allen and Marie and Florrie was busy packing up and they asked me how I come out. I told them and Allen just stood there stareing like a big rummy but Marie and Florrie both begin to cry and I almost felt like as if I would like to cry to only I am not no baby Al.

Well Al I told Florrie she might just is well quit packing and make up her mind that she was not going nowheres till I got money enough to go to Bedford where I belong. She kept right on crying and it got so I could not stand it no more so I went out to get a drink because I still had just about a dollar left yet.

It was about 2 oclock when I left the flat and pretty near 5 when I come back because I had ran in to some fans that knowed who I was and would not let me get away and besides I did not want to see no more of Allen and Marie till they was out of the house and on their way.

But when I come in Al they was nobody there. They was not nothing there except the furniture and a few of my things scattered round. I sit down for a few minutes because I guess I must of had to much to drink but finally I seen a note on the table addressed to me and I seen it was Florrie's writeing.

I do not remember just what was there in the note Al because I tore it up the minute I read it but it was something about I could not support no wife and Allen had gave her enough money to go back to Texas and she was going on the 6 oclock train and it would not do me no good to try and stop her.

Well Al they was not no danger of me trying to stop her. She was not no good and I wisht I had not of never saw either she or her sister or my brother-in-law.

For a minute I thought I would follow Allen and his

wife down to the deepo where the special train was to pull out of and wait till I see him and punch his jaw but I seen that would not get me nothing.

So here I am all alone Al and I will have to stay here till you send me the money to come home. You better send me $25 because I have got a few little debts I should ought to pay before I leave town. I am not going to Milwaukee Al because I did not get no decent deal and nobody cannot make no sucker out of me.

Please hurry up with the $25 Al old friend because I am sick and tired of Chi and want to get back there with my old pal.   Yours,   JACK.

P. S. Al I wish I had of took poor little Violet when she was so stuck on me.

IV. A New Busher Breaks In

Chicago, Illinois, March 2

FRIEND AL: Al that peace in the paper was all O. K. and the right dope just like you said. I seen president Johnson the president of the league to-day and he told me the peace in the papers was the right dope and Comiskey did not have no right to sell me to Milwaukee because the Detroit Club had never gave no wavers on me. He says the Detroit Club was late in fileing their claim and Comiskey must of tooken it for granted that they was going to wave but president Johnson was pretty sore about it at that and says Comiskey did not have no right to sell me till he was positive that they was not no team that wanted me.

It will probily cost Comiskey some money for acting

like he done and not paying no attention to the rules and I would not be supprised if president Johnson had him throwed out of the league.

Well I asked president Johnson should I report at once to the Detroit Club down south and he says No you better wait till you hear from Comiskey and I says What has Comiskey got to do with it now? And he says Comiskey will own you till he sells you to Detroit or somewheres else. So I will have to go out to the ball park to-morrow and see is they any mail for me there because I probily will get a letter from Comiskey telling me I am sold to Detroit.

If I had of thought at the time I would of knew that Detroit never would give no wavers on me after the way I showed Cobb and Crawford up last fall and I might of knew too that Detroit is in the market for good pitchers because they got a rotten pitching staff but they won't have no rotten staff when I get with them.

If necessary I will pitch every other day for Jennings and if I do we will win the pennant sure because Detroit has got a club that can get 2 or 3 runs every day and all as I need to win most of my games is 1 run. I can't hardly wait till Jennings works me against the White Sox and what I will do to them will be a plenty. It don't take no pitching to beat them anyway and when they get up against a pitcher like I they might as well leave their bats in the bag for all the good their bats will do them.

I guess Cobb and Crawford will be glad to have me on the Detroit Club because then they won't never have to hit against me except in practice and I won't pitch my best in practice because they will be teammates of mine and I don't never like to show none of my teammates up. At that though I don't suppose Jennings will let me do much pitching in practice because when he gets a hold of a good pitcher he won't want me to take no chances of throwing my arm away in practice.

Al just think how funny it will be to have me pitching for the Tigers in the same town where Violet lives and pitching on the same club with her husband. It will not be so funny for Violet and her husband though because when she has a chance to see me work regular she will find out what a mistake she made takeing that left-hander instead of a man that has got some future and soon will be makeing 5 or $6000 a year because I won't sign with Detroit for no less than $5000 at most. Of coarse I could of had her if I had of wanted to but still and all it will make her feel pretty sick to see me winning games for Detroit while her husband is batting fungos and getting splinters in his unie from slideing up and down the bench.

As for her husband the first time he opens his clam to me I will haul off and bust him one in the jaw but I guess he will know more than to start trouble with a man of my size and who is going to be one of their stars while he is just holding down a job because they feel sorry for him. I wish he could of got the girl I married instead of the one he got and I bet she would of drove him crazy. But I guess you can't drive a left-hander crazyer than he is to begin with.

I have not heard nothing from Florrie Al and I don't want to hear nothing. I and her is better apart and I wish she would sew me for a bill of divorce so she could not go round claiming she is my wife and disgraceing my name. If she would consent to sew me for a bill of divorce I would gladly pay all the expenses and settle with her for any sum of money she wants say about $75.00 or $100.00 and they is no reason I should give her a nichol after the way her and her sister Marie and her brother-in-law Allen grafted off of me. Probily I could sew her for a bill of divorce but they tell me it costs money to sew and if you just lay low and let the other side do the sewing it don't cost you a nichol.

It is pretty late Al and I have got to get up early to-morrow and go to the ball park and see is they any mail for me. I will let you know what I hear old pal.

Your old pal,   JACK.

Chicago, Illinois, March 4

AL: I am up against it again. I went out to the ball park office yesterday and they was nobody there except John somebody who is asst secretary and all the rest of them is out on the Coast with the team. Maybe this here John was trying to kid me but this is what he told me. First I says Is they a letter here for me? And he says No. And I says I was expecting word from Comiskey that I should join the Detroit Club and he says What makes you think you are going to Detroit? I says Comiskey asked wavers on me and Detroit did not give no wavers. He says Well that is not no sign that you are going to Detroit. If Comiskey can't get you out of the league he will probily keep you himself and it is a cinch he is not going to give no pitcher to Detroit no matter how rotten he is.

I says What do you mean? And he says You just stick round town till you hear from Comiskey and I guess you will hear pretty soon because he is comeing back from the Coast next Saturday. I says Well the only thing he can tell me is to report to Detroit because I won't never pitch again for the White Sox. Then John gets fresh and says I suppose you will quit the game and live on your saveings and then I blowed out of the office because I was scared I would loose my temper and break something.

So you see Al what I am up against. I won't never pitch for the White Sox again and I want to get with the Detroit Club but how can I if Comiskey won't let me go? All I can do is stick round till next Saturday and then I will see Comiskey and I guess when I tell him what I think of him he will be glad to let me go to Detroit or anywheres else. I will have something on him this time because I know that he did not pay no attention to the rules when he told me I was sold to Milwaukee and if he tries to slip something over on me I will tell president Johnson of the league all about it and then you will see where Comiskey heads in at.

Al old pal that $25.00 you give me at the station the other day is all shot to peaces and I must ask you to let me have $25.00 more which will make $75.00 all together includeing the $25.00 you sent me before I come home. I hate to ask you this favor old pal but I know you have got the money. If I am sold to Detroit I will get some advance money and pay up all my dedts incluseive.

If he don't let me go to Detroit I will make him come across with part of my salary for this year even if I don't pitch for him because I signed a contract and was ready to do my end of it and would of if he had not of been nasty and tried to slip something over on me. If he refuses to come across I will hire a attorney at law and he will get it all. So Al you see you have got a cinch on getting back what you lone me but I guess you know that Al without all this talk because you have been my old pal for a good many years and I have allways treated you square and tried to make you feel that I and you was equals and that my success was not going to make me forget my old friends.

Wherever I pitch this year I will insist on a salary of 5 or $6000 a year. So you see on my first pay day I will have enough to pay you up and settle the rest of

my dedts but I am not going to pay no more rent for
this rotten flat because they tell me if a man don't pay no
rent for a while they will put him out. Let them put me
out. I should not worry but will go and rent my old room
that I had before I met Florrie and got into all this
trouble.

The sooner you can send me that $35.00 the better
and then I will owe you $85.00 incluseive and I will
write and let you know how I come out with Comiskey.

Your pal,   JACK.

Chicago, Illinois, March 12

FRIEND AL: I got another big supprise for you and this
is it I am going to pitch for the White Sox after all. If
Comiskey was not a old man I guess I would of lost
my temper and beat him up but I am glad now that I
kept my temper and did not loose it because I forced
him to make a lot of consessions and now it looks like as
though I would have a big year both pitching and
money.

He got back to town yesterday morning and showed
up to his office in the afternoon and I was there waiting
for him. He would not see me for a while but finally
I acted like as though I was getting tired of waiting and
I guess the secretary got scared that I would beat it out
of the office and leave them all in the lerch. Anyway
he went in and spoke to Comiskey and then come out
and says the boss was ready to see me. When I went
into the office where he was at he says Well young man
what can I do for you? And I says I want you to give
me my release so as I can join the Detroit Club down
South and get in shape. Then he says What makes you
think you are going to join the Detroit Club? Because
we need you here. I says Then why did you try to sell

me to Milwaukee? But you could not because you could not get no wavers.

Then he says I thought I was doing you a favor by sending you to Milwaukee because they make a lot of beer up there. I says What do you mean? He says You been keeping in shape all this winter by trying to drink this town dry and besides that you tried to hold me up for more money when you allready had signed a contract allready and so I was going to send you to Milwaukee and learn you something and besides you tried to go with the Federal League but they would not take you because they was scared to.

I don't know where he found out all that stuff at Al and besides he was wrong when he says I was drinking to much because they is not nobody that can drink more than me and not be effected. But I did not say nothing because I was scared I would forget myself and call him some name and he is a old man. Yes I did say something. I says Well I guess you found out that you could not get me out of the league and then he says Don't never think I could not get you out of the league. If you think I can't send you to Milwaukee I will prove it to you that I can. I says You can't because Detroit won't give no wavers on me. He says Detroit will give wavers on you quick enough if I ask them.

Then he says Now you can take your choice you can stay here and pitch for me at the salery you signed up for and you can cut out the monkey business and drink water when you are thirsty or else you can go up to Milwaukee and drownd yourself in one of them brewrys. Which shall it be? I says How can you keep me or send me to Milwaukee when Detroit has allready claimed my services? He says Detroit has claimed a lot of things and they have even claimed the pennant but that is not no sign they will win it. He says And besides you would

not want to pitch for Detroit because then you would not
never have no chance to pitch against Cobb and show
him up.

Well Al when he says that I knowed he appresiated
what a pitcher I am even if he did try to sell me to Milwaukee or he would not of made that remark about the
way I can show Cobb and Crawford up. So I says Well
if you need me that bad I will pitch for you but I must
have a new contract. He says Oh I guess we can fix that
up O. K. and he steps out in the next room a while and
then he comes back with a new contract. And what do
you think it was Al? It was a contract for 3 years so
you can see I am sure of my job here for 3 years and
everything is all O. K.

The contract calls for the same salery a year for 3
years that I was going to get before for only 1 year
which is $2800.00 a year and then I will get in on the
city serious money too and the Detroit Club don't have
no city serious and have no chance to get into the World
Serious with the rotten pitching staff they got. So you see
Al he fixed me up good and that shows that he must
think a hole lot of me or he would of sent me to Detroit
or maybe to Milwaukee but I don't see how he could
of did that without no wavers.

Well Al I allmost forgot to tell you that he has gave
me a ticket to Los Angeles where the 2d team are practicing at now but where the 1st team will be at in about
a week. I am leaveing to-night and I guess before I go
I will go down to president Johnson and tell him that I
am fixed up all O. K. and have not got no kick comeing
so that president Johnson will not fine Comiskey for not
paying no attention to the rules or get him fired out of
the league because I guess Comiskey must be all O. K.
and good hearted after all.

I won't pay no attention to what he says about me

drinking this town dry because he is all wrong in regards to that. He must of been jokeing I guess because nobody but some boob would think he could drink this town dry but at that I guess I can hold more than anybody and not be effected. But I guess I will cut it out for a while at that because I don't want to get them sore at me after the contract they give me.

I will write to you from Los Angeles Al and let you know what the boys says when they see me and I will bet that they will be tickled to death. The rent man was round to-day but I seen him comeing and he did not find me. I am going to leave the furniture that belongs in the flat in the flat and allso the furniture I bought which don't amount to much because it was not no real Sir Cashion walnut and besides I don't want nothing round me to remind me of Florrie because the sooner her and I forget each other the better.

Tell the boys about my good luck Al but it is not no luck neither because it was comeing to me.

Yours truly, JACK.

Los Angeles, California, March 16

AL: Here I am back with the White Sox again and it seems to good to be true because just like I told you they are all tickled to death to see me. Kid Gleason is here in charge of the 2d team and when he seen me come into the hotel he jumped up and hit me in the stumach but he acts like that whenever he feels good so I could not get sore at him though he had no right to hit me in the stumach. If he had of did it in ernest I would of walloped him in the jaw.

He says Well if here ain't the old lady killer. He ment Al that I am strong with the girls but I am all threw with them now but he don't know nothing about the

troubles I had. He says Are you in shape? And I told
him Yes I am. He says Yes you look in shape like a
barrel. I says They is not no fat on me and if I am a
little bit bigger than last year it is because my mussels
is bigger. He says Yes your stumach mussels is emense
and you must of gave them plenty of exercise. Wait
till Bodie sees you and he will want to stick round you
all the time because you make him look like a broom
straw or something. I let him kid me along because what
is the use of getting mad at him? And besides he is all
O. K. even if he is a little rough.

I says to him A little work will fix me up all O. K.
and he says You bet you are going to get some work
because I am going to see to it myself. I says You will
have to hurry because you will be going up to Frisco
in a few days and I am going to stay here and join the
1st club. Then he says You are not going to do no such
a thing. You are going right along with me. I knowed
he was kidding me then because Callahan would not
never leave me with the 2d team no more after what I
done for him last year and besides most of the stars generally allways goes with the 1st team on the training trip.

Well I seen all the rest of the boys that is here with
the 2d team and they all acted like as if they was glad
to see me and why should not they be when they know
that me being here with the White Sox and not with
Detroit means that Callahan won't have to do no worrying about his pitching staff? But they is four or 5 young
recrut pitchers with the team here and I bet they is not
so glad to see me because what chance have they got?

If I was Comiskey and Callahan I would not spend
no money on new pitchers because with me and 1 or 2
of the other boys we got the best pitching staff in the
league. And instead of spending the money for new
pitching recruts I would put it all in a lump and buy Ty

Cobb or Sam Crawford off of Detroit or somebody else who can hit and Cobb and Crawford is both real hitters Al even if I did make them look like suckers. Who wouldn't?

Well Al to-morrow a.m. I am going out and work a little and in the p.m. I will watch the game between we and the Venice Club but I won't pitch none because Gleason would not dare take no chances of me hurting my arm. I will write to you in a few days from here because no matter what Gleason says I am going to stick here with the 1st team because I know Callahan will want me along with him for a attraction.

Your pal,   JACK.

San Francisco, California, March 20

FRIEND AL: Well Al here I am back in old Frisco with the 2d team but I will tell you how it happened Al. Yesterday Gleason told me to pack up and get ready to leave Los Angeles with him and I says No I am going to stick here and wait for the 1st team and then he says I guess I must of overlooked something in the papers because I did not see nothing about you being appointed manager of the club. I says No I am not manager but Callahan is manager and he will want to keep me with him. He says I got a wire from Callahan telling me to keep you with my club but of coarse if you know what Callahan wants better than he knows it himself why then go ahead and stay here or go jump in the Pacific Ocean.

Then he says I know why you don't want to go with me and I says Why? And he says Because you know I will make you work and won't let you eat everything on the bill of fair includeing the name of the hotel at which we are stopping at. That made me sore and I was just going to call him when he says Did not you marry

Mrs. Allen's sister? And I says Yes but that is not none of your business. Then he says Well I don't want to butt into your business but I heard you and your wife had some kind of a argument and she beat it. I says Yes, she give me a rotten deal. He says Well then I don't see where it is going to be very pleasant for you traveling round with the 1st club because Allen and his wife is both with that club and what do you want to be mixed up with them for? I says I am not scared of Allen or his wife or no other old hen.

So here I am Al with the 2d team but it is only for a while till Callahan gets sick of some of them pitchers he has got and sends for me so as he can see some real pitching. And besides I am glad to be here in Frisco where I made so many friends when I was pitching here for a short time till Callahan heard about my work and called me back to the big show where I belong at and nowheres else.   Yours truly,   Jack.

San Francisco, California, March 25

OLD PAL: Al I got a suprise for you. Who do you think I seen last night? Nobody but Hazel. Her name now is Hazel Levy because you know Al she married Kid Levy the middleweight and I wish he was champion of the world Al because then it would not take me more than about a minute to be champion of the world myself. I have not got nothing against him though because he married her and if he had not of I probily would of married her myself but at that she could not of treated me no worse than Florrie. Well they was setting at a table in the cafe where her and I use to go pretty near every night. She spotted me when I first come in and sends a waiter over to ask me to come and have a drink with them. I went over because they was no use being nasty and let bygones be bygones.

She interduced me to her husband and he asked me what I was drinking. Then she butts in and says Oh you must let Mr. Keefe buy the drinks because it hurts his feelings to have somebody else buy the drinks. Then Levy says Oh he is one of these here spendrifts is he? and she says Yes he don't care no more about a nichol than his right eye does. I says I guess you have got no holler comeing on the way I spend my money. I don't steal no moncy anyway. She says What do you mean? and I says I guess you know what I mean. How about that $30.00 that you borrowed off of me and never give it back? Then her husband cuts in and says You cut that line of talk out or I will bust you. I says Yes you will. And he says Yes I will.

Well Al what was the use of me starting trouble with him when he has got enough trouble right to home and besides as I say I have not got nothing against him. So I got up and blowed away from the table and I bet he was relieved when he seen I was not going to start nothing. I beat it out of there a while afterward because I was not drinking nothing and I don't have no fun setting round a place and lapping up ginger ail or something. And besides the music was rotten.

Al I am certainly glad I throwed Hazel over because she has grew to be as big as a horse and is all painted up. I don't care nothing about them big dolls no more or about no other kind neither. I am off of them all. They can all of them die and I should not worry.

Well Al I done my first pitching of the year this p.m. and I guess I showed them that I was in just as good a shape as some of them birds that has been working a month. I worked 4 innings against my old team the San Francisco Club and I give them nothing but fast ones but they sure was fast ones and you could hear them zip. Charlie O'Leary was trying to get out of the way of one of them and it hit his bat and went over first base for a base hit but at that Fournier would of eat it up if it had of been Chase playing first instead of Fournier.

That was the only hit they got off of me and they ought to of been ashamed to of tooken that one. But Gleason don't appresiate my work and him and I allmost come to blows at supper. I was pretty hungry and I ordered some stake and some eggs and some pie and some ice cream and some coffee and a glass of milk but Gleason would not let me have the pie or the milk and would not let me eat more than ½ the stake. And it is a wonder I did not bust him and tell him to mind his own business. I says What right have you got to tell me what to eat? And he says You don't need nobody to tell you what to eat you need somebody to keep you from floundering yourself. I says Why can't I eat what I want to when I have worked good?

He says Who told you you worked good and I says I did not need nobody to tell me. I know I worked good because they could not do nothing with me. He says Well it is a good thing for you that they did not start bunting because if you had of went to stoop over and pick up the ball you would of busted wide open. I says Why? and he says because you are hog fat and if you don't let up on the stable and fancy groceries we will have to pay 2 fairs to get you back to Chi. I don't remember now what I says to him but I says something you can bet on that. You know me Al.

I wish Al that Callahan would hurry up and order me to join the 1st team. If he don't Al I believe Gleason will starve me to death. A little slob like him don't realize that a big man like I needs good food and plenty of it.

Your pal,   JACK.

Salt Lake City, Utah, April 1

AL: Well Al we are on our way East and I am still
with the 2d team and I don't understand why Callahan
don't order me to join the 1st team but maybe it is because he knows that I am all right and have got the stuff
and he wants to keep them other guys round where he
can see if they have got anything.

The recrut pitchers that is along with our club have
not got nothing and the scout that reckommended them
must of been full of hops or something. It is not no common thing for a club to pick up a man that has got the
stuff to make him a star up here and the White
Sox was pretty lucky to land me but I don't understand
why they throw their money away on new pitchers when
none of them is no good and besides who would want
a better pitching staff than we got right now without no
raw recruts and bushers.

I worked in Oakland the day before yesterday but he
only let me go the 1st 4 innings. I bet them Oakland
birds was glad when he took me out. When I was in that
league I use to just throw my glove in the box and them
Oakland birds was licked and honest Al some of them
turned white when they seen I was going to pitch the
other day.

I felt kind of sorry for them and I did not give them
all I had so they got 5 or 6 hits and scored a couple of
runs. I was not feeling very good at that and besides we
got some awful excuses for a ball player on this club and
the support they give me was the rottenest I ever seen
gave anybody. But some of them won't be in this league
more than about 10 minutes more so I should not fret
as they say.

We play here this afternoon and I don't believe I will
work because the team they got here is not worth wasteing nobody on. They must be a lot of boobs in this

town Al because they tell me that some of them has got
½ a dozen wives or so. And what a man wants with 1
wife is a misery to me let alone a ½ dozen.

I will probily work against Denver because they got
a good club and was champions of the Western League
last year. I will make them think they are champions of
the Epworth League or something.

Yours truly,   JACK.

Des Moines, Iowa, April 10

FRIEND AL: We got here this a.m. and this is our last
stop and we will be in old Chi to-morrow to open the
season. The 1st team gets home to-day and I would be
there with them if Callahan was a real manager who
knowed something about manageing because if I am
going to open the season I should ought to have 1 day
of rest at home so I would have all my strength to open
the season. The Cleveland Club will be there to open
against us and Callahan must know that I have got them
licked any time I start against them.

As soon as my name is announced to pitch the Cleveland Club is licked or any other club when I am right
and they don't kick the game away behind me.

Gleason told me on the train last night that I was
going to pitch here to-day but I bet by this time he has
got orders from Callahan to let me rest and to not give
me no more work because suppose even if I did not
start the game to-morrow I probily will have to finish it.

Gleason has been sticking round me like as if I had a
million bucks or something. I can't even sit down and
smoke a cigar but what he is there to knock the ashes
off of it. He is O. K. and good-hearted if he is a little
rough and keeps hitting me in the stumach but I wish he
would leave me alone sometimes espesially at meals.

He was in to breakfast with me this a.m. and after I got threw I snuck off down the street and got something to eat. That is not right because it costs me money when I have to go away from the hotel and eat and what right has he got to try and help me order my meals? Because he don't know what I want and what my stumach wants.

My stumach don't want to have him punching it all the time but he keeps on doing it. So that shows he don't know what is good for me. But he is a old man Al otherwise I would not stand for the stuff he pulls. The 1st thing I am going to do when we get to Chi is I am going to a resturunt somewheres and get a good meal where Gleason or no one else can't get at me. I know allready what I am going to eat and that is a big stake and a apple pie and that is not all.

Well Al watch the papers and you will see what I done to that Cleveland Club and I hope Lajoie and Jackson is both in good shape because I don't want to pick on no cripples.   Your pal,   JACK.

Chicago, Illinois, April 16

OLD PAL: Yesterday was the 1st pay day old pal and I know I promised to pay you what I owe you and it is $75.00 because when I asked you for $35.00 before I went West you only sent me $25.00 which makes the hole sum $75.00. Well Al I can't pay you now because the pay we drawed was only for 4 days and did not amount to nothing and I had to buy a meal ticket and fix up about my room rent.

And then they is another thing Al which I will tell you about. I come into the clubhouse the day the season opened and the 1st guy I seen was Allen. I was going up to bust him but he come up and held his hand out and what was they for me to do but shake hands with him if he is going to be yellow like that? He says Well Jack I am glad they did not send you to Milwaukee and I bet you will have a big year. I says Yes I will have a big year O. K. if you don't sick another 1 of your sister-in-laws on to me. He says Oh don't let they be no hard feelings about that. You know it was not no fault of mine and I bet if you was to write to Florrie everything could be fixed up O. K.

I says I don't want to write to no Florrie but I will get a attorney at law to write to her. He says You don't even know where she is at and I says I don't care where she is at. Where is she? He says She is down to her home in Waco, Texas, and if I was you I would write to her myself and not let no attorney at law write to her because that would get her mad and besides what do you want a attorney at law to write to her about? I says I am going to sew her for a bill of divorce.

Then he says On what grounds? and I says Dessertion. He says You better not do no such thing or she will sew you for a bill of divorce for none support and then you will look like a cheap guy. I says I don't care what I look like. So you see Al I had to send Florrie $10.00 or maybe she would be mean enough to sew me for a bill of divorce on the ground of none support and that would make me look bad.

Well Al, Allen told me his wife wanted to talk to me and try and fix things up between I and Florrie but I give him to understand that I would not stand for no meeting with his wife and he says Well suit yourself about that but they is no reason you and I should quarrel.

You see Al he don't want no mix-up with me because he knows he could get nothing but the worst of it. I will be friends with him but I won't have nothing to do with Marie because if it had not of been for she and

Florrie I would have money in the bank besides not being in no danger of getting sewed for none support.

I guess you must of read about Joe Benz getting married and I guess he must of got a good wife and 1 that don't bother him all the time because he pitched the opening game and shut Cleveland out with 2 hits. He was pretty good Al, better than I ever seen him and they was a couple of times when his fast ball was pretty near as fast as mine.

I have not worked yet Al and I asked Callahan to-day what was the matter and he says I was waiting for you to get in shape. I says I am in shape now and I notice that when I was pitching in practice this a.m. they did not hit nothing out of the infield. He says That was because you are so spread out that they could not get nothing past you. He says The way you are now you cover more ground than the grandstand. I says Is that so? And he walked away.

We got out on a trip to Cleveland and Detroit and St. Louis in a few days and maybe I will take my regular turn then because the other pitchers has been getting away lucky because most of the hitters has not got their batting eye as yet but wait till they begin hitting and then it will take a man like I to stop them.

The 1st of May is our next pay day Al and then I will have enough money so as I can send you the $75.00.

Your pal,   JACK.

Detroit, Michigan, April 28

FRIEND AL: What do you think of a rotten manager that bawls me out and fines me $50.00 for losing a 1 to 0 game in 10 innings when it was my 1st start this season? And no wonder I was a little wild in the 10th when I had not had no chance to work and get control. I got a

good notion to quit this rotten club and jump to the
Federals where a man gets some kind of treatment.
Callahan says I throwed the game away on purpose but I
did not do no such a thing Al because when I throwed
that ball at Joe Hill's head I forgot that the bases was
full and besides if Gleason had not of starved me to
death the ball that hit him in the head would of killed
him.

And how could a man go to 1st base and the winning
run be forced in if he was dead which he should ought
to of been the lucky left handed stiff if I had of had my
full strenth to put on my fast one instead of being ½
starved to death and weak. But I guess I better tell you
how it come off. The papers will get it all wrong like
they generally allways does.

Callahan asked me this a.m. if I thought I was hard
enough to work and I was tickled to death, because I
seen he was going to give me a chance. I told him Sure
I was in good shape and if them Tigers scored a run off
me he could keep me setting on the bench the rest of
the summer. So he says All right I am going to start you
and if you go good maybe Gleason will let you eat some
supper.

Well Al when I begin warming up I happened to look
up in the grand stand and who do you think I seen?
Nobody but Violet. She smiled when she seen me but
I bet she felt more like crying. Well I smiled back at
her because she probily would of broke down and made
a seen or something if I had not of. They was not nobody warming up for Detroit when I begin warming
up but pretty soon I looked over to their bench and Joe
Hill Violet's husband was warming up. I says to myself
Well here is where I show that bird up if they got nerve
enough to start him against me but probily Jennings
don't want to waste no real pitcher on this game which

he knows we got cinched and we would of had it cinched Al if they had of got a couple of runs or even 1 run for me.

Well, Jennings come passed our bench just like he allways does and tried to pull some of his funny stuff. He says Hello are you still in the league? I says Yes but I come pretty near not being. I came pretty near being with Detroit. I wish you could of heard Gleason and Callahan laugh when I pulled that one on him. He says something back but it was not no hot comeback like mine.

Well Al if I had of had any work and my regular control I guess I would of pitched a 0 hit game because the only time they could touch me was when I had to ease up to get them over. Cobb was out of the game and they told me he was sick but I guess the truth is that he knowed I was going to pitch. Crawford got a couple of lucky scratch hits off of me because I got in the hole to him and had to let up. But the way that lucky left handed Hill got by was something awful and if I was as lucky as him I would quit pitching and shoot craps or something.

Our club can't hit nothing anyway. But batting against this bird was just like hitting fungos. His curve ball broke about ½ a inch and you could of wrote your name and address on his fast one while it was comeing up there. He had good control but who would not when they put nothing on the ball?

Well Al we could not get started against the lucky stiff and they could not do nothing with me even if my suport was rotten and I give a couple or 3 or 4 bases on balls but when they was men waiting to score I zipped them threw there so as they could not see them let alone hit them. Every time I come to the bench be-tween innings I looked up to where Violet was setting

and give her a smile and she smiled back and once I seen
her clapping her hands at me after I had made Moriarty
pop up in the pinch.

Well we come along to the 10th inning, 0 and 0, and
all of a sudden we got after him. Bodie hits one and
Schalk gets 2 strikes and 2 balls and then singles. Callahan tells Alcock to bunt and he does it but Hill sprawls
all over himself like the big boob he is and the bases is
full with nobody down. Well Gleason and Callahan argude about should they send somebody up for me or
let me go up there and I says Let me go up there because I can murder this bird and Callahan says Well they
is nobody out so go up and take a wallop.

Honest Al if this guy had of had anything at all I
would of hit 1 out of the park, but he did not have even
a glove. And how can a man hit pitching which is not
no pitching at all but just slopping them up? When I
went up there I hollered to him and says Stick 1 over
here now you yellow stiff. And he says Yes I can stick
them over allright and that is where I got something on
you.

Well Al I hit a foul off of him that would of been
a fare ball and broke up the game if the wind had not
of been against it. Then I swung and missed a curve that
I don't see how I missed it. The next 1 was a yard outside and this Evans calls it a strike. He has had it in
for me ever since last year when he tried to get funny
with me and I says something back to him that stung
him. So he calls this 3d strike on me and I felt like mur-
dering him. But what is the use?

I throwed down my bat and come back to the bench
and I was glad Callahan and Gleason was out on the
coaching line or they probily would of said something
to me and I would of cut loose and beat them up. Well
Al Weaver and Blackburne looked like a couple of rums

up there and we don't score where we ought to of had 3 or 4 runs with any kind of hitting.

I would of been all O. K. in spite of that peace of rotten luck if this big Hill had of walked to the bench and not said nothing like a real pitcher. But what does he do but wait out there till I start for the box and I says Get on to the bench you lucky stiff or do you want me to hand you something? He says I don't want nothing more of yourn. I allready got your girl and your goat.

Well Al what do you think of a man that would say a thing like that? And nobody but a left hander could of. If I had of had a gun I would of killed him deader than a doornail or something. He starts for the bench and I hollered at him Wait till you get up to that plate and then I am going to bean you. Honest Al I was so mad I could not see the plate or nothing. I don't even know who it was come up to bat 1st but whoever it was I hit him in the arm and he walks to first base. The next guy bunts and Chase tries to pull off 1 of them plays of hisn instead of playing safe and he don't get nobody. Well I kept getting madder and madder and I walks Stanage who if I had of been myself would not foul me.

Callahan has Scotty warming up and Gleason runs out from the bench and tells me I am threw but Callahan says Wait a minute he is going to let Hill hit and this big stiff ought to be able to get him out of the way and that will give Scotty a chance to get warm. Gleason says You better not take a chance because the big busher is hogwild, and they kept argueing till I got sick of listening to them and I went back to the box and got ready to pitch. But when I seen this Hill up there I forgot all about the ball game and I cut loose at his bean.

Well Al my control was all O. K. this time and I catched him square on the fourhead and he dropped like as if he had been shot. But pretty soon he gets up and gives me the laugh and runs to first base. I did not know the game was over till Weaver come up and pulled me off the field. But if I had not of been ½ starved to death and weak so as I could not put all my stuff on the ball you can bet that Hill never would of ran to first base and Violet would of been a widow and probily a lot better off than she is now. At that I never should ought to of tried to kill a left-hander by hitting him in the head.

Well Al they jumped all over me in the clubhouse and I had to hold myself back or I would of gave somebody the beating of their life. Callahan tells me I am fined $50.00 and suspended without no pay. I asked him What for and he says They would not be no use in telling you because you have not got no brains. I says Yes I have to got some brains and he says Yes but they is in your stumach. And then he says I wish we had of sent you to Milwaukee and I come back at him. I says I wish you had of.

Well Al I guess they is no chance of getting square treatment on this club and you won't be supprised if you hear of me jumping to the Federals where a man is treated like a man and not like no white slave.

Yours truly, JACK.

Chicago, Illinois, May 2

AL: I have got to disappoint you again Al. When I got up to get my pay yesterday they held out $150.00 on me. $50.00 of it is what I was fined for loosing a 1 to 0 10-inning game in Detroit when I was so weak that I should ought never to of been sent in there and the $100.00 is the advance money that I drawed last winter and which I had forgot all about and the club would of forgot about it to if they was not so tight fisted.

So you see all I get for 2 weeks' pay is about $80.00

and I sent $25.00 to Florrie so she can't come no none support business on me.

I am still suspended Al and not drawing no pay now and I got a notion to hire a attorney at law and force them to pay my salary or else jump to the Federals where a man gets good treatment.

Allen is still after me to come over to his flat some night and see his wife and let her talk to me about Florrie but what do I want to talk about Florrie for or talk about nothing to a nut lefthander's wife?

The Detroit Club is here and Cobb is playing because he knows I am suspended but I wish Callahan would call it off and let me work against them and I would certainly love to work against this Joe Hill again and I bet they would be a different story this time because I been getting something to eat since we been home and I got back most of my strenth.   Your old pal,   JACK.

Chicago, Illinois, May 5

FRIEND AL: Well Al if you been reading the papers you will know before this letter is received what I done. Before the Detroit Club come here Joe Hill had win 4 strate but he has not win no 5 strate or won't neither Al because I put a crimp in his winning streek just like I knowed I would do if I got a chance when I was feeling good and had all my strenth. Callahan asked me yesterday a.m. if I thought I had enough rest and I says Sure because I did not need no rest in the 1st place. Well, he says, I thought maybe if I layed you off a few days you would do some thinking and if you done some thinking once in a while you would be a better pitcher.

Well anyway I worked and I wish you could of saw them Tigers trying to hit me Cobb and Crawford incluseive. The 1st time Cobb come up Weaver catched a lucky line drive off of him and the next time I eased up a little and Collins run back and took a fly ball off of the fence. But the other times he come up he looked like a sucker except when he come up in the 8th and then he beat out a bunt but allmost anybody is liable to do that once in a while.

Crawford got a scratch hit between Chase and Blackburne in the 2d inning and in the 4th he was gave a three-base hit by this Evans who should ought to be writeing for the papers instead of trying to umpire. The ball was 2 feet foul and I bet Crawford will tell you the same thing if you ask him. But what I done to this Hill was awful. I give him my curve twice when he was up there in the 3d and he missed it a foot. Then I come with my fast ball right past his nose and I bet if he had not of ducked it would of drove that big horn of hisn clear up in the press box where them rotten reporters sits and smokes their hops. Then when he was looking for another fast one I slopped up my slow one and he is still swinging at it yet.

But the best of it was that I practally won my own game. Bodie and Schalk was on when I come up in the 5th and Hill hollers to me and says I guess this is where I shoot one of them bean balls. I says Go ahead and shoot and if you hit me in the head and I ever find it out I will write and tell your wife what happened to you. You see what I was getting at Al. I was insinuateing that if he beaned me with his fast one I would not never know nothing about it if somebody did not tell me because his fast one is not fast enough to hurt nobody even if it should hit them in the head. So I says to him Go ahead and shoot and if you hit me in the head and I ever find it out I will write and tell your wife what happened to you. See, Al?

Of coarse you could not hire me to write to Violet

but I did not mean that part of it in ernest. Well sure enough he shot at my bean and I ducked out of the way though if it had of hit me it could not of did no more than tickle. He takes 2 more shots and misses me and then Jennings hollers from the bench What are you doing pitching or trying to win a cigar? So then Hill sees what a monkey he is makeing out of himself and tries to get one over, but I have him 3 balls and nothing and what I done to that groover was a plenty. She went over Bush's head like a bullet and got between Cobb and Veach and goes clear to the fence. Bodie and Schalk scores and I would of scored to if anybody else beside Cobb had of been chaseing the ball. I got 2 bases and Weaver scores me with another wallop.

Say, I wish I could of heard what they said to that baby on the bench. Callahan was tickled to death and he says Maybe I will give you back that $50.00 if you keep that stuff up. I guess I will get that $50.00 back next pay day and if I do Al I will pay you the hole $75.00.

Well Al I beat them 5 to 4 and with good support I would of held them to 1 run but what do I care as long as I beat them? I wish though that Violet could of been there and saw it. Yours truly, JACK.

Chicago, Illinois, May 29

OLD PAL: Well Al I have not wrote to you for a long while but it is not because I have forgot you and to show I have not forgot you I am incloseing the $75.00 which I owe you. It is a money order Al and you can get it cashed by takeing it to Joe Higgins at the P. O.

Since I wrote to you Al I been East with the club and I guess you know what I done in the East. The Athaletics did not have no right to win that 1 game off of me and I will get them when they come here the week after next. I beat Boston and just as good as beat New York twice because I beat them 1 game all alone and then saved the other for Eddie Cicotte in the 9th inning and shut out the Washington Club and would of did the same thing if Johnson had of been working against me instead of this left handed stiff Boehling.

Speaking of left handers Allen has been going rotten and I would not be supprised if they sent him to Milwaukee or Frisco or somewheres.

But I got bigger news than that for you Al. Florrie is back and we are liveing together in the spair room at Allen's flat so I hope they don't send him to Milwaukee or nowheres else because it is not costing us nothing for room rent and this is no more than right after the way the Allens grafted off of us all last winter.

I bet you will be supprised to know that I and Florrie has made it up and they is a secret about it Al which I can't tell you now but maybe next month I will tell you and then you will be more supprised than ever. It is about I and Florrie and somebody else. But that is all I can tell you now.

We got in this a.m. Al and when I got to my room they was a slip of paper there telling me to call up a phone number so I called it up and it was Allen's flat and Marie answered the phone. And when I reckonized her voice I was going to hang up the phone but she says Wait a minute somebody wants to talk to you. And then Florrie come to the phone and I was going to hang up the phone again when she pulled this secret on me that I was telling you about.

So it is all fixed up between us Al and I wish I could tell you the secret but that will come later. I have tooken my baggage over to Allen's and I am there now writeing to you while Florrie is asleep. And after a while I am going out and mail this letter and get a glass of beer because I think I have got 1 comeing now on account of this secret. Florrie says she is sorry for the way she treated me and she cried when she seen me. So what is the use of me being nasty Al? And let bygones be bygones.   Your pal,   JACK.

Chicago, Illinois, June 16

FRIEND AL: Al I beat the Athaletics 2 to 1 to-day but I am writeing to you to give you the supprise of your life. Old pal I got a baby and he is a boy and we are going to name him Allen which Florrie thinks is after his uncle and aunt Allen but which is after you old pal. And she can call him Allen but I will call him Al because I don't never go back on my old pals. The baby was born over to the hospital and it is going to cost me a bunch of money but I should not worry. This is the secret I was going to tell you Al and I am the happyest man in the world and I bet you are most as tickled to death to hear about it as I am.

The baby was born just about the time I was makeing McInnis look like a sucker in the pinch but they did not tell me nothing about it till after the game and then they give me a phone messige in the clubhouse. I went right over there and everything was all O. K. Little Al is a homely little skate but I guess all babys is homely and don't have no looks till they get older and maybe he will look like Florrie or I then I won't have no kick comeing.

Be sure and tell Bertha the good news and tell her everything has came out all right except that the rent man is still after me about that flat I had last winter. And I am still paying the old man $10.00 a month for that house you got for me and which has not never done me no good. But I should not worry about money when I got a real family. Do you get that Al, a real family?

Well Al I am to happy to do no more writeing tonight but I wanted you to be the 1st to get the news and I would of sent you a telegram only I did not want to scare you.   Your pal,   JACK.

Chicago, Illinois, July 2

OLD PAL: Well old pal I just come back from St. Louis this a.m. and found things in pretty fare shape. Florrie and the baby is out to Allen's and we will stay there till I can find another place. The Dr. was out to look at the baby this a.m. and the baby was waveing his arm round in the air. And Florrie asked was they something the matter with him that he kept waveing his arm. And the Dr. says No he was just getting his exercise.

Well Al I noticed that he never waved his right arm but kept waveing his left arm and I asked the Dr. why was that. Then the Dr. says I guess he must be left handed. That made me sore and I says I guess you doctors don't know it all. And then I turned round and beat it out of the room.

Well Al it would be just my luck to have him left handed and Florrie should ought to of knew better than to name him after Allen. I am going to hire another Dr. and see what he has to say because they must be some way of fixing babys so as they won't be left handed. And if necessary I will cut his left arm off of him. Of coarse I would not do that Al. But how would I feel if a boy of mine turned out like Allen and Joe Hill and some of them other nuts?

We have a game with St. Louis to-morrow and a double header on the 4th of July. I guess probily Callahan will work me in one of the 4th of July games on account of the holiday crowd.   Your pal,   JACK.

P. S. Maybe I should ought to leave the kid left handed so as he can have some of their luck. The lucky stiffs.

v. The Busher's Kid

FRIEND AL: Well Al what do you think of little Al now? But I guess I better tell you first what he done. Maybe you won't believe what I am telling you but did you ever catch me telling you a lie? I guess you know you did not Al. Well we got back from the East this a.m. and I don't have to tell you we had a rotten trip and if it had not of been for me beating Boston once and the Athaletics two times we would of been ashamed to come home.

I guess these here other pitchers thought we was haveing a vacation and when they go up in the office to-morrow to get there checks they should ought to be arrested if they take them. I would not go nowheres near Comiskey if I had not of did better than them others but I can go and get my pay and feel all O. K. about it because I done something to ern it.

Me loseing that game in Washington was a crime and Callahan says so himself. This here Weaver throwed it away for me and I would not be surprised if he done it from spitework because him and Scott is pals and probily he did not want to see me winning all them games when Scott was getting knocked out of the box. And no wonder when he has not got no stuff. I wish I knowed for sure that Weaver was throwing me down and if I

knowed for sure I would put him in a hospital or somewheres.

But I was going to tell you what the kid done Al.
So here goes. We are still liveing at Allen's and his wife.
So I and him come home together from the train. Well
Florrie and Marie was both up and the baby was up
too—that is he was not up but he was woke up. I beat
it right into the room where he was at and Florrie come
in with me. I says Hello Al and what do you suppose he
done. Well Al he did not say Hello pa or nothing like
that because he is not only one month old. But he smiled
at me just like as if he was glad to see me and I guess
maybe he was at that.

I was tickled to death and I says to Florrie Did you
see that. And she says See what. I says The baby smiled
at me. Then she says They is something the matter with
his stumach. I says I suppose because a baby smiles that
is a sign they is something the matter with his stumach
and if he had the toothache he would laugh. She says
You think your smart but I am telling you that he was
not smileing at all but he was makeing a face because
they is something the matter with his stumach. I says I
guess I know the difference if somebody is smileing or
makeing a face. And she says I guess you don't know
nothing about babys because you never had none before. I says How many have you had. And then she
got sore and beat it out of the room.

I did not care because I wanted to be in there alone
with him and see would he smile at me again. And sure
enough Al he did. Then I called Allen in and when the
baby seen him he begin to cry. So you see I was right
and Florrie was wrong. It don't take a man no time at
all to get wise to these babys and it don't take them long
to know if a man is there father or there uncle.

When he begin to cry I chased Allen out of the room

and called Florrie because she should ought to know by
this time how to make him stop crying. But she was still
sore and she says Let him cry or if you know so much
about babys make him stop yourself. I says Maybe he is
sick. And she says I was just telling you that he had a
pane in his stumach or he would not of made that face
that you said was smileing at you.

I says Do you think we should ought to call the doctor
but she says No if you call the doctor every time he has
the stumach acke you might just as well tell him he
should bring his trunk along and stay here. She says All
babys have collect and they is not no use fusing about it
but come and get your breakfast.

Well Al I did not injoy my breakfast because the baby
was crying all the time and I knowed he probily wanted
I should come in and visit with him. So I just eat the
prunes and drunk a little coffee and did not wait for the
rest of it and sure enough when I went back in our room
and started talking to him he started smileing again and
pretty soon he went to sleep so you see Al he was smileing and not makeing no face and that was a hole lot of
bunk about him haveing the collect. But I don't suppose I should ought to find fault with Florrie for not
knowing no better because she has not never had no
babys before but still and all I should think she should
ought to of learned something about them by this time or
ask somebody.

Well Al little Al is woke up again and is crying and I
just about got time to fix him up and get him asleep
again and then I will have to go to the ball park because
we got a poseponed game to play with Detroit and Callahan will probily want me to work though I pitched the
next to the last game in New York and would of gave
them a good beating except for Schalk dropping that
ball at the plate but I got it on these Detroit babys and

when my name is announced to pitch they feel like forfiting the game. I won't try for no strike out record because I want them to hit the first ball and get the game over with quick so as I can get back here and take care of little Al.   Your pal,   JACK.

P. S. Babys is great stuff Al and if I was you I would not wait no longer but would hurry up and adopt 1 somewheres.

Chicago, Illinois, August 15

OLD PAL: What do you think Al. Kid Gleason is comeing over to the flat and look at the baby the day after to-morrow when we don't have no game skeduled but we have to practice in the a.m. because we been going so rotten. I had a hard time makeing him promise to come but he is comeing and I bet he will be glad he come when he has came. I says to him in the clubhouse Do you want to see a real baby? And he says You're real enough for me Boy.

I says No I am talking about babys. He says Oh I thought you was talking about ice cream soda or something. I says No I want you to come over to the flat to-morrow and take a look at my kid and tell me what you think of him. He says I can tell you what I think of him without takeing no look at him. I think he is out of luck. I says What do you mean out of luck. But he just laughed and would not say no more.

I asked him again would he come over to the flat and look at the baby and he says he had troubles enough without that and kidded along for a while but finally he seen I was in ernest and then he says he would come if I would keep the missus out of the room while he was there because he says if she seen him she would probily be sorry she married me.

He was just jokeing and I did not take no excepshun to

his remarks because Florrie could not never fall for him after seeing me because he is not no big stropping man like I am but a little runt and look at how old he is. But I am glad he is comeing because he will think more of me when he sees what a fine baby I got though he thinks a hole lot of me now because look what I done for the club and where would they be at if I had jumped to the Federal like I once thought I would. I will tell you what he says about little Al and I bet he will say he never seen no prettyer baby but even if he don't say nothing at all I will know he is kidding.

The Boston Club comes here to-morrow and plays 4 days includeing the day after to-morrow when they is not no game. So on account of the off day maybe I will work twice against them and if I do they will wish the grounds had of burned down.   Yours truly,   JACK.

Chicago, Illinois, August 17

AL: Well old pal what did I tell you about what I would do to that Boston Club? And now Al I have beat every club in the league this year because yesterday was the first time I beat the Boston Club this year but now I have beat all of them and most of them severel times.

This should ought to of gave me a record of 16 wins and 0 defeats because the only game I lost was throwed away behind me but instead of that my record is 10 games win and 6 defeats and that don't include the games I finished up and helped the other boys win which is about 6 more alltogether but what do I care about my record Al? because I am not the kind of man that is allways thinking about there record and playing for there record while I am satisfied if I give the club the best I got and if I win all O. K. And if I lose who's fault is it. Not mine Al.

I asked Callahan would he let me work against the Boston Club again before they go away and he says I guess I will have to because you are going better than anybody else on the club. So you see Al he is beginning to appresiate my work and from now on I will pitch in my regular turn and a hole lot offtener then that and probily Comiskey will see the stuff I am made from and will raise my salery next year even if he has got me signed for 3 years and for the same salery I am getting now.

But all that is not what I was going to tell you Al and what I was going to tell you was about Gleason comeing to see the baby and what he thought about him. I sent Florrie and Marie downtown and says I would take care of little Al and they was glad to go because Florrie says she should ought to buy some new shoes though I don't see what she wants of no new shoes when she is going to be tied up in the flat for a long time yet on account of the baby and nobody cares if she wears shoes in the flat or goes round in her bear feet. But I was glad to get rid of the both of them for a while because little Al acts better when they is not no women round and you can't blame him.

The baby was woke up when Gleason come in and I and him went right in the room where he was laying. Gleason takes a look at him and says Well that is a mighty fine baby and you must of boughten him. I says What do you mean? And he says I don't believe he is your own baby because he looks humaner than most babys. And I says Why should not he look human. And he says Why should he.

Then he goes to work and picks the baby right up and I was a-scared he would drop him because even I have not never picked him up though I am his father and would be a-scared of hurting him. I says Here, don't pick him up and he says Why not? He says Are you going to leave him on that there bed the rest of his life? I says No but you don't know how to handle him. He says I have handled a hole lot bigger babys than him or else Callahan would not keep me.

Then he starts patting the baby's head and I says Here, don't do that because he has got a soft spot in his head and you might hit it. He says I thought he was your baby and I says Well he is my baby and he says Well then they can't be no soft spot in his head. Then he lays little Al down because he seen I was in ernest and as soon as he lays him down the baby begins to cry. Then Gleason says See he don't want me to lay him down and I says Maybe he has got a pane in his stumach and he says I would not be supprised because he just took a good look at his father.

But little Al did not act like as if he had a pane in his stumach and he kept sticking his finger in his mouth and crying. And Gleason says He acts like as if he had a toothacke. I says How could he have a toothacke when he has not got no teeth? He says That is easy. I have saw a lot of pitchers complane that there arm was sore when they did not have no arm.

Then he asked me what was the baby's name and I told him Allen but that he was not named after my brother-in-law Allen. And Gleason says I should hope not. I should hope you would have better sense than to name him after a left hander. So you see Al he don't like them no better then I do even if he does jolly Allen and Russell along and make them think they can pitch.

Pretty soon he says What are you going to make out of him, a ball player? I says Yes I am going to make a hitter out of him so as he can join the White Sox and then maybe they will get a couple of runs once in a while. He says If I was you I would let him pitch and then you won't have to give him no educasion. Besides, he says, he looks now like he would divellop into a grate spitter.

Well I happened to look out of the window and seen Florrie and Marie comeing acrost Indiana Avenue and I told Gleason about it. And you ought to of seen him run. I asked him what was his hurry and he says it was in his contract that he was not to talk to no women but I knowed he was kidding because I allready seen him talking to severel of the players' wifes when they was on trips with us and they acted like as if they thought he was a regular comeedion though they really is not nothing funny about what he says only it is easy to make women laugh when they have not got no grouch on about something.

Well Al I am glad Gleason has saw the baby and maybe he will fix it with Callahan so as I won't have to go to morning practice every a.m. because I should ought to be home takeing care of little Al when Florrie is washing the dishs or helping Marie round the house. And besides why should I wear myself all out in practice because I don't need to practice pitching and I could hit as well as the rest of the men on our club if I never seen no practice.

After we get threw with Boston, Washington comes here and then we go to St. Louis and Cleveland and then come home and then go East again. And after that we are pretty near threw except the city serious. Callahan is not going to work me no more after I beat Boston again till it is this here Johnson's turn to pitch for Washington. And I hope it is not his turn to work the 1st game of the serious because then I would not have no rest between the last game against Boston and the 1st game against Washington.

But rest or no rest I will work against this here Johnson and show him up for giveing me that trimming in

Washington, the lucky stiff. I wish I had a team like the Athletics behind me and I would loose about 1 game every 6 years and then they would have to get all the best of it from these rotten umpires.

Your pal,   JACK.

New York, New York, September 16

FRIEND AL: Al it is not no fun running round the country no more and I wish this dam trip was over so as I could go home and see how little Al is getting along because Florrie has not wrote since we was in Philly which was the first stop on this trip. I am a-scared they is something the matter with the little fellow or else she would of wrote but then if they was something the matter with him she would of sent me a telegram or something and let me know.

So I guess they can't be nothing the matter with him. Still and all I don't see why she has not wrote when she knows or should ought to know that I would be worrying about the baby. If I don't get no letter to-morrow I am going to send her a telegram and ask her what is the matter with him because I am positive she would of wrote if they was not something the matter with him.

The boys has been trying to get me to go out nights and see a show or something but I have not got no heart to go to shows. And besides Callahan has not gave us no pass to no show on this trip. I guess probily he is sore on account of the rotten way the club has been going but still he should ought not to be sore on me because I have win 3 out of my last 4 games and would of win the other if he had not of started me against them with only 1 day's rest and the Athletics at that, who a man should ought not to pitch against if he don't feel good.

I asked Allen if he had heard from Marie and he says

Yes he did but she did not say nothing about little Al except that he was keeping her awake nights balling. So maybe Al if little Al is balling they is something wrong with him. I am going to send Florrie a telegram tomorrow—that is if I don't get no letter.

If they is something the matter with him I will ask Callahan to send me home and he won't want to do it neither because who else has he got that is a regular winner. But if little Al is sick and Callahan won't let me go home I will go home anyway. You know me Al.

Yours truly,   JACK.

Boston, Massachusetts, September 24

AL: I bet if Florrie was a man she would be a left-hander. What do you think she done now Al? I sent her a telegram from New York when I did not get no letter from her and she did not pay no atension to the telegram. Then when we got up here I sent her another telegram and it was not more than five minutes after I sent the 2d telegram till I got a letter from her. And it said the baby was all O. K. but she had been so busy takeing care of him that she had not had no time to write.

Well when I got the letter I chased out to see if I could catch the boy who had took my telegram but he had went allready so I was spending $.60 for nothing. Then what does Florrie do but send me a telegram after she got my second telegram and tell me that little Al is all O. K., which I knowed all about then because I had just got her letter. And she sent her telegram c.o.d. and I had to pay for it at this end because she had not paid for it and that was $.60 more but I bet if I had of knew what was in the telegram before I read it I would of told the boy to keep it and would not of gave him no

$.60 but how did I know if little Al might not of tooken sick after Florrie had wrote the letter?

I am going to write and ask her if she is trying to send us both to the Poor House or somewheres with her telegrams. I don't care nothing about the $.60 but I like to see a woman use a little judgement though I guess that is impossible.

It is my turn to work to-day and to-night we start West but we have got to stop off at Cleveland on the way. I have got a nosion to ask Callahan to let me go right on threw to Chi if I win to-day and not stop off at no Cleveland but I guess they would not be no use because I have got that Cleveland Club licked the minute I put on my glove. So probily Callahan will want me with him though it don't make no difference if we win or lose now because we have not got no chance for the pennant. One man can't win no pennant Al I don't care who he is.   Your pal,   JACK.

Chicago, Illinois, October 2

FRIEND AL: Well old pal I am all threw till the city serious and it is all fixed up that I am going to open the serious and pitch 3 of the games if nessary. The club has went to Detroit to wind up the season and Callahan did not take me along but left me here with a couple other pitchers and Billy Sullivan and told me all as I would have to do was go over to the park the next 3 days and warm up a little so as to keep in shape. But I don't need to be in no shape to beat them Cubs Al. But it is a good thing Al that Allen was tooken on the trip to Detroit or I guess I would of killed him. He has not been going good and he has been acting and talking nasty to everybody because he can't win no games.

Well the 1st night we was home after the trip little

Al was haveing a bad night and was balling pretty hard
and they could not nobody in the flat get no sleep. Florrie says he was haveing the collect and I says Why
should he have the collect all the time when he did not
drink nothing but milk? She says she guessed the milk
did not agree with him and upsetted his stumach. I says
Well he must take after his mother if his stumach gets
upsetted every time he takes a drink because if he took
after his father he could drink a hole lot and not never
be effected. She says You should ought to remember
he has only got a little stumach and not a great big
resservoire. I says Well if the milk don't agree with him
why don't you give him something else? She says Yes I
suppose I should ought to give him weeny worst or
something.

Allen must of heard us talking because he hollered
something and I did not hear what it was so I told him
to say it over and he says Give the little X-eyed brat
poison and we would all be better off. I says You better
take poison yourself because maybe a rotten pitcher
like you could get by in the league where you're going
when you die. Then I says Besides I would rather my
baby was X-eyed then to have him left handed. He says
It is better for him that he is X-eyed or else he might
get a good look at you and then he would shoot himself.
I says Is that so? and he shut up. Little Al is not no
more X-eyed than you or I are Al and that was what
made me sore because what right did Allen have to talk
like that when he knowed he was lying?

Well the next morning Allen nor I did not speak to
each other and I seen he was sorry for the way he had
talked and I was willing to fix things up because what is
the use of staying sore at a man that don't know no
better.

But all of a sudden he says When are you going to pay me what you owe me? I says What do you mean? And he says You been liveing here all summer and I been paying all the bills. I says Did not you and Marie ask us to come here and stay with you and it would not cost us nothing. He says Yes but we did not mean it was a life sentence. You are getting more money than me and you don't never spend a nichol. All I have to do is pay the rent and buy your food and it would take a millionare or something to feed you.

Then he says I would not make no holler about you grafting off of me if that brat would shut up nights and give somebody a chance to sleep. I says You should ought to get all the sleep you need on the bench. Besides, I says, who done the grafting all last winter and without no invatation? If he had of said another word I was going to bust him but just then Marie come in and he shut up.

The more I thought about what he said and him a rotten lefthander that should ought to be hussling freiht the more madder I got and if he had of opened his head to me the last day or 2 before he went to Detroit I guess I would of finished him. But Marie stuck pretty close to the both of us when we was together and I guess she knowed they was something in the air and did not want to see her husband get the worst of it though if he was my husband and I was a woman I would push him under a st. car.

But Al I won't even stand for him saying that I am grafting off of him and I and Florrie will get away from here and get a flat of our own as soon as the city serious is over. I would like to bring her and the kid down to Bedford for the winter but she wont listen to that.

I allmost forgot Al to tell you to be sure and thank Bertha for the little dress she made for little Al. I don't

know if it will fit him or not because Florrie has not
yet tried it on him yet and she says she is going to use it
for a dishrag but I guess she is just kidding.

I suppose you seen where Callahan took me out of
that game down to Cleveland but it was not because I
was not going good Al but it was because Callahan seen
he was makeing a mistake wasteing me on that bunch
who allmost any pitcher could beat. They beat us that
game at that but only by one run and it was not no
fault of mine because I was tooken out before they got
the run that give them the game.

Your old pal,   JACK.

Chicago, Illinois, October 4

FRIEND AL: Well Al the club winds up the season at
Detroit to-morrow and the serious starts the day after
to-morrow and I will be in there giveing them a battle.
I wish I did not have nobody but the Cubs to pitch
against all season and you bet I would have a record
that would make Johnson and Mathewson and some of
them other swell heads look like a dirty doose.

I and Florrie and Marie has been haveing a argument
about how could Florrie go and see the city serious
games when they is not nobody here that can take care
of the baby because Marie wants to go and see the games
to even though they is not no more chance of Callahan
starting Allen than a rabbit or something.

Florrie and Marie says I should ought to hire a nurse
to take care of little Al and Florrie got pretty sore when
I told her nothing doing because in the first place I can't
afford to pay no nurse a salary and in the second place I
would not trust no nurse to take care of the baby because how do I know the nurse is not nothing but a

grafter or a dope fiend maybe and should ought not to be left with the baby?

Of coarse Florrie wants to see me pitch and a man can't blame her for that but I won't leave my baby with no nurse Al and Florrie will have to stay home and I will tell her what I done when I get there. I might of gave my consent to haveing a nurse at that if it had not of been for the baby getting so sick last night when I was takeing care of him while Florrie and Marie and Allen was out to a show and if I had not of been home they is no telling what would of happened. It is a cinch that none of them bonehead nurses would of knew what to do.

Allen must of been out of his head because right after supper he says he would take the 2 girls to a show. I says All right go on and I will take care of the baby. Then Florrie says Do you think you can take care of him all O. K.? And I says Have not I tooken care of him before allready? Well, she says, I will leave him with you only don't run in to him every time he cries. I says Why not? And she says Because it is good for him to cry. I says You have not got no heart or you would not talk that way.

They all give me the laugh but I let them get away with it because I am not picking no fights with girls and why should I bust this Allen when he don't know no better and has not got no baby himself. And I did not want to do nothing that would stop him takeing the girls to a show because it is time he spent a peace of money on somebody.

Well they all went out and I went in on the bed and played with the baby. I wish you could of saw him Al because he is old enough now to do stunts and he smiled up at me and waved his arms and legs round and made

a noise like as if he was trying to say Pa. I did not think
Florrie had gave him enough covers so I rapped him up
in some more and took a blanket off of the big bed and
stuck it round him so as he could not kick his feet out
and catch cold.

I thought once or twice he was going off to sleep
but all of a sudden he begin to cry and I seen they was
something wrong with him. I give him some hot water
but that made him cry again and I thought maybe he
was to cold yet so I took another blanket off of Allen's
bed and wrapped that round him but he kept on crying
and trying to kick inside the blankets. And I seen then
that he must have collect or something.

So pretty soon I went to the phone and called up our
regular Dr. and it took him pretty near a hour to get
there and the baby balling all the time. And when he
come he says they was nothing the matter except that
the baby was to hot and told me to take all them blankets
off of him and then soaked me 2 dollars. I had a nosion
to bust his jaw. Well pretty soon he beat it and then
little Al begin crying again and kept getting worse and
worse so finally I got a-scared and run down to the
corner where another Dr. is at and I brung him up to
see what was the matter but he said he could not see
nothing the matter but he did not charge me a cent so
I thought he was not no robber like our regular doctor
even if he was just as much of a boob.

The baby did not cry none while he was there but
the minute he had went he started crying and balling
again and I seen they was not no use of fooling no
longer so I looked around the house and found the
medicine the doctor left for Allen when he had a stumach
acke once and I give the baby a little of it in a spoon
but I guess he did not like the taste because he hollered
like a Indian and finally I could not stand it no longer

so I called that second Dr. back again and this time he seen that the baby was sick and asked me what I had gave it and I told him some stumach medicine and he says I was a fool and should ought not to of gave the baby nothing. But while he was talking the baby stopped crying and went off to sleep so you see what I done for him was the right thing to do and them doctors was both off of there nut.

This second Dr. soaked me 2 dollars the 2d time though he had not did no more than when he was there the 1st time and charged me nothing but they is all a bunch of robbers Al and I would just as leave trust a policeman.

Right after the baby went to sleep Florrie and Marie and Allen come home and I told Florrie what had came off but instead of giveing me credit she says If you want to kill him why don't you take a ax? Then Allen butts in and says Why don't you take a ball and throw it at him? Then I got sore and I says Well if I did hit him with a ball I would kill him while if you was to throw that fast ball of yours at him and hit him in the head he would think the musketoes was biteing him and brush them off. But at that, I says, you could not hit him with a ball except you was aiming at something else.

I guess they was no comeback to that so him and Marie went to there room. Allen should ought to know better than to try and get the best of me by this time and I would shut up anyway if I was him after getting sent home from Detroit with some of the rest of them when he only worked 3 innings up there and they had to take him out or play the rest of the game by electrick lights.

I wish you could be here for the serious Al but you would have to stay at a hotel because we have not got no spair room and it would cost you a hole lot of money.

But you can watch the papers and you will see what I done.   Yours truly,   JACK.

Chicago, Illinois, October 6

DEAR OLD PAL: Probily before you get this letter you will of saw by the paper that we was licked in the first game and that I was tooken out but the papers don't know what really come off so I am going to tell you and you can see for yourself if it was my fault.

I did not never have no more stuff in my life then when I was warming up and I seen the Cubs looking over to our bench and shakeing there heads like they knowed they did not have no chance. O'Day was going to start Cheney who is there best bet and had him warming up but when he seen the smoke I had when I and Schalk was warming up he changed his mind because what was the use of useing his best pitcher when I had all that stuff and it was a cinch that no club in the world could score a run off of me when I had all that stuff?

So he told a couple others to warm up to and when my name was announced to pitch Cheney went and set on the bench and this here left-hander Pierce was announced for them.

Well Al you will see by the paper where I sent there 1st 3 batters back to the bench to get a drink of water and all 3 of them good hitters Leach and Good and this here Saier that hits a hole lot of home runs but would not never hit one off of me if I was O. K. Well we scored a couple in our half and the boys on the bench all says Now you got enough to win easy because they won't never score none off of you.

And they was right to because what chance did they have if this thing that I am going to tell you about had not of happened? We goes along seven innings and only

2 of there men had got to 1st base one of them on a bad peg of Weaver's and the other one I walked because this blind Evans don't know a ball from a strike. We had not did no more scoreing off of Pierce not because he had no stuff but because our club could not take a ball in there hands and hit it out of the infield.

Well Al I did not tell you that before I come out to the park I kissed little Al and Florrie good by and Marie says she was going to stay home to and keep Florrie Co. and they was not no reason for Marie to come to the game anyway because they was not a chance in the world for Allen to do nothing but hit fungos. Well while I was doing all this here swell pitching and make-ing them Cubs look like a lot of rummys I was thinking about little Al and Florrie and how glad they would be when I come home and told them what I done though of coarse little Al is not only a little over 3 months of age and how could he appresiate what I done? But Flor-rie would.

Well Al when I come in to the bench after there ½ of the 7th I happened to look up to the press box to see if the reporters had gave Schulte a hit on that one Weaver throwed away and who do you think I seen in a box right alongside of the press box? It was Florrie and Marie and both of them claping there hands and holler-ing with the rest of the bugs.

Well old pal I was never so supprised in my life and it just took all the heart out of me. What was they doing there and what had they did with the baby? How did I know that little Al was not sick or maybe dead and balling his head off and nobody round to hear him?

I tried to catch Florrie's eyes but she would not look at me. I hollered her name and the bugs looked at me like as if I was crazy and I was to Al. Well I seen they was not no use of standing out there in front of the stand so I come into the bench and Allen was setting there and I says Did you know your wife and Florrie was up there in the stand? He says No and I says What are they doing here? And he says What would they be doing here—mending there stockings? I felt like busting him and I guess he seen I was mad because he got up off of the bench and beat it down to the corner of the field where some of the others was getting warmed up though why should they have anybody warming up when I was going so good?

Well Al I made up my mind that ball game or no ball game I was not going to have little Al left alone no longer and I seen they was not no use of sending word to Florrie to go home because they was a big crowd and it would take maybe 15 or 20 minutes for somebody to get up to where she was at. So I says to Callahan You have got to take me out. He says What is the matter? Is your arm gone? I says No my arm is not gone but my baby is sick and home all alone. He says Where is your wife? And I says She is setting up there in the stand.

Then he says How do you know your baby is sick? And I says I don't know if he is sick or not but he is left home all alone. He says Why don't you send your wife home? And I says I could not get word to her in time. He says Well you have only got two innings to go and the way your going the game will be over in 10 minutes. I says Yes and before 10 minutes is up my baby might die and are you going to take me out or not? He says Get in there and pitch you yellow dog and if you don't I will take your share of the serious money away from you.

By this time our part of the inning was over and I had to go out there and pitch some more because he would not take me out and he has not got no heart Al. Well Al how could I pitch when I kept thinking maybe the baby was dying right now and maybe if I was home I could do something? And instead of paying attension to what I was doing I was thinking about little Al and looking up there to where Florrie and Marie was setting and before I knowed what come off they had the bases full and Callahan took me out.

Well Al I run to the clubhouse and changed my cloths and beat it for home and I did not even hear what Callahan and Gleason says to me when I went by them but I found out after the game that Scott went in and finished up and they batted him pretty hard and we was licked 3 and 2.

When I got home the baby was crying but he was not all alone after all Al because they was a little girl about 14 years of age there watching him and Florrie had hired her to take care of him so as her and Marie could go and see the game. But just think Al of leaveing little Al with a girl 14 years of age that did not never have no babys of her own! And what did she know about takeing care of him? Nothing Al.

You should ought to of heard me ball Florrie out when she got home and I bet she cried pretty near enough to flood the basemunt. We had it hot and heavy and the Allens butted in but I soon showed them where they was at and made them shut there mouth.

I had a good nosion to go out and get a hole lot of drinks and was just going to put on my hat when the doorbell rung and there was Kid Gleason. I thought he would be sore and probily try to ball me out and I was not going to stand for nothing but instead of balling me out he come and shook hands with me and inter-duced himself to Florrie and asked how was little Al.

Well we all set down and Gleason says the club was depending on me to win the serious because I was in the best shape of all the pitchers. And besides the Cubs

could not never hit me when I was right and he was
telling the truth to.

So he asked me if I would stand for the club hireing a
train nurse to stay with the baby the rest of the serious
so as Florrie could go and see her husband win the serious but I says No I would not stand for that and Florrie's place was with the baby.

So Gleason and Florrie goes out in the other room
and talks a while and I guess he was persuadeing her to
stay home because pretty soon they come back in the
room and says it was all fixed up and I would not have
to worry about little Al the rest of the serious but could
give the club the best I got. Gleason just left here a
little while ago and I won't work to-morrow Al but I will
work the day after and you will see what I can do when
I don't have nothing to worry me.   Your pal,   JACK.

Chicago, Illinois, October 8

OLD PAL: Well old pal we got them 2 games to one now
and the serious is sure to be over in three more days
because I can pitch 2 games in that time if nessary. I
shut them out to-day and they should ought not to of
had four hits but should ought to of had only 2 but
Bodie don't cover no ground and 2 fly balls that he
should ought to of eat up fell safe.

But I beat them anyway and Benz beat them yesterday but why should he not beat them when the club
made 6 runs for him? All they made for me was three
but all I needed was one because they could not hit me
with a shuvvel. When I come to the bench after the 5th
inning they was a note there for me from the boy that
answers the phone at the ball park and it says that somebody just called up from the flat and says the baby was

asleep and getting along fine. So I felt good Al and I was better than ever in the 6th.

When I got home Florrie and Marie was both there and asked me how did the game come out because I beat Allen home and I told them all about what I done and I bet Florrie was proud of me but I supose Marie is a little jellus because how could she help it when Callahan is depending on me to win the serious and her husband is wearing out the wood on the bench? But why should she be sore when it is me that is winning the serious for them? And if it was not for me Allen and all the rest of them would get about $500.00 apeace instead of the winner's share which is about $750.00 apeace.

Cicotte is going to work to-morrow and if he is lucky maybe he can get away with the game and that will leave me to finish up the day after to-morrow but if nessary I can go in to-morrow when they get to hitting Cicotte and stop them and then come back the following day and beat them again. Where would this club be at Al if I had of jumped to the Federal?   Yours truly,   JACK.

Chicago, Illinois, October 11

FRIEND AL: We done it again Al and I guess the Cubs won't never want to play us again not so long as I am with the club. Before you get this letter you will know what we done and who done it but probily you could of guessed that Al without seeing no paper.

I got 2 more of them phone messiges about the baby dureing the game and I guess that was what made me so good because I knowed then that Florrie was takeing care of him but I could not help feeling sorry for Florrie because she is a bug herself and it must of been pretty hard for her to stay away from the game espesially when she knowed I was going to pitch and she has been pretty good to sacrifice her own plesure for little Al.

Cicotte was knocked out of the box the day before yesterday and then they give this here Faber a good beating but I wish you could of saw what they done to Allen when Callahan sent him in after the game was gone allready. Honest Al if he had not of been my brother in law I would of felt like laughing at him because it looked like as if they would have to call the fire department to put the side out. They had Bodie and Collins hollering for help and with there tongue hanging out from running back to the fence.

Anyway the serious is all over and I won't have nothing to do but stay home and play with little Al but I don't know yet where my home is going to be at because it is a cinch I won't stay with Allen no longer. He has not came home since the game and I suppose he is out somewheres lapping up some beer and spending some of the winner's share of the money which he would not of had no chance to get in on if it had not of been for me.

I will write and let you know my plans for the winter and I wish Florrie would agree to come to Bedford but nothing doing Al and after her staying home and takeing care of the baby instead of watching me pitch I can't be too hard on her but must leave her have her own way about something. Your pal, JACK.

Chicago, Illinois, October 13

AL: I am all threw with Florrie Al and I bet when you hear about it you won't say it was not no fault of mine but no man liveing who is any kind of a man would act different from how I am acting if he had of been decieved like I been.

Al Florrie and Marie was out to all them games and

was not home takeing care of the baby at all and it is
not her fault that little Al is not dead and that he was
not killed by the nurse they hired to take care of him
while they went to the games when I thought they was
home takeing care of the baby. And all them phone
messiges was just fakes and maybe the baby was sick all
the time I was winning them games and balling his head
off instead of being asleep like they said he was.

Allen did not never come home at all the night before
last and when he come in yesterday he was a sight and
I says to him Where have you been? And he says I have
been down to the Y. M. C. A. but that is not none of your
business. I says Yes you look like as if you had been to
the Y. M. C. A. and I know where you have been and
you have been out lushing beer. And he says Suppose
I have and what are you going to do about it? And I
says Nothing but you should ought to be ashamed of
yourself and leaveing Marie here while you was out
lapping up beer.

Then he says Did you not leave Florrie home while
you was getting away with them games, you lucky
stiff? And I says Yes but Florrie had to stay home and
take care of the baby but Marie don't never have to
stay home because where is your baby? You have not
got no baby. He says I would not want no X-eyed baby
like yourn. Then he says So you think Florrie stayed to
home and took care of the baby do you? And I says
What do you mean? And he says You better ask her.

So when Florrie come in and heard us talking she
busted out crying and then I found out what they put
over on me. It is a wonder Al that I did not take some of
that cheap furniture them Allens got and bust it over
there heads, Allen and Florrie. This is what they done
Al. The club give Florrie $50.00 to stay home and take
care of the baby and she said she would and she was

to call up every so often and tell me the baby was all
O. K. But this here Marie told her she was a sucker so
she hired a nurse for part of the $50.00 and then her
and Marie went to the games and beat it out quick after
the games was over and come home in a taxicab and
chased the nurse out before I got home.

Well Al when I found out what they done I grabbed
my hat and goes out and got some drinks and I was so
mad I did not know where I was at or what come off
and I did not get home till this a.m. And they was all
asleep and I been asleep all day and when I woke up
Marie and Allen was out but Florrie and I have not
spoke to each other and I won't never speak to her again.

But I know now what I am going to do Al and I am
going to take little Al and beat it out of here and she
can sew me for a bill of divorce and I should not worry
because I will have little Al and I will see that he is
tooken care of because I guess I can hire a nurse as well
as they can and I will pick out a train nurse that knows
something. Maybe I and him and the nurse will come
to Bedford Al but I don't know yet and I will write and
tell you as soon as I make up my mind. Did you ever
hear of a man getting a rottener deal Al? And after
what I done in the serious too.   Your pal,   JACK.

Chicago, Illinois, October 17

OLD PAL: I and Florrie has made it up Al but we are
threw with Marie and Allen and I and Florrie and the
baby is staying at a hotel here on Cottage Grove Avenue
the same hotel we was at when we got married only of
coarse they was only the 2 of us then.

And now Al I want to ask you a favor and that is for
you to go and see old man Cutting and tell him I want
to ree-new the lease on that house for another year be-

cause I and Florrie has decided to spend the winter in Bedford and she will want to stay there and take care of little Al while I am away on trips next summer and not stay in no high-price flat up here. And may be you and Bertha can help her round the house when I am not there.

I will tell you how we come to fix things up Al and you will see that I made her apollojize to me and after this she will do what I tell her to and won't never try to put nothing over. We was eating breakfast—I and Florrie and Marie. Allen was still asleep yet because I guess he must of had a bad night and he was snoreing so as you could hear him in the next st. I was not saying nothing to nobody but pretty soon Florrie says to Marie I don't think you and Allen should ought to kick on the baby crying when Allen's snoreing makes more noise than a hole wagonlode of babys. And Marie got sore and says I guess a man has got a right to snore in his own house and you and Jack has been grafting off of us long enough.

Then Florrie says What did Allen do to help win the serious and get that $750.00? Nothing but set on the bench except when they was makeing him look like a sucker the 1 inning he pitched. The trouble with you and Allen is you are jellous of what Jack has did and you know he will be a star up here in the big league when Allen is tending bar which is what he should ought to be doing because then he could get stewed for nothing.

Marie says Take your brat and get out of the house. And Florrie says Don't you worry because we would not stay here no longer if you hired us. So Florrie went in her room and I followed her in and she says Let's pack up and get out.

Then I says Yes but we won't go nowheres together after what you done to me but you can go where you dam please and I and little Al will go to Bedford. Then she says You can't take the baby because he is mine and if you was to take him I would have you arrested for kidnaping. Besides, she says, what would you feed him and who would take care of him?

I says I would find somebody to take care of him and I would get him food from a resturunt. She says He can't eat nothing but milk and I says Well he has the collect all the time when he is eating milk and he would not be no worse off if he was eating watermelon. Well, she says, if you take him I will have you arrested and sew you for a bill of divorce for dessertion.

Then she says Jack you should not ought to find no fault with me for going to them games because when a woman has a husband that can pitch like you can do you think she wants to stay home and not see her husband pitch when a lot of other women is cheering him and makeing her feel proud because she is his wife?

Well Al as I said right along it was pretty hard on Florrie to have to stay home and I could not hardly blame her for wanting to be out there where she could see what I done so what was the use of argueing?

So I told her I would think it over and then I went out and I went and seen a attorney at law and asked him could I take little Al away and he says No I did not have no right to take him away from his mother and besides it would probily kill him to be tooken away from her and then he soaked me $10.00 the robber.

Then I went back and told Florrie I would give her another chance and then her and I packed up and took little Al in a taxicab over to this hotel. We are threw with the Allens Al and let me know right away if I can get that lease for another year because Florrie has gave up and will go to Bedford or anywheres else with me now.   Yours truly,   JACK.

Chicago, Illinois, October 18

FRIEND AL: Old pal I won't never forget your kindnus and this is to tell you that I and Florrie except your kind invatation to come and stay with you till we can find a house and I guess you won't regret it none because Florrie will livun things up for Bertha and Bertha will be crazy about the baby because you should ought to see how cute he is now Al and not yet four months old. But I bet he will be talking before we know it.

We are comeing on the train that leaves here at noon Saturday Al and the train leaves here about 12 oclock and I don't know what time it gets to Bedford but it leaves here at noon so we shall be there probily in time for supper.

I wish you would ask Ben Smith will he have a hack down to the deepo to meet us but I won't pay no more than $.25 and I should think he should ought to be glad to take us from the deepo to your house for nothing.

Your pal,   JACK.

P. S. The train we are comeing on leaves here at noon Al and will probily get us there in time for a late supper and I wonder if Bertha would have spair ribs and crout for supper. You know me Al.

VI. The Busher Beats It Hence

Chicago, Ill., Oct. 20

FRIEND AL: I guess may be you will begin to think I dont never do what I am going to do and that I change my mind a hole lot because I wrote and told you that I and Florrie and little Al would be in Bedford to-day

and here we are in Chi yet on the day when I told you
we would get to Bedford and I bet Bertha and you and
the rest of the boys will be dissapointed but Al I dont
feel like as if I should ought to leave the White Sox in
a hole and that is why I am here yet and I will tell you
how it come off but in the 1st place I want to tell you
that it wont make a diffrence of more than 5 or 6 or
may be 7 days at least and we will be down there and
see you and Bertha and the rest of the boys just as soon
as the N. Y. giants and the White Sox leaves here and
starts a round the world. All so I remember I told you
to fix it up so as a hack would be down to the deepo
to meet us to-night and you wont get this letter in time
to tell them not to send no hack so I supose the hack
will be there but may be they will be somebody else
that gets off of the train that will want the hack and
then every thing will be all O. K. but if they is not nobody else that wants the hack I will pay them ½ of what
they was going to charge me if I had of came and road
in the hack though I dont have to pay them nothing
because I am not going to ride in the hack but I want
to do the right thing and besides I will want a hack at
the deepo when I do come so they will get a peace of
money out of me any way so I dont see where they got
no kick comeing even if I dont give them a nichol now.

I will tell you why I am still here and you will see
where I am trying to do the right thing. You knowed
of coarse that the White Sox and the N. Y. giants was
going to make a trip a round the world and they been
after me for a long time to go a long with them but I
says No I would not leave Florrie and the kid because
that would not be fare and besides I would be paying
rent and grocerys for them some wheres and me not
getting nothing out of it and besides I would probily
be spending a hole lot of money on the trip because

though the club pays all of our regular expences they
would be a hole lot of times when I felt like blowing
my self and buying some thing to send home to the
Mrs and to good old friends of mine like you and Bertha
so I turned them down and Callahan acted like he was
sore at me but I dont care nothing for that because I
got other people to think a bout and not Callahan and
besides if I was to go a long the fans in the towns where
we play at would want to see me work and I would
have to do a hole lot of pitching which I would not be
getting nothing for it and it would not count in no
standing because the games is to be just for fun and
what good would it do me and besides Florrie says I
was not under no circumstance to go and of coarse I
would go if I wanted to go no matter what ever she
says but all and all I turned them down and says I would
stay here all winter or rather I would not stay here but
in Bedford. Then Callahan says All right but you know
before we start on the trip the giants and us is going to
play a game right here in Chi next Sunday and after
what you done in the city serious the fans would be
sore if they did not get no more chance to look at you
so will you stay and pitch part of the game here and I
says I would think it over and I come home to the hotel
where we are staying at and asked Florrie did she care
if we did not go to Bedford for an other week and she
says No she did not care if we dont go for 6 years so
I called Callahan up and says I would stay and he says
Thats the boy and now the fans will have an other treat
so you see Al he appresiates what I done and wants to
give the fans fare treatment because this town is nuts
over me after what I done to them Cubs but I could do
it just the same to the Athaletics or any body else if it
would of been them in stead of the Cubs. May be we
will leave here the a.m. after the game that is Monday

and I will let you know so as you can order an other
hack and tell Bertha I hope she did not go to no extra
trouble a bout getting ready for us and did not order
no spair ribs and crout but you can eat them up if she
all ready got them and may be she can order some more
for us when we come but tell her it dont make no diffrence and not to go to no trouble because most anything she has is O. K. for I and Florrie accept of coarse
we would not want to make no meal off of sardeens or
something.

Well Al I bet them N. Y. giants will wish I would of
went home before they come for this here exibishun
game because my arm feels grate and I will show them
where they would be at if they had to play ball in our
league all the time though I supose they is some pitchers
in our league that they would hit good against them if
they can hit at all but not me. You see in the papers
how I come out and I will write and tell you a bout it.

Your pal,   JACK.

Chicago, Ill., Oct. 25

OLD PAL: I have not only got a little time but I have
got some news for you and I knowed you would want
to hear all a bout it so I am writeing this letter and then
I am going to catch the train. I would be saying good
by to little Al instead of writeing this letter only Florrie
wont let me wake him up and he is a sleep but may be
by the time I get this letter wrote he will be a wake
again and I can say good by to him. I am going with
the White Sox and giants as far as San Francisco or
may be Van Coover where they take the boat at but I
am not going a round the world with them but only
just out to the coast to help them out because they is
a couple of men going to join them out there and untill

them men join them they will be short of men and they
got a hole lot of exibishun games to play before they get
out there so I am going to help them out. It all come off
in the club house after the game to-day and I will tell
you how it come off but 1st I want to tell you a bout
the game and honest Al them giants is the luckyest team
in the world and it is not no wonder they keep wining
the penant in that league because a club that has got
there luck could win ball games with out sending no
team on the field at all but staying down to the hotel.

They was a big crowd out to the park so Callahan
says to me I did not know if I was going to pitch you
or not but the crowd is out here to see you so I will
have to let you work so I warmed up but I knowed the
minute I throwed the 1st ball warming up that I was
not right and I says to Callahan I did not feel good but
he says You wont need to feel good to beat this bunch
because they heard a hole lot a bout you and you would
have them beat if you just throwed your glove out
there in the box. So I went in and tried to pitch but my
arm was so lame it pretty near killed me every ball I
throwed and I bet if I was some other pitchers they
would not never of tried to work with my arm so sore
but I am not like some of them yellow dogs and quit because I would not dissapoint the crowd or throw Callahan down when he wanted me to pitch and was depending on me. You know me Al. So I went in there but I did
not have nothing and if them giants could of hit at all
in stead of like a lot of girls they would of knock down
the fence because I was not my self. At that they should
not ought to of had only the 1 run off of me if Weaver
and them had not of begin kicking the ball a round like
it was a foot ball or something. Well Al what with dropping fly balls and booting them a round and this in that
the giants was gave 5 runs in the 1st 3 innings and they

should ought to of had just the 1 run or may be not that
and that ball Merkle hit in to the seats I was trying to
waist it and a man that is a good hitter would not never
of hit at it and if I was right this here Merkle could not
foul me in 9 years. When I was comeing into the bench
after the 3th inning this here smart alex Mcgraw came
passed me from the 3 base coaching line and he says
Are you going on the trip and I says No I am not going
on no trip and he says That is to bad because if you was
going we would win a hole lot of games and I give him
a hot come back and he did not say nothing so I went
in to the bench and Callahan says Them giants is not
such rotten hitters is they and I says No they hit pretty
good when a man has got a sore arm against them and
he says Why did not you tell me your arm was sore and
I says I did not want to dissapoint no crowd that come
out here to see me and he says Well I guess you need
not pitch no more because if I left you in there the crowd
might begin to get tired of watching you a bout 10
oclock to-night and I says What do you mean and he
did not say nothing more so I set there a while and then
went to the club house. Well Al after the game Callahan
come in to the club house and I was still in there yet
talking to the trainer and getting my arm rubbed and
Callahan says Are you getting your arm in shape for
next year and I says No but it give me so much pane I
could not stand it and he says I bet if you was feeling
good you could make them giants look like a sucker and
I says You know I could make them look like a sucker
and he says Well why dont you come a long with us
and you will get an other chance at them when you feel
good and I says I would like to get an other crack at
them but I could not go a way on no trip and leave the
Mrs and the baby and then he says he would not ask me
to make the hole trip a round the world but he wisht

I would go out to the coast with them because they was
hard up for pitchers and he says Mathewson of the
giants was not only going as far as the coast so if the
giants had there star pitcher that far the White Sox
should ought to have theren and then some of the other
boys coaxed me would I go so finely I says I would think
it over and I went home and seen Florrie and she says
How long would it be for and I says a bout 3 or 4 weeks
and she says If you dont go will we start for Bedford
right a way and I says Yes and then she says All right
go a head and go but if they was any thing should happen to the baby while I was gone what would they do
if I was not a round to tell them what to do and I says
Call a Dr. in but dont call no Dr. if you dont have to and
besides you should ought to know by this time what to
do for the baby when he got sick and she says Of coarse
I know a little but not as much as you do because you
know it all. Then I says No I dont know it all but I will
tell you some things before I go and you should not
ought to have no trouble so we fixed it up and her and
little Al is to stay here in the hotel untill I come back
which will be a bout the 20 of Nov. and then we will
come down home and tell Bertha not to get to in patient
and we will get there some time. It is going to cost me
$6.00 a week at the hotel for a room for she and the baby
besides there meals but the babys meals dont cost nothing yet and Florrie should not ought to be very hungry
because we been liveing good and besides she will get all
she can eat when we come to Bedford and it wont cost
me nothing for meals on the trip out to the coast because
Comiskey and Mcgraw pays for that.

I have not even had no time to look up where we play
at but we stop off at a hole lot of places on the way and
I will get a chance to make them giants look like a
sucker before I get threw and Mcgraw wont be so sorry

I am not going to make the hole trip. You will see by the papers what I done to them before we get threw and I will write as soon as we stop some wheres long enough so as I can write and now I am going to say good by to little Al if he is a wake or not a wake and wake him up and say good by to him because even if he is not only 5 months old he is old enough to think a hole lot of me and why not. I all so got to say good by to Florrie and fix it up with the hotel clerk a bout she and the baby staying here a while and catch the train. You will hear from me soon old pal.   Your pal,   JACK.

St. Joe, Miss., Oct. 29

FRIEND AL: Well Al we are on our way to the coast and they is quite a party of us though it is not no real White Sox and giants at all but some players from off of both clubs and then some others that is from other clubs a round the 2 leagues to fill up. We got Speaker from the Boston club and Crawford from the Detroit club and if we had them with us all the time Al I would not never loose a game because one or the other of them 2 is good for a couple of runs every game and that is all I need to win my games is a couple of runs or only 1 run and I would win all my games and would not never loose a game.

I did not pitch to-day and I guess the giants was glad of it because no matter what Mcgraw says he must of saw from watching me Sunday that I was a real pitcher though my arm was so sore I could not hardly raze it over my sholder so no wonder I did not have no stuff but at that I could of beat his gang with out no stuff if I had of had some kind of decent suport. I will pitch against them may be to-morrow or may be some day soon and my arm is all O. K. again now so I will show them up and make them wish Callahan had of left me to home. Some of the men has brung there wife a long and besides that there is some other men and there wife that is not no ball players but are going a long for the trip and some more will join the party out the coast before they get a bord the boat but of coarse I and Mathewson will drop out of the party then because why should I or him go a round the world and throw our arms out pitching games that dont count in no standing and that we dont get no money for pitching them out side of just our bare expences. The people in the towns we played at so far has all wanted to shake hands with Mathewson and I so I guess they know who is the real pitchers on these here 2 clubs no matter what them reporters says and the stars is all ways the men that the people wants to shake there hands with and make friends with them but Al this here Mathewson pitched to-day and honest Al I dont see how he gets by and either the batters in the National league dont know nothing a bout hitting or else he is such a old man that they feel sorry for him and may be when he was a bout 10 years younger then he is may be then he had some thing and was a pretty fare pitcher but all as he does now is stick the 1st ball right over with 0 on it and pray that they dont hit it out of the park. If a pitcher like he can get by in the National league and fool them batters they is not nothing I would like better then to pitch in the National league and I bet I would not get scored on in 2 to 3 years. I heard a hole lot a bout this here fade away that he is supposed to pitch and it is a ball that is throwed out between 2 fingers and falls in at a right hand batter and they is not no body cant hit it but if he throwed 1 of them things to-day he done it while I was a sleep and they was not no time when I was not wide a wake and looking right at him and after the game

was over I says to him Where is that there fade a way
I heard so much a bout and he says O I did not have
to use none of my regular stuff against your club and I
says Well you would have to use all you got if I was
working against you and he says Yes if you worked like
you done Sunday I would have to do some pitching or
they would not never finish the game. Then I says a bout
me haveing a sore arm Sunday and he says I wisht I had
a sore arm like yourn and a little sence with it and was
your age and I would not never loose a game so you see
Al he has heard a bout me and is jellus because he has
not got my stuff but they cant every body expect to have
the stuff that I got or ½ as much stuff. This smart alex
Mcgraw was trying to kid me to-day and says Why did
not I make friends with Mathewson and let him learn
me some thing a bout pitching and I says Mathewson
could not learn me nothing and he says I guess thats
right and I guess they is not nobody could learn you
nothing a bout nothing and if you was to stay in the
league 20 years probily you would not be no better then
you are now so you see he had to add mit that I am
good Al even if he has not saw me work when my arm
was O. K.

Mcgraw says to me to-night he says I wisht you was
going all the way and I says Yes you do. I says Your
club would look like a sucker after I had worked against
them a few times and he says May be thats right to because they would not know how to hit against a regular
pitcher after that. Then he says But I dont care nothing
a bout that but I wisht you was going to make the hole
trip so as we could have a good time. He says We got
Steve Evans and Dutch Schaefer going a long and they
is both of them funny but I like to be a round with
boys that is funny and dont know nothing a bout it. I
says Well I would go a long only for my wife and baby

and he says Yes it would be pretty tough on your wife to have you a way that long but still and all think how glad she would be to see you when you come back again and besides them dolls acrost the ocean will be pretty sore at I and Callahan if we tell them we left you to home. I says Do you suppose the people over there has heard a bout me and he says Sure because they have wrote a lot of letters asking me to be sure and bring you and Mathewson a long. Then he says I guess Mathewson is not going so if you was to go and him left here to home they would not be nothing to it. You could have things all your own way and probily could marry the Queen of europe if you was not all ready married. He was giveing me the strate dope this time Al because he did not crack a smile and I wisht I could go a long but it would not be fare to Florrie but still and all did not she leave me and beat it for Texas last winter and why should not I do the same thing to her only I am not that kind of a man. You know me Al.

We play in Kansas city to-morrow and may be I will work there because it is a big town and I have got to close now and write to Florrie.   Your old pal,   JACK.

Abilene, Texas, Nov. 4

AL: Well Al I guess you know by this time that I have worked against them 2 times since I wrote to you last time and I beat them both times and Mcgraw knows now what kind of a pitcher I am and I will tell you how I know because after the game yesterday he road down to the place we dressed at a long with me and all the way in the automobile he was after me to say I would go all the way a round the world and finely it come out that he wants I should go a long and pitch for his club and not pitch for the White Sox. He says his club is up

against it for pitchers because Mathewson is not going
and all they got left is a man named Hern that is a young
man and not got no experiense and Wiltse that is a left-
hander. So he says I have talked it over with Callahan
and he says if I could get you to go a long it was all
O. K. with him and you could pitch for us only I must
not work you to hard because he is depending on you
to win the penant for him next year. I says Did not
none of the other White Sox made no holler because
may be they might have to bat against me and he says
Yes Crawford and Speaker says they would not make
the trip if you was a long and pitching against them but
Callahan showed them where it would be good for them
next year because if they hit against you all winter the
pitchers they hit against next year will look easy to them.
He was crazy to have me go a long on the hole trip but
of coarse Al they is not no chance of me going on acct.
of Florrie and little Al but you see Mcgraw has cut out
his trying to kid me and is treating me now like a man
should ought to be treated that has did what I done.

They was not no game here to-day on acct. of it
raining and the people here was sore because they did
not see no game but they all come a round to look at
us and says they must have some speechs from the most
prommerent men in the party so I and Comiskey and
Mcgraw and Callahan and Mathewson and Ted Sullivan
that I guess is putting up the money for the trip made
speechs and they clapped there hands harder when I was
makeing my speech then when any 1 of the others was
makeing there speech. You did not know I was a speech
maker did you Al and I did not know it neither untill
to-day but I guess they is not nothing I cant do if I make
up my mind and 1 of the boys says that I done just as
well as Dummy Taylor could of.

I have not heard nothing from Florrie but I guess may

be she is to busy takeing care of little Al to write no letters and I am not worring none because she give me her word she would let me know was they some thing the matter.   Yours truly,   JACK.

San Dago, Cal., Nov. 9

FRIEND AL: Al some times I wisht I was not married at all and if it was not for Florrie and little Al I would go a round the world on this here trip and I guess the boys in Bedford would not be jellus if I was to go a round the world and see everything they is to be saw and some ot the boys down home has not never been no futher a way then Terre Haute and I dont mean you Al but some of the other boys. But of coarse Al when a man has got a wife and a baby they is not no chance for him to go a way on 1 of these here trips and leave them a lone so they is not no use I should even think a bout it but I can't help thinking a bout it because the boys keeps after me all the time to go. Callahan was talking a bout it to me to-day and he says he knowed that if I was to pitch for the giants on the trip his club would not have no chance of wining the most of the games on the trip but still and all he wisht I would go a long because he was a scared the people over in Rome and Paris and Africa and them other countrys would be awful sore if the 2 clubs come over there with out bringing none of there star pitchers along. He says We got Speaker and Crawford and Doyle and Thorp and some of them other real stars in all the positions accept pitcher and it will make us look bad if you and Mathewson don't neither 1 of you come a long. I says What is the matter with Scott and Benz and this here left hander Wiltse and he says They is not nothing the matter with none of them accept they is not no real stars like you and

Mathewson and if we cant show them forreners 1 of you 2 we will feel like as if we was cheating them. I says You would not want me to pitch my best against your club would you and he says O no I would not want you to pitch your best or get your self all wore out for next year but I would want you to let up enough so as we could make a run oncet in a while so the games would not be to 1 sided. I says Well they is not no use talking a bout it because I could not leave my wife and baby and he says Why dont you write and ask your wife and tell her how it is and can you go. I says No because she would make a big holler and besides of coarse I would go any way if I wanted to go with out no yes or no from her only I am not the kind of a man that runs off and leaves his family and besides they is not nobody to leave her with because her and her sister Allens wife has had a quarrle. Then Callahan says Where is Allen at now is he still in Chi. I says I dont know where is he at and I dont care where he is at because I am threw with him. Then Callahan says I asked him would he go on the trip before the season was over but he says he could not and if I knowed where was he I would wire a telegram to him and ask him again. I says What would you want him a long for and he says Because Mcgraw is shy of pitchers and I says I would try and help him find 1. I says Well you should ought not to have no trouble finding a man like Allen to go along because his wife probily would be glad to get rid of him. Then Callahan says Well I wisht you would get a hold of where Allen is at and let me know so as I can wire him a telegram. Well Al I know where Allen is at all O. K. but I am not going to give his adress to Callahan because Mcgraw has treated me all O. K. and why should I wish a man like Allen on to him and besides I am not going to give Allen no chance to go a round the world or no wheres else after the way he acted a bout I and Florrie haveing a room in his flat and asking me to pay for it when he give me a invatation to come there and stay. Well Al it is to late now to cry in the sour milk but I wisht I had not never saw Florrie untill next year and then I and her could get married just like we done last year only I dont know would I do it again or not but I guess I would on acct. of little Al.

Your pal,   JACK.

San Francisco, Cal., Nov. 14

OLD PAL: Well old pal what do you know a bout me being back here in San Francisco where I give the fans such a treat 2 years ago and then I was not nothing but a busher and now I am with a team that is going a round the world and are crazy to have me go a long only I cant because of my wife and baby. Callahan wired a telegram to the reporters here from Los Angeles telling them I would pitch here and I guess they is going to be 20 or 25000 out to the park and I will give them the best I got.

But what do you think Florrie has did Al. Her and the Allens has made it up there quarrel and is friends again and Marie told Florrie to write and tell me she was sorry we had that there argument and let by gones be by gones. Well Al it is all O. K. with me because I cant help not feeling sorry for Allen because I dont beleive he will be in the league next year and I feel sorry for Marie to because it must be pretty tough on her to see how well her sister done and what a misstake she made when she went and fell for a lefthander that could not fool a blind man with his curve ball and if he was to hit a man in the head with his fast ball they would think there nose iched. In Florries letter she says she thinks us and the Allens could find an other flat like the 1 we had last winter and all live in it to gether in stead

of going to Bedford but I have wrote to her before I
started writeing this letter all ready and told her that
her and I is going to Bedford and the Allens can go
where they feel like and they can go and stay on a boat
on Michigan lake all winter if they want to but I and
Florrie is comeing to Bedford. Down to the bottom of
her letter she says Allen wants to know if Callahan or
Mcgraw is shy of pitchers and may be he would change
his mind and go a long on the trip. Well Al I did not ask
either Callahan nor Mcgraw nothing a bout it because
I knowed they was looking for a star and not for no left-
hander that could not brake a pane of glass with his fast
1 so I wrote and told Florrie to tell Allen they was all
filled up and would not have no room for no more men.

It is pretty near time to go out to the ball park and I
wisht you could be here Al and hear them San Francisco
fans go crazy when they hear my name anounced to
pitch. I bet they wish they had of had me here this last
year.   Yours truly,   JACK.

Medford, Organ, Nov. 16

FRIEND AL: Well Al you know by this time that I did
not pitch the hole game in San Francisco but I was not
tooken out because they was hitting me Al but because
my arm went back on me all of a sudden and it was the
change in the clime it that done it to me and they could
not hire me to try and pitch another game in San Francisco. They was the biggest crowd there that I ever seen
in San Francisco and I guess they must of been 40000
people there and I wisht you could of heard them yell
when my name was anounced to pitch. But Al I would
not never of went in there but for the crowd. My arm
felt like a wet rag or some thing and I knowed I would
not have nothing and besides the people was packed in

a round the field and they had to have ground rules so when a man hit a pop fly it went in to the crowd some wheres and was a 2 bagger and all them giants could do against me was pop my fast ball up in the air and then the wind took a hold of it and dropped it in to the crowd the lucky stiffs. Doyle hit 3 of them pop ups in to the crowd so when you see them 3 2 base hits oposit his name in the score you will know they was not no real 2 base hits and the infielders would of catched them had it not of been for the wind. This here Doyle takes a awful wallop at a ball but if I was right and he swang at a ball the way he done in San Francisco the catcher would all ready be throwing me back the ball a bout the time this here Doyle was swinging at it. I can make him look like a sucker and I done it both in Kansas city and Bonham and if he will get up there and bat against me when I feel good and when they is not no wind blowing I will bet him a $25.00 suit of cloths that he cant foul 1 off of me. Well when Callahan seen how bad my arm was he says I guess I should ought to take you out and not run no chance of you getting killed in there and so I quit and Faber went in to finnish it up because it dont make no diffrence if he hurts his arm or dont. But I guess Mcgraw knowed my arm was sore to because he did not try and kid me like he done that day in Chi because he has saw enough of me since then to know I can make his club look rotten when I am O.K. and my arm is good. On the train that night he come up and says to me Well Jack we catched you off your strid to-day or you would of gave us a beating and then he says What your arm needs is more work and you should ought to make the hole trip with us and then you would be in fine shape for next year but I says You cant get me to make no trip so you might is well not do no more talking a bout it and then he says Well I am sorry and the girls over to Paris will be sorry to but I guess he was just jokeing a bout the last part of it.

Well Al we go to 1 more town in Organ and then to Washington but of coarse it is not the same Washington we play at in the summer but this is the state Washington and have not got no big league club and the boys gets there boat in 4 more days and I will quit them and then I will come strate back to Chi and from there to Bedford.   Your pal,   JACK.

Portland, Organ, Nov. 17

FRIEND AL: I have just wrote a long letter to Florrie but I feel like as if I should ought to write to you because I wont have no more chance for a long while that is I wont have no more chance to male a letter because I will be on the pacific Ocean and un less we should run passed a boat that was comeing the other way they would not be no chance of getting no letter maled. Old pal I am going to make the hole trip clear a round the world and back and so I wont see you this winter after all but when I do see you Al I will have a lot to tell you a bout my trip and besides I will write you a letter a bout it from every place we head in at.

I guess you will be surprised a bout me changeing my mind and makeing the hole trip but they was not no way for me to get out of it and I will tell you how it all come off. While we was still in that there Medford yesterday Mcgraw and Callahan come up to me and says was they not no chance of me changeing my mind a bout makeing the hole trip. I says No they was not. Then Callahan says Well I dont know what we are going to do then and I says Why and he says Comiskey just got a letter from president Wilson the President of the united states and in the letter president Wilson says he had got

an other letter from the king of Japan who says that they
would not stand for the White Sox and giants comeing
to Japan un less they brought all there stars a long and
president Wilson says they would have to take there
stars a long because he was a scared if they did not take
there stars a long Japan would get mad at the united
states and start a war and then where would we be at.
So Comiskey wired a telegram to president Wilson and
says Mathewson could not make the trip because he was
so old but would everything be all O.K. if I was to go
a long and president Wilson wired a telegram back and
says Yes he had been talking to the priest from Japan
and he says Yes it would be all O.K. I asked them would
they show me the letter from president Wilson because
I thought may be they might be kiding me and they
says they could not show me no letter because when
Comiskey got the letter he got so mad that he tore it up.
Well Al I finely says I did not want to brake up there trip
but I knowed Florrie would not stand for letting me go
so Callahan says All right I will wire a telegram to a
friend of mine in Chi and have him get a hold of Allen
and send him out here and we will take him a long and I
says It is to late for Allen to get here in time and Mcgraw
says No they was a train that only took 2 days from Chi
to where ever it was the boat is going to sale from because the train come a round threw canada and it was
down hill all the way. Then I says Well if you will wire
a telegram to my wife and fix things up with her I will
go a long with you but if she is going to make a holler
it is all off. So we all 3 went to the telegram office to
gether and we wired Florrie a telegram that must of
cost $2.00 but Callahan and Mcgraw payed for it out of
there own pocket and then we waited a round a long
time and the anser come back and the anser was longer
than the telegram we wired and it says it would not

make no difference to her but she did not know if the
baby would make a holler but he was hollering most
of the time any way so that would not make no diffrence
but if she let me go it was on condishon that her and the
Allens could get a flat to gether and stay in Chi all
winter and not go to no Bedford and hire a nurse to take
care of the baby and if I would send her a check for the
money I had in the bank so as she could put it in her
name and draw it out when she need it. Well I says at
1st I would not stand for nothing like that but Callahan
and Mcgraw showed me where I was makeing a mistake
not going when I could see all them diffrent countrys
and tell Florrie all a bout the trip when I come back
and then in a year or 2 when the baby was a little older
I could make an other trip and take little Al and Florrie
a long so I finely says O.K. I would go and we wires
still an other telegram to Florrie and told her O.K. and
then I set down and wrote her a check for ½ the money
I got in the bank and I got $500.00 all together there so
I wrote the check for ½ of that or $250.00 and maled it
      and if she cant get a long on that she would be a
              because I am not only going to be a way
until   You should ought to of heard the boys
cheer when Callahan tells them I am going to make the
hole trip but when he tells them I am going to pitch
for the giants and not for the White Sox I bet Crawford
and Speaker and them wisht I was going to stay to home
but it is just like Callahan says if they bat against me all
winter the pitchers they bat against next season will look
easy to them and you wont be supprised Al if Crawford and Speaker hits a bout 500 next year and if they
hit good you will know why it is. Steve Evans asked me
was I all fixed up with cloths and I says No but I was
going out and buy some cloths includeing a full dress
suit of evening cloths and he says You dont need no full

dress suit of evening cloths because you look funny enough with out them. This Evans is a great kidder Al and no body never gets sore at the stuff he pulls some thing like Kid Gleason. I wisht Kid Gleason was going on the trip Al but I will tell him all a bout it when I come back.

Well Al old pal I wisht you was going a long to and I bet we could have the time of our life but I will write to you right a long Al and I will send Bertha some post cards from the different places we head in at. I will try and write you a letter on the boat and male it as soon as we get to the 1st station which is either Japan or Yokohama I forgot which. Good by Al and say good by to Bertha for me and tell her how sorry I and Florrie is that we cant come to Bedford this winter but we will spend all the rest of the winters there and her and Florrie will have a plenty of time to get acquainted. Good by old pal.

Your pal,   JACK.

Seattle, Wash., Nov. 18

AL: Well Al it is all off and I am not going on no trip a round the world and back and I been looking for Callahan or Mcgraw for the last ½ hour to tell them I have changed my mind and am not going to make no trip because it would not be fare to Florrie and besides that I think I should ought to stay home and take care of little Al and not leave him to be tooken care of by no train nurse because how do I know what would she do to him and I am not going to tell Florrie nothing a bout it but I am going to take the train to-morrow night right back to Chi and supprise her when I get there and I bet both her and little Al will be tickled to death to see me. I supose Mcgraw and Callahan will be sore at me for a while but when I tell them I want to do the right thing and not give my famly no raw deal I guess they will see where I am right.

We was to play 2 games here and was to play 1 of them in Tacoma and the other here but it rained and so we did not play neither 1 and the people was pretty mad a bout it because I was announced to pitch and they figured probily this would be there only chance to see me in axion and they made a awful holler but Comiskey says No they would not be no game because the field neither here or in Tacoma was in no shape for a game and he would not take no chance of me pitching and may be slipping in the mud and straneing myself and then where would the White Sox be at next season. So we been laying a round all the p.m. and I and Dutch Schaefer had a long talk to gether while some of the rest of the boys was out buying some cloths to take on the trip and Al I bought a full dress suit of evening cloths at Portland yesterday and now I owe Callahan the money for them and am not going on no trip so probily I wont never get to ware them and it is just $45.00 throwed a way but I would rather throw $45.00 a way then go on a trip a round the world and leave my family all winter.

Well Al I and Schaefer was talking to gether and he says Well may be this is the last time we will ever see the good old US and I says What do you mean and he says People that gos acrost the pacific Ocean most generally all ways has there ship recked and then they is not no more never heard from them. Then he asked me was I a good swimmer and I says Yes I had swam a good deal in the river and he says Yes you have swam in the river but that is not nothing like swimming in the pacific Ocean because when you swim in the pacific Ocean you cant move your feet because if you move your feet the sharks comes up to the top of the water and bites at them and even if they did not bite your feet clean off there bite is poison and gives you the hidero-fobeya and when you get that you start barking like a dog and the water runs in to your mouth and chokes you to death. Then he says Of coarse if you can swim with out useing your feet you are all O.K. but they is very few can do that and espesially in the pacific Ocean because they got to keep useing there hands all the time to scare the sord fish a way so when you dont dare use your feet and your hands is busy you got nothing left to swim with but your stumach mussles. Then he says You should ought to get a long all O. K. because your stumach muscles should ought to be strong from the exercise they get so I guess they is not no danger from a man like you but men like Wiltse and Mike Donlin that is not hog fat like you has not got no chance. Then he says Of coarse they have been times when the boats got acrost all O.K. and only a few lives lost but it dont offten happen and the time the old Minneapolis club made the trip the boat went down and the only thing that was saved was the catchers protector that was full of air and could not do nothing else but flote. Then he says May be you would flote to if you did not say noth-ing for a few days.

I asked him how far would a man got to swim if some thing went wrong with the boat and he says O not far because they is a hole lot of ilands a long the way that a man could swim to but it would not do a man no good to swim to these here ilands because they dont have nothing to eat on them and a man would probily starve to death un less he happened to swim to the sandwich ilands. Then he says But by the time you been out on the pacific Ocean a few months you wont care if you get any thing to eat or not. I says Why not and he says the pacific Ocean is so ruff that not nothing can set still not even the stuff you eat. I asked him how long did it take to make the trip acrost if they was not no ship reck and he says they should ought to get acrost a long in febuery if the weather was good. I says Well if we dont get there until febuery we won't have no time to train for next season and he says You wont need to do no training because this trip will take all the weight off of you and every thing else you got. Then he says But you should not ought to be scared of getting sea sick because they is 1 way you can get a way from it and that is to not eat nothing at all while you are on the boat and they tell me you dont eat hardly nothing any way so you wont miss it. Then he says Of coarse if we should have good luck and not get in to no ship reck and not get shot by 1 of them war ships we will have a grate time when we get acrost because all the girls in europe and them places is nuts over ball players and espesially stars. I asked what did he mean saying we might get shot by 1 of them war ships and he says we would have to pass by Swittserland and the Swittserland war ships was all the time shooting all over the ocean and of coarse they was not trying to hit no body but they was as wild as most of them lefthanders and how could you tell what was they going to do next.

Well Al after I got threw talking to Schaefer I run in to Jack Sheridan the umpire and I says I did not think I would go on no trip and I told him some of the things Schaefer was telling me and Sheridan says Schaefer was kidding me and they was not no danger at all and of coarse Al I did not believe ½ of what Schaefer was telling me and that has not got nothing to do with me changeing my mind but I dont think it is not hardly fare for me to go a way on a trip like that and leave Florrie and the baby and suppose some of them things really did happen like Schaefer said though of coarse he was kidding me but if 1 of them was to happen they would not be no body left to take care of Florrie and little Al and I got a $1000.00 insurence policy but how do I know after I am dead if the insurence co. comes acrost and gives my famly the money.

Well Al I will male this letter and then try again and find Mcgraw and Callahan and then I will look up a time table and see what train can I get to Chi. I don't know yet when I will be in Bedford and maybe Florrie has hired a flat all ready but the Allens can live in it by them self and if Allen says any thing a bout I paying for ½ of the rent I will bust his jaw.   Your pal,   JACK.

Victoria, Can., Nov. 19

DEAR OLD AL: Well old pal the boat gos to-night I am going a long and I would not be takeing no time to write this letter only I wrote to you yesterday and says I was not going and you probily would be expecting to see me blow in to Bedford in a few days and besides Al I got a hole lot of things to ask you to do for me if any thing happens and I want to tell you how it come a bout that I changed my mind and am going on the trip. I am glad now that I did not write Florrie no letter yesterday and tell her I was not going because now I would have to write her an other letter and tell her I was going and she would be expecting to see me the day after she got the 1st letter and in stead of seeing me she would get this 2nd. letter and not me at all. I have all ready wrote her a good by letter to-day though and while I was writeing it Al I all most broke down and cried and espesially when I thought a bout leaveing little Al so long and may be when I see him again he wont be no baby no more or may be some thing will of happened to him or that train nurse did some thing to him or may be I wont never see him again no more because it is pretty near a cinch that some thing will either happen to I or him. I would give all most any thing I got Al to be back in Chi with little Al and Florrie and I wisht she had not of never wired that telegram telling me I could make the trip and if some thing happens to me think how she will feel when ever she thinks a bout wireing me that telegram and she will feel all most like as if she was a murder.

Well Al after I had wrote you that letter yesterday I found Callahan and Mcgraw and I tell them I have changed my mind and am not going on no trip. Callahan says Whats the matter and I says I dont think it would be fare to my wife and baby and Callahan says Your wife says it would be all O.K. because I seen the telegram my self. I says Yes but she dont know how dangerus the trip is and he says Whos been kiding you and I says They has not no body been kiding me. I says Dutch Schaefer told me a hole lot of stuff but I did not believe none of it and that has not got nothing to do with it. I says I am not a scared of nothing but supose some thing should happen and then where would my wife and my baby be at. Then Callahan says Schaefer has been giveing you a lot of hot air and they is not no more danger on this trip then they is in bed. You been in a hole lot more danger when you was pitching some of them days when you had a sore arm and you would be takeing more chances of getting killed in Chi by 1 of them taxi cabs or the dog catcher then on the Ocean. This here boat we are going on is the Umpires of Japan and it has went acrost the Ocean a million times with out nothing happening and they could not nothing happen to a boat that the N. Y. giants was rideing on because they is to lucky. Then I says Well I have made up my mind to not go on no trip and he says All right then

I guess we might is well call the trip off and I says Why and he says You know what president Wilson says a bout Japan and they wont stand for us comeing over there with out you a long and then Mcgraw says Yes it looks like as if the trip was off because we dont want to take no chance of starting no war between Japan and the united states. Then Callahan says You will be in fine with Comiskey if he has to call the trip off because you are a scared of getting hit by a fish. Well Al we talked and argued for a hour or a hour and ½ and some of the rest of the boys come a round and took Callahan and Mcgraw side and finely Callahan says it looked like as if they would have to posepone the trip a few days untill he could get a hold of Allen or some body and get them to take my place so finely I says I would go because I would not want to brake up no trip after they had made all there plans and some of the players wifes was all ready to go and would be dissapointed if they was not no trip. So Mcgraw and Callahan says Thats the way to talk and so I am going Al and we are leaveing to-night and may be this is the last letter you will ever get Allen me but if they does not nothing happen Al a long and I you a lot of letters and tell you all a bout you must not be looking for no more letters for a while untill we get to Japan where I can male a letter and may be its likely as not we wont never get to Japan.

Here is the things I want to ask you to try and do Al and I am not asking you to do nothing if we get threw the trip all right but if some thing happens and I should be drowned here is what I am asking you to do for me and that is to see that the insurence co. dont skin Florrie out of that $1000.00 policy and see that she all so gets that other $250.00 out of the bank and find her some place down in Bedford to live if she is willing to live down there because she can live there a hole lot

cheaper then she can live in Chi and besides I know
Bertha would treat her right and help her out all she
could. All so Al I want you and Bertha to help take
care of little Al untill he grows up big enough to take
care of him self and if he looks like as if he was going
to be lefthanded dont let him Al but make him use his
right hand for every thing. Well Al they is 1 good thing
and that is if I get drowned Florrie wont have to buy
no lot in no cemetary and hire no herse.

Well Al old pal you all ways been a good friend of
mine and I all ways tried to be a good friend of yourn
and if they was ever any thing I done to you that was
not O.K. remember by gones is by gones. I want you to
all ways think of me as your best old pal. Good by old
pal.   Your old pal,   JACK.

P.S. Al if they should not nothing happen and if we
was to get acrost the Ocean all O.K. I am going to ask
Mcgraw to let me work the 1st game against the White
Sox in Japan because I should certainly ought to be
right after giveing my arm a rest and not doing nothing
at all on the trip acrost and I bet if Mcgraw lets me work
Crawford and Speaker will wisht the boat had of sank.
You know me Al.

THE BIG TOWN

Preface

THIS book deals with the adventures of a man and his wife and his sister-in-law who move to New York from a small Middle Western city. Because the writer and she who jokingly married him moved to New York from the Middle West, and because the writer has almost as many sisters-in-law as Solomon, several Nordic blondes have inquired whether the hero and heroines of the book are not actually us. Fortunately most of the inquirers made the inquiry of me, the possessor of a notoriously sweet disposition. Two of them, however, asked the madam herself and were both shot down.

In the first place, the ladies of the book are supposed to have inherited enough money to make them and the gent more or less independent. Nothing like that in our family.

In the second place, the sister-in-law of the book has a hard time getting a man. The sisters-in-law in real life acquired permanent men while still in their nonage, you might say, and didn't have to move out of the Middle West to do it. And though none of them, perhaps, can be said to have done as well as the madam herself, at least from an esthetic standpoint, still it is something to boast of that none of them was obliged to go Democratic.

The contents of *The Big Town* were written mostly in a furnished house in Greenwich, Connecticut, and the author wishes to thank the rats for staying out of the room while he worked. It was winter time and the furnished house was a summer cottage, but we didn't

realize that when we rented it. Nor, apparently, did the
rats.

R. W. L.

March 1925.

1. Quick Returns

THIS is just a clipping from one of the New York papers;
a little kidding piece that they had in about me two years
ago. It says:

HOOSIER CLEANS UP IN WALL STREET. Employees
of the brokerage firm of H. L. Krause & Co. are authority
for the statement that a wealthy Indiana speculator made
one of the biggest killings of the year in the Street yesterday afternoon. No very definite information was obtain-
able, as the Westerner's name was known to only one of
the firm's employees, Francis Griffin, and he was unable
to recall it last night.

You'd think I was a millionaire and that I'd made a
sucker out of Morgan or something, but it's only a kid,
see? If they'd of printed the true story they wouldn't of
had no room left for that day's selections at Pimlico, and
God knows that would of been fatal.

But if you want to hear about it, I'll tell you.

Well, the War wound up in the fall of 1918. The only
member of my family that was killed in it was my wife's
stepfather. He died of grief when it ended with him two
hundred thousand dollars ahead. I immediately had a
black bandage sewed round my left funny bone, but
when they read us the will I felt all right again and tore
it off. Our share was seventy-five thousand dollars. This

was after we had paid for the inheritance tax and the amusement stamps on a horseless funeral.

My young sister-in-law, Katie, dragged down another seventy-five thousand dollars and the rest went to the old bird that had been foreman in Papa's factory. This old geezer had been starving to death for twenty years on the wages my step father-in-law give him, and the rest of us didn't make no holler when his name was read off for a small chunk, especially as he didn't have no teeth to enjoy it with.

I could of had this old foreman's share, maybe, if I'd of took advantage of the offer "Father" made me just before his daughter and I was married. I was over in Niles, Michigan, where they lived, and he insisted on me seeing his factory, which meant smelling it too. At that time I was knocking out about eighteen hundred dollars per annum selling cigars out of South Bend, and the old man said he would start me in with him at only about a fifty per cent cut, but we would also have the privilege of living with him and my wife's kid sister.

"They's a lot to be learnt about this business," he says, "but if you would put your mind on it you might work up to manager. Who knows?"

"My nose knows," I said, and that ended it.

The old man had lost some jack and went into debt a good many years ago, and for a long wile before the war begin about all as he was able to do was support himself and the two gals and pay off a part of what he owed. When the war broke loose and leather went up to hell and gone I and my wife thought he would get prosperous, but before this country went in his business went on about the same as usual.

"I don't know how they do it," he would say. "Other leather men is getting rich on contracts with the Allies, but I can't land a one."

I guess he was trying to sell razor strops to Russia.

Even after we got into it and he begin to clean up, with the factory running day and night, all as we knew was that he had contracts with the U. S. Government, but he never confided in us what special stuff he was turning out. For all as we knew, it may of been medals for the ground navy.

Anyway, he must of been hitting a fast clip when the armistice come and ended the war for everybody but Congress! It's a cinch he wasn't amongst those arrested for celebrating too loud on the night of November 11. On the contrary they tell me that when the big news hit Niles the old bird had a stroke that he didn't never recover from, and though my wife and Katie hung round the bedside day after day in the hopes he would tell how much he was going to leave he was keeping his fiscal secrets for Oliver Lodge or somebody, and it wasn't till we seen the will that we knew we wouldn't have to work no more, which is pretty fair consolation even for the loss of a step-father-in-law that ran a perfume mill.

"Just think," said my wife, "after all his financial troubles, Papa died a rich man!"

"Yes," I said to myself, "and a patriot. His only regret was that he just had one year to sell leather to his country."

If the old codger had of only been half as fast a salesman as his two daughters this clipping would of been right when it called me a wealthy Hoosier. It wasn't two weeks after we seen the will when the gals had disposed of the odor factory and the old home in Niles, Michigan. Katie, it seemed, had to come over to South Bend and live with us. That was agreeable to me, as I figured that if two could live on eighteen hundred dollars a year three could struggle along some way on the income off one hundred and fifty thousand dollars.

Only for me, though, Ella and Sister Kate would of shot the whole wad into a checking account so as the bank could enjoy it wile it lasted. I argued and fought and finally persuaded them to keep five thousand apiece for pin money and stick the rest into bonds.

The next thing they done was run over to Chi and buy all the party dresses that was vacant. Then they come back to South Bend and wished somebody would give a party. But between you and I the people we'd always ran round with was birds that was ready for bed as soon as they got home from the first show, and even though it had been printed in the *News-Times* that we had fell heir to a lot of jack we didn't have to hire no extra clerical help to tend to invitations received from the demi-Monday.

Finally Ella said we would start something ourselves. So she got a lot of invitations printed and sent them to all our friends that could read and hired a cater and a three-piece orchestra and everything, and made me buy a dress suit.

Well, the big night arrived and everybody come that had somebody to leave their baby with. The hosts wore evening clothes and the rest of the merrymakers prepared for the occasion with a shine or a clean collar. At first the cat had everybody's tongue, but when we sat down to eat some of the men folks begun to get comical. For instance, they would say to my wife or Katie, "Ain't you afraid you'll catch cold?" And they'd say to me, "I didn't know you was a waiter at the Oliver." Before the fish course everybody was in a fair way to get the giggles.

After supper the musicians come and hid behind a geranium and played a jazz. The entire party set out the first dance. The second was a solo between Katie and I, and I had the third with my wife. Then Kate and the

Mrs. had one together, wile I tried holds with a lady named Mrs. Eckhart, who seemed to think that somebody had ast her to stand for a time exposure. The men folks had all drifted over behind the plant to watch the drummer, but after the stalemate between Mrs. Eckhart and I, I grabbed her husband and took him out in the kitchen and showed him a bottle of bourbon that I'd been saving for myself, in the hopes it would loosen him up. I told him it was my last bottle, but he must of thought I said it was the last bottle in the world. Anyway, when he got through they was international prohibition.

We went back in the ballroom and sure enough he ast Katie to dance. But he hadn't no sooner than win one fall when his wife challenged him to take her home and that started the epidemic that emptied the house of everybody but the orchestra and us. The orchestra had been hired to stay till midnight, which was still two hours and a half distance, so I invited both of the gals to dance with me at once, but it seems like they was surfeited with that sport and wanted to cry a little. Well, the musicians had ran out of blues, so I chased them home.

"Some party!" I said, and the two girls give me a dirty look like it was my fault or something. So we all went to bed and the ladies beat me to it on account of being so near ready.

Well, they wasn't no return engagements even hinted at and the only other times all winter when the gals had a chance to dress up was when some secondhand company would come to town with a show and I'd have to buy a box. We couldn't ask nobody to go with us on account of not having no friends that you could depend on to not come in their stocking feet.

Finally it was summer and the Mrs. said she wanted to get out of town.

"We've got to be fair to Kate," she said.

"We don't know no young unmarried people in South Bend and it's no fun for a girl to run round with her sister and brother-in-law. Maybe if we'd go to some resort somewheres we might get acquainted with people that could show her a good time."

So I hired us rooms in a hotel down to Wawasee Lake and we stayed there from the last of June till the middle of September. During that time I caught a couple of bass and Kate caught a couple of carp from Fort Wayne. She was getting pretty friendly with one of them when along come a wife that he hadn't thought was worth mentioning. The other bird was making a fight against the gambling fever, but one night it got the best of him and he dropped forty-five cents in the nickel machine and had to go home and make a new start.

About a week before we was due to leave I made the remark that it would seem good to be back in South Bend and get some home cooking.

"Listen!" says my wife. "I been wanting for a long wile to have a serious talk with you and now's as good a time as any. Here are I and Sis and you with an income of over eight thousand dollars a year and having pretty near as good a time as a bird with habitual boils. What's more, we can't never have a good time in South Bend, but have got to move somewheres where we are un- known."

"South Bend is certainly all of that," I said.

"No, it isn't," said the Mrs. "We're acquainted there with the kind of people that makes it impossible for us to get acquainted with the other kind. Kate could live there twenty years and never meet a decent man. She's a mighty attractive girl, and if she had a chance they's nobody she couldn't marry. But she won't never have a chance in South Bend. And they's no use of you saying

'Let her move,' because I'm going to keep her under my eye till she's married and settled down. So in other words, I want us to pack up and leave South Bend for good and all and move somewheres where we'll get something for our money."

"For instance, where?" I ast her.

"They's only one place," she said; "New York City."

"I've heard of it," said I, "but I never heard that people who couldn't enjoy themselves on eight thousand a year in South Bend could go to New York and tear it wide open."

"I'm not planning to make no big splurge," she says. "I just want to be where they's Life and fun; where we can meet real live people. And as for not living there on eight thousand, think of the families that's already living there on half of that and less!"

"And think of the Life and fun they're having!" I says.

"But when you talk about eight thousand a year," said the Mrs., "why do we have to hold ourselves to that? We can sell some of those bonds and spend a little of our principal. It will just be taking money out of one investment and putting it in another."

"What other?" I ast her.

"Kate," said the wife. "You let me take her to New York and manage her and I'll get her a husband that'll think our eight thousand a year fell out of his vest."

"Do you mean," I said, "that you'd let a sister of yours marry for money?"

"Well," she says, "I know a sister of hers that wouldn't mind if she had."

So I argued and tried to compromise on somewheres in America, but it was New York or nothing with her. You see, she hadn't never been here, and all as she knew about it she'd read in books and magazines, and for some reason another when authors starts in on that subject it ain't very long till they've got a weeping jag. Besides, what chance did I have when she kept reminding me that it was her stepfather, not mine, that had croaked and made us all rich?

When I had give up she called Kate in and told her, and Kate squealed and kissed us both, though God knows I didn't deserve no remuneration or ask for none.

Ella had things all planned out. We was to sell our furniture and take a furnished apartment here, but we would stay in some hotel till we found a furnished apartment that was within reason.

"Our stay in some hotel will be life-long," I said.

The furniture, when we come to sell it, wasn't worth nothing, and that's what we got. We didn't have nothing to ship, as Ella found room for our books in my collar box. I got two lowers and an upper in spite of the Government, and with two taxi drivers and the baggage-man thronging the station platform we pulled out of South Bend and set forth to see Life.

The first four miles of the journey was marked by considerable sniveling on the part of the heiresses.

"If it's so painful to leave the Bend let's go back," I said.

"It isn't leaving the Bend," said the Mrs., "but it makes a person sad to leave any place."

"Then we're going to have a muggy trip," said I. "This train stops pretty near everywheres to either discharge passengers or employees."

They were still sobbing when we left Mishawaka and I had to pull some of my comical stuff to get their minds off. My wife's mighty easy to look at when she hasn't got those watery blues, but I never did see a gal that knocked you for a goal when her nose was in full bloom.

Katie had brought a flock of magazines and started in on one of them at Elkhart, but it's pretty tough trying to read with the Northern Indiana mountains to look out at, to say nothing about the birds of prey that kept prowling up and down the aisle in search of a little encouragement or a game of rhum.

I noticed a couple of them that would of give a lady an answer if she'd approached them in a nice way, but I've done some traveling myself and I know what kind of men it is that allows themselves to be drawed into a flirtation on trains. Most of them has made the mistake of getting married some time, but they don't tell you that. They tell you that you and a gal they use to be stuck on is as much alike as a pair of corsets, and if you ever come to Toledo to give them a ring, and they hand you a telephone number that's even harder to get than the ones there are; and they ask you your name and address and write it down, and the next time they're up at the Elks they show it to a couple of the brothers and tell what they'd of done if they'd only been going all the way through.

"Say, I hate to talk about myself! But say!"

Well, I didn't see no sense in letting Katie waste her time on those kind of guys, so every time one of them looked our way I give him the fish eye and the non-stop signal. But this was my first long trip since the Government started to play train, and I didn't know the new rules in regards to getting fed; otherwise I wouldn't of never cleaned up in Wall Street.

In the old days we use to wait till the boy come through and announced that dinner was now being served in the dining car forward; then we'd saunter into the washroom and wash our hands if necessary, and ramble into the diner and set right down and enjoy as big a meal as we could afford. But the Government wants to be economical, so they've cut down the number of trains, to say nothing about the victuals; and they's two or three times as many people traveling, because they can't throw their money away fast enough at home. So the result is that the wise guys keeps an eye on their watch and when it's about twenty minutes to dinner time they race to the diner and park against the door and get quick action; and after they've eat the first time they go out and stand in the vestibule and wait till it's their turn again, as one Federal meal don't do nothing to your appetite only whet it, you might say.

Well, anyway, I was playing the old rules and by the time I and the two gals started for the diner we run up against the outskirts of a crowd pretty near as big as the ones that waits outside restaurant windows to watch a pancake turn turtle. About eight o'clock we got to where we could see the wealthy dining car conductor in the distance, but it was only about once every quarter of an hour that he raised a hand, and then he seemed to of had all but one of his fingers shot off.

I have often heard it said that the way to a man's heart is through his stomach, but every time I ever seen men and women keep waiting for their eats it was always the frail sex that give the first yelp, and personally I've often wondered what would of happened in the trenches Over There if ladies had of been occupying them when the rations failed to show up. I guess the bombs bursting round would of sounded like Sweet and Low sang by a quextette of deef mutes.

Anyway, my two charges was like wild animals, and when the con finally held up two fingers I didn't have no more chance or desire to stop them than as if they was the Center College Football Club right after opening prayer.

The pair of them was ushered to a table for four where they already was a couple of guys making the best of it, and it wasn't more than ten minutes later when one

of these birds dipped his bill in the finger bowl and staggered out, but by the time I took his place the other
gent and my two gals was talking like barbers.

The guy was Francis Griffin that's in the clipping. But
when Ella introduced us all as she said was, "This is
my husband," without mentioning his name, which she
didn't know at that time, or mine, which had probably
slipped her memory.

Griffin looked at me like I was a side dish that he
hadn't ordered. Well, I don't mind snubs except when I
get them, so I ast him if he wasn't from Sioux City—
you could tell he was from New York by his blue collar.

"From Sioux City!" he says. "I should hope not!"

"I beg your pardon," I said. "You look just like a
photographer I used to know out there."

"I'm a New Yorker," he said, "and I can't get home too
soon."

"Not on this train, you can't," I said.

"I missed the Century," he says.

"Well," I says with a polite smile, "the Century's loss
is our gain."

"Your wife's been telling me," he says, "that you're
moving to the Big Town. Have you ever been there?"

"Only for a few hours," I says.

"Well," he said, "when you've been there a few weeks
you'll wonder why you ever lived anywhere else. When
I'm away from old Broadway I always feel like I'm only
camping out."

Both the gals smiled their appreciation, so I says:
"That certainly expresses it. You'd ought to remember
that line and give it to Georgie Cohan."

"Old Georgie!" he says. "I'd give him anything I got
and welcome. But listen! Your wife mentioned something
about a good hotel to stop at wile you're looking for a
home. Take my advice and pick out one that's near the

center of things; you'll more than make up the difference in taxi bills. I lived up in the Hundreds one winter and it averaged me ten dollars a day in cab fares."

"You must of had a pleasant home life," I says.

"Me!" he said. "I'm an old bachelor."

"Old!" says Kate, and her and the Mrs. both giggled.

"But seriously," he says, "if I was you I would go right to the Baldwin, where you can get a room for twelve dollars a day for the three of you; and you're walking distance from the theaters or shops or cafés or anywheres you want to go."

"That sounds grand!" said Ella.

"As far as I'm concerned," I said, "I'd just as lief be overseas from any of the places you've mentioned. What I'm looking for is a home with a couple of beds and a cookstove in the kitchen, and maybe a bath."

"But we want to see New York first," said Katie, "and we can do that better without no household cares."

"That's the idear!" says Griffin. "Eat, drink and be merry; to-morrow we may die."

"I guess we won't drink ourselves to death," I said, "not if the Big Town's like where we been living."

"Oh, say!" says our new friend. "Do you think little old New York is going to stand for prohibition? Why, listen! I can take you to thirty places to-morrow night where you can get all you want in any one of them."

"Let's pass up the other twenty-nine," I says.

"But that isn't the idear," he said. "What makes we New Yorkers sore is to think they should try and wish a law like that on Us. Isn't this supposed to be a government of the people, for the people and by the people?"

"People!" I said. "Who and the hell voted for prohibition if it wasn't the people?"

"The people of where?" he says. "A lot of small-time hicks that couldn't buy a drink if they wanted it."

"Including the hicks," I says, "that's in the New York State legislature."

"But not the people of New York City," he said. "And you can't tell me it's fair to spring a thing like this without warning on men that's got their fortunes tied up in liquor that they can't never get rid of now, only at a sacrifice."

"You're right," I said. "They ought to give them some warning. Instead of that they was never even a hint of what was coming off till Maine went dry seventy years ago."

"Maine?" he said. "What the hell is Maine?"

"I don't know," I said. "Only they was a ship or a boat or something named after it once, and the Spaniards sunk it and we sued them for libel or something."

"You're a smart Aleck," he said. "But speaking about war, where was you?"

"In the shipyards at South Bend painting a duck boat," I says. "And where was you?"

"I'd of been in there in a few more weeks," he says. "They wasn't no slackers in the Big Town."

"No," said I, "and America will never forget New York for coming in on our side."

By this time the gals was both giving me dirty looks, and we'd eat all we could get, so we paid our checks and went back in our car and I felt kind of apologetic, so I dug down in the old grip and got out a bottle of bourbon that a South Bend pal of mine, George Hull, had give me the day before; and Griffin and I went in the washroom with it and before the evening was over we was pretty near ready to forget national boundaries and kiss.

The old bourb' helped me save money the next morning, as I didn't care for no breakfast. Ella and Kate went in with Griffin and you could of knocked me over with a coupling pin when the Mrs. come back and reported that he'd insisted on paying the check. "He told us all about himself," she said. "His name is Francis Griffin and he's in Wall Street. Last year he cleared twenty thousand dollars in commissions and everything."

"He's a piker," I says. "Most of them never even think under six figures."

"There you go!" said the Mrs. "You never believe nothing. Why shouldn't he be telling the truth? Didn't he buy our breakfast?"

"I been buying your breakfast for fivo years," I said, "but that don't prove that I'm knocking out twenty thousand per annum in Wall Street."

Francis and Katie was setting together four or five seats ahead of us.

"You ought to of seen the way he looked at her in the diner," said the Mrs. "He looked like he wanted to eat her up."

"Everybody gets desperate in a diner these days," I said. "Did you and Kate go fifty-fifty with him? Did you tell him how much money we got?"

"I should say not!" says Ella. "But I guess we did say that you wasn't doing nothing just now and that we was going to New York to see Life, after being cooped up in a small town all these years. And Sis told him you'd made us put pretty near everything in bonds, so all we can spend is eight thousand a year. He said that wouldn't go very far in the Big Town."

"I doubt if it ever gets as far as the Big Town," I said. "It won't if he makes up his mind to take it away from us."

"Oh, shut up!" said the Mrs. "He's all right and I'm for him, and I hope Sis is too. They'd make a stunning couple. I wished I knew what they're talking about."

"Well," I said, "they're both so reserved that I suppose they're telling each other how they're affected by cucumbers."

When they come back and joined us Ella said: "We was just remarking how well you two young things seemed to be getting along. We was wondering what you found to say to one another all this time."

"Well," said Francis, "just now I think we were discussing you. Your sister said you'd been married five years and I pretty near felt like calling her a fibber. I told her you looked like you was just out of high school."

"I've heard about you New Yorkers before," said the Mrs. "You're always trying to flatter somebody."

"Not me," said Francis. "I never say nothing without meaning it."

"But sometimes," says I, "you'd ought to go on and explain the meaning."

Along about Schenectady my appetite begin to come back. I'd made it a point this time to find out when the diner was going to open, and then when it did our party fell in with the door.

"The wife tells me you're on the stock exchange," I says to Francis when we'd give our order.

"Just in a small way," he said. "But they been pretty good to me down there. I knocked out twenty thousand last year."

"That's what he told us this morning," said Ella.

"Well," said I, "they's no reason for a man to forget that kind of money between Rochester and Albany, even if this is a slow train."

"Twenty thousand isn't a whole lot in the Big Town," said Francis, "but still and all, I manage to get along and enjoy myself a little on the side."

"I suppose it's enough to keep one person," I said.

"Well," says Francis, "they say two can live as cheap as one."

Then him and Kate and Ella all giggled, and the waiter brought in a part of what he thought we'd ordered and we eat what we could and ast for the check. Francis said he wanted it and I was going to give in to him after a long hard struggle, but the gals reminded him that he'd paid for breakfast, so he said all right, but we'd all have to take dinner with him some night.

I and Francis set a wile in the washroom and smoked, and then he went to entertain the gals, but I figured the wife would go right to sleep like she always does when they's any scenery to look out at, so I stuck where I was and listened to what a couple of toothpick salesmen from Omsk would of done with the League of Nations if Wilson had of had sense enough to leave it to them.

Pulling into the Grand Central Station, Francis apologized for not being able to steer us over to the Baldwin and see us settled, but said he had to rush right downtown and report on his Chicago trip before the office closed. To see him when he parted with the gals you'd of thought he was going clear to Siberia to compete in the Olympic Games, or whatever it is we're in over there.

Well, I took the heiresses to the Baldwin and got a regular Big Town welcome. Ella and Kate set against a pillar wile I tried different tricks to make an oil-haired clerk look at me. New York hotel clerks always seem to of just dropped something and can't take their eyes off the floor. Finally I started to pick up the register and the guy give me the fish eye and ast what he could do for me.

"Well," I said, "when I come to a hotel I don't usually want to buy a straw hat."

He ast me if I had a reservation and I told him no.

"Can't do nothing for you then," he says. "Not till to-morrow morning anyway."

So I went back to the ladies.

"We'll have to go somewheres else," I said. "This joint's a joint. They won't give us nothing till to-morrow."

"But we can't go nowheres else," said the Mrs. "What would Mr. Griffin think, after recommending us to come here?"

"Well," I said, "if you think I'm going to park myself in a four-post chair all night just because we got a tip on a hotel from Wall Street you're Queen of the Cuckoos."

"Are you sure they haven't anything at all?" she says.

"Go ask them yourself!" I told her.

Well, she did, and in about ten minutes she come back and said everything was fixed.

"They'll give us a single room with bath and a double room with bath for fifteen dollars a day," she said.

" 'Give us' is good!" said I.

"I told him we'd wired for reservations and it wasn't our fault if the wire didn't get here," she said. "He was awfully nice."

Our rooms was right close to each other on the twenty-first floor. On the way up we decided by two votes to one that we'd dress for dinner. I was still monkeying with my tie when Katie come in for Ella to look her over. She had on the riskiest dress she'd bought in Chi.

"It's a pretty dress," she said, "but I'm afraid maybe it's too daring for just a hotel dining room."

Say, we hadn't no sooner than set down in the hotel dining room when two other gals come in that made my team look like they was dressed for a sleigh ride with Doc Cook.

"I guess you don't feel so daring now," I said. "Compared to that baby in black you're wearing Jess Willard's ulster."

"Do you know what that black gown cost?" said Ella. "Not a cent under seven hundred dollars."

"That would make the material twenty-one hundred dollars a yard," I says.

"I'd like to know where she got it," said Katie.

"Maybe she cut up an old stocking," said I.

"I wished now," said the Mrs., "that we'd waited till we got here before we bought our clothes."

"You can bet one thing," says Katie. "Before we're ast out anywheres on a real party we'll have something to wear that isn't a year old."

"First thing to-morrow morning," says the Mrs., "we'll go over on Fifth Avenue and see what we can see."

"They'll only be two on that excursion," I says.

"Oh, we don't want you along," said Ella. "But I do wished you'd go to some first-class men's store and get some ties and shirts and things that don't look like an embalmer."

Well, after a wile one of the waiters got it in his head that maybe we hadn't came in to take a bath, so he fetched over a couple of programs.

"Never mind them," I says. "What's ready? We're in a hurry."

"The Long Island Duckling's very nice," he said. "And how about some nice au gratin potatoes and some nice lettuce and tomato salad with Thousand Island dressing, and maybe some nice French pastry?"

"Everything seems to be nice here," I said. "But wait a minute. How about something to drink?"

He give me a mysterious smile.

"Well," he said, "they're watching us pretty close here, but we serve something we call a cup. It comes from the bar and we're not supposed to know what the bartender puts in it."

"We'll try and find out," I said. "And rush this order through, as we're starved."

So he frisked out and was back again in less than an hour with another guy to help carry the stuff, though Lord knows he could of parked the three ducklings on one eyelid and the whole meal on the back of his hand. As for the cup, when you tasted it they wasn't no big mystery about what the bartender had put in it—a bottle of seltzer and a prune and a cherry and an orange peel, and maybe his finger. The check come to eighteen dollars and Ella made me tip him the rest of a twenty.

Before dinner the gals had been all for staying up a wile and looking the crowd over, but when we was through they both owned up that they hadn't slept much on the train and was ready for bed.

Ella and Kate was up early in the morning. They had their breakfast without me and went over to stun Fifth Avenue. About ten o'clock Francis phoned to say he'd call round for us that evening and take us to dinner. The gals didn't get back till late in the afternoon, but from one o'clock on I was too busy signing for packages to get lonesome. Ella finally staggered in with some more and I told her about our invitation.

"Yes, I know," she said.

"How do you know?" I ast her.

"He told us," she said. "We had to call him up to get a check cashed."

"You got plenty nerve!" I said. "How does he know your checks is good?"

"Well, he likes us," she said. "You'll like us too when you see us in some of the gowns we bought."

"Some!" I said.

"Why, yes," said the Mrs. "You don't think a girl can go round in New York with one evening dress!"

"How much money did you spend to-day?" I ast her.

"Well," she said, "things are terribly high—that is, nice things. And then, of course, there's suits and hats and things besides the gowns. But remember, it's our money. And as I told you, it's an investment. When young Mister Wall Street sees Kate to-night it'll be all off."

"I didn't call on you for no speech," I says. "I ast you how much you spent."

"Not quite sixteen hundred dollars."

I was still out on my feet when the phone rung. Ella answered it and then told me it was all right about the tickets.

"What tickets?" I said.

"Why, you see," she says, "after young Griffin fixing us up with that check and inviting us to dinner and everything we thought it would be nice to take him to a show to-night. Kate wanted to see *Ups and Downs,* but the girl said she couldn't get us seats for it. So I ast that nice clerk that took care of us yesterday and he's fixed it."

"All right," I said, "but when young Griffin starts a party, why and the hell not let him finish it?"

"I suppose he would of took us somewheres after dinner," says the Mrs., "but I couldn't be sure. And between you and I, I'm positive that if he and Kate is throwed together a whole evening, and her looking like she'll look to-night, we'll get mighty quick returns on our investment."

Well, to make a short story out of it, the gals finally got what they called dressed, and I wished Niles, Michigan, or South Bend could of seen them. If boxers wore bathing skirts I'd of thought I was in the ring with a couple of bantams.

"Listen!" I said. "What did them two girdles cost?"

"Mine was three hundred and Kate's three hundred and fifty," said the Mrs.

"Well," I says, "don't you know that you could of went to any cut-rate drugstore and wrapped yourself up just as warm in thirty-two cents' worth of adhesive tape? Listen!" I said. "What's the use of me paying a burglar for tickets to a show like *Ups and Downs* when I could set round here and look at you for nothing?"

Then Griffin rung up to say that he was waiting and we went downstairs. Francis took us in the same dining room we'd been in the night before, but this time the waiters all fought each other to get to us first.

I don't know what we eat, as Francis had something on the hip that kind of dazed me for a wile, but afterwards I know we got a taxi and went to the theater. The tickets was there in my name and only cost me thirteen dollars and twenty cents.

Maybe you seen this show wile it was here. Some show! I didn't read the program to see who wrote it, but I guess the words was by Noah and the music took the highest awards at the St. Louis Fair. They had a good system on the gags. They didn't spring none but what you'd heard all your life and knew what was coming, so instead of just laughing at the point you laughed all the way through it.

I said to Ella, I said, "I bet the birds that run this don't want prohibition. If people paid $3.30 apiece and come in here sober they'd come back the next night with a machine gun."

"I think it's dandy," she says, "and you'll notice every seat is full. But listen! Will you do something for me? When this is over suggest that we go up to the Castle Roof for a wile."

"What for?" I said. "I'm sleepy."

"Just this once," she says. "You know what I told you about quick returns!"

Well, I give in and made the suggestion, and I never seen people so easy coaxed. I managed to get a ringside table for twenty-two bucks. Then I ast the boy how about getting a drink and he ast me if I knew any of the head waiters.

"I do," says Francis. "Tell Hector it's for Frank Griffin's party."

So we ordered four Scotch highballs and some chicken à la King, and then the dinge orchestra tore loose some jazz and I was expecting a dance with Ella, but before she could ask me Francis had ast her, and I had one with Kate.

"Your Wall Street friend's a fox," I says, "asking an old married lady to dance so's to stand in with the family."

"Old married lady!" said Kate. "Sis don't look a day over sixteen to-night."

"How are you and Francis coming?" I ast her.

"I don't know," she says. "He acts kind of shy. He hasn't hardly said a word to me all evening."

Well, they was another jazz and I danced it with Ella; then her and Francis had another one and I danced again with Kate. By this time our food and refreshments was served and the show was getting ready to start.

I could write a book on what I don't remember about that show. The first sip of their idear of a Scotch highball put me down for the count of eight and I was practic'lly unconscious till the waiter woke me up with a check for forty bucks.

Francis seen us home and said he would call up again soon, and when Ella and I was alone I made the remark that I didn't think he'd ever strain his larnix talking to Kate.

"He acts gun-shy when he's round her," I says. "You seem to be the one that draws him out."

"It's a good sign," she says. "A man's always embarrassed when he's with a girl he's stuck on. I'll bet you anything you want to bet that within a week something'll happen."

Well, she win. She'd of win if she'd of said three days instead of a week. It was a Wednesday night when we had that party, and on the Friday Francis called up and said he had tickets for the Palace. I'd been laid up mean wile with the Scotch influenza, so I told the gals to cut me out. I was still awake yet when Ella come in a little after midnight.

"Well," I said, "are we going to have a brother-in-law?"

"Mighty soon," she says.

So I ast her what had come off.

"Nothing—to-night," she says, "except this: He wrote me a note. He wants me to go with him to-morrow afternoon and look at a little furnished apartment. And he ast me if I could come without Sis, as he wants to pull a surprise on her. So I wondered if you couldn't think of some way to fix it so's I can sneak off for a couple of hours."

"Sure!" I said. "Just tell her you didn't sleep all night and you're wore out and you want to take a nap."

So she pulled this gag at lunch Saturday and Katie said she was tired too. She went up to her room and Ella snuck out to keep her date with Francis. In less than an hour she romped into our room again and throwed herself on the bed.

"Well," I says, "it must of been a little apartment if it didn't only take you this long to see it."

"Oh, shut up!" she said. "I didn't see no apartment. And don't say a word to me or I'll scream."

Well, I finally got her calmed down and she give me the details. It seems that she'd met Francis, and he'd got a taxi and they'd got in the taxi and they hadn't no sooner than got in the taxi when Francis give her a kiss.

"Quick returns," I says.

"I'll kill you if you say another word!" she says.

So I managed to keep still.

Well, I didn't know Francis' home address, and Wall Street don't run Sundays, so I spent the Sabbath training on a quart of rye that a bell hop picked up at a bargain sale somewheres for fifteen dollars. Mean wile Katie had been let in on the secret and staid in our room all day, moaning like a prune-fed calf.

"I'm afraid to leave her alone," says Ella. "I'm afraid she'll jump out the window."

"You're easily worried," I said. "What I'm afraid of is that she won't."

Monday morning finally come, as it generally always does, and I told the gals I was going to some first-class men's store and buy myself some ties and shirts that didn't look like a South Bend embalmer.

So the only store I knew about was H. L. Krause & Co. in Wall Street, but it turned out to be an office. I ast for Mr. Griffin and they ast me my name and I made one up, Sam Hall or something, and out he come.

If I told you the rest of it you'd think I was bragging. But I did bust a few records. Charley Brickley and Walter Eckersall both kicked five goals from field in one football game, and they was a bird named Robertson or something out at Purdue that kicked seven. Then

they was one of the old-time ball players, Bobby Lowe or
Ed Delehanty, that hit four or five home runs in one
afternoon. And out to Toledo that time Dempsey made
big Jess set down seven times in one round.

Well, listen! In a little less than three minutes I floored
this bird nine times and I kicked him for eight goals
from the field and I hit him over the fence for ten home
runs. Don't talk records to me!

So that's what they meant in the clipping about a
Hoosier cleaning up in Wall Street. But it's only a kid,
see?

II. Ritchey

WELL, I was just getting used to the Baldwin and
making a few friends round there when Ella suddenly
happened to remember that it was Griffin who had
recommended it. So one day, wile Kate was down to
the chiropodist's, Ella says it was time for us to move
and she had made up her mind to find an apartment
somewheres.

"We could get along with six rooms," she said. "All
as I ask is for it to be a new building and on some good
street, some street where the real people lives."

"You mean Fifth Avenue," said I.

"Oh, no," she says. "That's way over our head. But
we'd ought to be able to find something, say, on Riverside Drive." "A six room apartment," I says, "in a new
building on Riverside Drive? What was you expecting
to pay?"

"Well," she said, "you remember that time I and Kate
visited the Kitchells in Chi? They had a dandy apartment

on Sheridan Road, six rooms and brand new. It cost them seventy-five dollars a month. And Sheridan Road is Chicago's Riverside Drive."

"Oh, no," I says. "Chicago's Riverside Drive is Canal Street. But listen: Didn't the Kitchells have their own furniture?"

"Sure they did," said Ella.

"And are you intending to furnish us all over complete?" I asked her.

"Of course not," she says. "I expect to get a furnished apartment. But that don't only make about twenty five dollars a month difference."

"Listen," I said: "It was six years ago that you visited the Kitchells; beside which, that was Chi and this is the Big Town. If you find a six room furnished apartment for a hundred dollars in New York City to-day, we'll be on Pell Street in Chinatown, and maybe Katie can marry into a laundry or a joss house."

"Well," said the wife, "even if we have to go to $150 a month for a place on the Drive, remember half of it's my money and half of it's Kate's, and none of it's yours."

"You're certainly letter perfect in that speech," I says.

"And further and more," said Ella, "you remember what I told you the other day. Wile one reason we moved to New York was to see Life, the main idear was to give Kate a chance to meet real men. So every nickel we spend making ourself look good is just an investment."

"I'd rather feel good than look good," I says, "and I hate to see us spending so much money on a place to live that they won't be nothing left to live on. For three or four hundred a month you might get a joint on the Drive with a bed and two chairs, but I can't drink furniture."

"This trip wasn't planned as no spree for you," says Ella. "On the other hand, I believe Sis would stand a whole lot better show of landing the right kind of a man if the rumor was to get out that her brother-in-law stayed sober once in a wile."

"Well," I said, "I don't think my liberal attitude on the drink question affected the results of our deal in Wall Street. That investment would of turned out just as good whether I was a teetotaler or a lush."

"Listen," she says: "The next time you mention ancient history like that, I'll make a little investment in a lawyer. But what's the use of arguing? I and Kate has made up our mind to do things our own way with our own money, and to-day we're going up on the Drive with a real estate man. We won't pay no more than we can afford. All as we want is a place that's good enough and big enough for Sis to entertain her gentleman callers in it, and she certainly can't do that in this hotel."

"Well," I says, "all her gentleman callers that's been around here in the last month, she could entertain them in one bunch in a telephone booth."

"The reason she's been let alone so far," says the Mrs., "is because I won't allow her to meet the kind of men that stays at hotels. You never know who they are."

"Why not?" I said. "They've all got to register their name when they come in, which is more than you can say for people that lives in $100 apartments on Riverside Drive."

Well, my arguments went so good that for the next three days the two gals was on a home-seekers' excursion and I had to spend my time learning the eastern intercollegiate kelly pool rules up to Doyle's. I win about seventy-five dollars.

When the ladies come home the first two nights they was all wore out and singing the landlord blues, but on the third afternoon they busted in all smiles.

"We've found one," says Ella. "Six rooms, too."

"Where at?" I asked her.

"Just where we wanted it," she says. "On the Drive. And it fronts right on the Hudson."

"No!" I said. "I thought they built them all facing the other way."

"It almost seems," said Katie, "like you could reach out and touch New Jersey."

"It's what you might call a near beer apartment," I says.

"And it's almost across the street from Grant's Tomb," says Ella.

"How many rooms has he got?" I says.

"We was pretty lucky," said Ella. "The people that had it was forced to go south for the man's health. He's a kind of a cripple. And they decided to sublet it furnished. So we got a bargain."

"Come on," I says. "What price?"

"Well," she says, "they don't talk prices by the month in New York. They give you the price by the year. So it sounds a lot more than it really is. We got it for $4,000."

"Sweet patootie!" I said. "That's only half your income."

"Well, what of it?" says Ella. "It won't only be for about a year and it's in the nicest kind of a neighborhood and we can't meet nothing only the best kind of people. You know what I told you."

And she give me a sly wink.

Well, it seems like they had signed up a year's lease and paid a month's rent in advance, so what was they left for me to say? All I done was make the remark that I didn't see how we was going to come even close to a trial balance.

"Why not?" said Katie. "With our rent paid we can get along easy on $4,000 a year if we economize."

"Yes," I said. "You'll economize just like the rest of the Riverside Drivers, with a couple of servants and a car and four or five new evening dresses a month. By the end of six months the bank'll be figuring our account in marks."

"What do you mean 'our' account?" says Ella.

"But speaking about a car," said Katie, "do you suppose we could get a good one cheap?"

"Certainly," I said. "They're giving away the good ones for four double coupons."

"But I mean an inexpensive one," says Kate.

"You can't live on the River and ride in a flivver," I said. "Besides, the buses limp right by the door."

"Oh, I love the buses!" said Ella.

"Wait till you see the place," says Katie to me. "You'll go simply wild! They's a colored boy in uniform to open the door and they's two elevators."

"How high do we go?" I said.

"We're on the sixth floor," says Katie.

"I should think we could get that far in one elevator," I says.

"What was it the real estate man told us?" said Ella. "Oh, yes, he said the sixth floor was the floor everybody tried to get on."

"It's a wonder he didn't knock it," I said.

Well, we was to have immediate possession, so the next morning we checked out of this joint and swooped up on the Drive. The colored boy, who I nicknamed George, helped us up with the wardrobe. Ella had the key and inside of fifteen minutes she'd found it.

We hadn't no sooner than made our entree into our new home when I knew what ailed the previous tenant. He'd crippled himself stumbling over the furniture. The living room was big enough to stage the high hurdles, and that's what was in it, only they'd planted them every two feet apart. If a stew with the blind staggers had of walked in there in the dark, the folks on the floor below would of thought he'd knocked the head pin for a goal.

"Come across the room," said Ella, "and look at the view."

"I guess I can get there in four downs," I said, "but you better have a substitute warming up."

"Well," she says, when I'd finally fell acrost the last white chalk mark, "what do you think of it?"

"It's a damn pretty view," I says, "but I've often seen the same view from the top of a bus for a thin dime."

Well, they showed me over the whole joint and it did look O. K., but not $4,000 worth. The best thing in the place was a half full bottle of rye in the kitchen that the cripple hadn't gone south with. I did.

We got there at eleven o'clock in the morning, but at three p.m. the gals was still hanging up their Follies costumes, so I beat it out and over to Broadway and got myself a plate of pea soup. When I come back, Ella and Katie was laying down exhausted. Finally I told Ella that I was going to move back to the hotel unless they served meals in this dump, so her and Kate got up and went marketing. Well, when you move from Indiana to the Big Town, of course you can't be expected to do your own cooking, so what we had that night was from the delicatessen, and for the next four days we lived on dill pickles with dill pickles.

"Listen," I finally says: "The only reason I consented to leave the hotel was in the hopes I could get a real home cook meal once in a wile and if I don't get a real home cook meal once in a wile, I leave this dive."

"Have a little bit of patience," says Ella. "I advertised in the paper for a cook the day before we come here, the day we rented this apartment. And I offered eight dollars a week."

"How many replies did you get?" I asked her.

"Well," she said, "I haven't got none so far, but it's probably too soon to expect any."

"What did you advertise in, the world almanac?" I says.

"No, sir," she says. "I advertised in the two biggest New York papers, the ones the real estate man recommended."

"Listen," I said: "Where do you think you're at, in Niles, Michigan? If you get a cook here for eight dollars a week, it'll be a one-armed leper that hasn't yet reached her teens."

"What would you do, then?" she asked me.

"I'd write to an employment agency," I says, "and I'd tell them we'll pay good wages."

So she done that and in three days the phone rung and the agency said they had one prospect on hand and did we want her to come out and see us. So Ella said we did and out come a colleen for an interview. She asked how much we was willing to pay.

"Well," said Ella, "I'd go as high as twelve dollars. Or I'd make it fifteen if you done the washing."

Kathleen Mavourneen turned her native color.

"Well," I said, "how much do you want?"

"I'll work for ninety dollars a month," she said, only I can't get the brogue. "That's for the cookin' only. No washin'. And I would have to have a room with a bath and all day Thursdays and Sunday evenin's off."

"Nothing doing," said Ella, and the colleen started for the door.

"Wait a minute," I says. "Listen: Is that what you gals is getting in New York?"

"We're a spalpeen if we ain't," says the colleen bawn.

Well, I was desperate, so I called the wife to one side and says: "For heaven's sakes, take her on a month's trial. I'll pay the most of it with a little piece of money I picked up last week down to Doyle's. I'd rather do that than get dill pickled for a goal."

"Could you come right away?" Ella asked her.

"Not for a couple days," says Kathleen.

"It's off, then," I said. "You cook our supper to-night or go back to Greece."

"Well," she says, "I guess I could make it if I hurried."

So she went away and come back with her suitcase, and she cooked our supper that night. And Oh darlint!

Well, Beautiful Katie still had the automobile bug and it wasn't none of my business to steer her off of it and pretty near every day she would go down to the "row" and look them over. But every night she'd come home whistling a dirge.

"I guess I've seen them all," she'd say, "but they're too expensive or else they look like they wasn't."

But one time we was all coming home in a taxi from a show and come up Broadway and all of a sudden she yelled for the driver to stop.

"That's a new one in that window," she says, "and one I never see before."

Well, the dive was closed at the time and we couldn't get in, but she insisted on going down there the first thing in the morning and I and Ella must go along. The car was a brand new model Bam Eight.

"How much?" I asked him.

"Four thousand," he says.

"When could I get one?" says Katie.

"I don't know," said the salesman.

"What do you mean?" I asked him. "Haven't they made none of them?"

"I don't know," says the salesman. "This is the only one we got."

"Has anybody ever rode in one?" I says.

"I don't know," said the guy.

So I asked him what made it worth four thousand.

"Well," he says, "what made this lady want one?"

"I don't know," I said.

"Could I have this one that's on the floor?" says Katie.

"I don't know," said the salesman.

"Well, when do you think I could get one?" says Katie.

"We can't promise no deliveries," says the salesman.

Well, that kind of fretted me, so I asked him if they wasn't a salesman we could talk to.

"You're talking to one," he said.

"Yes, I know," said I. "But I used to be a kind of a salesman myself, and when I was trying to sell things, I didn't try and not sell them."

"Yes," he says, "but you wasn't selling automobiles in New York in 1920. Listen," he says: "I'll be frank with you. We got the New York agency for this car and was glad to get it because it sells for four thousand and anything that sells that high, why the people will eat up, even if it's a pearl-handle ketchup bottle. If we ever do happen to get a consignment of these cars, they'll sell like oil stock. The last word we got from the factory was that they'd send us three cars next September. So that means we'll get two cars a year from next October and if we can spare either of them, you can have one."

So then he begin to yawn and I said, "Come on, girls," and we got a taxi and beat it home. And I wouldn't of said nothing about it, only if Katie had of been able to buy her Bam, what come off might of never came off.

It wasn't only two nights later when Ella come in from shopping all excited. "Well," she said, "talk about experiences! I just had a ride home and it wasn't in a street car and it wasn't in a taxi and it wasn't on the subway and it wasn't on a bus."

"Let's play charades," said I.

"Tell us, Sis," says Katie.

"Well," said the wife, "I was down on Fifth Avenue, waiting for a bus, and all of a sudden a big limousine drew up to the curb with a livery chauffeur, and a man got out of the back seat and took off his hat and asked if he couldn't see me home. And of course I didn't pay no attention to him."

"Of course not," I said.

"But," says Ella, "he says, 'Don't take no offense. I think we're next door neighbors. Don't you live acrost the hall on the sixth floor of the Lucius?' So of course I had to tell him I did."

"Of course," I said.

"And then he said," says Ella, "'Is that your sister living with you?' 'Yes,' I said, 'she lives with my husband and I.' 'Well,' he says, 'if you'll get in and let me take you home, I'll tell you what a beautiful girl I think she is.' So I seen then that he was all right, so I got in and come home with him. And honestly, Sis, he's just wild about you!"

"What is he like?" says Katie.

"He's stunning," says the wife. "Tall and wears dandy clothes and got a cute mustache that turns up."

"How old?" says Kate, and the Mrs. kind of stalled.

"Well," she said, "he's the kind of a man that you can't tell how old they are, but he's not old. I'd say he was, well, maybe he's not even that old."

"What's his name?" asked Kate.

"Trumbull," said the Mrs. "He said he was keeping bachelor quarters, but I don't know if he's really a bachelor or a widower. Anyway, he's a dandy fella and must have lots of money. Just imagine living alone in one of these apartments!"

"Imagine living in one of them whether you're a bachelor or a Mormon," I says.

"Who said he lived alone?" asked Katie.

"He did," says the Mrs. "He told me that him and his servants had the whole apartment to themselves. And that's what makes it so nice, because he's asked the three of us over there to dinner to-morrow night."

"What makes it so nice?" I asked her.

"Because it does," said Ella, and you can't ever beat an argument like that.

So the next night the two girls donned their undress uniforms and made me put on the oysters and horse radish and we went acrost the hall to meet our hero. The door was opened by a rug peddler and he showed us into a twin brother to our own living room, only you could get around it without being Houdini.

"Mr. Trumbull will be right out," said Omar.

The ladies was shaking like an aspirin leaf, but in a few minutes, in come mine host. However old Ella had thought he wasn't, she was wrong. He'd seen baseball when the second bounce was out. If he'd of started his career as a barber in Washington, he'd of tried to wish a face massage on Zachary Taylor. The only thing young about him was his teeth and his clothes. His dinner suit made me feel like I was walking along the station platform at Toledo, looking for hot boxes.

"Ah, here you are!" he says. "It's mighty nice of you to be neighborly. And so this is the young sister. Well," he says to me, "you had your choice, and as far as I can see, it was heads you win and tails you win. You're lucky."

So when he'd spread all the salve, he rung the bell and in come Allah with cocktails. I don't know what was in them, but when Ella and Katie had had two apiece, they both begin to trill.

Finally we was called in to dinner and every other course was hootch. After the solid and liquid diet, he turned on the steam piano and we all danced. I had one with Beautiful Katie and the rest of them was with my wife, or, as I have nicknamed them, quarrels. Well, the steam run out of three of us at the same time, the piano inclusive, and Ella sat down in a chair that was made for Eddie Foy's family and said how comfortable it was.

"Yes," says Methuselah, "that's my favorite chair. And I bet you wouldn't believe me if I told you how much it cost."

"Oh, I'd like to know," says Ella.

"Two hundred dollars," says mine host.

"Do you still feel comfortable?" I asked her.

"Speaking about furniture," said the old bird, "I've got a few bits that I'm proud of. Would you like to take a look at them?"

So the gals said they would and we had to go through the entire apartment, looking at bits. The best bits I seen was tastefully wrapped up in kegs and cases. It seemed like every time he opened a drawer, a cork popped up. He was a hundred per cent proofer than the governor of New Jersey. But he was giving us a lecture on the furniture itself, not the polish.

"I picked up this dining room suit for eighteen hundred," he says.

"Do you mean the one you've got on?" I asked him, and the gals give me a dirty look.

"And this rug," he says, stomping on an old rag carpet. "How much do you suppose that cost?"

It was my first guess, so I said fifty dollars.

"That's a laugh," he said. "I paid two thousand for that rug."

"The guy that sold it had the laugh," I says.

Finally he steered us into his bedroom.

"Do you see that bed?" he says. "That's Marie Antoinette's bed. Just a cool thousand."

"What time does she usually get in?" I asked him.

"Here's my hobby," he said, opening up a closet, "dressing gowns and bathrobes."

Well, they was at least a dozen of them hanging on hangers. They was all colors of the rainbow including the Scandinavian. He dragged one down that was redder than Ella's and Katie's cheeks.

"This is my favorite bathrobe," he said. "It's Rose D. Barry."

So I asked him if he had all his household goods and garments named after some dame.

"This bathrobe cost me an even two hundred," he says.

"I always take baths bare," I said. "It's a whole lot cheaper."

"Let's go back in the living room," says Katie.

"Come on," said Ella, tugging me by the sleeve.

"Wait a minute," I says to her. "I don't know how much he paid for his toothbrush."

Well, when we got back in the living room, the two gals acted kind of drowsy and snuggled up together on the davenport and I and the old bird was left to ourself.

"Here's another thing I didn't show you," he says, and pulls a pair of African golf balls out of a drawer in his desk. "These dice is real ivory and they cost me twelve and a half berries."

"You mean up to now," I said.

"All right," he said. "We'll make it a twenty-five dollar limit."

Well, I didn't have no business in a game with him,

but you know how a guy gets sometimes. So he took them first and rolled a four.

"Listen," I says: "Do you know how many times Willard set down in the first round?"

And sure enough he sevened.

"Now solid ivory dice," I said, "how many days in the week?"

So out come a natural. And as sure as I'm setting here, I made four straight passes with the whole roll riding each time and with all that wad parked on the two thousand dollar rug, I shot a five and a three. "Ivory," I said, "we was invited here to-night, so don't make me pay for the entertainment. Show me eighter from Decatur."

And the lady from Decatur showed.

Just then they was a stir on the davenport, and Ella woke up long enough to make the remark that we ought to go home. It was the first time she ever said it in the right place.

"Oh," I says, "I've got to give Mr. Trumbull a chance to get even."

But I wasn't in earnest.

"Don't bother about that," said Old Noah. "You can accommodate me some other time."

"You're certainly a sport," I says.

"And thanks for a wonderful time," said Ella. "I hope we'll see you again soon."

"Soon is to-morrow night," said mine host. "I'm going to take you all up the river to a place I know."

"Well," I says to Katie, when we was acrost the hall and the door shut, "how do you like him?"

"Oh, shut up!" says Katie.

So the next night he come over and rung our bell and said Ritchey was waiting with the car and would we come down when we was ready. Well, the gals had only

had all day to prepare for the trip, so in another half
hour they had their wraps on and we went downstairs.
They wasn't nothing in front but a Rools-Royce with a
livery chauffeur that looked like he'd been put there by
a rubber stamp.

"What a stunning driver!" said Katie when we'd
parked ourself in the back seat.

"Ritchey?" says mine host. "He is a nice looking boy,
but better than that, he's a boy I can trust."

Well, anyway, the boy he could trust took us out to a
joint called the Indian Inn where you wouldn't of never
knew they was an eighteenth amendment only that the
proprietor was asking twenty berries a quart for stuff
that used to cost four. But that didn't seem to bother
Methuselah and he ordered two of them. Not only that
but he got us a table so close to the orchestra that the
cornet player thought we was his mute.

"Now, what'll we eat?" he says.

So I looked at the program and the first item I seen
was "Guinea Hen, $4.50."

"That's what Katie'll want," I says to myself, and
sure enough that's what she got.

Well, we eat and then we danced and we danced and
we danced, and finally along about eleven I and Ella was
out on the floor pretending like we was enjoying ourself,
and we happened to look over to the table and there was
Katie and Trumbull setting one out and to look at either
you could tell that something was wrong.

"Dance the next one with her," says Ella, "and find
out what's the matter."

So I danced the next one with Katie and asked her.

"He squeezed my hand," she says. "I don't like him."

"Well," said I, "if you'd of ordered guinea hen on me
I wouldn't of stopped at your hand. I'd of went at your
throat."

"I've got a headache," she says. "Take me out to the car."

So they was nothing to it but I had to take her out to the car and come back and tell Ella and Trumbull that she wasn't feeling any too good and wanted to go home.

"She don't like me," says the old guy. "That's the whole trouble."

"Give her time," says Ella. "Remember she's just a kid."

"Yes, but what a kid!" he says.

So then he paid the check without no compotition and we went out and clumb in the big limmie. Katie was pretending like she was asleep and neither Ella or Trumbull acted like they wanted to talk, so the conversation on the way home was mostly one-sided, with me in the title role. Katie went in the apartment without even thanking mine host for the guinea hen, but he kept Ella and I outside long enough to say that Ritchey and the car was at our service any time we wanted them.

So Ella told her that the next noon at breakfast. "And you'd ought to be ashamed of yourself," says Ella, "for treating a man like that like that."

"He's too fresh," says Katie.

"Well," said Ella, "if he was a little younger, you wouldn't mind him being fresh."

"No," said Katie, "if he was fresh, I wouldn't care if he was fresh. But what's the number of the garage?"

And she didn't lose no time taking advantage of the old bird. That same afternoon it seemed she had to go shopping and the bus wasn't good enough no more. She was out in Trumbull's limmie from two o'clock till pretty near seven. The old guy himself come to our place long about five and wanted to know if we knew where she was at. "I haven't no idear," said Ella. "I expected her home long ago. Did you want to use the car?"

"What's the difference," I said, "if he wanted to use the car or not? He's only the owner."

"Well," says Trumbull, "when I make an offer I mean it, and that little girl is welcome to use my machine whenever she feels like it."

So Ella asked him to stay to dinner and he said he would if we'd allow him to bring in some of his hootch, and of course I kicked on that proposition, but he insisted. And when Katie finally did get home, we was all feeling good and so was she and you'd never of thought they'd been any bad feelings the night before.

Trumbull asked her what she'd been buying.

"Nothing," she says. "I was looking at dresses, but they want too much money."

"You don't need no dresses," he says.

"No, of course not," said Katie. "But lots of girls is wearing them."

"Where did you go?" said Ella.

"I forget," says Katie. "What do you say if we play cards?"

So we played rummy till we was all blear-eyed and the old guy left, saying we'd all go somewheres next day. After he'd gone Ella begin to talk serious.

"Sis," she says, "here's the chance of a lifetime. Mr. Trumbull's head over heels in love with you and all as you have to do is encourage him a little. Can't you try and like him?"

"They's nobody I have more respect for," said Katie, "unless it's George Washington."

And then she give a funny laugh and run off to bed.

"I can't understand Sis no more," said Ella, when we was alone.

"Why not?" I asked her.

"Why, look at this opportunity staring her in the face," says the Mrs.

"Listen," I said: "The first time I stared you in the face, was you thinking about opportunity?"

Well, to make a short story out of it, I was the only one up in the house the next morning when Kathleen said we had a caller. It was the old boy.

"I'm sorry to be so early," he says, "but I just got a telegram and it means I got to run down to Washington for a few days. And I wanted to tell you that wile I'm gone Ritchey and the car is at your service."

So I thanked him and he said good-by and give his regards to the Mrs. and especially Katie, so when they got up I told them about it and I never seen a piece of bad news received so calm as Katie took it.

"But now he's gone," I said at the breakfast table, "why not the three of us run out to Bridgeport and call on the Wilmots?"

They're cousins of mine.

"Oh, fine!" said Ella.

"Wait a minute," says Katie. "I made a kind of an engagement with a dressmaker for to-day."

Well, as I say, to make a short story out of it, it seems like she'd made engagements with the dressmaker every day, but they wasn't no dresses ever come home.

In about a week Trumbull come back from Washington and the first thing he done was look us up and we had him in to dinner and I don't remember how the conversation started, but all of a sudden we was on the subject of his driver, Ritchey.

"A great boy," says Trumbull, "and a boy you can trust. If I didn't like him for nothing else, I'd like him for how he treats his family."

"What family?" says Kate.

"Why," says Trumbull, "his own family: his wife and two kids."

"My heavens!" says Katie, and kind of fell in a swoon.

So it seems like we didn't want to live there no more and we moved back to the Baldwin, having sublet the place on the Drive for three thousand a year.

So from then on, we was paying a thousand per annum for an apartment we didn't live in two weeks. But as I told the gals, we was getting pretty near as much for our money as the people that rented New York apartments and lived in them, too.

iii. Lady Perkins

ALONG the first week in May they was a couple hot days, and Katie can't stand the heat. Or the cold, or the medium. Anyway, when it's hot she always says: "I'm simply stifling." And when it's cold: "I'm simply frozen." And when it ain't neither one: "I wished the weather would do one thing another." I don't s'pose she knows what she's saying when she says any one of them things, but she's one of these here gals that can't bear to see a conversation die out and thinks it's her place to come through with a wise crack whenever they's a vacuum.

So during this hot spell we was having dinner with a bird named Gene Buck that knowed New York like a book, only he hadn't never read a book, and Katie made the remark that she was simply stifling.

"If you think this is hot," says our friend, "just wait till the summer comes. The Old Town certainly steams up in the Old Summer Time."

So Kate asked him how people could stand it.

"They don't," he says. "All the ones that's got a piece

of change ducks out somewheres where they can get the air."

"Where do they go?" Katie asked him.

"Well," he says, "the most of my pals goes to Newport or Maine or up in the Adirondacks. But of course them places is out of most people's reach. If I was you folks I'd go over on Long Island somewheres and either take a cottage or live in one of them good hotels."

"Where, for instance?" says my Mrs.

"Well," he said, "some people takes cottages, but the rents is something fierce, and besides, the desirable ones is probably all eat up by this time. But they's plenty good hotels where you get good service and swell meals and meet good people; they won't take in no riffraff. And they give you a pretty fair rate if they know you're going to make a stay."

So Ella asked him if they was any special one he could recommend.

"Let's think a minute," he says.

"Let's not strain ourself," I said.

"Don't get cute!" said the Mrs. "We want to get some real information and Mr. Buck can give it to us."

"How much would you be willing to pay?" said Buck.

It was Ella's turn to make a wise crack.

"Not no more than we have to," she says.

"I and my sister has got about eight thousand dollars per annum between us," said Katie, "though a thousand of it has got to go this year to a man that cheated us up on Riverside Drive.

"It was about a lease. But Papa left us pretty well off; over a hundred and fifty thousand dollars."

"Don't be so secret with Mr. Buck," I says. "We've knew him pretty near a week now. Tell him about them four-dollar stockings you bought over on Fifth Avenue and the first time you put them on they got as many runs as George Sisler."

"Well," said Buck, "I don't think you'd have no trouble getting comfortable rooms in a good hotel on seven thousand dollars. If I was you I'd try the Hotel Decker. It's owned by a man named Decker."

"Why don't he call it the Griffith?" I says.

"It's located at Tracy Estates," says Buck. "That's one of the garden spots of Long Island. It's a great big place, right up to the minute, and they give you everything the best. And they's three good golf courses within a mile of the hotel."

The gals told him they didn't play no golf.

"You don't know what you've missed," he says.

"Well," I said, "I played a game once myself and missed a whole lot."

"Do they have dances?" asked Kate.

"Plenty of them," says Buck, "and the guests is the nicest people you'd want to meet. Besides all that, the meals is included in the rates, and they certainly set a nasty table."

"I think it sounds grand," said the Mrs. "How do you get there?"

"Go over to the Pennsylvania Station," says Buck, "and take the Long Island Railroad to Jamaica. Then you change to the Haverton branch. It don't only take a half hour altogether."

"Let's go over to-morrow morning and see can we get rooms," said Katie.

So Ella asked how that suited me.

"Go just as early as you want to," I says. "I got a date to run down to the Aquarium and see the rest of the fish."

"You won't make no mistake stopping at the Decker," says Buck.

So the gals thanked him and I paid the check so as he would have more to spend when he joined his pals up to Newport.

Well, when Ella and Kate come back the next afternoon, I could see without them telling me that it was all settled. They was both grinning like they always do when they've pulled something nutty.

"It's a good thing we met Mr. Buck," said the Mrs., "or we mightn't never of heard of this place. It's simply wonderful. A double room with a bath for you and I and a room with a bath for Katie. The meals is throwed in, and we can have it all summer."

"How much?" I asked her.

"Two hundred a week," she said. "But you must remember that's for all three of us and we get our meals free."

"And I s'pose they also furnish knobs for the bedroom doors," says I.

"We was awful lucky," said the wife. "These was the last two rooms they had, and they wouldn't of had those only the lady that had engaged them canceled her reservation."

"I wished I'd met her when I was single," I says.

"So do I," says Ella.

"But listen," I said. "Do you know what two hundred a week amounts to? It amounts to over ten thousand a year, and our income is seven thousand."

"Yes," says Katie, "but we aren't only going to be there twenty weeks, and that's only four thousand."

"Yes," I said, "and that leaves us three thousand for the other thirty-two weeks, to pay for board and room and clothes and show tickets and a permanent wave every other day."

"You forget," said Kate, "that we still got our principal, which we can spend some of it and not miss it."

"And you also forget," said the Mrs., "that the money belongs to Sis and I, not you."

"I've got a sweet chance of forgetting that," I said. "It's hammered into me three times a day. I hear about it pretty near as often as I hear that one of you's lost their new silk bag."

"Well, anyway," says Ella, "it's all fixed up and we move out there early tomorrow morning, so you'll have to do your packing to-night."

I'm not liable to celebrate the anniversary of the next day's trip. Besides the trunks, the gals had a suitcase and a grip apiece and I had a suitcase. So that give me five pieces of baggage to wrestle, because of course the gals had to carry their parasol in one hand and their wrist watch in the other. A redcap helped load us on over to the station, but oh you change at Jamaica! And when we got to Tracy Estates we seen that the hotel wasn't only a couple of blocks away, so the ladies said we might as well walk and save taxi fare.

I don't know how I covered them two blocks, but I do know that when I reeled into the Decker my hands and arms was paralyzed and Ella had to do the registering.

Was you ever out there? Well, I s'pose it's what you might call a family hotel, and a good many of the guests belongs to the cay-nine family. A few of the couples that can't afford dogs has got children, and you're always tripping over one or the other. They's a dining room for the grown-ups and another for the kids, wile the dogs and their nurses eats in the grill-room à la carte. One part of the joint is bachelor quarters. It's located right next to the dogs' dormitories, and they's a good deal of rivalry between the dogs and the souses to see who can make the most noise nights. They's also a ballroom and a couple card rooms and a kind of a summer parlor where the folks sets round in the evening and listen to a three-piece orchestra that don't know they's been any music wrote since Poets and Peasants. The men get up about eight o'clock and go down to New York to Business. They don't never go to work. About nine the women begins limping downstairs and either goes to call on their dogs or take them for a walk in the front yard. This is a great big yard with a whole lot of benches strewed round it, but you can't set on them in the daytime because the women or the nurses uses them for a place to read to the dogs or kids, and in the evenings you would have to share them with the waitresses, which you have already had enough of them during the day.

When the women has prepared themselves for the long day's grind with a four-course breakfast, they set round on the front porch and discuss the big questions of the hour, like for instance the last trunk murder or whether an Airedale is more loving than a Golden Bantam. Once in a wile one of them cracks that it looks like they was bound to be a panic pretty soon and a big drop in prices, and so forth. This shows they're broad-minded and are giving a good deal of thought to up-to-date topics. Every so often one of them'll say: "The present situation can't keep up." The hell it can't!

By one o'clock their appetites is whetted so keen from brain exercise that they make a bum out of a plate of soup and an order of Long Island duckling, which they figure is caught fresh every day, and they wind up with salad and apple pie à la mode and a stein of coffee. Then they totter up to their rooms to sleep it off before Dear gets home from Business.

Saturday nights everybody puts on their evening clothes like something was going to happen. But it don't. Sunday mornings the husbands and bachelors gets up

earlier than usual to go to their real business, which is
golf. The womenfolks are in full possession of the hotel
till Sunday night supper and wives and husbands don't
see one another all day long, but it don't seem as long as
if they did. Most of them's approaching their golden-
wedding jubilee and haven't nothing more to say to each
other that you could call a novelty. The husband may
make the remark, Sunday night, that he would of broke
one hundred and twenty in the afternoon round if the
caddy hadn't of handed him a spoon when he asked for
a nut pick, and the wife'll probably reply that she's got
to go in Town some day soon and see a chiropodist. The
rest of the Sabbath evening is spent in bridge or listening to the latest song hit from *The Bohemian Girl*.

The hotel's got all the modern conveniences like
artificial light and a stopper in the bathtubs. They even
got a barber and a valet, but you can't get a shave wile
he's pressing your clothes, so it's pretty near impossible
for a man to look their best at the same time.

Well, the second day we was there I bought me a
deck of cards and got so good at solitary that pretty soon
I could play fifty games between breakfast and lunch
and a hundred from then till suppertime. During the
first week Ella and Kate got on friendly terms with over
a half dozen people—the head waiter, our waitress,
some of the clerks and the manager and the two telephone gals. It wasn't from lack of trying that they didn't
meet even more people. Every day one or the other of
them would try and swap a little small talk with one of
the other squatters, but it generally always wound up as
a short monologue.

Ella said to me one day, she says: "I don't know if we
can stick it out here or not. Every hotel I was ever at
before, it was easy enough to make a lot of friends, but
you could stick a bottle of cream alongside one of these

people and it'd stay sweet a week. Unless they looked at it. I'm sick of talking to you and Sis and the hired help, and Kate's so lonesome that she cries herself to sleep nights."

Well, if I'd of only had sense enough to insist on staying we'd of probably packed up and took the next train to Town. But instead of that I said: "What's to prevent us from going back to New York?"

"Don't be silly!" says the Mrs. "We come out here to spend the summer and here is where we're going to spend the summer."

"All right," I says, "and by September I'll be all set to write a book on one-handed card games."

"You'd think," says Ella, "that some of these women was titled royalties the way they snap at you when you try and be friends with them. But they's only one in the bunch that's got any handle to her name; that's Lady Perkins."

I asked her which one was that.

"You know," says Ella. "I pointed her out to you in the dining room. She's a nice-looking woman, about thirty-five, that sets near our table and walks with a cane."

"If she eats like some of the rest of them," I says, "she's lucky they don't have to w'eel her."

"She's English," says Ella. "They just come over and her husband's in Texas on some business and left her here. She's the one that's got that dog."

"That dog!" I said. "You might just as well tell me she's the one that don't play the mouth organ. They've all got a dog."

"She's got two," said the wife. "But the one I meant is that big German police dog that I'm scared to death of him. Haven't you saw her out walking with him and the little chow?"

"Yes," I said, "if that's what it is. I always wondered

what the boys in the Army was talking about when they said they eat chow."

"They probably meant chowchow," says the Mrs. "They wouldn't of had these kind of chows, because in the first place, who would eat a dog, and besides these kind costs too much."

"Well," I says, "I'm not interested in the price of chows, but if you want to get acquainted with Lady Perkins, why I can probably fix it for you."

"Yes, you'll fix it!" said Ella. "I'm beginning to think that if we'd of put you in storage for the summer the folks round here wouldn't shy away from us like we was leopards that had broke out of a pest-house. I wished you would try and dress up once in a wile and not always look like you was just going to do the chores. Then maybe I and Sis might get somewheres."

Well, of course when I told her I could probably fix it up with Lady Perkins, I didn't mean nothing. But it wasn't only the next morning when I started making good. I was up and dressed and downstairs about half past eight, and as the gals wasn't ready for their breakfast yet I went out on the porch and set down. They wasn't nobody else there, but pretty soon I seen Lady Perkins come up the path with her two whelps. When she got to the porch steps their nurse popped out of the servants' quarters and took them round to the grillroom for their breakfast. I s'pose the big one ordered sauerkraut and kalter Aufschnitt, wile the chow had tea and eggs fo yung. Anyway, the Perkins dame come up on the porch and flopped into the chair next to mine.

In a few minutes Ed Wurz, the manager of the hotel, showed, with a bag of golf instruments and a trick suit. He spotted me and asked me if I didn't want to go along with him and play.

"No," I said. "I only played once in my life."

"That don't make no difference," he says. "I'm a bum myself. I just play shinny, you might say."

"Well," I says, "I can't anyway, on account of my dogs. They been giving me a lot of trouble."

Of course I was referring to my feet, but he hadn't no sooner than went on his way when Lady Perkins swung round on me and says: "I didn't know you had dogs. Where do you keep them?"

At first I was going to tell her "In my shoes," but I thought I might as well enjoy myself, so I said: "They're in the dog hospital over to Haverton."

"What ails them?" she asked me.

Well, I didn't know nothing about cay-nine diseases outside of hydrophobia, which don't come till August, so I had to make one up.

"They got blanny," I told her.

"Blanny!" she says. "I never heard of it before."

"No," I said. "It hasn't only been discovered in this country just this year. It got carried up here from Peru some way another."

"Oh, it's contagious, then!" says Lady Perkins.

"Worse than measles or lockjaw," says I. "You take a dog that's been in the same house with a dog that's got blanny, and it's a miracle if they don't all get it."

She asked me if I'd had my dogs in the hotel.

"Only one day," I says, "the first day we come, about a week ago. As soon as I seen what was the matter with them, I took them over to Haverton in a sanitary truck."

"Was they mingling with the other dogs here?" she says.

"Just that one day," I said.

"Heavens!" said Lady Perkins. "And what's the symptoms?"

"Well," I said, "first you'll notice that they keep their tongue stuck out a lot and they're hungry a good deal of the time, and finally they show up with a rash."

"Then what happens?" she says.

"Well," said I, "unless they get the best of treatment, they kind of dismember."

Then she asked me how long it took for the symptoms to show after a dog had been exposed. I told her any time between a week and four months.

"My dogs has been awful hungry lately," she says, "and they most always keeps their tongue stuck out. But they haven't no rash."

"You're all right, then," I says. "If you give them treatments before the rash shows up, they's no danger."

"What's the treatment?" she asked me.

"You rub the back of their neck with some kind of dope," I told her. "I forget what it is, but if you say the word, I can get you a bottle of it when I go over to the hospital this afternoon."

"I'd be ever so much obliged," she says, "and I hope you'll find your dear ones a whole lot better."

"Dear ones is right," I said. "They cost a pile of jack, and the bird I bought them off of told me I should ought to get them insured, but I didn't. So if anything happens to them now, I'm just that much out."

Next she asked me what kind of dogs they was.

"Well," I said, "you might maybe never of heard of them, as they don't breed them nowheres only way down in Dakota. They call them yaphounds—I don't know why; maybe on account of the noise they make. But they're certainly a grand-looking dog and they bring a big price."

She set there a wile longer and then got up and went inside, probably to the nursery to look for signs of rash.

Of course I didn't tell the Mrs. and Kate nothing about

this incidence. They wouldn't of believed it if I had of, and besides, it would be a knock-out if things broke right and Lady Perkins come up and spoke to me wile they was present, which is just what happened.

During the afternoon I strolled over to the drugstore and got me an empty pint bottle. I took it up in the room and filled it with water and shaving soap. Then I laid low till evening, so as Perk would think I had went to Haverton.

I and Ella and Kate breezed in the dining room kind of late and we hadn't no more than ordered when I seen the Lady get up and start out. She had to pass right past us, and when I looked at her and smiled she stopped.

"Well," she said, "how's your dogs?"

I got up from the table.

"A whole lot better, thank you," says I, and then I done the honors. "Lady Perkins," I said, "meet the wife and sister-in-law."

The two gals staggered from their chairs, both pop-eyed. Lady Perkins bowed to them and told them to set down. If she hadn't the floor would of bounced up and hit them in the chin.

"I got a bottle for you," I said. "I left it upstairs and I'll fetch it down after supper."

"I'll be in the red card room," says Perk, and away she went.

I wished you could of see the two gals. They couldn't talk for a minute, for the first time in their life. They just set there with their mouth open like a baby blackbird. Then they both broke out with a rash of questions that come so fast I couldn't understand none of them, but the general idear was, What the hell!

"They's no mystery about it," I said. "Lady Perkins was setting out on the porch this morning and you two was late getting down to breakfast, so I took a walk, and when I come back she noticed that I kind of limped and asked me what ailed my feet. I told her they always swoll up in warm weather and she said she was troubled the same way and did I know any medicine that shrank them. So I told her I had a preparation and would bring her a bottle of it."

"But," says Kate, "I can't understand a woman like she speaking to a man she don't know."

"She's been eying me all week," I said. "I guess she didn't have the nerve to break the ice up to this morning; then she got desperate."

"She must of," said Ella.

"I wished," said Kate, "that when you introduce me to people you'd give them my name."

"I'm sorry," I said, "but I couldn't recall it for a minute, though your face is familiar."

"But listen," says the wife. "What ails your dogs is a corn. You haven't got no swelled feet and you haven't got no medicine for them."

"Well," I says, "what I give her won't hurt her. It's just a bottle of soap and water that I mixed up, and pretty near everybody uses that once in a wile without no bad after effects."

Now, the whole three of us had been eating pretty good ever since we'd came to the Decker. After living à la carte at Big Town prices for six months, the American plan was sweet patootie. But this night the gals not only skrimped themselves but they was in such a hurry for me to get through that my molars didn't hardly have time to identify what all was scampering past them. Ella finally got so nervous that I had to take off the feed bag without dipping my bill into the stewed rhubarb.

"Lady Perkins will get tired waiting for you," she says. "And besides, she won't want us horning in there and interrupting them after their game's started."

"Us!" said I. "How many do you think it's going to take to carry this bottle?"

"You don't mean to say we can't go with you!" said Kate.

"You certainly can't," I says. "I and the nobility won't have our little romance knocked for a gool by a couple of country gals that can't get on speaking terms with nobody but the chambermaid."

"But they'll be other people there," says Kate. "She can't play cards alone."

"Who told you she was going to play cards?" I says. "She picked the red card room because we ain't liable to be interrupted there. As for playing cards alone, what else have I done all week? But when I get there she won't have to play solitary. It'll be two-handed hearts; where if you was to crowd in, it couldn't be nothing but rummy."

Well, they finally dragged me from the table, and the gals took a seat in the lobby wile I went upstairs after the medicine. But I hadn't no sooner than got a hold of the bottle when Ella come in the room.

"Listen," she says. "They's a catch in this somewheres. You needn't to try and tell me that a woman like Lady Perkins is trying to start a flirtation with a yahoo. Let's hear what really come off."

"I already told you," I said. "The woman's nuts over me and you should ought to be the last one to find fault with her judgment."

Ella didn't speak for a wile. Then she says: "Well, if you're going to forget your marriage vows and flirt with an old hag like she, I guess two can play at that little game. They's several men round this hotel that I like their looks and all as they need is a little encouragement."

"More than a little, I guess," says I, "or else they'd of

already been satisfied with what you and Kate has give them. They can't neither one of you pretend that you been fighting on the defense all week, and the reason you haven't copped nobody is because this place is a hotel, not a home for the blind."

I wrapped a piece of newspaper round the bottle and started for the door. But all of a sudden I heard snuffles and stopped.

"Look here," I said. "I been kidding you. They's no need for you to get sore and turn on the tear ducks. I'll tell you how this thing happened if you think you can see a joke."

So I give her the truth, and afterwards I says: "They'll be plenty of time for you and Kate to get acquainted with the dame, but I don't want you tagging in there with me to-night. She'd think we was too cordial. To-morrow morning, if you can manage to get up, we'll all three of us go out on the porch and lay for her when she brings the whelps back from their hike. She's sure to stop and inquire about my kennel. And don't forget, wile she's talking, that we got a couple of yaphounds that's suffering from blanny, and if she asks any questions let me do the answering, as I can think a lot quicker. You better tell Kate the secret, too, before she messes everything up, according to custom."

Then I and the Mrs. come downstairs and her and Katie went out to listen to the music wile I beat it to the red card room. I give Perkie the bottle of rash poison and she thanked me and said she would have the dogs' governess slap some of it onto them in the morning. She was playing bridge w'ist with another gal and two dudes. To look at their faces they wasn't playing for just pins. I had sense enough to not talk, but I stood there watching them a few minutes. Between hands Perk introduced me to the rest of the party. She had to ask my name first.

The other skirt at the table was a Mrs. Snell and one of the dudes was a Doctor Platt. I didn't get the name of Lady Perkins' partner.

"Mr. Finch," says Perk, "is also a dog fancier. But his dogs is sick with a disease called blanny and he's got them over to the dog hospital at Haverton."

"What kind of dogs?" asked Platt.

"I never heard of the breed before," says Perk. "They're yaphounds."

"They raise them in South Dakota," I says.

Platt gives me a funny look and said: "I been in South Dakota several times and I never heard of a yaphound neither; or I never heard of a disease named blanny."

"I s'pose not," says I. "You ain't the only old-fashioned doctor that left themselves go to seed when they got out of school. I bet you won't admit they's such a thing as appendicitis."

Well, this got a laugh from Lady Perkins and the other dude, but it didn't go very big with Doc or Mrs. Snell. Wile Doc was trying to figure out a come-back I said I must go and look after my womenfolks. So I told the party I was glad to of met them and walked out.

I found Ella and Katie in the summer parlor, and they wasn't alone. A nice-looking young fella named Codd was setting alongside of them, and after we was introduced Ella leaned over and w'ispered to me that he was Bob Codd, the famous aviator. It come out that he had invented some new kind of an aeroplane and had came to demonstrate it to the Williams Company. The company—Palmer Williams and his brother, you know—they've got their flying field a couple miles from the hotel. Well, a guy with nerve enough to go up in one of them things certainly ain't going to hesitate about speaking to a strange gal when he likes their looks. So this Codd baby had give himself an introduction to my Mrs.

and Kate, and I guess they hadn't sprained an ankle running away from him.

Of course Ella wanted to know how I'd came out with Lady Perkins. I told her that we hadn't had much chance to talk because she was in a bridge game with three other people, but I'd met them and they'd all seemed to fall for me strong. Ella wanted to know who they was and I told her their names, all but the one I didn't get. She squealed when I mentioned Mrs. Snell.

"Did you hear that, Sis?" she says to Kate. "Tom's met Mrs. Snell. That's the woman, you know, that wears them funny clothes and has the two dogs."

"You're describing every woman in the hotel," I said.

"But this is *the* Mrs. Snell," said the wife. "Her husband's the sugar man and she's the daughter of George Henkel, the banker. They say she's a wonderful bridge player and don't never play only for great big stakes. I'm wild to meet her."

"Yes," I said, "if they's one person you should ought to meet, it's a wonderful bridge player that plays for great big stakes, especially when our expenses is making a bum out of our income and you don't know a grand slam from no dice."

"I don't expect to gamble with her," says Ella. "But she's just the kind of people we want to know."

Well, the four of us set there and talked about this and that, and Codd said he hadn't had time to get his machine put together yet, but when he had her fixed and tested her a few times he would take me up for a ride.

"You got the wrong number," I says. "I don't feel flighty."

"Oh, I'd just love it!" said Kate.

"Well," says Codd, "you ain't barred. But I don't want

to have no passengers along till I'm sure she's working O. K."

When I and Ella was upstairs she said that Codd had told them he expected to sell his invention to the Williamses for a cold million. And he had took a big fancy to Kate.

"Well," I said, "they say that the reckless aviators makes the best ones, so if him and Kate gets married he'll be better than ever. He won't give a damn after that."

"You're always saying something nasty about Sis," said the Mrs.; "but I know you just talk to hear yourself talk. If I thought you meant it I'd walk out on you."

"I'd hate to lose you," I says, "but if you took her along I wouldn't write it down as a total loss."

The following morning I and the two gals was down on the porch bright and early and in a few minutes, sure enough, along came Lady Perkins, bringing the menagerie back from the parade. She turned them over to the nurse and joined us. She said that Martha, the nurse, had used the rash poison and it had made a kind of a lather on the dogs' necks and she didn't know whether to wash it off or not, but it had dried up in the sun. She asked me how many times a day the dope should ought to be put on, and I told her before every meal and at bedtime.

"But," I says, "it's best to not take the dogs right out in the sun where the lather'll dry. The blanny germ can't live in that kind of lather, so the longer it stays moist, why, so much the better."

Then she asked me was I going to Haverton to see my pets that day and I said yes, and she said she hoped I'd find them much improved. Then Ella cut in and said she understood that Lady Perkins was very fond of bridge.

"Yes, I am," says Perk. "Do you people play?"

"No, we don't," says Ella, "but we'd like to learn."

"It takes a long wile to learn to play good," said Perk. "But I do wished they was another real player in the hotel so as we wouldn't have to take Doctor Platt in. He knows the game, but he don't know enough to keep still. I don't mind people talking wile the cards is being dealt, but once the hands is picked up they ought to be absolute silence. Last night I lost about three hundred and seventy dollars just because he talked at the wrong time."

"Three hundred and seventy dollars!" said Kate. "My, you must play for big stakes!"

"Yes, we do," says Lady Perkins; "and when a person is playing for sums like that it ain't no time to trifle, especially when you're playing against an expert like Mrs. Snell."

"The game must be awfully exciting," said Ella. "I wished we could watch it sometime."

"I guess it wouldn't hurt nothing," says Perkie; "not if you kept still. Maybe you'd bring me luck."

"Was you going to play to-night?" asked Kate.

"No," says the Lady. "They's going to be a little dance here to-night and Mr. Snell's dance mad, so he insists on borrowing his wife for the occasion. Doctor Platt likes to dance too."

"We're all wild about it," says Kate. "Is this an invitation affair?"

"Oh, no," says Perk. "It's for the guests of the hotel."

Then she said good-by to us and went in the dining room. The rest of our conversation all day was about the dance and what should we wear, and how nice and democratic Lady Perkins was, and to hear her talk you wouldn't never know she had a title. I s'pose the gals thought she ought to stop every three or four steps and declare herself.

I made the announcement about noon that I wasn't going to partake in the grand ball. My corn was the alibi. But they wasn't no way to escape from dressing up and escorting the two gals into the grand ballroom and then setting there with them.

The dance was a knock-out. Outside of Ella and Kate and the aviator and myself, they was three couple. The Snells was there and so was Doctor Platt. He had a gal with him that looked like she might be his mother with his kid sister's clothes on. Then they was a pair of young shimmy shakers that ought to of been give their bottle and tucked in the hay at six p.m. A corn wouldn't of bothered them the way they danced; their feet wasn't involved in the transaction.

I and the Mrs. and Kate was the only ones there in evening clothes. The others had attended these functions before and knew that they wouldn't be enough suckers on hand to make any difference whether you wore a monkey suit or rompers. Besides, it wasn't Saturday night.

The music was furnished by the three-piece orchestra that usually done their murder in the summer parlor.

Ella was expecting me to introduce her and Kate to the Snell gal, but her and her husband was so keen for dancing that they called it off in the middle of the second innings and beat it upstairs. Then Ella said she wouldn't mind meeting Platt, but when he come past us and I spoke to him he give me a look like you would expect from a flounder that's been wronged.

So poor Codd danced one with Kate and one with Ella, and so on, and so on, till finally it got pretty late, a quarter to ten, and our party was the only merry-makers left in the joint. The orchestra looked over at us to see if we could stand some more punishment. The Mrs. told me to go and ask them to play a couple more dances before they quit. They done what I asked them, but maybe I got my orders mixed up.

The next morning I asked Wurz, the manager, how often the hotel give them dances.

"Oh," he says, "once or twice a month."

I told him I didn't see how they could afford it.

Kate went out after supper this next evening to take an automobile ride with Codd. So when I and Ella had set in the summer parlor a little wile, she proposed that we should go in and watch the bridge game. Well, I wasn't keen for it, but when you tell wife you don't want to do something she always says, "Why not?" and even if you've got a reason she'll make a monkey out of it. So we rapped at the door of the red card room and Lady Perkins said, "Come in," and in we went.

The two dudes and Mrs. Snell was playing with her again, but Perk was the only one that spoke.

"Set down," she said, "and let's see if you can bring me some luck."

So we drawed up a couple of chairs and set a little ways behind her. Her and the anonymous dude was partners against Doc and Mrs. Snell, and they didn't change all evening. I haven't played only a few games of bridge, but I know a little about it, and I never see such hands as Perkie held. It was a misdeal when she didn't have the ace, king and four or five others of one suit and a few picture cards and aces on the side. When she couldn't get the bid herself she doubled the other pair and made a sucker out of them. I don't know what they was playing a point, but when they broke up Lady Perkins and her dude was something like seven hundred berries to the good.

I and Ella went to bed wile they was settling up, but we seen her on the porch in the morning. She smiled at us and says: "You two are certainly grand mascots! I hope you can come in and set behind me again to-night. I ain't even yet, but one more run of luck like last night's and I'll be a winner. Then," she says, "I s'pose I'll have to give my mascots some kind of a treat."

Ella was tickled to death and couldn't hardly wait to slip Sis the good news. Kate had been out late and overslept herself and we was half through breakfast when she showed up. The Mrs. told her about the big game and how it looked like we was in strong with the nobility, and Kate said she had some good news of her own; that Codd had as good as told her he was stuck on her.

"And he's going to sell his invention for a million," says Ella. "So I guess we wasn't as crazy coming out to this place as some people thought we was."

"Wait till the machine's made good," I said.

"It has already," says Kate. "He was up in it yesterday and everything worked perfect and he says the Williamses was wild over it. And what do you think's going to come off to-morrow morning? He's going to take me up with him."

"Oh, no, Sis!" said Ella. "S'pose something should happen!"

"No hope," says I.

"But even if something should happen," said Katie, "what would I care as long as it happened to Bob and I together!"

I told the waitress to bring me another order of fried mush.

"To-night," said Kate, "Bob's going in Town to a theater party with some boys he went to college with. So I can help you bring Lady Perkins good luck."

Something told me to crab this proposition and I tried, but it was passed over my veto. So the best I could do was to remind Sis, just before we went in the gambling den, to keep her mouth shut wile the play was going on.

Perk give us a smile of welcome and her partner smiled too.

For an hour the game went along about even. Kate acted like she was bored, and she didn't have nothing to say after she'd told them, wile somebody was dealing, that she was going to have an aeroplane ride in the morning. Finally our side begin to lose, and lose by big scores. They was one time when they was about sixteen hundred points to the bad. Lady Perkins didn't seem to be enjoying herself and when Ella addressed a couple of remarks to her the cat had her tongue.

But the luck switched round again and Lady Perk had all but caught up when the blow-off come.

It was the rubber game, with the score nothing and nothing. The Doc dealt the cards. I was setting where I could see his hand and Perk's both. Platt had the king, jack and ten and five other hearts. Lady Perkins held the ace and queen of hearts, the other three aces and everything else in the deck.

The Doc bid two hearts. The other dude and Mrs. Snell passed.

"Two without," says Lady Perkins.

"Three hearts," says Platt.

The other two passed again and Perk says: "Three without."

Katie had came strolling up and was pretty near behind Perk's chair.

"Well," says Platt, "it looks like——"

But we didn't find out what it looked like, as just then Katie says: "Heavens! Four aces! Don't you wished you was playing penny ante?"

It didn't take Lady Perkins no time at all to forget her title.

"You fool!" she screams, w'eeling round on Kate. "Get out of here, and get out of here quick, and don't never come near me again! I hope your aeroplane falls a million feet. You little fool!"

I don't know how the hand come out. We wasn't there to see it played.

Lady Perkins got part of her hope. The aeroplane fell all right, but only a couple of miles instead of a million feet. They say that they was a defect or something in poor Codd's engine. Anyway, he done an involuntary nose dive. Him and his invention was spilled all over Long Island. But Katie had been awake all night with the hysterics and Ella hadn't managed to get her to sleep till nine a.m. So when Codd had called for her Ella'd told him that Sis would go some other day. Can you beat it?

Wile I and Ella was getting ready for supper I made the remark that I s'posed we'd live in a vale of tears for the next few days.

"No," said Ella. "Sis is taking it pretty calm. She's sensible. She says if that could of happened, why the invention couldn't of been no good after all. And the Williamses probably wouldn't of give him a plugged dime for it."

Lady Perkins didn't only speak to me once afterwards. I seen her setting on the porch one day, reading a book. I went up to her and said: "Hello." They wasn't no answer, so I thought I'd appeal to her sympathies.

"Maybe you're still interested in my dogs," I said. "They was too far gone and the veter'nary had to order them shot."

"That's good," said Perk, and went on reading.

IV. Only One

ABOUT a week after this, the Mrs. made the remark that the Decker wasn't big enough to hold both she and Perkins.

"She treats us like garbage," says the Mrs., "and if I stay here much longer I'll forget myself and do her nose in a braid."

But Perk left first and saved us the trouble. Her husband was down in Texas looking after some oil gag and he wired her a telegram one day to come and join him as it looked like he would have to stay there all summer. If I'd of been him I'd of figured that Texas was a sweet enough summer resort without adding your wife to it.

We was out on the porch when her ladyship and two dogs shoved off.

"Three of a kind," said the Mrs.

And she stuck her tongue out at Perk and felt like that made it all even. A woman won't stop at nothing to revenge insults. I've saw them stagger home in a new pair of 3 double A shoes because some fresh clerk told them the 7 Ds they tried on was too small. So anyway we decided to stay on at the Decker and the two gals prettied themselves up every night for dinner in the hopes that somebody besides the head waiter would look at them twice, but we attracted about as much attention as a dirty finger nail in the third grade.

That is, up till Herbert Daley come on the scene.

Him and Katie spotted each other at the same time. It was the night he come to the Decker. We was pretty near through dinner when the head waiter showed him to a table a little ways from us. The majority of the guests out there belongs to the silly sex and a new man is always a riot, even with the married ones. But Daley would of knocked them dead anywheres. He looked like he was born and raised in Shubert's chorus and the minute he danced in all the womenfolks forgot the feed bag and feasted their eyes on him. As for Daley, after he'd glanced at the bill of fare, he let his peepers roll over towards our table and then they quit rolling. A cold stare from Kate might have scared him off, but if they was ever a gal with "Welcome" embroidered on her pan, she's it.

It was all I could do to tear Ella and Sis from the dining room, though they was usually in a hurry to romp out to the summer parlor and enjoy a few snubs. I'd just as soon of set one place as another, only for the waitress, who couldn't quit till we did and she generally always had a date with the big ski jumper the hotel hires to destroy trunks.

Well, we went out and listened a wile to the orchestra, which had brought a lot of new jazz from the Prince of Pilsen, and we waited for the new dude to show up, but he didn't, and finally I went in to the desk to buy a couple of cigars and there he was, talking to Wurz, the manager. Wurz introduced us and after we'd shook hands Daley excused himself and said he was going upstairs to write a letter. Then Wurz told me he was Daley the horseman.

"He's just came up from the South," says Wurz. "He's going to be with us till the meetings is over at Jamaica and Belmont. He's got a whale of a stable and he expects to clean up round New York with Only One, which he claims can beat any horse in the world outside of Man o' War. They's some other good ones in the bunch, too, and he says he'll tell me when he's going to bet on them. I don't only bet once in a long wile and then never more than $25 at a crack, but I'll take this baby's tips as often as he comes through with them. I guess a man won't make no mistake following a bird that bets five and ten thousand at a clip, though of course it don't mean much to him if he win or lose. He's dirty with it."

I asked Wurz if Daley was married and he said no.

"And listen," he says: "It looks like your little sister-in-law had hit him for a couple of bases. He described where she was setting in the dining room and asked who she was."

"Yes," I said, "I noticed he was admiring somebody at our table, but I thought maybe it was me."

"He didn't mention you," says Wurz, "only to make sure you wasn't Miss Kate's husband."

"If he was smart he'd know that without asking," I said. "If she was my wife I'd be wearing weeds."

I went back to the gals and told them I'd met the guy. They was all steamed up.

"Who is he?" says Kate.

"His name is Herbert Daley," I told her. "He's got a stable over to Jamaica."

"A stable!" says Ella, dropping her jaw. "A man couldn't dress like he and run a livery."

So I had to explain that he didn't run no livery, but owned a string of race horses.

"How thrilling!" says Katie. "I love races! I went to the Grand Circuit once, the time I was in Columbus."

"These is different," I says. "These is thurlbreds."

"So was they thurlbreds!" she says. "You always think a thing can't be no good if you wasn't there."

I let her win that one.

"We must find out when the race is and go," said the Mrs.

"They's six of them every day," I said, "but it costs about five smackers apiece to get in, to say nothing about what you lose betting."

"Betting!" says Katie. "I just love to bet and I never lose. Don't you remember the bet I made with Sammy Pass on the baseball that time? I took him for a five-pound box of candy. I just felt that Cincinnati was going to win."

"So did the White Sox," I says. "But if you bet with the boys over to Jamaica, the only candy they'll take you for is an all-day sucker."

"What did Mr. Daley have to say?" asked Ella.

"He had to say he was pleased to meet me," I told her. "He proved it by chasing upstairs to write a letter."

"Probably to his wife," said Kate.

"No," I said. "Wurz tells me he ain't got no wife. But he's got plenty of jack, so Wurz says."

"Well, Sis," says the Mrs., "that's no objection to him, is it?"

"Don't be silly!" said Katie. "He wouldn't look at me."

"I guess not!" I says. "He was so busy doing it in the dining room, that half his soup never got past his chin. And listen: I don't like to get you excited, but Wurz told me he asked who you was."

"O Sis!" said the Mrs. "It looks like a Romance."

"Wurz didn't say nothing about a Romance," said I. "He may be interested like the rubes who stare with their mouth open at Ringling's 'Strange People.'"

"Oh, you can't tease Sis like that," said Ella. "She's as pretty as a picture to-night and nobody could blame a man from admiring her."

"Especially when we don't know nothing about him," I says. "He may be a snow-eater or his upstairs rooms is unfurnished or something."

"Well," says Ella, "if he shows up again to-night, don't you forget to introduce us."

"Better not be in no hurry," I said.

"Why not?" said Ella. "If him and Sis likes each other's looks, why, the sooner they get acquainted, it won't hurt nothing."

"I don't know," I says. "I've noticed that most of the birds you chose for a brother-in-law only stayed in the family as long as they was strangers."

"Nobody said nothing about Mr. Daley as a brother-in-law," says Ella.

"Oh!" I said. "Then I suppose you want Katie to meet him so as she can land a hostler's job."

Well, in about a half hour, the gals got their wish and Daley showed up. I didn't have to pull no strategy to land him. He headed right to where we was setting like him and I was old pals. I made the introductions and he drawed up a chair and parked. The rest of the guests stared at us goggle-eyed.

"Some hotel!" says Daley.

"We like it," says the Mrs. "They's so many nice people lives here."

"We know by hearsay," I said, but she stepped on my foot.

"It's handy for me," said Daley. "I have a few horses over to the Jamaica race track and it's a whole lot easier to come here than go in Town every night."

"Do you attend the races every day?" says Katie.

"Sure," he says. "It's my business. And they's very few afternoons when one of my nags ain't entered."

"My! You must have a lot of them!" said Kate.

"Not many," says Daley. "About a hundred. And I only shipped thirty."

"Imagine!" said Kate.

"The army's got that many," I said.

"The army ain't got none like mine," says Daley. "I guess they wished they had of had. I'd of been glad to of helped them out, too, if they'd asked me."

"That's why I didn't enlist," I said. "Pershing never even suggested it."

"Oh, I done my bit all right," says Daley. "Two hundred thousand in Liberty Bonds is all."

"Just like throwing it away!" I says.

"Two hundred thousand!" says Ella. "And you've still got money left?"

She said this in a joking way, but she kept the receiver to her ear.

"I ain't broke yet," says Daley, "and I don't expect to be."

"You don't half know this hotel," I says.

"The Decker does charge good prices," said Daley, "but still and all, a person is willing to pay big for the opportunity of meeting young ladies like the present company."

"O Mr. Daley!" said Kate. "I'm afraid you're a flatter."

"I bet he makes them pretty speeches to every woman he meets," says Ella.

"I haven't met none before who I felt like making them," says Daley.

Wile they was still talking along these lines, the orchestra begin to drool a Perfect Day, so I ducked out on the porch for air. The gals worked fast wile I was gone and when I come back it was arranged that Daley was to take us to the track next afternoon in his small car.

His small car was a toy that only had enough room for the people that finds fault with Wilson. I suppose he had to leave his big car in New York on account of the Fifty-ninth Street bridge being so frail.

Before we started I asked our host if they was a chance to get anything to drink over to the track and he says no, but pretty near everybody brought something along on the hip, so I said for them to wait a minute wile I went up to the room and filled a flask. When we was all in the car, the Mrs. wanted to know if it wasn't risky, me taking the hootch along.

"It's against the prohibition law," she says.

"So am I," I said.

"They's no danger," says Daley. "They ain't began to force prohibition yet. I only wished they had. It would save me a little worry about my boy."

"Your boy!" said Katie, dropping her jaw a foot.

"Well, I call him my boy," says Daley. "I mean little Sid Mercer, that rides for me. He's the duke of them all when he lays off the liquor. He's gave me his word that he won't touch nothing as long as he's under contract to me, and he's kept straight so far, but I can't help from worr'ing about him. He ought to be good, though, when I pay him $20,000 for first call, and leave him make all he can on the side. But he ain't got much stren'th of character, you might say, and if something upsets him, he's liable to bust things wide open.

"I remember once he was stuck on a gal down in Louisville and he was supposed to ride Great Scott for Bradley in the Derby. He was the only one that could handle Scott right, and with him up Scott would of win as far as from here to Dallas. But him and the gal had a brawl the day before the race and that night the kid got stiff. When it come time for the race he couldn't of kept a seat on a saw horse. Bradley had to hustle round and dig up another boy and Carney was the only one left that could ride at all and him and Great Scott was strangers. So Bradley lose the race and canned Mercer."

"Whisky's a terrible thing," says Ella. A woman'll sometimes pretend for a long wile like she's stupid and all of a sudden pull a wise crack that proves she's a thinker.

"Well," says Daley, "when Bradley give him the air,

I took him, and he's been all right. I guess maybe I
know how to handle men."

"Men only?" says Katie, smiling.

"Men and horses," said Daley. "I ain't never tried to
handle the fair sex and I don't know if I could or not.
But I've just met one that I think could handle me." And
he give her a look that you could pour on a waffle.

Daley had a table saved for him in the clubhouse and
we eat our lunch. The gals had clubhouse sandwiches,
probably figuring they was caught fresh there. They was
just one of Daley's horses entered that day and he told
us he wasn't going to bet on it, as it hadn't never showed
nothing and this was just a try-out. He said, though,
that they was other horses on the card that looked good
and maybe he would play them after he'd been round
and talked to the boys.

"Yes," says Kate, "but the men you'll talk to knows
all about the different horses and they'll tell you what
horses to bet on and how can I win?"

"Why," says Daley, "if I decide to make a little bet
on So-and-So I'll tell you about it and you can bet on
the same horse."

"But if I'm betting with you," says Kate, "how can we
bet on the same horse?"

"You're betting with me, but you ain't betting against
me," said Daley. "This ain't a bet like you was betting
with your sister on a football game or something. We
place our bets with the bookmakers, that makes their
living taking bets. Whatever horse we want to bet on,
they take the bet."

"They must be crazy!" says Katie. "Your friends tell
you what horse is going to win and you bet on them and
the bookbinders is stung."

"My friends makes mistakes," says Daley, "and besides, I ain't the only guy out here that bets. Pretty

near everybody at the track bets and the most of them don't know a race horse from a corn plaster. A bookmaker that don't finish ahead on the season's a cuckoo. Now," he says, "if you'll excuse me for a few minutes, I'll go down to the paddock and see what's new."

So wile he was gone we had a chance to look round and they was plenty to see. It was a Saturday and a big crowd out. Lots of them was gals that you'd have to have a pick to break through to their regular face. Since they had their last divorce, about the only excitement they could enjoy was playing a long shot. Which reminds me that they's an old saying that nobody loves a fat man, but you go out to a race track or down to Atlantic City or any place where the former wifes hangs out and if you'll notice the birds with them, the gents that broke up their home, you'll find out that the most of them is guys with chins that runs into five and six figures and once round their waist is a sleeper jump.

Besides the Janes and the fat rascals with them, you seen a flock of ham actors that looked like they'd spent the night in a Chinese snowstorm, and maybe a half a dozen losers'-end boxers that'd used the bridge of their nose to block with and always got up in the morning just after the clock had struck ten, thinking they'd been counted out.

Pretty near everybody wore a pair of field glasses on a strap and when the race was going on they'd look through them and tell the world that the horse they'd bet on was three len'ths in front and just as good as in, but I never heard of a bookie paying off on that dope, and personally when someone would insist on lending me a pair to look through I couldn't tell if the things out there racing was horses or gnats.

Daley was back with us in a few minutes and says to

Kate: "I guess you'll have to bet on yourself in the first race."

So she asked him what did he mean and he said: "I had a tip on a filly named Sweet and Pretty."

"O Mr. Daley!" says Kate.

"They don't expect her to win," says Daley, "but she's six, two and even, and I'm going to play her place and show."

Then he explained what that was and he said he was going to bet a thousand each way and finally the gals decided to go in for $10 apiece to show. It tickled them to death to find out that they didn't have to put up nothing. We found seats down in front wile Daley went to place the bets. Pretty soon the horses come out and Kate and Ella both screamed when they seen how cute the jockeys was dressed. Sweet and Pretty was No. 10 and had a combination of colors that would knock your eye out. Daley come back and explained that every owner had their own colors and of course the gals wanted to know what his was and he told them Navy blue and orange sleeves with black whoops on them and a blue cap.

"How beautiful!" says Ella. "I can't hardly wait to see them!"

"You must have wonderful taste in colors!" says Kate.

"Not only in colors," he says.

"O Mr. Daley!" she says again.

Well, the race was ran and No. 10 was a Sweet and Pretty last.

"Now," I says, "you O Mr. Daley."

The gals had yelped themself hoarse and didn't have nothing to say, but I could tell from their face that it would take something more than a few pretty speeches to make up for that twenty men.

"Never mind that!" said Daley. "She got a rotten ride. We'll get that back on the next one."

His hunch in the next one was Sena Day and he was betting a thousand on her to place at 4 to 1. He made the gals go in for $20 apiece, though they didn't do it with no pep. I went along with him to place the bets and he introduced me to a bookie so as I could bet a few smackers of my own when I felt like it. You know they's a law against betting unless it's a little bet between friends and in order to be a bookie's friend he's got to know your name. A quick friendship sprung up between I and a guy named Joe Meyer, and he not only give me his card but a whole deck of them. You see the law also says that when you make one of these bets with your pals he can't give you no writing to show for it, but he's generally always a man that makes a lot of friends and it seems like they all want to make friendly bets with him, and he can't remember where all his buddies lives, so he makes them write their name and address on the cards and how much the friendly wager is for and who on, and so forth, and the next day he mails them the bad news and they mail him back a check for same. Once in a wile, of course, you get the bad news and forget to mail him the check and he feels blue over it as they's nothing as sad as breaking up an old friendship.

I laid off Sena Day and she win. Daley smiled at the gals.

"There!" he says. "I'm sorry we didn't play her on the nose, but I was advised to play safe."

"Fine advice!" said Kate. "It's cost Sis and I $60 so far."

"What do you mean?" says Daley.

"We lose $20 on the first race," she says, "and you

tell us we'll get it back on the next one and we bet the horse'll come second and it don't."

So we had to explain that if a horse win, why it placed, too, and her and Ella had grabbed $160 on that race and was $140 ahead. He was $2,000 winners himself.

"We'll have a drink on Sena," he says. "I don't believe they was six people out here that bet a nickel on her."

So Katie told him he was wonderful and him and the gals had a sarsaparilla or something and I poured my own. He'd been touting Cleopatra in the third race, but her and everybody else was scratched out of it except Captain Alcock and On Watch. On Watch was 9 to 10 and Alcock even money and Daley wouldn't let us bet.

"On Watch is best," he says, "but he's giving away twenty pounds and you can't tell. Anyway, it ain't worth it at that price."

"Only two horses in the race?" asked Ella.

"That's all," he says.

"Well, then, listen," she says, all excited: "Why not bet on one of them for place?"

Daley laughed and said it was a grand idear only he didn't think the bookbinders would stand for it.

"But maybe they don't know," she says.

"I guess they do," said Daley. "It's almost impossible to keep a secret like that round a race track."

"Besides," I said, "the bookworms owes you and Kate $70 apiece and if you put something like that over on them and they find it out, they'll probably get even by making you a check on the West Bank of the Hudson River."

So we decided to play fair and lay off the race entirely. On Watch come through and the gals felt pretty bad about it till we showed them that they'd of only grabbed off nine smackers apiece if they'd of plunged on him for $20 straight.

Along toward time for the next race, Daley steered us down by the paddock and we seen some of the nags close up. Daley and the gals raved over this one and that one, and wasn't this one a beauty, and so forth. Personally they was all just a horse to me and I never seen one yet that wasn't homelier than the City Hall. If they left it up to me to name the world's champion eyesore, I'd award the elegant barb' wire wash rag to a horse rode by a woman in a derby hat. People goes to the Horse Show to see the Count de Fault; they don't know a case of withers from an off hind hock. And if the Sport of Kings was patronized by just birds that admires equine charms, you could park the Derby Day crowd in a phone booth.

A filly named Tamarisk was the favorite in the fourth race and Daley played her for eight hundred smackers at 4 to 5. The gals trailed along with $8 apiece and she win from here to Worcester. The fifth was the one that Daley had an entry in—a dog named Fly-by-Night. It was different in the daytime. Mercer had the mount and done the best he could, which was finish before supper. Nobody bet, so nobody was hurt.

"He's just a green colt," Daley told us. "I wanted to see how he'd behave."

"Well," I said, "I thought he behaved like a born caboose."

Daley liked the Waterbury entry in the last and him and the gals played it and win. All told, Daley was $4,000 ahead on the day and Ella and Kate had picked up $160 between them. They wanted to kiss everybody on the way out. Daley sent us to the car to wait for him. He wanted to see Mercer a minute. After a wile he come out and brought Mercer along and introduced him. He's a good-looking kid only for a couple of blotches on his pan and got an under lip and chin that kind of lags behind. He was about Kate's height, and take away his Adams apple and you could mail him to Duluth for six cents. Him and Kate got personal right away and she told him how different he looked now than in his riding make-up. He said he had a new outfit that he'd of wore if he'd knew she was looking on. So I said I hoped he didn't expect to ride Fly-by-Night round the track and keep a suit new, and he laughed, and Daley didn't seem to enjoy the conversation and said we'd have to be going, but when we started off, Kate and Mercer give each other a smile with a future in it. She's one of these gals that can't help from looking open house, even if the guy takes after a pelican.

Daley moved to our table that night and after that we eat breakfast and supper with him pretty near every day. After breakfast the gals would go down to New York to spend what they had win the day before, and I'll admit that Daley give us many a winner. I begin betting a little of my own jack, but I stuck the proceeds in the old sock. I ain't superstitious about living off a woman's money as long as you're legally married, but at the clip the two gals was going, it looked like their old man's war profits was on the way to join their maker, and the more jack I laid by, the less sooner I would have to go to work.

We'd meet every afternoon at the track and after the races Daley'd bring us back to the hotel. After supper we'd set round and chin or play rummy or once in a wile we'd go in Town to a show or visit one of the road houses near the Decker. The mail service on Long Island's kind of rotten and they's a bunch of road houses that hasn't heard of prohibition.

During the time we'd lived in Town Katie had got acquainted with three or four birds that liked her well enough to take her places where they wasn't no cover charge, but since we'd moved to the Decker we hadn't heard from none of them. That is, till a few days after we'd met Daley, when she told us that one of the New York boys, a guy named Goldberg, had called up and wanted her to come in and see a show with him. He's a golf champion or something. Well, Daley offered to drive her in, but she said no, she'd rather go on the train and Goldberg was going to meet her. So she went, and Daley tried to play cards with Ella and I, but he was too restless and finally snuck up to his room.

They wasn't no question about his feelings toward Kate. He was always trying to fix it to be alone with her, but I guess it was the first time in her life when she didn't have to do most of the leading and she kept him at arm's len'th. Her and Ella had many a battle. Ella told her that the first thing she knowed he'd get discouraged and walk out on her; that she'd ought to quit monking and give him to understand that she was ready to yes him when he spoke up. But Katie said she guessed she could run her own love affairs as she'd had a few more of them than Ella.

So Ella says: "Maybe you have, but which one of us has got the husband?"

"You, thank the Lord!" says Katie.

"Thank him twice," I said.

Kate didn't come home from her New York party till two o'clock and she overslept herself till it was too late to go down again and shop. So we all drove over to the track with Daley and most of the way over he acted like a child. Katie kept talking about what a good show she seen and had a grand time, and so forth, and he pretended he wasn't listening. Finally she cut it out and give him the old oil and by the time we got to the club-house he'd tossed in the sponge.

That was the last day at Jamaica and a couple of his horses was in. We was all down on them and they both copped, though Mercer had to give one of them a dude ride to pull us through. Daley got maudlin about what a grand rider the kid was and a grand little fella besides, and he had half a notion to bring him along with us back to the hotel and show him a good time. But Kate said what was the use of an extra man, as it would kind of spoil things and she was satisfied with just Daley. So of course that tickled him and everybody was feeling good and after supper him and Kate snuck out alone for the first time. Ella made me set up till they come back, so as she could get the news. Well, Daley had asked her all right, but she told him she wanted a little wile to think.

"Think!" says Ella. "What does she want to think for?"

"The novelty, I suppose," said I.

Only One was in the big stake race the next day, when we shifted over to Belmont. They was five or six others in with him, all of them pretty good, and the price on him was 3 to 1. He hadn't started yet since Daley'd brought him here, but they'd been nursing him along and Mercer and the trainer said he was right.

I suppose of course you've been out to Belmont. At that time they run the wrong way of the track, like you deal cards. Daley's table was in a corner of the club-house porch and when you looked up the track, the horses was coming right at you. Even the boys with the trick glasses didn't dast pretend they could tell who's ahead.

The Belmont national hymn is Whispering. The joint's so big and scattered round that a German could sing without disturbing the party at the next table. But they seems to be a rule that when they's anything to be said, you got to murmur it with the lips stuck to the opponent's earlobe. They shush you if you ask out loud for a toothpick. Everywheres you'll see two or three guys with their heads together in a whispering scene. One of them has generally always just been down to the horses' dining room and had lunch with Man o' War or somebody and they told him to play Sea Mint in the next race as Cleopatra had walked the stall all night with her foal. A little ways off they'll be another pair of shushers and one of them's had a phone call from Cleopatra's old dam to put a bet on Cleo as Captain Alcock had got a hold of some wild oats and they couldn't make him do nothing but shimmy.

If they's ten horses in a race you can walk from one end of the clubhouse to the other and get a whisper on all ten of them. I remember the second time Man o' War run there. They was only one horse that wanted to watch him from the track and the War horse was 1 to 100. So just before the race, if you want to call it that, I seen a wise cracker that I'd got acquainted with, that had always been out last night with Madden or Waterbury, so just kidding I walked up to him and asked him who he liked. So he motioned me to come over against the wall where they wasn't nobody near us and whispered, "Man o' War's unbeatable." You see if that remark had of been overheard and the news allowed to spread round, it might of forced the price to, say, 1 to a lump of coal, and spoiled the killing.

Well, wile the Jamaica meeting was on, the gals had spent some of their spare time figuring out how much they'd of been ahead if Daley had of let them bet more than ten to twenty smackers a race. So this day at Belmont, they said that if he liked Only One so much, he should ought to leave them raise the ante just once and play fifty apiece.

But he says: "No, not this time. I'm pretty sure he'll win, but he's in against a sweet field and he ain't raced for a month. I'll bet forty on the nose for the two of you, and if he looks good you can gamble some real money the next time he runs."

So Ella and Kate had to be satisfied with $20 apiece. Daley himself bet $2,000 and I piked along with $200 that I didn't tell the gals nothing about. We all got 3 to 1. A horse named Streak of Lightning was favorite at 6 to 5. It was a battle. Only One caught the Streak in the last step and win by a flea's jaw. Everybody was in hysterics and the gals got all messed up clawing each other.

"Nobody but Mercer could of did it!" says Daley, as soon as he could talk.

"He's some jockey!" yelled Kate. "O you Sid!"

Pretty soon the time was give out and Only One had broke the track record for the distance, whatever it was.

"He's a race horse!" said Daley. "But it's too bad he had to extend himself. We won't get no price the next time out."

Well, altogether the race meant $14,000 to Daley, and he said we'd all go to Town that night and celebrate. But when we got back to the Decker, they was a telegram for him and he had to pack up and beat it for Kentucky.

Daley being away didn't stop us from going to the track. He'd left orders with Ernest, his driver, to take us wherever we wanted to go and the gals had it so bad now that they couldn't hardly wait till afternoon. They kept on trimming the books, too. Kate got a phone call every morning that she said was from this Goldberg and he was giving her tips. Her and Ella played them and I wished I had. I would of if I'd knew who they was from. They was from Mercer, Daley's boy. That's who they was from.

I and Ella didn't wise up till about the third night after Daley'd went. That night, Kate took the train to Town right after supper, saying she had a date with Goldberg. It was a swell night and along about eight, I and Ella decided we might as well have a ride. So we got a hold of Ernest and it wound up by us going to New York too. We seen a picture and batted round till midnight and then Ella says why not go down to the Pennsylvania Station and pick Kate up when she come to take the train, and bring her home. So we done it. But when Katie showed up for the train, it was Mercer that was with her, not Goldberg.

Well, Mercer was pretty near out to the car with us when he happened to think that Daley's driver mustn't see him. So he said good night and left us. But he didn't do it quick enough. Daley's driver had saw him and I seen that he'd saw him and I knowed that he wasn't liable to be stuck on another of Daley's employs that was getting ten times as much money as him and all the cheers, and never had to dirty himself up changing a tire. And I bet it was all Ernest could do was wait till Daley come back so as he could explode the boom.

Kate and Ella didn't know Ernest was hep and I didn't tell them for fear of spoiling the show, so the women done their brawling on the way home in a regular race track whisper. The Mrs. told Kate she was a hick to be monking round with a jockey when Daley was ready and willing to give her a modern home with a platinum stopper in the washbowl. Kate told Ella that she wasn't going to marry nobody for their money, and besides, Mercer was making more than enough to support a wife, and how that boy can dance!

"But listen," she says: "I ain't married to neither one of them yet and don't know if I want to be."

"Well," says Ella, "you won't have no chance to marry Daley if he finds out about you and Mercer."

"He won't find out unless you tell him," said Kate.

"Well, I'll tell him," says Ella, "unless you cut this monkey business out."

"I'll cut it out when I get good and ready," says Kate. "You can tell Daley anything you please."

She knew they wasn't no chance of Ella making good.

"Daley'll be back in a couple of days," says the Mrs. "When he comes he'll want his answer and what are you going to say?"

"Yes or no, according to which way I make up my mind," said Kate. "I don't know yet which one I like best."

"That's ridic'lous!" Ella says. "When a girl says she can't make up her mind, it shows they's nothing to make up. Did you ever see me when I couldn't make up my mind?"

"No," said Katie, "but you never had even one whole man to choose between."

The last half of the ride neither of them were talking. That's a world's record in itself. They kind of made up the next morning after I'd told Ella that the surest way to knock Daley's chances for a gool was to paste Mercer.

"Just lay off of it," I told her. "The best man'll win in fair competition, which it won't be if you keep plugging for Daley."

We had two more pretty fair days at the track on Kate's tips that Mercer give her. We also went on a party with him down Town, but we used the train, not Daley's car.

Daley showed up on a Wednesday morning and had Ernest take him right over to the track. I suppose it was on this trip that Ernest squealed. Daley didn't act no different when we joined him on the clubhouse porch, but that night him and Kate took a ride alone and come back engaged.

They'd been pointing Only One for the Merrick Handicap, the fourth race on Saturday. It was worth about $7,000 to the winner. The distance was seven furlongs and Only One had top weight, 126 pounds. But Thursday he done a trial over the distance in 1.22, carrying 130 pounds, so it looked like a set-up.

Thursday morning I and Ella happened to be in Katie's room when the telephone rung. It was Mercer on the other end. He asked her something and she says: "I told you why in my note."

So he said something else and she says: "Not with no jailbird."

And she hung up.

Well, Ella wanted to know what all the pleasantries was about, but Kate told her to mind her own business.

"You got your wish and I'm engaged to Daley," she says, "and that's all you need to know."

For a gal that was going to marry a dude that was supposed to have all the money in the world, she didn't act just right, but she wouldn't been Kate if she had of, so I didn't think much about it.

Friday morning I got a wire from one of the South Bend boys, Goat Anderson, sent from Buffalo, saying he'd be in New York that night and would I meet him at the Belmont at seven o'clock. So I went in Town from the track and waited round till pretty near nine, but he didn't show up. I started to walk across to the Pennsylvania Station and on the way I dropped in at a place where they was still taking a chance. I had one up at the bar and was throwing it into me when a guy in the back part yelled "Hey! Come here!" It was Mercer yelling and it was me he wanted.

He was setting at a table all alone with a highball. It didn't take no Craig Kennedy to figure out that it wasn't his first one.

"Set down before I bat you down!" he says.

"Listen," I says: "I wished you was champion of the world. You'd hold onto the title just long enough for me to reach over and sock you where most guys has a chin."

"Set down!" he says. "It's your wife I'm going to beat up, not you."

"You ain't going to beat up nobody's wife or nobody's husband," I says, "and if you don't cut out that line of gab you'll soon be asking the nurse how you got there."

"Set down and come clean with me," he says. "Was your wife the one that told Daley about your sister-in-law and I?"

"If she did, what of it?" I says.

"I'm asking you, did she?" he says.

"No, she didn't," I said. "If somebody told him his driver told him. He seen you the other night."

"Ernest!" he says. "Frank and Ernest! I'll Ernest him right in the jaw!"

"You're a fine matchmaker!" I says. "He could knock you for a row of flat tires. Why don't you try and get mad at Dempsey?"

"Set down and have a drink," says Mercer.

"I didn't mean that about your wife. You and her has treated me all right. And your sister-in-law, too, even if she did give me the air. And called me a jailbird. But that's all right. It's Daley I'm after and it's Daley I'm going to get."

"Sweet chance!" I says. "What could you do to him?"

"Wait and see!" said Mercer, and smiled kind of silly.

"Listen," I says. "Have you forgot that you're supposed to ride Only One to-morrow?"

"Supposed to ride is right," he says, and smiled again.

"Ain't you going to ride him?" I said.

"You bet I am!" he says.

"Well, then," I said, "you better call it a day and go home."

"I'm over twenty-one," he says, "and I'm going to set here and enjoy myself. But remember, I ain't keeping you up."

Well, they wasn't nothing I could do only set there and wait for him to get stiff and then see him to his hotel. We had a drink and we had another and a couple more. Finally he opened up. I wished you could of heard him. It took him two hours to tell his story, and everything he said, he said it over and over and repeated it four and five times. And part of the time he talked so thick that I couldn't hardly get him.

"Listen," he says. "Can you keep a secret? Listen," he says. "I'm going to take a chance with you on account of your sister-in-law. I loved that little gal. She's give me the air, but that don't make no difference; I loved that little gal and I don't want her to lose no money. So I'm going to tell you a secret and if you don't keep your clam shut I'll roll you for a natural. In the first place," he says, "how do you and Daley stack up?"

"That ain't no secret," I said. "I think he's all right. He's been a good friend of mine."

"Oh," says Mercer, "so he's been a good friend of yours, has he? All right, then. I'm going to tell you a secret. Do you remember the day I met you and the gals in the car? Well, a couple of days later, Daley was feeling pretty good about something and he asked me how I liked his gal? So I told him she looked good. So he says, 'I'm going to marry that gal,' he says. He says,

'She likes me and her sister and brother-in-law is encouraging it along,' he says. 'They know I've got a little money and they're making a play for me. They're a couple of rats and I'm the cheese. They're going to make a meal off of me. They think they are,' he says. 'But the brother-in-law's a smart Aleck that thinks he's a wise cracker. He'd be a clown in a circus, only that's work. And his wife's fishing for a sucker with her sister for bait. Well, the gal's a pip and I'm going to marry her,' he says, 'but as soon as we're married, it's good-by, family-in-law! Me and them is going to be perfect strangers. They think they'll have free board and lodging at my house,' he says, 'but they won't get no meal unless they come to the back door for it, and when they feel sleepy they can make up a lower for themself on my cement porch.' That's the kind of a friend of yours this baby is," says Mercer.

I didn't say nothing and he went on.

"He's your friend as long as he can use you," he says. "He's been my friend since I signed to ride for him, that is, up till he found out I was stealing his gal. Then he shot my chances for a bull's-eye by telling her about a little trouble I had, five or six years ago. I and a girl went to a party down in Louisville and I seen another guy wink at her and I asked him what he meant by it and he said he had St. Vitus' dance. So I pulled the iron and knocked off a couple of his toes, to cure him. I was in eleven months and that's what Daley told Kate about. And of course he made her promise to not tell, but she wrote me a good-by note and spilled it. That's the kind of a pal he is.

"After I got out I worked for Bradley, and when Bradley turned me loose, he give me a $10,000 contract."

"He told us twenty," I said.

"Sure he did," says Mercer. "He always talks double.

When he gets up after a tough night, both his heads aches. And if he ever has a baby he'll invite you over to see the twins. But anyway, what he pays me ain't enough and after to-morrow I'm through riding. What's ten or fifteen thousand a year when you can't drink nothing and you starve to death for the fear you'll pick up an ounce! Listen," he says. "I got a brother down in Oklahoma that's in the oil lease game. He cleaned up $25,000 last year and he wants me to go in with him. And with what I've saved up and what I'm going to win to-morrow, I should worry if we don't make nothing in the next two years."

"How are you going to win to-morrow?" I said. "The price'll be a joke."

"The price on who?" says Mercer.

"Only One," I said.

He give a silly laugh and didn't say nothing for a minute. Then he asked if Daley done the betting for I and the two gals. I told him he had did it at first, but now I was doing it.

"Well," he says, "you do it to-morrow, see? That little lady called me a jailbird, but I don't want her to lose her money."

So I asked him what he meant and he asked me for the tenth or eleventh time if I could keep a secret. He made me hold up my hand and swear I wouldn't crack what he was going to tell me.

"Now," he says, "what's the name of the horse I'm riding to-morrow?"

"Only One," I said.

"That ain't all of it," said Mercer. "His name to-morrow is Only One Left. See? Only One Left."

"Do you mean he's going to get left at the post?" I says.

"You're a Ouija board!" says Mercer. "Your name is

Ouija and the horse's name is Only One Left. And listen," he says. "Everything but three horses is going to be scratched out of this race and we'll open at about 1 to 3 and back up to 1 to 5. And Daley's going to bet his right eye. But they's a horse in the race named Sap and that's the horse my two thousand smackers is going down on. And you're a sap, too, if you don't string along with me."

"Suppose you can't hold Only One?"

"Get the name right," said Mercer. "Only One Left. And don't worry about me not handling him. He thinks I'm Billy Sunday and everything I say he believes. Do you remember the other day when I beat Streak of Lightning? Well, the way I done that was whispering in One's ear, coming down the stretch. I says to him, 'One,' I says, 'this Lightning hoss has been spilling it round that your father's grandmother was a zebra. Make a bum out of him!' That's what I whispered to him and he got sore and went past Lightning like he was standing still. And to-morrow, just before we're supposed to go, I'll say to him, 'One, we're back at Jamaica. You're facing the wrong way.' And when Sap and the other dog starts, we'll be headed towards Rhode Island and in no hurry to get there."

"Mercer," I said, "I don't suppose they's any use talking to you, but after all, you're under contract to give Daley the best you've got and it don't look to me just like you was treating him square."

"Listen!" he says. "Him and square don't rhyme. And besides, I won't be under contract to nobody by this time to-morrow. So you save your sermon for your own parish."

I don't know if you'll think I done right or not. Or I don't care. But what was the sense of me tipping off a guy that had said them sweet things about I and Ella?

And even if I don't want a sister-in-law of mine running round with a guy that's got a jail record, still Daley squealing on him was rotten dope. And besides, I don't never like to break a promise, especially to a guy that shoots a man's toes off just for having St. Vitus' dance.

Well, anyway, the third race was over and the Merrick Handicap was next, and just like Mercer had said, they all quit but our horse and Sap and a ten-ton truck named Honor Bright. He was 20 to 1 and Sap was 6. Only One was 1 to 3 and Daley hopped on him with fifteen thousand men. Before post time the price was 1 to 5 and 1 to 6.

Daley was off his nut all afternoon and didn't object when I said I'd place the gals' money and save him the trouble. Kate and Ella had figured out what they had win up to date. It was about $1,200 and Daley told them to bet it all.

"You'll only make $400 between you," he says, "but it's a cinch."

"And four hundred's pretty good interest on $1,200," says Kate. "About ten per cent, ain't it?"

I left them and went downstairs. I wrote out a card for a hundred smackers on Sap. Then my feet caught cold and I didn't turn it in. I walked down towards the paddock and got there just as the boys was getting ready to parade. I seen Mercer and you wouldn't of never knew he'd fell off the wagon.

Daley was down there, too, and I heard him say: "Well, Sid, how about you?"

"Never better," says Mercer. "If I don't win this one I'll quit riding."

Then he seen me and smiled.

I chased back to the clubhouse, making up my mind on the way. I decided to not bet a nickel for the gals on anything. If Mercer was crossing me, I'd give Ella and

Kate their $400 like they had win it, and say nothing. Personally, I was going to turn in the card I'd wrote on Sap. That was my idear when I got to Joe Meyer. But all of a sudden I had the hunch that Mercer was going through; they wasn't a chance in the world for him to weaken. I left Meyer's stand and went to a bookie named Haynes, who I'd bet with before.

Sap had went up to 8 to 1, and instead of a hundred smackers I bet a thousand.

He finished ahead by three len'ths, probably the most surprised horse in history. Honor Bright got the place, but only by a hair. Only One, after being detained for some reason another, come faster at the end than any horse ever run before. And Mercer give him an unmerciful walloping, pretending to himself, probably, that the hoss was its master.

We come back to our table. The gals sunk down in their chairs. Ella was blubbering and Kate was as white as a ghost. Daley finally joined us, looking like he'd had a stroke. He asked for a drink and I give him my flask.

"I can't understand it!" he says. "I don't know what happened!"

"You don't!" hollered Kate. "I'll tell you what happened. You stole our money! Twelve hundred dollars! You cheat!"

"Oh, shut your fool mouth!" says Daley.

And another Romance was knocked for a row of sour apple trees.

Kate brought the mail in the dining room Monday morning. They was a letter for her and one for me. She read hers and they was a couple of tears in her eyes.

"Mercer's quit riding," she says. "This is a farewell note. He's going to Oklahoma."

Ella picked up my envelope.

"Who's this from?" she says.

"Give it here," I said, and took it away from her. "It's just the statement from Haynes, the bookie."

"Well, open it up," she said.

"What for?" said I. "You know how much you lose, don't you?"

"He might of made a mistake, mightn't he?" she says.

So I opened up the envelope and there was the check for $8,000.

"Gosh!" I said. "It looks like it was me that made the mistake!" And I laid the check down where her and Kate could see it. They screamed and I caught Ella just as she was falling off the chair.

"What does this mean?" says Kate.

"Well," I said, "I guess I was kind of rattled Saturday, and when I come to make my bet I got balled up and wrote down Sap. And I must of went crazy and played him for a thousand men."

"But where's our statement, mine and Sis'?" says Ella.

"That's my mistake again," I said. "I wrote out your ticket, but I must of forgot to turn it in."

They jumped up and come at me, and before I could duck I was kissed from both sides at once.

"O Sis!" yelps the Mrs. "Just think! We didn't lose our twelve hundred! We didn't lose nothing at all. We win eight thousand dollars!"

"Try and get it!" I says.

v. Katie Wins a Home

OH YES, we been back here quite a wile. And we're liable to be here quite a wile. This town's good enough for me and it suits the Mrs. too, though they didn't neither one of us appreciate it till we'd give New York a try. If I was running the South Bend Boosters' club, I'd make everybody spend a year on the Gay White Way. They'd be so tickled when they got to South Bend that you'd never hear them razz the old burg again. Just yesterday we had a letter from Katie, asking us would we come and pay her a visit. She's a regular New Yorker now. Well, I didn't have to put up no fight with my Mrs. Before I could open my pan she says, "I'll write and tell her we can't come; that you're looking for a job and don't want to go nowheres just now."

Well, they's some truth in that. I don't want to go nowheres and I'll take a job if it's the right kind. We could get along on the interest from Ella's money, but I'm tired of laying round. I didn't do a tap of work all the time I was east and I'm out of the habit, but the days certainly do drag when a man ain't got nothing to do and if I can find something where I don't have to travel, I'll try it out.

But the Mrs. has still got most of what the old man left her and all and all, I'm glad we made the trip. I more than broke even by winning pretty close to $10,-000 on the ponies down there. And we got Katie off our hands, which was one of the objects of us going in the first place—that and because the two gals wanted to see Life. So I don't grudge the time we spent, and we had some funny experiences when you look back at them. Anybody does that goes on a tour like that with a cuckoo like Katie. You hear a lot of songs and gags about mother-in-laws. But I could write a book of them about sister-in-laws that's twenty years old and pretty and full of peace and good will towards Men.

Well, after the blow-off with Daley, Long Island got too slow, besides costing us more than we could afford. So the gals suggested moving back in Town, to a hotel called the Graham on Sixty-seventh Street that somebody had told them was reasonable.

They called it a family hotel, but as far as I could see, Ella and I was the only ones there that had ever forced two dollars on the clergy. Outside of the transients, they was two song writers and a couple of gals that had their hair pruned and wrote for the papers, and the rest of the lodgers was boys that had got penned into a sixteen-foot ring with Benny Leonard by mistake. They looked like they'd spent many an evening hanging onto the ropes during the rush hour.

When we'd staid there two days, Ella and Katie was ready to pack up again.

"This is just a joint," said Ella. "The gals may be all right, but they're never in, only to sleep. And the men's impossible; a bunch of low prize-fighters."

I was for sticking, on account of the place being cheap, so I said:

"Second prize ain't so low. And you're overlooking the two handsome tune thiefs. Besides, what's the difference who else lives here as long as the rooms is clean and they got a good restaurant? What did our dude cellmates out on Long Island get us? Just trouble!"

But I'd of lose the argument as usual only for Kate oversleeping herself. It was our third morning at the Graham and her and Ella had it planned to go and look for a better place. But Katie didn't get up till pretty near noon and Ella went without her. So it broke so's Sis had just came downstairs and turned in her key when the two bellhops reeled in the front door bulging with baggage and escorting Mr. Jimmy Ralston. Yes, Jimmy Ralston the comedian. Or comic, as he calls it.

Well, he ain't F. X. Bushman, as you know. But no one that seen him could make the mistake of thinking he wasn't somebody. And he looked good enough to Kate so as she waited till the clerk had him fixed up, and then ast who he was. The clerk told her and she told us when the Mrs. come back from her hunt. Ella begin to name a few joints where we might move, but it seemed like Sis had changed her mind.

"Oh," she says, "let's stay here a wile longer, a week anyway."

"What's came over you!" ast Ella. "You just said last night that you was bored to death here."

"Maybe we won't be so bored now," said Kate, smiling. "The Graham's looking up. We're entertaining a celebrity—Jimmy Ralston of the Follies."

Well, they hadn't none of us ever seen him on the stage, but of course we'd heard of him. He'd only just started with the Follies, but he'd made a name for himself at the Winter Garden, where he broke in two or three years ago. And Kate said that a chorus gal she'd met—Jane Abbott—had told her about Ralston and what a scream he was on a party.

"He's terribly funny when he gets just the right number of drinks," says Kate.

"Well, let's stay then," says Ella. "It'll be exciting to know a real actor."

"I would like to know him," says Katie, "not just because he's on the stage, but I think it'd be fun to set and listen to him talk. He must say the screamingest things! If we had him round we wouldn't have to play cards or nothing for entertainment. Only they say it makes people fat to laugh."

"If I was you, I'd want to get fat," I said. "Looking like an E string hasn't started no landslide your way."

"Is he attractive?" ast the Mrs.

"Well," said Kate, "he isn't handsome, but he's striking looking. You wouldn't never think he was a comedian. But then, ain't it generally always true that the driest people have sad faces?"

"That's a joke!" I said. "Did you ever see Bryan when he didn't look like somebody was tickling his feet?"

"We'll have to think up some scheme to get introduced to him," says Ella.

"It'll be tough," I says. "I don't suppose they's anybody in the world harder to meet than a member of the Follies, unless it's an Elk in a Pullman washroom."

"But listen," says Kate: "We don't want to meet him till we've saw the show. It'd be awfully embarrassing to have him ask us how we liked the Follies and we'd have to say we hadn't been to it."

"Yes," said the Mrs., "but still if we tell him we haven't been to it, he may give us free passes."

"Easy!" I said. "And it'd take a big load off his mind. They say it worries the Follies people half sick wondering what to do with all their free passes."

"Suppose we go to-night!" says Kate. "We can drop in a hotel somewheres and get seats. The longer we don't go, the longer we won't meet him."

"And the longer we don't meet him," I says, "the longer till he gives you the air."

"I'm not thinking of Mr. Ralston as a possible suitor," says Katie, swelling up. "But I do want to get acquainted with a man that don't bore a person to death."

"Well," I says, "if this baby's anything like the rest of your gentleman friends, he won't hardly be round long enough for that."

I didn't make no kick about going to the show. We

hadn't spent no money since we'd moved back to Town and I was as tired as the gals of setting up in the room, playing rummy. They said we'd have to dress, and I kicked just from habit, but I'd got past minding that end of it. They was one advantage in dolling up every time you went anywheres. It meant an hour when they was no chance to do something even sillier.

We couldn't stop to put on the nose bag at the Graham because the women was scared we'd be too late to get tickets. Besides, when you're dressed for dinner, you at least want the waiter to be the same. So we took a taxi down to the Spencer, bought Follies seats in the ninth row, and went in to eat. It's been in all the papers that the price of food has came down, but the hotel man can't read. They fined us eleven smackers for a two-course banquet that if the Woman's Guild, here, would dast soak you four bits a plate for it, somebody'd write a nasty letter to the *News-Times*.

We got in the theater a half hour before the show begin. I put in the time finding out what the men will wear, and the gals looked up what scenes Ralston'd be in. He was only on once in each act. They don't waste much time on a comedian in the Follies. It don't take long to spring the two gags they can think up for him in a year, and besides, he just interferes with the big gal numbers, where Bunny Granville or somebody dreams of the different flappers he danced with at the prom, and the souvenirs they give him; and one by one the different gals writhes in, dressed like the stage director thinks they dress at the female colleges—a Wesley gal in pink tights, a Vassar dame in hula-hula, and a Smith gal with a sombrero and a sailor suit. He does a couple of steps with them and they each hand him a flower or a vegetable to remember them by. The song winds up:

> *But my most exclusive token*
> *Is a little hangnail broken*
> *Off the gal from Gussie's School for Manicures.*

And his real sweet patootie comes on made up as a scissors.

You've saw Ralston? He's a good comedian; no getting away from that. The way he fixes up his face, you laugh just to look at him. I yelled when I first seen him. He was supposed to be an office boy and he got back late from lunch and the boss ast him what made him late and he said he stopped to buy the extra. So the boss ast him what extra and he says the extra about the New York society couple getting married. So the boss said, "Why, they wouldn't print an extra about that. They's a New York society couple married most every day." So Ralston said, "Yes, but this couple is both doing it for the first time."

I don't remember what other gags he had, and they're old anyway by now. But he was a hit, especially with Ella and Kate. They screamed so loud I thought we'd get the air. If he didn't say a word, he'd be funny with that fool make-up and that voice.

I guess if it wasn't for me the gals would of insisted on going back to the stage door after the show and waiting for him to come out. I've saw Katie bad a lot of times, but never as cuckoo as this. It wasn't no case of love at first or second sight. You couldn't be stuck on this guy from seeing him. But she'd always been kind of stage-struck and was crazy over the idear of getting acquainted with a celebrity, maybe going round to places with him, and having people see her with Jimmy Ralston, the comedian. And then, of course, most anybody wants to meet a person that can make you laugh.

I managed to persuade them that the best dope would be to go back to the Graham and wait for him to come home; maybe we could fix it up with the night clerk to introduce us. I told them that irregardless of what you read in books, they's some members of the theatrical profession that occasionally visits the place where they sleep. So we went to the hotel and set in the lobby for an hour and a half, me trying to keep awake wile the gals played Ralston's part of the show over again a couple thousand times. They's nothing goes so big with me as listening to people repeat gags out of a show that I just seen.

The clerk had been tipped off and when Ralston finally come in and went to get his key, I strolled up to the desk like I was after mine. The clerk introduced us.

"I want you to meet my wife and sister-in-law," I said.

"Some other time," says Ralston. "They's a matinee to-morrow and I got to run off to bed."

So off he went and I got bawled out for Ziegfeld having matinees. But I squared myself two days afterwards when we went in the restaurant for lunch. He was just having breakfast and the three of us stopped by his table. I don't think he remembered ever seeing me before, but anyway he got up and shook hands with the women. Well, you couldn't never accuse Ella of having a faint heart, and she says:

"Can't we set down with you, Mr. Ralston? We want to tell you how much we enjoyed the Follies."

So he says, sure, set down, but I guess we would of anyway.

"We thought it was a dandy show," says Katie.

"It ain't a bad troupe," says Ralston.

"If you'll pardon me getting personal," said Ella, "we thought you was the best thing in it."

He looked like he'd strain a point and forgive her.

"We all just yelled!" says Katie. "I was afraid they'd put us out, you made us laugh so hard."

"Well," says Ralston, "I guess if they begin putting people out for that, I'd have to leave the troupe."

"It wouldn't be much of a show without you," says Ella.

"Well, all that keeps me in it is friendship for Ziggy," says Ralston. "I said to him last night, I says, 'Ziggy, I'm going to quit the troupe. I'm tired and I want to rest a wile.' So he says, 'Jim, don't quit or I'll have to close the troupe. I'll give you fifteen hundred a week to stay.' I'm getting a thousand now. But I says to him, I said, 'Ziggy, it ain't a question of money. What I want is a troupe of my own, where I get a chance to do serious work. I'm sick of making a monkey of myself in front of a bunch of saps from Nyack that don't appreciate no art but what's wrapped up in a stocking.' So he's promised that if I'll stick it out this year, he'll star me next season in a serious piece."

"Is he giving you the five hundred raise?" I ast him.

"I wouldn't take it," said Ralston. "I don't need money."

"At that, a person can live pretty cheap at this hotel," I says.

"I didn't move here because it was cheap," he said. "I moved here to get away from the pests—women that wants my autograph or my picture. And all they could say was how much they enjoyed my work and how did I think up all them gags, and so forth. No real artist likes to talk about himself, especially to people that don't understand. So that's the reason why I left the Ritz, so's I'd be left alone, not to save money. And I don't save no money, neither. I've got the best suite in the house—bedroom, bath, and study."

"What do you study?" ast Kate.

"The parts I want to play," he says; "Hamlet and Macbeth and Richard."

"But you're a comedian," says Kate.

"It's just a stepping stone," said Ralston.

He'd finished his breakfast and got up.

"I must go to my study and work," he says. "We'll meet again."

"Yes, indeed," says Ella. "Do you always come right back here nights after the show?"

"When I can get away from the pests," he says.

"Well," says Ella, "suppose you come up to our rooms to-night and we'll have a bite to eat. And I think the husband can give you a little liquid refreshments if you ever indulge."

"Very little," he says. "What is your room number?"

So the Mrs. told him and he said he'd see us after the show that night, and walked out.

"Well," said Ella, "how do you like him?"

"I think he's wonderful!" says Katie. "I didn't have no idear he was so deep, wanting to play Hamlet."

"Pretty near all comedians has got that bug," I says.

"Maybe he's different when you know him better," said Ella.

"I don't want him to be different," says Kate.

"But he was so serious," said the Mrs. "He didn't say nothing funny."

"Sure he did," I says. "Didn't he say artists hate to talk about themselfs?"

Pretty soon the waiter come in with our lunch. He ast us if the other gentleman was coming back.

"No," said Ella. "He's through."

"He forgot his check," says the dish smasher.

"Oh, never mind!" says Ella. "We'll take care of that."

"Well," I says, "I guess the bird was telling the truth when he said he didn't need no money."

I and the gals spent the evening at a picture show and stopped at a delicatessen on the way home to stock up for the banquet. I had a quart and a pint of yearling rye, and a couple of bottles of McAllister that they'd fined me fifteen smackers apiece for and I wanted to save them, so I told Kate that I hoped her friend would get comical enough on the rye.

"He said he drunk very little," she reminded me.

"Remember, don't make him talk about himself," said the Mrs. "What we want is to have him feel at home, like he was with old friends, and then maybe he'll warm up. I hope we don't wake the whole hotel, laughing."

Well, Ralston showed up about midnight. He'd remembered his date and apologized for not getting there before.

"I like to walk home from the theater," he says. "I get some of my funniest idears wile I walk."

I come to the conclusion later that he spent practically his whole life riding.

Ella's and my room wasn't no gymnasium for size and after the third drink, Ralston tried to get to the dresser to look at himself in the glass, and knocked a $30 vase for a corpse. This didn't go very big with the Mrs., but she forced a smile and would of accepted his apology if he'd made any. All he done was mumble something about cramped quarters. They was even more cramped when we set the table for the big feed, and it was my tough luck to have our guest park himself in the chair nearest the clothes closet, where my two bottles of Scotch had been put to bed. The fourth snifter finished the pint of rye and I said I'd get the other quart, but before I could stop her, Ella says:

"Let Mr. Ralston get it. It's right there by him."

So the next thing you know, James has found the good stuff and he comes out with both bottles of it.

"McAllister!" he says. "That's my favorite. If I'd knew you had that, I wouldn't of drank up all your rye."

"You haven't drank it all up," I says. "They's another bottle of it in there."

"It can stay there as long as we got this," he says, and helped himself to the corkscrew.

Well, amongst the knickknacks the gals had picked up at the delicatessen was a roast chicken and a bottle of olives, and at the time I thought Ralston was swallowing bones, stones, and all. It wasn't till the next day that we found all these keepsakes on the floor, along with a couple dozen assorted cigarette butts.

Katie's chorus gal friend had told her how funny the guy was when he'd had just the right number of shots, but I'd counted eight and begin to get discouraged before he started talking.

"My mother could certainly cook a chicken," he says.

"Is your mother living?" Kate ast him.

"No," he says. "She was killed in a railroad wreck. I'll never forget when I had to go and identify her. You wouldn't believe a person could get that mangled! No," he says, "my family's all gone. I never seen my father. He was in the pesthouse with smallpox when I was born and he died there. And my only sister died of jaundice. I can still——"

But Kate was scared we'd wake up the hotel, laughing, so she says: "Do you ever give imitations?"

"You mustn't make Mr. Ralston talk about himself," says Ella.

"Imitations of who?" said Ralston.

"Oh, other actors," said Katie.

"No," he says. "I leave it to the other actors to give imitations of me."

"I never seen none of them do it," says Kate.

"They all do it, but they don't advertise it," he says. "Every comic in New York is using my stuff."

"Oh!" said Ella. "You mean they steal your idears."

"Can't you go after them for it?" ast Katie.

"You could charge them with petit larceny," I said.

"I wouldn't be mean," said Ralston. "But they ain't a comic on the stage to-day that I didn't give him every laugh he's got."

"You ain't only been on the stage three or four years," I says. "How did Hitchcock and Ed Wynn and them fellas get by before they seen you?"

"They wasn't getting by," he says. "I'm the baby that put them on their feet. Take Hitchy. Hitchy come to me last spring and says, 'Jim, I've ran out of stuff. Have you got any notions I could use?' So I says, 'Hitchy, you're welcome to anything I got.' So I give him a couple of idears and they're the only laughs in his troupe. And you take Wynn. He opened up with a troupe that looked like a flop and one day I seen him on Broadway, wearing a long pan, and I says, 'What's the matter, Eddie?' And he brightened up and says, 'Hello, there, Jim! You're just the boy I want to see.' So I says, 'Well, Eddie, I'm only too glad to do anything I can.' So he says, 'I got a flop on my hands unlest I can get a couple of idears, and you're the baby that can give them to me.' So I said, 'All right, Eddie.' And I give him a couple of notions to work on and they made his show. And look at Stone! And Errol! And Jolson and Tinney! Every one of them come to me at one time another, hollering for help. 'Jim, give me a couple of notions!' 'Jim, give me a couple of gags!' And not a one of them went away empty-handed."

"Did they pay you?" ast Ella.

Ralston smiled.

"I wouldn't take no actor's money," he says. "They're all brothers to me. They can have anything I got, and I can have anything they got, only they haven't got nothing."

Well, I can't tell you all he said, as I was asleep part of the time. But I do remember that he was the one that had give Bert Williams the notion of playing coon parts, and learnt Sarah Bernhardt to talk French.

Along about four o'clock, when they was less than a pint left in the second McAllister bottle, he defied all the theater managers in New York.

"I ain't going to monkey with them much longer!" he says. "I'll let you folks in on something that'll cause a sensation on Broadway. I'm going to quit the Follies!"

We was all speechless.

"That's the big secret!" he says. "I'm coming out as a star under my own management and in a troupe wrote and produced by myself!"

"When?" ast Kate.

"Just as soon as I decide who I'm going to let in as part owner," said Ralston. "I've worked for other guys long enough! Why should I be satisfied with $800 a week when Ziegfeld's getting rich off me!"

"When did he cut you $200?" I says. "You was getting $1,000 last time I seen you."

He didn't pay no attention.

"And why should I let some manager produce my play," he says, "and pay me maybe $1,200 a week when I ought to be making six or seven thousand!"

"Are you working on your play now?" Kate ast him.

"It's done," he says. "I'm just trying to make up my mind who's the right party to let in on it. Whoever it is, I'll make him rich."

"I've got some money to invest," says Katie. "Suppose you tell us about the play."

"I'll give you the notion, if you'll keep it to yourself," says Ralston. "It's a serious play with a novelty idear that'll be a sensation. Suppose I go down to my suite and get the script and read it to you."

"Oh, if you would!" says Kate.

"It'll knock you dead!" he says.

And just the thought of it was fatal to the author. He got up from his chair, done a nose dive acrost the table and laid there with his head in the chili sauce.

I called up the clerk and had him send up the night bellhop with our guest's key. I and the boy acted as pall bearers and got him to his "suite," where we performed the last sad rites. Before I come away I noticed that the "suite" was a ringer for Ella's and mine—a dinky little room with a bath. The "study" was prettily furnished with coat hangers.

When I got back to my room Katie'd ducked and the Mrs. was asleep, so I didn't get a chance to talk to them till we was in the restaurant at noon. Then I ast Kate if she'd figured out just what number drink it was that had started him being comical.

"Now listen," she says: "I don't think that Abbott girl ever met him in her life. Anyway, she had him all wrong. We expected he'd do stunts, like she said, but he ain't that kind that shows off or acts smart. He's too much of a man for that. He's a bigger man than I thought."

"I and the bellhop remarked that same thing," I says.

"And you needn't make fun of him for getting faint," says Katie. "I called him up a wile ago to find out how he was and he apologized and said they must of been something in that second bottle of Scotch."

So I says:

"You tell him they was, but they ain't."

Well, it couldn't of been the Scotch or no other brew that ruined me. Or if it was, it worked mighty slow. I didn't even look at a drink for three days after the party in our room. But the third day I felt rotten, and that night I come down with a fever. Ella got scared and called a doctor and he said it was flu, and if I didn't watch my step it'd be something worse. He advised taking me to a hospital and I didn't have pep enough to say no.

So they took me and I was pretty sick for a couple of weeks—too sick for the Mrs. to give me the news. And it's a wonder I didn't have a relapse when she finally did.

"You'll probably yelp when you hear this," she says. "I ain't crazy about it myself, but it didn't do me no good to argue at first and it's too late for argument now. Well, to begin with, Sis is in love with Ralston."

"What of it!" I said. "She's going through the city directory and she's just got to the R's."

"No, it's the real thing this time," said the Mrs. "Wait till you hear the rest of it. She's going on the stage!"

"I've got nothing against that," I says. "She's pretty enough to get by in the Follies chorus, and if she can earn money that way, I'm for it."

"She ain't going into no chorus," said Ella. "Ralston's quit the Follies and she's going in his show."

"The one he wrote?" I ast.

"Yes," said the Mrs.

"And who's going to put it on?" I ast her.

"That's it," she says. "They're going to put it on themself, Ralston and Sis. With Sis's money. She sold her bonds, fifty thousand dollars' worth."

"But listen," I says. "Fifty thousand dollars! What's the name of the play, Ringling's Circus?"

"It won't cost all that," said Ella. "They figure it'll

take less than ten thousand to get started. But she insisted on having the whole thing in a checking account, where she can get at it. If the show's a big success in New York they're going to have a company in Chicago and another on the road. And Ralston says her half of the profits in New York ought to run round $5,000 a week. But anyway, she's sure of $200 a week salary for acting in it."

"Where did she get the idear she can act?" I says.

"She's always had it," said the Mrs., "and I think she made him promise to put her in the show before she agreed to back it. Though she says it's a wonderful investment! She won't be the leading woman, of course. But they's only two woman's parts and she's got one of them."

"Well," I said, "if she's going to play a sap and just acts normal, she'll be a sensation."

"I don't know what she'll be," says Ella. "All I know is that she's mad over Ralston and believes everything he says. And even if you hadn't of been sick we couldn't of stopped her."

So I ast what the play was like, but Ella couldn't tell me.

Ralston had read it out loud to she and Kate, but she couldn't judge from just hearing it that way. But Kate was tickled to death with it. And they'd already been rehearsing a week, but Sis hadn't let Ella see the rehearsals. She said it made her nervous.

"Ralston thinks the main trouble will be finding a theater," said the Mrs. "He says they's a shortage of them and the men that owns them won't want to let him have one on account of jealousy."

"Has the Follies flopped?" I ast her.

"No," she says, "but they've left town."

"They always do, this time of year," I said.

"That's what I thought," says the Mrs., "but Ralston says they'd intended to stay here all the year round, but when the news come out that he'd left, they didn't dast. He's certainly got faith in himself. He must have, to give up a $600 a week salary. That's what he says he was really getting."

"You say Katie's in love," I says. "How about him?"

"I don't know and she don't know," says Ella. "He calls her dearie and everything and holds her hands, but when they're alone together, he won't talk nothing but business. Still, as I say, he calls her dearie."

"Actors calls every gal that," I says. "It's because they can't remember names."

Well, to make a short story out of it, they had another couple weeks' rehearsals that we wasn't allowed to see, and they finally got a theater—the Olney. They had to guarantee a $10,000 business to get it. They didn't go to Atlantic City or nowheres for a tryout. They opened cold. And Ralston didn't tell nobody what kind of a show it was.

Of course he done what they generally always do on a first night. He sent out free passes to everybody that's got a dress suit, and they's enough of them in New York to pretty near fill up a theater. These invited guests is supposed to be for the performance wile it's going on. After it's through, they can go out and ride it all over the island.

Well, the rules wasn't exactly lived up to at "Bridget Sees a Ghost." On account of Ralston writing the play and starring in it, the gang thought it would be comical and they come prepared to laugh. It was comical all right, and they laughed. They didn't only laugh; they yelled. But they yelled in the wrong place.

The programme said it was "a Daring Drama in Three Acts." The three acts was what made it daring.

It took nerve to even have one. In the first place, this was two years after the armistice and the play was about the war, and I don't know which the public was most interested in by this time—the war or Judge Parker.

Act 1 was in July, 1917. Ralston played the part of Francis Shaw, a captain in the American army. He's been married a year, and when the curtain goes up, his wife's in their New York home, waiting for him to come in from camp on his weekly leave. She sets reading the war news in the evening paper, and she reads it out loud, like people always do when they're alone, waiting for somebody. Pretty soon in comes Bridget, the Irish maid—our own dear Katie. And I wished you could of heard her brogue. And seen her gestures. What she reminded me most like was a gal in a home talent minstrels giving an imitation of Lew Fields playing the part of the block system on the New York Central. Her first line was, "Ain't der Captain home yed?" But I won't try and give you her dialect.

"No," says Mrs. Shaw. "He's late." So Katie says better late than never, and the wife says, yes, but she's got a feeling that some day it'll be never; something tells her that if he ever goes to France, he won't come back. So Bridget says, "You been reading the war news again and it always makes you sad." "I hate wars!" says Mrs. Shaw, and that line got one of the biggest laughs.

After this they was a couple of minutes when neither of them could think of nothing to add, and then the phone rung and Bridget answered it. It was Capt. Shaw, saying he'd be there pretty soon; so Bridget goes right back to the kitchen to finish getting dinner, but she ain't no sooner than left the stage when Capt.

Shaw struts in. He must of called up from the public booth on his front porch.

The audience had a tough time recognizing him without his comic make-up, but when they did they give him a good hand. Mrs. Shaw got up to greet him, but he brushed by her and come down to the footlights to bow. Then he turned and went back to his Mrs., saying "Maizie!" like this was the last place he expected to run acrost her. They kissed and then he ast her "Where is Bobbie, our dear little one?"—for fear she wouldn't know whose little one he meant. So she rung the bell and back come Bridget, and he says "Well, Bridget!" and Bridget says, "Well, it's the master!" This line was another riot. "Bring the little one, Bridget," says Mrs. Shaw, and the audience hollered again.

Wile Bridget was after the little one, the Captain celebrated the reunion by walking round the room, looking at the pictures. Bridget brings the baby in and the Captain uncovers its face and says, "Well, Bobbie!" Then he turns to his wife and says, "Let's see, Maizie. How old is he?" "Two weeks," says Maizie. "Two weeks!" says Captain Shaw, surprised. "Well," he says, "I hope by the time he's old enough to fight for the Stars and Stripes, they won't be no such a thing as war." So Mrs. Shaw says, "And I hope his father won't be called on to make the supreme sacrifice for him and we others that must stay home and wait. I sometimes think that in wartime, it's the women and children that suffers most. Take him back to his cozy cradle, Bridget. We mothers must be careful of our little ones. Who knows when the kiddies will be our only comfort!" So Bridget beat it out with the little one and I bet he hated to leave all the gaiety.

"Well," says Shaw to his wife, "and what's the little woman been doing?"

"Just reading," she says, "reading the news of this horrible war. I don't never pick up the paper but what I think that some day I'll see your name amongst the dead."

"Well," says the Captain bravely, "they's no danger wile I stay on U. S. soil. But only for you and the little one, I would welcome the call to go Over There and take my place in the battle line. The call will come soon, I believe, for they say France needs men." This rumor pretty near caused a riot in the audience and Ralston turned and give us all a dirty look.

Then Bridget come in again and said dinner was ready, and Shaw says, "It'll seem funny to set down wile I eat." Which was the first time I ever knew that army captains took their meals off the mantelpiece.

Wile the Shaws was out eating, their maid stayed in the living room, where she'd be out of their way. It seems that Ralston had wrote a swell speech for her to make in this spot, about what a tough thing war is, to come along and separate a happy young couple like the Shaws that hadn't only been married a year. But the speech started "This is terrible!" and when Bridget got that much of it out, some egg in the gallery hollered "You said a mouthful, kid!" and stopped the show.

The house finally quieted down, but Katie was dumb for the first time in her life. She couldn't say the line that was the cue for the phone to ring, and she had to go over and answer a silent call. It was for the Captain, and him and his wife both come back on the stage.

"Maizie," he says, after he'd hung up, "it's came! That was my general! We sail for France in half an hour!"

"O husband!" says Maizie. "This is the end!"

"Nonsense!" says Shaw with a brave smile. "This war means death for only a small per cent of our men."

"And almost no captains," yells the guy in the gallery.

Shaw gets ready to go, but she tells him to wait till she puts on her wraps; she'll go down to the dock and see him off.

"No, darling," he says. "Our orders is secret. I can't give you the name of our ship or where we're sailing from."

So he goes and she flops on the couch w'ining because he wouldn't tell her whether his ship left from Times Square or Grand Central.

They rung the curtain down here to make you think six days has passed. When it goes up again, Maizie's setting on the couch, holding the little one. Pretty soon Bridget comes in with the evening paper.

"They's a big headline, mum," she says. "A troopship has been torpedoed."

Well, when she handed her the paper, I could see the big headline. It said, "Phillies Hit Grimes Hard." But Maizie may of had a bet on Brooklyn. Anyway, she begin trembling and finally fell over stiff. So Bridget picked up the paper and read it out loud:

"Amongst the men lost was Capt. F. Shaw of New York."

Down went the curtain again and the first act was over, and some jokesmith in the audience yelled "Author! Author!"

"He's sunk!" said the egg in the gallery.

Well, Maizie was the only one in the whole theater that thought Shaw was dead. The rest of us just wished it. Still you couldn't blame her much for getting a wrong idear, as it was Nov. 11, 1918—over a year later—when the second act begins, and she hadn't heard from him in all that time. It wasn't never brought

out why. Maybe he'd forgot her name or maybe it
was Burleson's fault, like everything else.

The scene was the same old living room and Maizie
was setting on the same old couch, but she was all
dressed up like Elsie Ferguson. It comes out that she's
expecting a gentleman friend, a Mr. Thornton, to
dinner. She asks Bridget if she thinks it would be
wrong of her to accept the guy the next time he proposed. He's ast her every evening for the last six months
and she can't stall him much longer. So Bridget says
it's all right if she loves him, but Maizie don't know
if she loves him or not, but he looks so much like her
late relic that she can't hardly tell the difference and
besides, she has got to either marry or go to work, or
her and the little one will starve. They's a knock at the
door and Thornton comes in. Him and the absent
Captain looks as much alike as two brothers, yours
and mine. Bridget ducks and Thornton proposes. Maizie
says, "Before I answer, I must tell you a secret. Captain Shaw didn't leave me all alone. I have a little
one, a boy." "Oh, I love kiddies," says Thornton. "Can
I see him?" So she says it's seven o'clock and the little
one's supposed to of been put to bed, but she has
Bridget go get him.

The little one's entrance was the sensation of this
act. In Act 1 he was just three or four towels, but now
Bridget can't even carry him acrost the stage, and
when she put him on his feet, he comes up pretty
near to her shoulder. And when Thornton ast him
would he like to have a new papa, he says, "Yes, because my other papa's never coming back."

Well, they say a woman can't keep a secret, but
if Thornton had been nosing round for six months and
didn't know till now that they was a spanker like

Bobbie in the family circle, I wouldn't hardly call Maizie the town gossip.

After the baby'd went back to read himself to sleep and Mrs. Shaw had yessed her new admirer, Bridget dashed in yelling that the armistice was signed and held up the evening paper for Maizie and Thornton to see. The great news was announced in code. It said: "Phillies Hit Grimes Hard." And it seemed kind of silly to not come right out and say "Armistice Signed!" Because as I recall, even we saps out here in South Bend had knew it since three o'clock that morning.

The last act was in the same place, on Christmas Eve, 1918.

Maizie and her second husband had just finished doing up presents for the little one. We couldn't see the presents, but I suppose they was giving him a cocktail shaker and a shaving set. Though when he come on the stage you could see he hadn't aged much since Act 2. He hadn't even begin to get bald.

Thornton and the Mrs. went off somewheres and left the kid alone, but all of a sudden the front door opened and in come old Cap Shaw, on crutches. He seen the kid and called to him. "Who are you?" says the little one. "I'm Santa Claus," says the Cap, "and I've broughten you a papa for Christmas." "I don't want no papa," says Bobbie. "I've just got a new one." Then Bridget popped in and seen "the master" and hollered, "A ghost!" So he got her calmed down and she tells him what's came off. "It was in the paper that Capt. F. Shaw of New York was lost," she says. "It must of been another Capt. F. Shaw!" he says.

"It's an odd name," hollered the guy in the gallery.

The Captain thinks it all over and decides it's his move. He makes Bridget promise to never tell that she seen him and he says good-by to she and the kid and goes out into the night.

Maizie comes in, saying she heard a noise and what was it? Was somebody here? "Just the boy with the evening paper," says Bridget. And the cat's got Bobbie's tongue. And Maizie don't even ask for the paper. She probably figured to herself it was the old story; that Grimes was still getting his bumps.

Well, I wished you could of read what the papers wrote up about the show. One of them said that Bridget seen a ghost at the Olney theater last night and if anybody else wanted to see it, they better go quick because it wouldn't be walking after this week. Not even on crutches. The mildest thing they said about Ralston was that he was even funnier than when he was in the Follies and tried to be. And they said the part of Bridget was played by a young actress that they hoped would make a name for herself, because Ralston had probably called her all he could think of.

We waited at the stage door that night and when Kate come out, she was crying. Ralston had canned her from the show.

"That's nothing to cry about," I says. "You're lucky! It's just like as if a conductor had put you off a train a couple of minutes before a big smash-up."

The programme had been to all go somewheres for supper and celebrate the play's success. But all Katie wanted now was to get in a taxi and go home and hide.

On the way, I ast her how much she was in so far.

"Just ten thousand," she says.

"Ten thousand!" I said. "Why, they was only one piece of scenery and that looked like they'd bought it secondhand from the choir boys' minstrels. They couldn't of spent one thousand, let alone ten."

"We had to pay the theater a week's rent in advance,"

she says. "And Jimmy give five thousand to a man for the idear."

"The idear for what?" I ast.

"The idear for the play," she said.

"That stops me!" I says. "This baby furnishes idears for all the good actors in the world, but when he wants one for himself, he goes out and pays $5,000 for it. And if he got a bargain, you're Mrs. Fiske."

"Who sold him the idear?" ast Ella.

"He wouldn't tell me," says Kate.

"Ponzi," I said.

Ralston called Kate up the next noon and made a date with her at the theater. He said that he was sorry he'd been rough. Before she went I ast her to give me a check for the forty thousand she had left so's I could buy back some of her bonds.

"I haven't got only $25,000," she says. "I advanced Jimmy fifteen thousand for his own account, so's he wouldn't have to bother me every time they was bills to meet."

So I said: "Listen: I'll go see him with you and if he don't come clean with that money, I'll knock him deader'n his play."

"Thank you!" she says. "I'll tend to my own affairs alone."

She come back late in the afternoon, all smiles.

"Everything's all right," she said. "I give him his choice of letting me be in the play or giving me my money."

"And which did he choose?" I ast her.

"Neither one," she says. "We're going to get married."

"Bridget" went into the ashcan Saturday night and the wedding come off Monday. Monday night they left for Boston, where the Follies was playing. Kate told us they'd took Ralston back at the same salary he was getting before.

"How much is that?" I ast her.

"Four hundred a week," she says.

Well, two or three days after they'd left, I got up my nerve and says to the Mrs.:

"Do you remember what we moved to the Big Town for? We done it to see Life and get Katie a husband. Well, we got her a kind of a husband and I'll tell the world we seen Life. How about moseying back to South Bend?"

"But we haven't no home there now."

"Nor we ain't had none since we left there," I says. "I'm going down and see what's the first day we can get a couple of lowers."

"Get uppers if it's quicker," says the Mrs.

So here we are, really enjoying ourselfs for the first time in pretty near two years. And Katie's in New York, enjoying herself, too, I suppose. She ought to be, married to a comedian. It must be such fun to just set and listen to him talk.

THE
SHORT STORIES

ALIBI IKE

HIS RIGHT name was Frank X. Farrell, and I guess the X stood for "Excuse me." Because he never pulled a play, good or bad, on or off the field, without apologizin' for it.

"Alibi Ike" was the name Carey wished on him the first day he reported down South. O' course we all cut out the "Alibi" part of it right away for the fear he would overhear it and bust somebody. But we called him "Ike" right to his face and the rest of it was understood by everybody on the club except Ike himself.

He ast me one time, he says:

"What do you all call me Ike for? I ain't no Yid."

"Carey give you the name," I says. "It's his nickname for everybody he takes a likin' to."

"He mustn't have only a few friends then," says Ike. "I never heard him say 'Ike' to nobody else."

But I was goin' to tell you about Carey namin' him. We'd been workin' out two weeks and the pitchers was showin' somethin' when this bird joined us. His first day out he stood up there so good and took such a reef at the old pill that he had everyone lookin'. Then him and Carey was together in left field, catchin' fungoes, and it was after we was through for the day that Carey told me about him.

"What do you think of Alibi Ike?" ast Carey.

"Who's that?" I says.

"This here Farrell in the outfield," says Carey.

"He looks like he could hit," I says.

"Yes," says Carey, "but he can't hit near as good as he can apologize."

Then Carey went on to tell me what Ike had been pullin' out there. He'd dropped the first fly ball that was hit to him and told Carey his glove wasn't broke in good yet, and Carey says the glove could easy of been Kid Gleason's gran'father. He made a whale of a catch out o' the next one and Carey says "Nice work!" or somethin' like that, but Ike says he could of caught the ball with his back turned only he slipped when he started after it and, besides that, the air currents fooled him.

"I thought you done well to get to the ball," says Carey.

"I ought to been settin' under it," says Ike.

"What did you hit last year?" Carey ast him.

"I had malaria most o' the season," says Ike. "I wound up with .356."

"Where would I have to go to get malaria?" says Carey, but Ike didn't wise up.

I and Carey and him set at the same table together for supper. It took him half an hour longer'n us to eat because he had to excuse himself every time he lifted his fork.

"Doctor told me I needed starch," he'd say, and then toss a shoveful o' potatoes into him. Or, "They ain't much meat on one o' these chops," he'd tell us, and grab another one. Or he'd say: "Nothin' like onions for a cold," and then he'd dip into the perfumery.

"Better try that apple sauce," says Carey. "It'll help your malaria."

"Whose malaria?" says Ike. He'd forgot already why he didn't only hit .356 last year.

I and Carey begin to lead him on.

"Whereabouts did you say your home was?" I ast him.

"I live with my folks," he says. "We live in Kansas City—not right down in the business part—outside a ways."

"How's that come?" says Carey. "I should think you'd get rooms in the post office."

But Ike was too busy curin' his cold to get that one.

"Are you married?" I ast him.

"No," he says. "I never run round much with girls, except to shows onct in a wile and parties and dances and roller skatin'."

"Never take 'em to the prize fights, eh?" says Carey.

"We don't have no real good bouts," says Ike. "Just bush stuff. And I never figured a boxin' match was a place for the ladies."

Well, after supper he pulled a cigar out and lit it. I was just goin' to ask him what he done it for, but he beat me to it.

"Kind o' rests a man to smoke after a good workout," he says. "Kind o' settles a man's supper, too."

"Looks like a pretty good cigar," says Carey.

"Yes," says Ike. "A friend o' mine give it to me—a fella in Kansas City that runs a billiard room."

"Do you play billiards?" I ast him.

"I used to play a fair game," he says. "I'm all out o' practice now—can't hardly make a shot."

We coaxed him into a four-handed battle, him and Carey against Jack Mack and I. Say, he couldn't play billiards as good as Willie Hoppe; not quite. But to hear him tell it, he didn't make a good shot all evenin'. I'd leave him an awful-lookin' layout and he'd gather 'em up in one try and then run a couple o' hundred, and be-

tween every carom he'd say he'd put too much stuff on
the ball, or the English didn't take, or the table wasn't
true, or his stick was crooked, or somethin'. And all the
time he had the balls actin' like they was Dutch soldiers
and him Kaiser William. We started out to play fifty
points, but we had to make it a thousand so as I and
Jack and Carey could try the table.

The four of us set round the lobby a wile after we was
through playin', and when it got along toward bedtime
Carey whispered to me and says:

"Ike'd like to go to bed, but he can't think up no
excuse."

Carey hadn't hardly finished whisperin' when Ike got
up and pulled it:

"Well, good night, boys," he says. "I ain't sleepy, but
I got some gravel in my shoes and it's killin' my feet."

We knowed he hadn't never left the hotel since we'd
came in from the grounds and changed our clo'es. So
Carey says:

"I should think they'd take them gravel pits out o' the
billiard room."

But Ike was already on his way to the elevator,
limpin'.

"He's got the world beat," says Carey to Jack and I.
"I've knew lots o' guys that had an alibi for every mistake they made; I've heard pitchers say that the ball
slipped when somebody cracked one off'n 'em; I've
heard infielders complain of a sore arm after heavin' one
into the stand, and I've saw outfielders tooken sick with
a dizzy spell when they've misjudged a fly ball. But this
baby can't even go to bed without apologizin', and I bet
he excuses himself to the razor when he gets ready to
shave."

"And at that," says Jack, "he's goin' to make us a good
man."

"Yes," says Carey, "unless rheumatism keeps his battin' average down to .400."

Well, sir, Ike kept whalin' away at the ball all through the trip till everybody knowed he'd won a job. Cap had him in there regular the last few exhibition games and told the newspaper boys a week before the season opened that he was goin' to start him in Kane's place.

"You're there, kid," says Carey to Ike, the night Cap made the 'nnouncement. "They ain't many boys that wins a big league berth their third year out."

"I'd of been up here a year ago," says Ike, "only I was bent over all season with lumbago."

II

It rained down in Cincinnati one day and somebody organized a little game o' cards. They was shy two men to make six and ast I and Carey to play.

"I'm with you if you get Ike and make it seven-handed," says Carey.

So they got a hold of Ike and we went up to Smitty's room.

"I pretty near forgot how many you deal," says Ike. "It's been a long wile since I played."

I and Carey give each other the wink, and sure enough, he was just as ig'orant about poker as billiards. About the second hand, the pot was opened two or three ahead of him, and they was three in when it come his turn. It cost a buck, and he throwed in two.

"It's raised, boys," somebody says.

"Gosh, that's right, I did raise it," says Ike.

"Take out a buck if you didn't mean to tilt her," says Carey.

"No," says Ike, "I'll leave it go."

Well, it was raised back at him and then he made another mistake and raised again. They was only three left in when the draw come. Smitty'd opened with a pair o' kings and he didn't help 'em. Ike stood pat. The guy that'd raised him back was flushin' and he didn't fill. So Smitty checked and Ike bet and didn't get no call. He tossed his hand away, but I grabbed it and give it a look. He had king, queen, jack and two tens. Alibi Ike he must have seen me peekin', for he leaned over and whispered to me.

"I overlooked my hand," he says. "I thought all the wile it was a straight."

"Yes," I says, "that's why you raised twice by mistake."

They was another pot that he come into with tens and fours. It was tilted a couple o' times and two o' the strong fellas drawed ahead of Ike. They each drawed one. So Ike throwed away his little pair and come out with four tens. And they was four treys against him. Carey'd looked at Ike's discards and then he says:

"This lucky bum busted two pair."

"No, no, I didn't," says Ike.

"Yes, yes, you did," says Carey, and showed us the two fours.

"What do you know about that?" says Ike. "I'd of swore one was a five spot."

Well, we hadn't had no pay day yet, and after a wile everybody except Ike was goin' shy. I could see him gettin' restless and I was wonderin' how he'd make the get-away. He tried two or three times. "I got to buy some collars before supper," he says.

"No hurry," says Smitty. "The stores here keeps open all night in April."

After a minute he opened up again.

"My uncle out in Nebraska ain't expected to live," he says. "I ought to send a telegram."

"Would that save him?" says Carey.

"No, it sure wouldn't," says Ike, "but I ought to leave my old man know where I'm at."

"When did you hear about your uncle?" says Carey.

"Just this mornin'," says Ike.

"Who told you?" ast Carey.

"I got a wire from my old man," says Ike.

"Well," says Carey, "your old man knows you're still here yet this afternoon if you was here this mornin'. Trains leavin' Cincinnati in the middle o' the day don't carry no ball clubs."

"Yes," says Ike, "that's true. But he don't know where I'm goin' to be next week."

"Ain't he got no schedule?" ast Carey.

"I sent him one openin' day," says Ike, "but it takes mail a long time to get to Idaho."

"I thought your old man lived in Kansas City," says Carey.

"He does when he's home," says Ike.

"But now," says Carey, "I s'pose he's went to Idaho so as he can be near your sick uncle in Nebraska."

"He's visitin' my other uncle in Idaho."

"Then how does he keep posted about your sick uncle?" ast Carey.

"He don't," says Ike. "He don't even know my other uncle's sick. That's why I ought to wire and tell him."

"Good night!" says Carey.

"What town in Idaho is your old man at?" I says.

Ike thought it over.

"No town at all," he says. "But he's near a town."

"Near what town?" I says.

"Yuma," says Ike.

Well, by this time he'd lost two or three pots and he was desperate. We was playin' just as fast as we could, because we seen we couldn't hold him much longer. But he was tryin' so hard to frame an escape that he couldn't pay no attention to the cards, and it looked like we'd get his whole pile away from him if we could make him stick.

The telephone saved him. The minute it begun to ring, five of us jumped for it. But Ike was there first.

"Yes," he says, answerin' it. "This is him. I'll come right down."

And he slammed up the receiver and beat it out o' the door without even sayin' good-by.

"Smitty'd ought to locked the door," says Carey.

"What did he win?" ast Carey.

We figured it up—sixty-odd bucks.

"And the next time we ask him to play," says Carey, "his fingers will be so stiff he can't hold the cards."

Well, we set round a wile talkin' it over, and pretty soon the telephone rung again. Smitty answered it. It was a friend of his'n from Hamilton and he wanted to know why Smitty didn't hurry down. He was the one that had called before and Ike had told him he was Smitty.

"Ike'd ought to split with Smitty's friend," says Carey.

"No," I says, "he'll need all he won. It costs money to buy collars and to send telegrams from Cincinnati to your old man in Texas and keep him posted on the health o' your uncle in Cedar Rapids, D. C."

III

And you ought to heard him out there on that field! They wasn't a day when he didn't pull six or seven, and it didn't make no difference whether he was goin' good or bad. If he popped up in the pinch he should of made a base hit and the reason he didn't was so-and-so. And if he cracked one for three bases he ought to had a home run, only the ball wasn't lively, or the wind brought it back, or he tripped on a lump o' dirt, roundin' first base.

They was one afternoon in New York when he beat all records. Big Marquard was workin' against us and he was good.

In the first innin' Ike hit one clear over that right field stand, but it was a few feet foul. Then he got another foul and then the count come to two and two. Then Rube slipped one acrost on him and he was called out.

"What do you know about that!" he says afterward on the bench. "I lost count. I thought it was three and one, and I took a strike."

"You took a strike all right," says Carey. "Even the umps knowed it was a strike."

"Yes," says Ike, "but you can bet I wouldn't of took it if I'd knew it was the third one. The score board had it wrong."

"That score board ain't for you to look at," says Cap. "It's for you to hit that old pill against."

"Well," says Ike, "I could of hit that one over the score board if I'd knew it was the third."

"Was it a good ball?" I says.

"Well, no, it wasn't," says Ike. "It was inside."

"How far inside?" says Carey.

"Oh, two or three inches or half a foot," says Ike.

"I guess you wouldn't of threatened the score board with it then," says Cap.

"I'd of pulled it down the right foul line if I hadn't thought he'd call it a ball," says Ike.

Well, in New York's part o' the innin' Doyle cracked

one and Ike run back a mile and a half and caught it with one hand. We was all sayin' what a whale of a play it was, but he had to apologize just the same as for gettin' struck out.

"That stand's so high," he says, "that a man don't never see a ball till it's right on top o' you."

"Didn't you see that one?" ast Cap.

"Not at first," says Ike; "not till it raised up above the roof o' the stand."

"Then why did you start back as soon as the ball was hit?" says Cap.

"I knowed by the sound that he'd got a good hold of it," says Ike.

"Yes," says Cap, "but how'd you know what direction to run in?"

"Doyle usually hits 'em that way, the way I run," says Ike.

"Why don't you play blindfolded?" says Carey.

"Might as well, with that big high stand to bother a man," says Ike. "If I could of saw the ball all the time I'd of got it in my hip pocket."

Along in the fifth we was one run to the bad and Ike got on with one out. On the first ball throwed to Smitty, Ike went down. The ball was outside and Meyers throwed Ike out by ten feet.

You could see Ike's lips movin' all the way to the bench and when he got there he had his piece learned.

"Why didn't he swing?" he says.

"Why didn't you wait for his sign?" says Cap.

"He give me his sign," says Ike.

"What is his sign with you?" says Cap.

"Pickin' up some dirt with his right hand," says Ike.

"Well, I didn't see him do it," Cap says.

"He done it all right," says Ike.

Well, Smitty went out and they wasn't no more argument till they come in for the next innin'. Then Cap opened it up.

"You fellas better get your signs straight," he says.

"Do you mean me?" says Smitty.

"Yes," Cap says. "What's your sign with Ike?"

"Slidin' my left hand up to the end o' the bat and back," says Smitty.

"Do you hear that, Ike?" ast Cap.

"What of it?" says Ike.

"You says his sign was pickin' up dirt and he says it's slidin' his hand. Which is right?"

"I'm right," says Smitty. "But if you're arguin' about him goin' last innin', I didn't give him no sign."

"You pulled your cap down with your right hand, didn't you?" ast Ike.

"Well, s'pose I did," says Smitty. "That don't mean nothin'. I never told you to take that for a sign, did I?"

"I thought maybe you meant to tell me and forgot," says Ike.

They couldn't none of us answer that and they wouldn't of been no more said if Ike had of shut up. But wile we was settin' there Carey got on with two out and stole second clean.

"There!" says Ike. "That's what I was tryin' to do and I'd of got away with it if Smitty'd swang and bothered the Indian."

"Oh!" says Smitty. "You was tryin' to steal then, was you? I thought you claimed I give you the hit and run."

"I didn't claim no such a thing," says Ike. "I thought maybe you might of gave me a sign, but I was goin' anyway because I thought I had a good start."

Cap prob'ly would of hit him with a bat, only just about that time Doyle booted one on Hayes and Carey come acrost with the run that tied.

Well, we go into the ninth finally, one and one, and Marquard walks McDonald with nobody out.

"Lay it down," says Cap to Ike.

And Ike goes up there with orders to bunt and cracks the first ball into that right-field stand! It was fair this time, and we're two ahead, but I didn't think about that at the time. I was too busy watchin' Cap's face. First he turned pale and then he got red as fire and then he got blue and purple, and finally he just laid back and busted out laughin'. So we wasn't afraid to laugh ourselfs when we seen him doin' it, and when Ike come in everybody on the bench was in hysterics.

But instead o' takin' advantage, Ike had to try and excuse himself. His play was to shut up and he didn't know how to make it.

"Well," he says, "if I hadn't hit quite so quick at that one I bet it'd of cleared the center-field fence."

Cap stopped laughin'.

"It'll cost you plain fifty," he says.

"What for?" says Ike.

"When I say 'bunt' I mean 'bunt,'" says Cap.

"You didn't say 'bunt,'" says Ike.

"I says 'Lay it down,'" says Cap. "If that don't mean 'bunt,' what does it mean?"

"'Lay it down' means 'bunt' all right," says Ike, "but I understood you to say 'Lay on it.'"

"All right," says Cap, "and the little misunderstandin' will cost you fifty."

Ike didn't say nothin' for a few minutes. Then he had another bright idear.

"I was just kiddin' about misunderstandin' you," he says. "I knowed you wanted me to bunt."

"Well, then, why didn't you bunt?" ast Cap.

"I was goin' to on the next ball," says Ike. "But I thought if I took a good wallop I'd have 'em all fooled.

So I walloped at the first one to fool 'em, and I didn't have no intention o' hittin' it."

"You tried to miss it, did you?" says Cap.

"Yes," says Ike.

"How'd you happen to hit it?" ast Cap.

"Well," Ike says, "I was lookin' for him to throw me a fast one and I was goin' to swing under it. But he come with a hook and I met it right square where I was swingin' to go under the fast one."

"Great!" says Cap. "Boys," he says, "Ike's learned how to hit Marquard's curve. Pretend a fast one's comin' and then try to miss it. It's a good thing to know and Ike'd ought to be willin' to pay for the lesson. So I'm goin' to make it a hundred instead o' fifty."

The game wound up 3 to 1. The fine didn't go, because Ike hit like a wild man all through that trip and we made pretty near a clean-up. The night we went to Philly I got him cornered in the car and I says to him:

"Forget them alibis for a wile and tell me somethin'. What'd you do that for, swing that time against Marquard when you was told to bunt?"

"I'll tell you," he says. "That ball he throwed me looked just like the one I struck out in the first innin' and I wanted to show Cap what I could of done to that other one if I'd knew it was the third strike."

"But," I says, "the one you struck out on in the first innin' was a fast ball."

"So was the one I cracked in the ninth," says Ike.

IV

You've saw Cap's wife, o' course. Well, her sister's about twict as good-lookin' as her, and that's goin' some.

Cap took his missus down to St. Louis the second trip and the other one come down from St. Joe to visit her. Her name is Dolly, and some doll is right.

Well, Cap was goin' to take the two sisters to a show and he wanted a beau for Dolly. He left it to her and she picked Ike. He'd hit three on the nose that afternoon— off'n Sallee, too.

They fell for each other that first evenin'. Cap told us how it come off. She begin flatterin' Ike for the star game he'd played and o' course he begin excusin' himself for not doin' better. So she thought he was modest and it went strong with her. And she believed everything he said and that made her solid with him—that and her make-up. They was together every mornin' and evenin' for the five days we was there. In the afternoons Ike played the grandest ball you ever see, hittin' and runnin' the bases like a fool and catchin' everything that stayed in the park.

I told Cap, I says: "You'd ought to keep the doll with us and he'd make Cobb's figures look sick."

But Dolly had to go back to St. Joe and we come home for a long serious.

Well, for the next three weeks Ike had a letter to read every day and he'd set in the clubhouse readin' it till mornin' practice was half over. Cap didn't say nothin' to him, because he was goin' so good. But I and Carey wasted a lot of our time tryin' to get him to own up who the letters was from. Fine chanct!

"What are you readin'?" Carey'd say. "A bill?"

"No," Ike'd say, "not exactly a bill. It's a letter from a fella I used to go to school with."

"High school or college?" I'd ask him.

"College," he'd say.

"What college?" I'd say.

Then he'd stall a wile and then he'd say:

"I didn't go to the college myself, but my friend went there."

"How did it happen you didn't go?" Carey'd ask him.

"Well," he'd say, "they wasn't no colleges near where I lived."

"Didn't you live in Kansas City?" I'd say to him.

One time he'd say he did and another time he didn't. One time he says he lived in Michigan.

"Where at?" says Carey.

"Near Detroit," he says.

"Well," I says, "Detroit's near Ann Arbor and that's where they got the university."

"Yes," says Ike, "they got it there now, but they didn't have it there then."

"I come pretty near goin' to Syracuse," I says, "only they wasn't no railroads runnin' through there in them days."

"Where'd this friend o' yours go to college?" says Carey.

"I forget now," says Ike.

"Was it Carlisle?" ast Carey.

"No," says Ike, "his folks wasn't very well off."

"That's what barred me from Smith," I says.

"I was goin' to tackle Cornell's," says Carey, "but the doctor told me I'd have hay fever if I didn't stay up North."

"Your friend writes long letters," I says.

"Yes," says Ike; "he's tellin' me about a ball player."

"Where does he play?" ast Carey.

"Down in the Texas League—Fort Wayne," says Ike.

"It looks like a girl's writin'," Carey says.

"A girl wrote it," says Ike. "That's my friend's sister, writin' for him."

"Didn't they teach writin' at this here college where he went?" says Carey.

"Sure," Ike says, "they taught writin', but he got his hand cut off in a railroad wreck."

"How long ago?" I says.

"Right after he got out o' college," says Ike.

"Well," I says, "I should think he'd of learned to write with his left hand by this time."

"It's his left hand that was cut off," says Ike; "and he was left-handed."

"You get a letter every day," says Carey. "They're all the same writin'. Is he tellin' you about a different ball player every time he writes?"

"No," Ike says. "It's the same ball player. He just tells me what he does every day."

"From the size o' the letters, they don't play nothin' but double-headers down there," says Carey.

We figured that Ike spent most of his evenin's answerin' the letters from his "friend's sister," so we kept tryin' to date him up for shows and parties to see how he'd duck out of 'em. He was bugs over spaghetti, so we told him one day that they was goin' to be a big feed of it over to Joe's that night and he was invited.

"How long'll it last?" he says.

"Well," we says, "we're goin' right over there after the game and stay till they close up."

"I can't go," he says, "unless they leave me come home at eight bells."

"Nothin' doin'," says Carey. "Joe'd get sore."

"I can't go then," says Ike.

"Why not?" I ast him.

"Well," he says, "my landlady locks up the house at eight and I left my key home."

"You can come and stay with me," says Carey.

"No," he says, "I can't sleep in a strange bed."

"How do you get along when we're on the road?" says I.

"I don't never sleep the first night anywheres," he says. "After that I'm all right."

"You'll have time to chase home and get your key right after the game," I told him.

"The key ain't home," says Ike. "I lent it to one o' the other fellas and he's went out o' town and took it with him."

"Couldn't you borry another key off'n the landlady?" Carey ast him.

"No," he says, "that's the only one they is."

Well, the day before we started East again, Ike come into the clubhouse all smiles.

"Your birthday?" I ast him.

"No," he says.

"What do you feel so good about?" I says.

"Got a letter from my old man," he says. "My uncle's goin' to get well."

"Is that the one in Nebraska?" says I.

"Not right in Nebraska," says Ike. "Near there."

But afterwards we got the right dope from Cap. Dolly'd blew in from Missouri and was going to make the trip with her sister.

V

Well, I want to alibi Carey and I for what come off in Boston. If we'd of had any idear what we was doin', we'd never did it. They wasn't nobody outside o' maybe Ike and the dame that felt worse over it than I and Carey.

The first two days we didn't see nothin' of Ike and her

except out to the park. The rest o' the time they was sight-seein' over to Cambridge and down to Revere and out to Brook-a-line and all the other places where the rubes go.

But when we come into the beanery after the third game Cap's wife called us over.

"If you want to see somethin' pretty," she says, "look at the third finger on Sis's left hand."

Well, o' course we knowed before we looked that it wasn't goin' to be no hangnail. Nobody was su'prised when Dolly blew into the dinin' room with it—a rock that Ike'd bought off'n Diamond Joe the first trip to New York. Only o' course it'd been set into a lady's-size ring instead o' the automobile tire he'd been wearin'.

Cap and his missus and Ike and Dolly ett supper together, only Ike didn't eat nothin', but just set there blushin' and spillin' things on the table-cloth. I heard him excusin' himself for not havin' no appetite. He says he couldn't never eat when he was clost to the ocean. He'd forgot about them sixty-five oysters he destroyed the first night o' the trip before.

He was goin' to take her to a show, so after supper he went upstairs to change his collar. She had to doll up, too, and o' course Ike was through long before her.

If you remember the hotel in Boston, they's a little parlor where the piano's at and then they's another little parlor openin' off o' that. Well, when Ike come down Smitty was playin' a few chords and I and Carey was harmonizin'. We seen Ike go up to the desk to leave his key and we called him in. He tried to duck away, but we wouldn't stand for it.

We ast him what he was all duded up for and he says he was goin' to the theayter.

"Goin' alone?" says Carey.

"No," he says, "a friend o' mine's goin' with me."

"What do you say if we go along?" says Carey.

"I ain't only got two tickets," he says.

"Well," says Carey, "we can go down there with you and buy our own seats; maybe we can all get together."

"No," says Ike. "They ain't no more seats. They're all sold out."

"We can buy some off'n the scalpers," says Carey.

"I wouldn't if I was you," says Ike. "They say the show's rotten."

"What are you goin' for, then?" I ast.

"I didn't hear about it bein' rotten till I got the tickets," he says.

"Well," I says, "if you don't want to go I'll buy the tickets from you."

"No," says Ike, "I wouldn't want to cheat you. I'm stung and I'll just have to stand for it."

"What are you goin' to do with the girl, leave her here at the hotel?" I says.

"What girl?" says Ike.

"The girl you ett supper with," I says.

"Oh," he says, "we just happened to go into the dinin' room together, that's all. Cap wanted I should set down with 'em."

"I noticed," says Carey, "that she happened to be wearin' that rock you bought off'n Diamond Joe."

"Yes," says Ike. "I lent it to her for a wile."

"Did you lend her the new ring that goes with it?" I says.

"She had that already," says Ike. "She lost the set out of it."

"I wouldn't trust no strange girl with a rock o' mine," says Carey.

"Oh, I guess she's all right," Ike says. "Besides, I was

tired o' the stone. When a girl asks you for somethin', what are you goin' to do?"

He started out toward the desk, but we flagged him.

"Wait a minute!" Carey says. "I got a bet with Sam here, and it's up to you to settle it."

"Well," says Ike, "make it snappy. My friend'll be here any minute."

"I bet," says Carey, "that you and that girl was engaged to be married."

"Nothin' to it," says Ike.

"Now look here," says Carey, "this is goin' to cost me real money if I lose. Cut out the alibi stuff and give it to us straight. Cap's wife just as good as told us you was roped."

Ike blushed like a kid.

"Well, boys," he says, "I may as well own up. You win, Carey."

"Yatta boy!" says Carey. "Congratulations!"

"You got a swell girl, Ike," I says.

"She's a peach," says Smitty.

"Well, I guess she's O. K.," says Ike. "I don't know much about girls."

"Didn't you never run round with 'em?" I says.

"Oh, yes, plenty of 'em," says Ike. "But I never seen none I'd fall for."

"That is, till you seen this one," says Carey.

"Well," says Ike, "this one's O. K., but I wasn't thinkin' about gettin' married yet a wile."

"Who done the askin'—her?" says Carey.

"Oh, no," says Ike, "but sometimes a man don't know what he's gettin' into. Take a good-lookin' girl, and a man gen'ally almost always does about what she wants him to."

"They couldn't no girl lasso me unless I wanted to be lassoed," says Smitty.

"Oh, I don't know," says Ike. "When a fella gets to feelin' sorry for one of 'em it's all off."

Well, we left him go after shakin' hands all round. But he didn't take Dolly to no show that night. Some time wile we was talkin' she'd came into that other parlor and she'd stood there and heard us. I don't know how much she heard. But it was enough. Dolly and Cap's missus took the midnight train for New York. And from there Cap's wife sent her on her way back to Missouri.

She'd left the ring and a note for Ike with the clerk. But we didn't ask Ike if the note was from his friend in Fort Wayne, Texas.

VI

When we'd came to Boston Ike was hittin' plain .397. When we got back home he'd fell off, to pretty near nothin'. He hadn't drove one out o' the infield in any o' them other Eastern parks, and he didn't even give no excuse for it.

To show you how bad he was, he struck out three times in Brooklyn one day and never opened his trap when Cap ast him what was the matter. Before, if he'd whiffed oncet in a game he'd of wrote a book tellin' why.

Well, we dropped from first place to fifth in four weeks and we was still goin' down. I and Carey was about the only ones in the club that spoke to each other, and all as we did was remind ourself o' what a boner we'd pulled.

"It's goin' to beat us out o' the big money," says Carey.

"Yes," I says. "I don't want to knock my own ball club, but it looks like a one-man team, and when that one man's dauber's down we couldn't trim our whiskers."

"We ought to knew better," says Carey.

"Yes," I says, "but why should a man pull an alibi for bein' engaged to such a bearcat as she was?"

"He shouldn't," says Carey. "But I and you knowed he would or we'd never started talkin' to him about it. He wasn't no more ashamed o' the girl than I am of a regular base hit. But he just can't come clean on no subjec'."

Cap had the whole story, and I and Carey was as pop'lar with him as an umpire.

"What do you want me to do, Cap?" Carey'd say to him before goin' up to hit.

"Use your own judgment," Cap'd tell him. "We want to lose another game."

But finally, one night in Pittsburgh, Cap had a letter from his missus and he come to us with it.

"You fellas," he says, "is the ones that put us on the bum, and if you're sorry I think they's a chancet for you to make good. The old lady's out to St. Joe and she's been tryin' her hardest to fix things up. She's explained that Ike don't mean nothin' with his talk; I've wrote and explained that to Dolly, too. But the old lady says that Dolly says that she can't believe it. But Dolly's still stuck on this baby, and she's pinin' away just the same as Ike. And the old lady says she thinks if you two fellas would write to the girl and explain how you was always kiddin' with Ike and leadin' him on, and how the ball club was all shot to pieces since Ike quit hittin', and how he acted like he was goin' to kill himself, and this and that, she'd fall for it and maybe soften down. Dolly, the old lady says, would believe you before she'd believe I and the old lady, because she thinks it's her we're sorry for, and not him."

Well, I and Carey was only too glad to try and see what we could do. But it wasn't no snap. We wrote about eight letters before we got one that looked good. Then we give it to the stenographer and had it wrote out on a typewriter and both of us signed it.

It was Carey's idear that made the letter good. He stuck in somethin' about the world's serious money that our wives wasn't goin' to spend unless she took pity on a "boy who was so shy and modest that he was afraid to come right out and say that he had asked such a beautiful and handsome girl to become his bride."

That's prob'ly what got her, or maybe she couldn't of held out much longer anyway. It was four days after we sent the letter that Cap heard from his missus again. We was in Cincinnati.

"We've won," he says to us. "The old lady says that Dolly says she'll give him another chance. But the old lady says it won't do no good for Ike to write a letter. He'll have to go out there."

"Send him to-night," says Carey.

"I'll pay half his fare," I says.

"I'll pay the other half," says Carey.

"No," says Cap, "the club'll pay his expenses. I'll send him scoutin'."

"Are you goin' to send him to-night?"

"Sure," says Cap. "But I'm goin' to break the news to him right now. It's time we win a ball game."

So in the clubhouse, just before the game, Cap told him. And I certainly felt sorry for Rube Benton and Red Ames that afternoon! I and Carey was standin' in front o' the hotel that night when Ike come out with his suitcase.

"Sent home?" I says to him.

"No," he says, "I'm goin' scoutin'."

"Where to?" I says. "Fort Wayne?"

"No, not exactly," he says.

"Well," says Carey, "have a good time."

"I ain't lookin' for no good time," says Ike. "I says I was goin' scoutin'."

"Well, then," says Carey, "I hope you see somebody you like."

"And you better have a drink before you go," I says.

"Well," says Ike, "they claim it helps a cold."

RHYTHM

This story is slightly immoral, but so, I guess, are all
stories based on truth. It concerns, principally, Harry
Hart whose frankness and naturalness were the traits
that endeared him to fellow members of the Friars' Club
and all red-blooded she-girls who met him in and out
of show business. Music writers have never been noted
for self-loathing and Harry was a refreshing exception
to the general run. That was before *Upsy Daisy* began
its year's tenancy of the Casino.

You can judge what sort of person he was by listening
in on a talk he had at the club one night with Sam Rose,
lyricist of *Nora's Nightie, Sheila's Shirt* and a hundred
popular songs. They were sitting alone at the table
nearest the senile piano.

"Sam," said Harry, "I was wondering if they's a
chance of you and I getting together."

"What's happened to Kane?" asked Sam.

"It's off between he and I," Harry replied. "That dame
ruined him. I guess she married him to make an honest
man of him. Anyways, he got so honest that I couldn't
stand it no more. You know how I am, Sam—live and
let live. I don't question nobody's ethics or whatever
you call them, as long as they don't question mine.
We're all trying to get along; that's the way I look at it.
At that, I've heard better lyrics than he wrote for those
two rhythm numbers of mine in *Lottie;* in fact, between
you and I, I thought he made a bum out of those two

337

numbers. They sold like hymns, so I was really able to bear up when we reached the parting of the ways.

"But I'll tell you the climax just to show you how silly a guy can get. You remember our *Yes, Yes, Eulalie.* Well, they was a spot for a swell love duet near the end of the first act and I had a tune for it that was a smash. You know I'm not bragging when I say that; I don't claim it as my tune, but it was and is a smash. I mean the 'Catch Me' number."

"I'll say it's a smash!" agreed Sam.

"But a smash in spite of the words," said Harry.

"You're right," said Sam.

"Well, the first time I played this tune for him, he went nuts over it and I gave him a lead sheet and he showed it to his wife. It seems she plays piano a little and she played this melody and she told him I had stole it from some opera; she thought it was *Gioconda,* but she wasn't sure. So the next day Kane spoke to me about it and I told him it wasn't *Gioconda;* it was Donizetti's *Linda di Chamounix.* Well, he said he didn't feel like it was right to work on a melody that had been swiped from somewhere. So I said, 'Ain't it kind of late for you to be having all those scruples?' So he said, 'Maybe it is, but better late than never.' So I said, 'Listen, Benny —this is your wife talking, not you.' And he said, 'Let's leave her out of this,' and I said, 'I wished to heaven we could.'

"I said, 'Benny, you'll admit that's a pretty melody,' and he said yes, he admitted it. So I said: 'Well, how many of the dumb-bells that goes to our shows has ever heard *Linda di Chamounix* or ever will hear it? When I put this melody in our troupe I'm doing a million people a favor; I'm giving them a chance to hear a beautiful piece of music that they wouldn't never hear otherwise. Not only that, but they'll hear it at its best because I've improved it.' So Benny said, 'The first four bars is exactly the same and that's where people will notice.'

"So then I said: 'Now listen here, Benny—up to the present you haven't never criticized my music and I haven't criticized your lyrics. But now you say I'm a tune thief. I don't deny it, but if I wasn't, you'd of had a sweet time making a living for yourself, let alone get married. However, laying that to one side, I was over to my sister's house the other night and she had a soprano singer there and she sung a song something about "I love you, I love you; 'tis all my heart can say." It was a mighty pretty song and it come out about twenty or thirty years ago.'

"So then Benny said, 'What of it?' So I said, 'Just this: I can recall four or five lyrics of yours where "I love you" comes in and I bet you've used the words "heart" and "say" and "all" at least twice apiece during your remarkable career as a song writer. Well, did you make those words up or did you hear them somewhere?' That's what I said to him and of course he was stopped. But his ethics was ravaged just the same and it was understood we'd split up right after *Eulalie*. And as I say, his words wasn't no help to my Donizetti number; they'd of slayed it if it could of been slayed."

"Well?" said Sam.

"Well," said Harry, "Conrad Green wired me yesterday to come and see him, so I was up there today. He's so dumb that he thinks I'm better than Friml. And he's got a book by Jack Prendergast that he wanted Kane and I to work on. So I told him I wouldn't work with Kane and he said to get who I wanted. So that's why I gave you a ring."

"It sounds good to me," said Sam. "How is the book?"

"I only skimmed it through, but I guess it's all right. It's based on *Cinderella*, so what with that idear combined with your lyrics and my tunes, it looks like we ought to give the public a novelty at least."

"Have you got any new tunes?"

"New?" Hart laughed. "I'm dirty with them." He sat down at the piano. "Get this rhythm number. If it ain't a smash, I'm Gatti-Casazza!"

He played it, beautifully, first in F sharp—a catchy refrain that seemed to be waltz time in the right hand and two-four in the left.

"It's pretty down here, too," he said, and played it again, just as surely, in B natural, a key whose mere mention is henbane to the average pianist.

"A wow!" enthused Sam Rose. "What is it?"

"Don't you know?"

"The Volga boat song."

"No," said Hart. "It's part of Aïda's number when she finds out the fella is going to war. And nobody that comes to our shows will spot it except maybe Deems Taylor and Alma Gluck."

"It's so pretty," said Sam, "that it's a wonder it never goes popular."

"The answer is that Verdi didn't know rhythm!" said Hart.

Or go back and observe our hero at the Bucks' house on Long Island. Several of the boys and girls were there and thrilled to hear that Harry Hart was coming. He hardly had time to taste his first cocktail before they were after him to play something.

"Something of your own!" pleaded the enraptured Helen Morse.

"If you mean something I made up," he replied with engaging frankness, "why, that's impossible; not exactly impossible, but it would be the homeliest tune you ever listened to. However, my name is signed to some mighty pretty things and I'll play you one or two of those."

Thus, without the conventional show of reluctance, Harry played the two "rhythm numbers" and the love-song that were making Conrad Green's *Upsy Daisy* the hit of the season. And he was starting in on another, a thing his informal audience did not recognize, when he overheard his hostess introducing somebody to Mr. Rudolph Friml.

"Good night!" exclaimed Hart. "Let somebody play that can play!" And he resigned his seat at the piano to the newcomer and moved to a far corner of the room.

"I hope Friml didn't hear me," he confided to a Miss Silloh. "I was playing a thing he wrote himself and letting you people believe it was mine."

Or catch him in the old days at a football game with Rita Marlowe of Goldwyn. One of the college bands was playing "Yes, Sir! That's My Baby!"

"Walter Donaldson. There's the boy that can write the hits!" said Hart.

"Just as if you couldn't!" said his companion.

"I don't class with him," replied her modest escort.

Later on, Rita remarked that he must have been recognized by people in the crowd. Many had stared.

"Let's not kid ourselves, girlie," he said. "They're staring at you, not me."

Still later, on the way home from the game, he told her he had saved over $25,000 and expected to average at least $40,000 a year income while his vogue lasted.

"I'm good as long as I don't run out of pretty tunes," he said, "and they's no reason why I should with all those old masters to draw from. I'm telling you my financial status because—well, I guess you know why."

Rita did know, and it was the general opinion, shared

by the two principals, that she and Harry were engaged.

When *Upsy Daisy* had been running two months and its hit numbers were being sung, played, and whistled almost to cloyment, Hart was discovered by Spencer Deal. That he was the pioneer in a new American jazz, that his rhythms would revolutionize our music —these things and many more were set forth by Deal in a four-thousand-word article called "Harry Hart, Harbinger," printed by the erudite *Webster's Weekly*. And Harry ate it up, though some of the words nearly choked him.

Interesting people were wont to grace Peggy Leech's drawing-room on Sunday afternoons. Max Reinhardt had been there. Reinald Werrenrath had been there. So had Heifetz and Jeritza and Michael Arlen, and Noel Coward and Dudley Malone. And Charlie Chaplin, and Gene Tunney. In fact, Peggy's Sunday afternoons could be spoken of as salons and her apartment as a hotbed of culture.

It was to Peggy's that Spencer Deal escorted Hart a few weeks after the appearance of the article in *Webster's*. Deal, in presenting him, announced that he was at work on a "blue" symphony that would make George Gershwin's ultra rhythms and near dissonants sound like the doxology. "Oh!" exclaimed pretty Myra Hampton. "Will he play some of it for us?"

"Play, play, play!" said Hart querulously. "Don't you think I ever want a rest! Last night it was a party at Broun's and they kept after me and wouldn't take 'No' and finally I played just as rotten as I could, to learn them a lesson. But they didn't even know it was rotten. What do you do for a living?"

"I'm an actress," confessed the embarrassed young lady.

"Well, would you like it if, every time you went anywhere socially, people asked you to act?"

"Yes," she answered, but he had moved away.

He seemed to be seeking seclusion; sat down as far as possible from the crowd and looked hurt. He accepted a highball proffered by his hostess, but neglected to thank her. Not a bit discouraged, she brought him Signor Parelli of the Metropolitan.

"Mr. Hart," she said, "this is Mr. Parelli, one of the Metropolitan's conductors."

"Yay?" said Hart.

"Perhaps some day Mr. Parelli will conduct one of your operas."

"I hope so," said the polite Parelli.

"Do you?" said Hart. "Well, if I ever write an opera, I'll conduct it myself, or at least I won't take no chance of having it ruined by a foreigner."

The late war increased people's capacity for punishment and in about twenty minutes Peggy's guests began to act as if they would live in spite of Harry's refusal to perform. In fact, one of them, Roy Lattimer, full of Scotch courage and not so full of musical ability, went to the piano himself and began to play.

"Began" is all, for he had not completed four bars before Hart plunged across the room and jostled him off the bench.

"I hope you don't call yourself a pianist!" he said, pronouncing it as if it meant a cultivator of, or dealer in, peonies. And for two hours, during which everybody but Spencer Deal and the unfortunate hostess walked out on him, Harry played and played and played. Nor in all that time did he play anything by Kern, Gershwin, Stephen Jones, or Isham Jones, Samuels, Youmans, Friml, Stamper, Tours, Berlin, Tierney, Hubbell, Hein, or Gitz-Rice.

It was during this epoch that Harry had occasion one day to walk up Fifth Avenue from Forty-fifth Street to the Plaza. He noticed that almost everyone he passed on the line of march gazed at him intently. He recalled that his picture had been in two rotogravure sections the previous Sunday. It must have been a better likeness than he had thought.

New York was burning soft coal that winter and when Hart arrived in the Plaza washroom he discovered a smudge on the left side of his upper lip. It made him look as if he had had a mustache, had decided to get it removed and then had changed his mind when the barber was half through.

Harry's date at the Plaza was with Rita Marlowe. He had put it off as long as he could. If the girl had any pride or sense, she'd have taken a hint. Why should he waste his time on a second-rate picture actress when he was hobnobbing with women like Elinor Deal and Thelma Warren and was promised an introduction to Mrs. Wallace Gerard? Girls ought to know that when a fella who has been taking them out three and four times a week and giving them a ring every morning, night, and noon between whiles—they ought to know that when a fella stops calling them up and taking them out and won't even talk to them when they call up, there is only one possible answer. Yet this dame insists on you meeting her and probably having a scene. Well, she'll get a scene. No, she won't. No use being brutal. Just make it apparent in a nice way that things ain't like they used to be and get it over as quick as possible.

"Where can we go?" asked Rita. "I mean, to talk."

"Nowheres that'll take much time," said Harry. "I've got a date with Paul Whiteman to look over part of my symphony."

"I don't want to interrupt your work," said Rita.

"Maybe it would be better if you came up to the house tonight."

"I can't tonight," he told her.

"When can you?"

"I'll give you a ring. It's hard to get away. You see—"

"I think I do," said Rita, and left him.

"About time," said Harry to himself.

His symphony went over fairly "big." The critics seemed less impressed than with the modern compositions of Gershwin and Deems Taylor. "But then," Harry reflected, "Gershwin was ahead of me and of course Taylor has friends on the paper."

A party instigated by Spencer Deal followed the concert and Harry met Mrs. Wallace Gerard, who took a great interest in young composers and had been known to give them substantial aid. Hart accepted an invitation to play to her at her Park Avenue apartment. He made the mistake of thinking she wanted to be petted, not played to, and his first visit was his last.

He had been engaged by Conrad Green to do the music for a new show, with a book by Guy Bolton. He balked at working again with Sam Rose, whose lyrics were hopelessly proletarian. Green told him to pick his own lyricist and Harry chose Spencer Deal. The result of the collaboration was a score that required a new signature at the beginning of each bar, and a collection of six-syllable rhymes that has as much chance of being unriddled, let alone sung, by chorus girls as a pandect on biotaxy by Ernest Boyd.

"Terrible!" was Green's comment on advice of his musical adviser, Frank Tours.

"You're a fine judge!" said Hart. "But it don't make no difference what you think. Our contract with you is to write music and lyrics for this show and that's what we've done. If you don't like it, you can talk to my law-yer."

"Your lawyer is probably one of mine, too," replied Green. "He must be if he practices in New York. But that is neither here or there. If you think you can compel me to accept a score which Tours tells me that if it was orchestrated, Stokowski himself couldn't even read the triangle part, to say nothing of lyrics which you would have to ring up every night at seven o'clock to get the words in the opening chorus all pronounced in time for Bayside people to catch the one-twenty train—well, Hart, go along home now, because you and I are going to see each other in court every day for the next forty years."

A year or so later, Harry's total cash on hand and in bank amounted to $214.60, including the $56 he had cleaned up on the sale of sheet music and mechanical records of his symphony. He read in the Sunday papers that Otto Harbach had undertaken a book for Willis Merwin and the latter was looking around for a com-poser. Merwin was one of the younger producers and had been a pal of Harry's at the Friars'. Hart sought him there. He found Merwin and came to the point at once.

"It's too late," said the young entrepreneur. "I did consider you at first, but—well, I didn't think you were interested now in anything short of oratorio. The stuff you used to write would have been great, but this piece couldn't stand the ponderous junk you've been turning out lately. It needs light treatment and I've signed Don-aldson and Gus Kahn."

"Maybe I could interpolate—" Harry began.

"I don't believe so," Merwin interrupted. "I don't recall a spot where we could use either a fugue or a dirge."

On his way out, Hart saw Benny Kane, his collaborator of other years. Benny made as if to get up and greet him, but changed his mind and sank back in his sequestered chair.

"He don't look as cocky as he used to," thought Harry, and wished that Kane had been more cordial. "What I'll have to do is turn out a hit song, just to tide me over. Of course I can write the words myself, but Benny had good idears once in a while."

Hart stopped in at his old publishers' where, in the halcyon days, he had been as welcome as more beer at the Pastry Cooks' Ball. He had left them for a more esthetic firm at the suggestion of Spencer Deal.

"Well, Harry," said Max Wise, one of the partners, "you're quite a stranger. We don't hear much of you lately."

"Maybe you will again," said Hart. "What would you say if I was to write another smash?"

"I'd say," replied Wise, "that it wasn't any too soon."

"How would you like to have me back here?"

"With a smash, yes. Go get one and you'll find the door wide open. Who are you working with?"

"I haven't nobody."

"You could do a lot worse," said Wise, "than team up again with Benny Kane. You and him parting company was like separating Baltimore and Ohio or pork and beans."

"He hasn't done nothing since he left me," said Hart.

"No," replied Wise, "but you can't hardly claim to have been glutting the country with sensations yourself!"

Hart went back to his hotel and wished there was no such thing as pride. He'd like to give Benny a ring.

He answered the telephone and recognized Benny's voice.

"I seen you at the Friars' today," said Benny, "and

it reminded me of an idear. Where could we get to-gether?"

"At the club," Harry replied. "I'll be there in a half-hour."

"I was thinking," said Benny, when they were seated at the table near the piano, "that nobody has wrote a rhythm song lately about 'I love you'; that is, not in the last two or three months. And one time you was telling me about being over to your sister's and they was a soprano there that sung a song that went 'I love you, I love you; 'tis all my heart can say.'"

"What of it?"

"Well," said Benny, "let's take that song and I'll just fix up the words a little and you can take the tune and put it into your rhythm and we're all set. That is, if the tune's O. K. What is it like?"

"Oh, 'Arcady' and 'Marcheta' and maybe that 'Buzz Around' song of Dave Stamper's. But then, what ain't?"

"Well, let's go to it."

"Where is your ethics?"

"Listen," said Benny Kane—"I and Rae was talking this afternoon, and we didn't disgust ethics. She was just saying she thought that all God's children had shoes except her."

"All right," said Hart. "I can remember enough of the tune. But I'll look the song up tomorrow and give it to you and you can rewrite the words."

"Fine! And now how about putting on the feed bag?"

"No," said Harry. "I promised to call up a dame."

Whereupon he kept his ancient promise.

"You've got a lot of nerve," said Rita at the other end of the wire, "imagining a girl would wait for you this long. And I'd say 'No' and say it good and loud, except that my piano has just been tuned and you've never played me your symphony."

"I ain't going to, neither," said Harry. "But I want to try out a new rhythm number that ought to be a smash. It starts off 'I love you, I love you.'"

"It sounds wonderful!" said Rita.

HAIRCUT

I GOT another barber that comes over from Carterville and helps me out Saturdays, but the rest of the time I can get along all right alone. You can see for yourself that this ain't no New York City and besides that, the most of the boys works all day and don't have no leisure to drop in here and get themselves prettied up.

You're a newcomer, ain't you? I thought I hadn't seen you round before. I hope you like it good enough to stay. As I say, we ain't no New York City or Chicago, but we have pretty good times. Not as good, though, since Jim Kendall got killed. When he was alive, him and Hod Meyers used to keep this town in an uproar. I bet they was more laughin' done here than any town its size in America.

Jim was comical, and Hod was pretty near a match for him. Since Jim's gone, Hod tries to hold his end up just the same as ever, but it's tough goin' when you ain't got nobody to kind of work with.

They used to be plenty fun in here Saturdays. This place is jam-packed Saturdays, from four o'clock on. Jim and Hod would show up right after their supper, round six o'clock. Jim would set himself down in that big chair, nearest the blue spittoon. Whoever had been settin' in that chair, why they'd get up when Jim come in and give it to him.

You'd of thought it was a reserved seat like they have sometimes in a theayter. Hod would generally always stand or walk up and down, or some Saturdays, of course, he'd be settin' in this chair part of the time, gettin' a haircut.

Well, Jim would set there a w'ile without openin' his mouth only to spit, and then finally he'd say to me, "Whitey,"—my right name, that is, my right first name, is Dick, but everybody round here calls me Whitey— Jim would say, "Whitey, your nose looks like a rosebud tonight. You must of been drinkin' some of your aw de cologne."

So I'd say, "No, Jim, but you look like you'd been drinkin' somethin' of that kind or somethin' worse."

Jim would have to laugh at that, but then he'd speak up and say, "No, I ain't had nothin' to drink, but that ain't sayin' I wouldn't like somethin'. I wouldn't even mind if it was wood alcohol."

Then Hod Meyers would say, "Neither would your wife." That would set everybody to laughin' because Jim and his wife wasn't on very good terms. She'd of divorced him only they wasn't no chance to get alimony and she didn't have no way to take care of herself and the kids. She couldn't never understand Jim. He *was* kind of rough, but a good fella at heart.

Him and Hod had all kinds of sport with Milt Sheppard. I don't suppose you've seen Milt. Well, he's got an Adam's apple that looks more like a mushmelon. So I'd be shavin' Milt and when I'd start to shave down here on his neck, Hod would holler, "Hey, Whitey, wait a minute! Before you cut into it, let's make up a pool and see who can guess closest to the number of seeds."

And Jim would say, "If Milt hadn't of been so hoggish, he'd of ordered a half a cantaloupe instead of a whole one and it might not of stuck in his throat."

All the boys would roar at this and Milt himself would force a smile, though the joke was on him. Jim certainly was a card!

There's his shavin' mug, settin' on the shelf, right next to Charley Vail's. "Charles M. Vail." That's the druggist. He comes in regular for his shave, three times a week. And Jim's is the cup next to Charley's. "James H. Kendall." Jim won't need no shavin' mug no more, but I'll leave it there just the same for old time's sake. Jim certainly was a character!

Years ago, Jim used to travel for a canned goods concern over in Carterville. They sold canned goods. Jim had the whole northern half of the State and was on the road five days out of every week. He'd drop in here Saturdays and tell his experiences for that week. It was rich.

I guess he paid more attention to playin' jokes than makin' sales. Finally the concern let him out and he come right home here and told everybody he'd been fired instead of sayin' he'd resigned like most fellas would of.

It was a Saturday and the shop was full and Jim got up out of that chair and says, "Gentlemen, I got an important announcement to make. I been fired from my job."

Well, they asked him if he was in earnest and he said he was and nobody could think of nothin' to say till Jim finally broke the ice himself. He says, "I been sellin' canned goods and now I'm canned goods myself."

You see, the concern he'd been workin' for was a factory that made canned goods. Over in Carterville. And now Jim said he was canned himself. He was certainly a card!

Jim had a great trick that he used to play w'ile he was travelin'. For instance, he'd be ridin' on a train and they'd come to some little town like—well, like—we'll say, like Benton. Jim would look out the train window and read the signs on the stores.

For instance, they'd be a sign, "Henry Smith, Dry Goods." Well, Jim would write down the name and the name of the town and when he got to wherever he was goin' he'd mail back a postal card to Henry Smith at Benton and not sign no name to it, but he'd write on the card, well, somethin' like "Ask your wife about that book agent that spent the afternoon last week," or "Ask your Missus who kept her from gettin' lonesome the last time you was in Carterville." And he'd sign the card, "A Friend."

Of course, he never knew what really come of none of these jokes, but he could picture what *probably* happened and that was enough.

Jim didn't work very steady after he lost his position with the Carterville people. What he did earn, doin' odd jobs round town, why he spent pretty near all of it on gin and his family might of starved if the stores hadn't of carried them along. Jim's wife tried her hand at dressmakin', but they ain't nobody goin' to get rich makin' dresses in this town.

As I say, she'd of divorced Jim, only she seen that she couldn't support herself and the kids and she was always hopin' that some day Jim would cut out his habits and give her more than two or three dollars a week.

They was a time when she would go to whoever he was workin' for and ask them to give her his wages, but after she done this once or twice, he beat her to it by borrowin' most of his pay in advance. He told it all round town, how he had outfoxed his Missus. He certainly was a caution!

But he wasn't satisfied with just outwittin' her. He was sore the way she had acted, tryin' to grab off his pay. And he made up his mind he'd get even. Well, he waited till Evans's Circus was advertised to come to town. Then he told his wife and two kiddies that he was goin' to take them to the circus. The day of the circus, he told them he would get the tickets and meet them outside the entrance to the tent.

Well, he didn't have no intentions of bein' there or buyin' tickets or nothin'. He got full of gin and laid round Wright's poolroom all day. His wife and the kids waited and waited and of course he didn't show up. His wife didn't have a dime with her, or nowhere else, I guess. So she finally had to tell the kids it was all off and they cried like they wasn't never goin' to stop.

Well, it seems, w'ile they was cryin', Doc Stair came along and he asked what was the matter, but Mrs. Kendall was stubborn and wouldn't tell him, but the kids told him and he insisted on takin' them and their mother in the show. Jim found this out afterwards and it was one reason why he had it in for Doc Stair.

Doc Stair come here about a year and a half ago. He's a mighty handsome young fella and his clothes always look like he has them made to order. He goes to Detroit two or three times a year and w'ile he's there he must have a tailor take his measure and then make him a suit to order. They cost pretty near twice as much, but they fit a whole lot better than if you just bought them in a store.

For a w'ile everybody was wonderin' why a young doctor like Doc Stair should come to a town like this where we already got old Doc Gamble and Doc Foote that's both been here for years and all the practice in town was always divided between the two of them.

Then they was a story got round that Doc Stair's gal had throwed him over, a gal up in the Northern Peninsula somewheres, and the reason he come here was to hide himself away and forget it. He said himself that he thought they wasn't nothin' like general practice in a place like ours to fit a man to be a good all round doctor. And that's why he'd came.

Anyways, it wasn't long before he was makin' enough to live on, though they tell me that he never dunned nobody for what they owed him, and the folks here certainly has got the owin' habit, even in my business. If I had all that was comin' to me for just shaves alone, I could go to Carterville and put up at the Mercer for a week and see a different picture every night. For instance, they's old George Purdy—but I guess I shouldn't ought to be gossipin'.

Well, last year, our coroner died, died of the flu. Ken Beatty, that was his name. He was the coroner. So they had to choose another man to be coroner in his place and they picked Doc Stair. He laughed at first and said he didn't want it, but they made him take it. It ain't no job that anybody would fight for and what a man makes out of it in a year would just about buy seeds for their garden. Doc's the kind, though, that can't say no to nothin' if you keep at him long enough.

But I was goin' to tell you about a poor boy we got here in town—Paul Dickson. He fell out of a tree when he was about ten years old. Lit on his head and it done somethin' to him and he ain't never been right. No harm in him, but just silly. Jim Kendall used to call him cuckoo; that's a name Jim had for anybody that was off their head, only he called people's head their bean. That was another of his gags, callin' head bean and callin' crazy people cuckoo. Only poor Paul ain't crazy, but just silly.

You can imagine that Jim used to have all kinds of fun with Paul. He'd send him to the White Front Garage for a left-handed monkey wrench. Of course they ain't no such a thing as a left-handed monkey wrench.

And once we had a kind of a fair here and they was a baseball game between the fats and the leans and before the game started Jim called Paul over and sent him way down to Schrader's hardware store to get a key for the pitcher's box.

They wasn't nothin' in the way of gags that Jim couldn't think up, when he put his mind to it.

Poor Paul was always kind of suspicious of people, maybe on account of how Jim had kept foolin' him. Paul wouldn't have much to do with anybody only his own mother and Doc Stair and a girl here in town named Julie Gregg. That is, she ain't a girl no more, but pretty near thirty or over.

When Doc first come to town, Paul seemed to feel like here was a real friend and he hung round Doc's office most of the w'ile; the only time he wasn't there was when he'd go home to eat or sleep or when he seen Julie Gregg doin' her shoppin'.

When he looked out Doc's window and seen her, he'd run downstairs and join her and tag along with her to the different stores. The poor boy was crazy about Julie and she always treated him mighty nice and made him feel like he was welcome, though of course it wasn't nothin' but pity on her side.

Doc done all he could to improve Paul's mind and he told me once that he really thought the boy was gettin' better, that they was times when he was as bright and sensible as anybody else.

But I was goin' to tell you about Julie Gregg. Old Man Gregg was in the lumber business, but got to drinkin' and lost the most of his money and when he died, he didn't leave nothin' but the house and just enough insurance for the girl to skimp along on.

Her mother was a kind of a half invalid and didn't hardly ever leave the house. Julie wanted to sell the place and move somewheres else after the old man died, but the mother said she was born here and would die here. It was tough on Julie, as the young people round this town—well, she's too good for them.

She's been away to school and Chicago and New York and different places and they ain't no subject she can't talk on, where you take the rest of the young folks here and you mention anything to them outside of Gloria Swanson or Tommy Meighan and they think you're delirious. Did you see Gloria in *Wages of Virtue?* You missed somethin'!

Well, Doc Stair hadn't been here more than a week when he come in one day to get shaved and I recognized who he was as he had been pointed out to me, so I told him about my old lady. She's been ailin' for a couple years and either Doc Gamble or Doc Foote, neither one, seemed to be helpin' her. So he said he would come out and see her, but if she was able to get out herself, it would be better to bring her to his office where he could make a completer examination.

So I took her to his office and w'ile I was waitin' for her in the reception room, in come Julie Gregg. When somebody comes in Doc Stair's office, they's a bell that rings in his inside office so as he can tell they's somebody to see him.

So he left my old lady inside and come out to the front office and that's the first time him and Julie met and I guess it was what they call love at first sight. But it wasn't fifty-fifty. This young fella was the slickest lookin' fella she'd ever seen in this town and she went wild over him. To him she was just a young lady that wanted to see the doctor.

She'd came on about the same business I had. Her mother had been doctorin' for years with Doc Gamble and Doc Foote and without no results. So she'd heard they was a new doc in town and decided to give him a try. He promised to call and see her mother that same day.

I said a minute ago that it was love at first sight on her part. I'm not only judgin' by how she acted afterwards but how she looked at him that first day in his office. I ain't no mind reader, but it was wrote all over her face that she was gone.

Now Jim Kendall, besides bein' a jokesmith and a pretty good drinker, well, Jim was quite a lady-killer. I guess he run pretty wild durin' the time he was on the road for them Carterville people, and besides that, he'd had a couple little affairs of the heart right here in town. As I say, his wife could of divorced him, only she couldn't.

But Jim was like the majority of men, and women, too, I guess. He wanted what he couldn't get. He wanted Julie Gregg and worked his head off tryin' to land her. Only he'd of said bean instead of head.

Well, Jim's habits and his jokes didn't appeal to Julie and of course he was a married man, so he didn't have no more chance than, well, than a rabbit. That's an expression of Jim's himself. When somebody didn't have no chance to get elected or somethin', Jim would always say they didn't have no more chance than a rabbit.

He didn't make no bones about how he felt. Right in here, more than once, in front of the whole crowd, he said he was stuck on Julie and anybody that could get her for him was welcome to his house and his wife and kids included. But she wouldn't have nothin' to do with him; wouldn't even speak to him on the street. He finally seen he wasn't gettin' nowheres with his usual line so he decided to try the rough stuff. He went right up to her house one evenin' and when she opened the door he forced his way in and grabbed her. But she broke loose and before he could stop her, she run in the next room and locked the door and phoned to Joe Barnes. Joe's the marshal. Jim could hear who she was phonin' to and he beat it before Joe got there.

Joe was an old friend of Julie's pa. Joe went to Jim the next day and told him what would happen if he ever done it again.

I don't know how the news of this little affair leaked out. Chances is that Joe Barnes told his wife and she told somebody else's wife and they told their husband. Anyways, it did leak out and Hod Meyers had the nerve to kid Jim about it, right here in this shop. Jim didn't deny nothin' and kind of laughed it off and said for us all to wait; that lots of people had tried to make a monkey out of him, but he always got even.

Meanw'ile everybody in town was wise to Julie's bein' wild mad over the Doc. I don't suppose she had any idear how her face changed when him and her was together; of course she couldn't of, or she'd of kept away from him. And she didn't know that we was all noticin' how many times she made excuses to go up to his office or pass it on the other side of the street and look up in his window to see if he was there. I felt sorry for her and so did most other people.

Hod Meyers kept rubbin' it into Jim about how the Doc had cut him out. Jim didn't pay no attention to the kiddin' and you could see he was plannin' one of his jokes.

One trick Jim had was the knack of changin' his voice. He could make you think he was a girl talkin' and he could mimic any man's voice. To show you how good he was along this line, I'll tell you the joke he played on me once.

You know, in most towns of any size, when a man is

dead and needs a shave, why the barber that shaves him soaks him five dollars for the job; that is, he don't soak *him*, but whoever ordered the shave. I just charge three dollars because personally I don't mind much shavin' a dead person. They lay a whole lot stiller than live customers. The only thing is that you don't feel like talkin' to them and you get kind of lonesome.

Well, about the coldest day we ever had here, two years ago last winter, the phone rung at the house w'ile I was home to dinner and I answered the phone and it was a woman's voice and she said she was Mrs. John Scott and her husband was dead and would I come out and shave him.

Old John had always been a good customer of mine. But they live seven miles out in the country, on the Streeter road. Still I didn't see how I could say no.

So I said I would be there, but would have to come in a jitney and it might cost three or four dollars besides the price of the shave. So she, or the voice, it said that was all right, so I got Frank Abbott to drive me out to the place and when I got there, who should open the door but old John himself! He wasn't no more dead than, well, than a rabbit.

It didn't take no private detective to figure out who had played me this little joke. Nobody could of thought it up but Jim Kendall. He certainly was a card!

I tell you this incident just to show you how he could disguise his voice and make you believe it was somebody else talkin'. I'd of swore it was Mrs. Scott had called me. Anyways, some woman.

Well, Jim waited till he had Doc Stair's voice down pat; then he went after revenge.

He called Julie up on a night when he knew Doc was over in Carterville. She never questioned but what it was Doc's voice. Jim said he must see her that night; he couldn't wait no longer to tell her somethin'. She was all excited and told him to come to the house. But he said he was expectin' an important long distance call and wouldn't she please forget her manners for once and come to his office. He said they couldn't nothin' hurt her and nobody would see her and he just *must* talk to her a little w'ile. Well, poor Julie fell for it.

Doc always keeps a night light in his office, so it looked to Julie like they was somebody there.

Meanw'ile Jim Kendall had went to Wright's poolroom, where they was a whole gang amusin' themselves. The most of them had drank plenty of gin, and they was a rough bunch even when sober. They was always strong for Jim's jokes and when he told them to come with him and see some fun they give up their card games and pool games and followed along.

Doc's office is on the second floor. Right outside his door they's a flight of stairs leadin' to the floor above. Jim and his gang hid in the dark behind these stairs.

Well, Julie come up to Doc's door and rung the bell and they was nothin' doin'. She rung it again and she rung it seven or eight times. Then she tried the door and found it locked. Then Jim made some kind of a noise and she heard it and waited a minute, and then she says, "Is that you, Ralph?" Ralph is Doc's first name.

They was no answer and it must of came to her all of a sudden that she'd been bunked. She pretty near fell downstairs and the whole gang after her. They chased her all the way home, hollerin', "Is that you, Ralph?" and "Oh, Ralphie, dear, is that you?" Jim says he couldn't holler it himself, as he was laughin' too hard.

Poor Julie! She didn't show up here on Main Street for a long, long time afterward.

And of course Jim and his gang told everybody in town, everybody but Doc Stair. They was scared to tell him, and he might of never knowed only for Paul Dickson. The poor cuckoo, as Jim called him, he was here in the shop one night when Jim was still gloatin' yet over what he'd done to Julie. And Paul took in as much of it as he could understand and he run to Doc with the story.

It's a cinch Doc went up in the air and swore he'd make Jim suffer. But it was a kind of a delicate thing, because if it got out that he had beat Jim up, Julie was bound to hear of it and then she'd know that Doc knew and of course knowin' that he knew would make it worse for her than ever. He was goin' to do somethin', but it took a lot of figurin'.

Well, it was a couple days later when Jim was here in the shop again, and so was the cuckoo. Jim was goin' duck-shootin' the next day and had came in lookin' for Hod Meyers to go with him. I happened to know that Hod had went over to Carterville and wouldn't be home till the end of the week. So Jim said he hated to go alone and he guessed he would call it off. Then poor Paul spoke up and said if Jim would take him he would go along. Jim thought a w'ile and then he said, well, he guessed a half-wit was better than nothin'.

I suppose he was plottin' to get Paul out in the boat and play some joke on him, like pushin' him in the water. Anyways, he said Paul could go. He asked him had he ever shot a duck and Paul said no, he'd never even had a gun in his hands. So Jim said he could set in the boat and watch him and if he behaved himself, he might lend him his gun for a couple of shots. They made a date to meet in the mornin' and that's the last I seen of Jim alive.

Next mornin', I hadn't been open more than ten minutes when Doc Stair come in. He looked kind of nervous. He asked me had I seen Paul Dickson. I said no, but I knew where he was, out duck-shootin' with Jim Kendall. So Doc says that's what he had heard, and he couldn't understand it because Paul had told him he wouldn't never have no more to do with Jim as long as he lived.

He said Paul had told him about the joke Jim had played on Julie. He said Paul had asked him what he thought of the joke and the Doc had told him that anybody that would do a thing like that ought not to be let live.

I said it had been a kind of a raw thing, but Jim just couldn't resist no kind of a joke, no matter how raw. I said I thought he was all right at heart, but just bubblin' over with mischief. Doc turned and walked out.

At noon he got a phone call from old John Scott. The lake where Jim and Paul had went shootin' is on John's place. Paul had came runnin' up to the house a few minutes before and said they'd been an accident. Jim had shot a few ducks and then give the gun to Paul and told him to try his luck. Paul hadn't never handled a gun and he was nervous. He was shakin' so hard that he couldn't control the gun. He let fire and Jim sunk back in the boat, dead.

Doc Stair, bein' the coroner, jumped in Frank Abbott's flivver and rushed out to Scott's farm. Paul and old John was down on the shore of the lake. Paul had rowed the boat to shore, but they'd left the body in it, waitin' for Doc to come.

Doc examined the body and said they might as well fetch it back to town. They was no use leavin' it there or callin' a jury, as it was a plain case of accidental shootin'.

Personally I wouldn't never leave a person shoot a

gun in the same boat I was in unless I was sure they knew somethin' about guns. Jim was a sucker to leave a new beginner have his gun, let alone a half-wit. It probably served Jim right, what he got. But still we miss him round here. He certainly was a card!

Comb it wet or dry?

CHAMPION

MIDGE KELLY scored his first knockout when he was seventeen. The knockee was his brother Connie, three years his junior and a cripple. The purse was a half dollar given to the younger Kelly by a lady whose electric had just missed bumping his soul from his frail little body.

Connie did not know Midge was in the house, else he never would have risked laying the prize on the arm of the least comfortable chair in the room, the better to observe its shining beauty. As Midge entered from the kitchen, the crippled boy covered the coin with his hand, but the movement lacked the speed requisite to escape his brother's quick eye.

"Watcha got there?" demanded Midge.

"Nothin'," said Connie.

"You're a one legged liar!" said Midge.

He strode over to his brother's chair and grasped the hand that concealed the coin.

"Let loose!" he ordered.

Connie began to cry.

"Let loose and shut up your noise," said the elder, and jerked his brother's hand from the chair arm.

The coin fell onto the bare floor. Midge pounced on it. His weak mouth widened in a triumphant smile.

"Nothin', huh?" he said. "All right, if it's nothin' you don't want it."

"Give that back," sobbed the younger.

"I'll give you a red nose, you little sneak! Where'd you steal it?"

"I didn't steal it. It's mine. A lady give it to me after she pretty near hit me with a car."

"It's a crime she missed you," said Midge.

Midge started for the front door. The cripple picked up his crutch, rose from his chair with difficulty, and, still sobbing, came toward Midge. The latter heard him and stopped.

"You better stay where you're at," he said.

"I want my money," cried the boy.

"I know what you want," said Midge.

Doubling up the fist that held the half dollar, he landed with all his strength on his brother's mouth. Connie fell to the floor with a thud, the crutch tumbling on top of him. Midge stood beside the prostrate form.

"Is that enough?" he said. "Or do you want this, too?"

And he kicked him in the crippled leg.

"I guess that'll hold you," he said.

There was no response from the boy on the floor. Midge looked at him a moment, then at the coin in his hand, and then went out into the street, whistling.

An hour later, when Mrs. Kelly came home from her day's work at Faulkner's Steam Laundry, she found Connie on the floor, moaning. Dropping on her knees beside him, she called him by name a score of times. Then she got up and, pale as a ghost, dashed from the house. Dr. Ryan left the Kelly abode about dusk and walked toward Halsted Street. Mrs. Dorgan spied him as he passed her gate.

"Who's sick, Doctor?" she called.

"Poor little Connie," he replied. "He had a bad fall."

"How did it happen?"

"I can't say for sure, Margaret, but I'd almost bet he was knocked down."

"Knocked down!" exclaimed Mrs. Dorgan. "Why, who—?"

"Have you seen the other one lately?"

"Michael? No, not since mornin'. You can't be thinkin'—"

"I wouldn't put it past him, Margaret," said the doctor gravely. "The lad's mouth is swollen and cut, and his poor, skinny little leg is bruised. He surely didn't do it to himself and I think Helen suspects the other one."

"Lord save us!" said Mrs. Dorgan. "I'll run over and see if I can help."

"That's a good woman," said Doctor Ryan, and went on down the street.

Near midnight, when Midge came home, his mother was sitting at Connie's bedside. She did not look up.

"Well," said Midge, "what's the matter?"

She remained silent. Midge repeated his question.

"Michael, you know what's the matter," she said at length.

"I don't know nothin'," said Midge.

"Don't lie to me, Michael. What did you do to your brother?"

"Nothin'."

"You hit him."

"Well, then, I hit him. What of it? It ain't the first time."

Her lips pressed tightly together, her face like chalk, Ellen Kelly rose from her chair and made straight for him. Midge backed against the door.

"Lay off'n me, Ma. I don't want to fight no woman."

Still she came on breathing heavily.

"Stop where you're at, Ma," he warned.

There was a brief struggle and Midge's mother lay on the floor before him.

"You ain't hurt, Ma. You're lucky I didn't land good. And I told you to lay off'n me."

"God forgive you, Michael!"

Midge found Hap Collins in the showdown game at the Royal.

"Come on out a minute," he said.

Hap followed him out on the walk.

"I'm leavin' town for a w'ile," said Midge.

"What for?"

"Well, we had a little run-in up to the house. The kid stole a half buck off'n me, and when I went after it he cracked me with his crutch. So I nailed him. And the old lady came at me with a chair and I took it off'n her and she fell down."

"How is Connie hurt?"

"Not bad."

"What are you runnin' away for?"

"Who the hell said I was runnin' away? I'm sick and tired o' gettin' picked on; that's all. So I'm leavin' for a w'ile and I want a piece o' money."

"I ain't only got six bits," said Happy.

"You're in bad shape, ain't you? Well, come through with it."

Happy came through.

"You oughtn't to hit the kid," he said.

"I ain't astin' you who can I hit," snarled Midge. "You try to put somethin' over on me and you'll get the same dose. I'm goin' now."

"Go as far as you like," said Happy, but not until he was sure that Kelly was out of hearing.

Early the following morning, Midge boarded a train for Milwaukee. He had no ticket, but no one knew the difference. The conductor remained in the caboose.

On a night six months later, Midge hurried out of the

"stage door" of the Star Boxing Club and made for Duane's saloon, two blocks away. In his pocket were twelve dollars, his reward for having battered up one Demon Dempsey through the six rounds of the first preliminary.

It was Midge's first professional engagement in the manly art. Also it was the first time in weeks that he had earned twelve dollars.

On the way to Duane's he had to pass Niemann's. He pulled his cap over his eyes and increased his pace until he had gone by. Inside Niemann's stood a trusting bartender, who for ten days had staked Midge to drinks and allowed him to ravage the lunch on a promise to come in and settle the moment he was paid for the "prelim."

Midge strode into Duane's and aroused the napping bartender by slapping a silver dollar on the festive board.

"Gimme a shot," said Midge.

The shooting continued until the wind-up at the Star was over and part of the fight crowd joined Midge in front of Duane's bar. A youth in the early twenties, standing next to young Kelly, finally summoned sufficient courage to address him.

"Wasn't you in the first bout?" he ventured.

"Yeh," Midge replied.

"My name's Hersch," said the other.

Midge received the startling information in silence.

"I don't want to butt in," continued Mr. Hersch, "but I'd like to buy you a drink."

"All right," said Midge, "but don't overstrain yourself."

Mr. Hersch laughed uproariously and beckoned to the bartender.

"You certainly gave that wop a trimmin' tonight," said the buyer of the drink, when they had been served. "I thought you'd kill him."

"I would if I hadn't let up," Midge replied. "I'll kill 'em all."

"You got the wallop all right," the other said admiringly.

"Have I got the wallop?" said Midge. "Say, I can kick like a mule. Did you notice them muscles in my shoulders?"

"Notice 'em? I couldn't help from noticin' 'em," said Hersch. "I says to the fella settin' alongside o' me, I says: 'Look at them shoulders! No wonder he can hit,' I says to him."

"Just let me land and it's good-by, baby," said Midge. "I'll kill 'em all."

The oral manslaughter continued until Duane's closed for the night. At parting, Midge and his new friend shook hands and arranged for a meeting the following evening.

For nearly a week the two were together almost constantly. It was Hersch's pleasant role to listen to Midge's modest revelations concerning himself, and to buy every time Midge's glass was empty. But there came an evening when Hersch regretfully announced that he must go home to supper.

"I got a date for eight bells," he confided. "I could stick till then, only I must clean up and put on the Sunday clo'es, 'cause she's the prettiest little thing in Milwaukee."

"Can't you fix it for two?" asked Midge.

"I don't know who to get," Hersch replied. "Wait, though. I got a sister and if she ain't busy, it'll be O. K. She's no bum for looks herself."

So it came about that Midge and Emma Hersch and

Emma's brother and the prettiest little thing in Milwaukee foregathered at Wall's and danced half the night away. And Midge and Emma danced every dance together, for though every little onestep seemed to induce a new thirst of its own, Lou Hersch stayed too sober to dance with his own sister.

The next day, penniless at last in spite of his phenomenal ability to make someone else settle, Midge Kelly sought out Doc Hammond, matchmaker for the Star, and asked to be booked for the next show.

"I could put you on with Tracy for the next bout," said Doc.

"What's they in it?" asked Midge.

"Twenty if you cop," Doc told him.

"Have a heart," protested Midge. "Didn't I look good the other night?"

"You looked all right. But you aren't Freddie Welsh yet by a consid'able margin."

"I ain't scared of Freddie Welsh or none of 'em," said Midge.

"Well, we don't pay our boxers by the size of their chests," Doc said. "I'm offerin' you this Tracy bout. Take it or leave it."

"All right; I'm on," said Midge, and he passed a pleasant afternoon at Duane's on the strength of his booking.

Young Tracy's manager came to Midge the night before the show.

"How do you feel about this go?" he asked.

"Me?" said Midge, "I feel all right. What do you mean, how do I feel?"

"I mean," said Tracy's manager, "that we're mighty anxious to win, 'cause the boy's got a chanct in Philly if he cops this one."

"What's your proposition?" asked Midge.

"Fifty bucks," said Tracy's manager.

"What do you think I am, a crook? Me lay down for fifty bucks. Not me!"

"Seventy-five, then," said Tracy's manager.

The market closed on eighty and the details were agreed on in short order. And the next night Midge was stopped in the second round by a terrific slap on the forearm.

This time Midge passed up both Niemann's and Duane's, having a sizable account at each place, and sought his refreshment at Stein's farther down the street.

When the profits of his deal with Tracy were gone, he learned, by firsthand information from Doc Hammond and the matchmakers at the other "clubs," that he was no longer desired for even the cheapest of preliminaries. There was no danger of his starving or dying of thirst while Emma and Lou Hersch lived. But he made up his mind, four months after his defeat by Young Tracy, that Milwaukee was not the ideal place for him to live.

"I can lick the best of 'em," he reasoned, "but there ain't no more chanct for me here. I can maybe go east and get on somewheres. And besides—"

But just after Midge had purchased a ticket to Chicago with the money he had "borrowed" from Emma Hersch "to buy shoes," a heavy hand was laid on his shoulders and he turned to face two strangers.

"Where are you goin', Kelly?" inquired the owner of the heavy hand.

"Nowheres," said Midge. "What the hell do you care?"

The other stranger spoke:

"Kelly, I'm employed by Emma Hersch's mother to see that you do right by her. And we want you to stay here till you've done it."

"You won't get nothin' but the worst of it, monkeying with me," said Midge.

Nevertheless, he did not depart for Chicago that night. Two days later, Emma Hersch became Mrs. Kelly, and the gift of the groom, when once they were alone, was a crushing blow on the bride's pale cheek.

Next morning, Midge left Milwaukee as he had entered it—by fast freight.

"They's no use kiddin' ourself any more," said Tommy Haley. "He might get down to thirty-seven in a pinch, but if he done below that a mouse could stop him. He's a welter; that's what he is and he knows it as well as I do. He's growed like a weed in the last six mont's. I told him, I says, 'If you don't quit growin' they won't be nobody for you to box, only Willard and them.' He says, 'Well, I wouldn't run away from Willard if I weighed twenty pounds more.'"

"He must hate himself," said Tommy's brother.

"I never seen a good one that didn't," said Tommy. "And Midge is a good one; don't make no mistake about that. I wisht we could of got Welsh before the kid growed so big. But it's too late now. I won't make no holler, though, if we can match him up with the Dutchman."

"Who do you mean?"

"Young Goetz, the welter champ. We mightn't not get so much dough for the bout itself, but it'd roll in afterward. What a drawin' card we'd be, 'cause the people pays their money to see the fella with the wallop, and that's Midge. And we'd keep the title just as long as Midge could make the weight."

"Can't you land no match with Goetz?"

"Sure, 'cause he needs the money. But I've went careful with the kid so far and look at the results I got! So what's the use of takin' a chanct? The kid's comin' every minute and Goetz is goin' back faster'n big Johnson did. I think we could lick him now; I'd bet my life on it. But six mont's from now they won't be no risk. He'll of licked hisself before that time. Then all as we'll have to do is sign up with him and wait for the referee to stop it. But Midge is so crazy to get at him now that I can't hardly hold him back."

The brothers Haley were lunching in a Boston hotel. Dan had come down from Holyoke to visit with Tommy and to watch the latter's protege go twelve rounds, or less, with Bud Cross. The bout promised little in the way of a contest, for Midge had twice stopped the Baltimore youth and Bud's reputation for gameness was all that had earned him the date. The fans were willing to pay the price to see Midge's hay-making left, but they wanted to see it used on an opponent who would not jump out of the ring the first time he felt its crushing force. Bud Cross was such an opponent, and his willingness to stop boxing-gloves with his eyes, ears, nose, and throat had long enabled him to escape the horrors of honest labor. A game boy was Bud, and he showed it in his battered, swollen, discolored face.

"I should think," said Dan Haley, "that the kid'd do whatever you tell him after all you done for him."

"Well," said Tommy, "he's took my dope pretty straight so far, but he's so sure of hisself that he can't see no reason for waitin'. He'll do what I say, though; he'd be a sucker not to."

"You got a contrac' with him?"

"No, I don't need no contrac'. He knows it was me that drug him out o' the gutter and he ain't goin' to turn me down now, when he's got the dough and bound to get more. Where'd he of been at if I hadn't listened to him when he first come to me? That's pretty near two

years ago now, but it seems like last week. I was settin'
in the s'loon acrost from the Pleasant Club in Philly,
waitin' for McCann to count the dough and come over,
when this little bum blowed in and tried to stand the
house off for a drink. They told him nothin' doin' and
to beat it out o' there, and then he seen me and come
over to where I was settin' and ast me wasn't I a boxin'
man and I told him who I was. Then he ast me for
money to buy a shot and I told him to set down and
I'd buy it for him.

"Then we got talkin' things over and he told me his
name and told me about fightin' a couple o' prelims out
to Milwaukee. So I says, 'Well, boy, I don't know how
good or how rotten you are, but you won't never get
nowheres trainin' on that stuff.' So he says he'd cut it
out if he could get on in a bout and I says I would give
him a chanct if he played square with me and didn't
touch no more to drink. So we shook hands and I took
him up to the hotel with me and give him a bath and
the next day I bought him some clo'es. And I staked him
to eats and sleeps for over six weeks. He had a hard time
breakin' away from the polish, but finally I thought he
was fit and I give him his chanct. He went on with
Smiley Sayer and stopped him so quick that Smiley
thought sure he was poisoned.

"Well, you know what he's did since. The only beatin'
in his record was by Tracy in Milwaukee before I got
hold of him, and he's licked Tracy three times in the
last year.

"I've gave him all the best of it in a money way and
he's got seven thousand bucks in cold storage. How's
that for a kid that was in the gutter two years ago? And
he'd have still more yet if he wasn't so nuts over clo'es
and got to stop at the good hotels and so forth."

"Where's his home at?"

"Well, he ain't really got no home. He came from Chicago and his mother canned him out o' the house for bein' no good. She give him a raw deal, I guess, and he says he won't have nothin' to do with her unlest she comes to him first. She's got a pile o' money, he says, so he ain't worryin' about her."

The gentleman under discussion entered the café and swaggered to Tommy's table, while the whole room turned to look.

Midge was the picture of health despite a slightly colored eye and an ear that seemed to have no opening. But perhaps it was not his healthiness that drew all eyes. His diamond horse-shoe tie pin, his purple cross-striped shirt, his orange shoes, and his light blue suit fairly screamed for attention.

"Where you been?" he asked Tommy. "I been lookin' all over for you."

"Set down," said his manager.

"No time," said Midge. "I'm goin' down to the w'arf and see 'em unload the fish."

"Shake hands with my brother Dan," said Tommy.

Midge shook with the Holyoke Haley.

"If you're Tommy's brother, you're O. K. with me," said Midge, and the brothers beamed with pleasure.

Dan moistened his lips and murmured an embarrassed reply, but it was lost on the young gladiator.

"Leave me take twenty," Midge was saying. "I prob'ly won't need it, but I don't like to be caught short."

Tommy parted with a twenty dollar bill and recorded the transaction in a small black book the insurance company had given him for Christmas.

"But," he said, "it won't cost you no twenty to look at them fish. Want me to go along?"

"No," said Midge hastily. "You and your brother here prob'ly got a lot to say to each other."

"Well," said Tommy, "don't take no bad money and don't get lost. And you better be back at four o'clock and lay down a w'ile."

"I don't need no rest to beat this guy," said Midge. "He'll do enough layin' down for the both of us."

And laughing even more than the jest called for, he strode out through the fire of admiring and startled glances.

The corner of Boylston and Tremont was the nearest Midge got to the wharf, but the lady awaiting him was doubtless a more dazzling sight than the catch of the luckiest Massachusetts fisherman. She could talk, too— probably better than the fish.

"O you Kid!" she said, flashing a few silver teeth among the gold. "O you fighting man!"

Midge smiled up at her.

"We'll go somewheres and get a drink," he said. "One won't hurt."

In New Orleans, five months after he had rearranged the map of Bud Cross for the third time, Midge finished training for his championship bout with the Dutchman.

Back in his hotel after the final workout, Midge stopped to chat with some of the boys from up north, who had made the long trip to see a champion de-throned, for the result of this bout was so nearly a fore-gone conclusion that even the experts had guessed it.

Tommy Haley secured the key and the mail and ascended to the Kelly suite. He was bathing when Midge came in, half an hour later.

"Any mail?" asked Midge.

"There on the bed," replied Tommy from the tub.

Midge picked up the stack of letters and postcards and glanced them over. From the pile he sorted out three letters and laid them on the table. The rest he

.tossed into the waste-basket. Then he picked up the three and sat for a few moments holding them, while his eyes gazed off into space. At length he looked again at the three unopened letters in his hand; then he put one in his pocket and tossed the other two at the basket. They missed their target and fell on the floor.

"Hell!" said Midge, and stooping over picked them up.

He opened one postmarked Milwaukee and read:

Dear Husband:

I have wrote to you so manny times and got no anser and I dont know if you ever got them, so I am writeing again in the hopes you will get this letter and anser. I dont like to bother you with my trubles and I would not only for the baby and I am not asking you should write to me but only send a little money and I am not asking for myself but the baby has not been well a day sence last Aug. and the dr. told me she cant live much longer unless I give her better food and thats impossible the way things are. Lou has not been working for a year and what I make dont hardley pay for the rent. I am not asking for you to give me any money, but only you should send what I loaned when convenient and I think it amts. to about $36.00. Please try and send that amt. and it will help me, but if you cant send the whole amt. try and send me something.

Your wife,

Emma.

Midge tore the letter into a hundred pieces and scattered them over the floor.

"Money, money, money!" he said. "They must think I'm made o' money. I s'pose the old woman's after it too."

He opened his mother's letter:

dear Michael Connie wonted me to rite and say you must beet the dutchman and he is sur you will and wonted me to say we wont you to rite and tell us about it, but I

gess you havent no time to rite or we herd from you long
beffore this but I wish you would rite jest a line or 2 boy
becaus it wuld be better for Connie then a barl of medisin.
It wuld help me to keep things going if you send me money
now and then when you can spair it but if you cant send
no money try and fine time to rite a letter onley a few lines
and it will please Connie. jest think boy he hasent got out
of bed in over 3 yrs. Connie says good luck.

Your Mother,

Ellen F. Kelly.

"I thought so," said Midge. "They're all alike."
The third letter was from New York. It read:

Hon:—This is the last letter you will get from me before
your champ, but I will send you a telegram Saturday, but
I can't say as much in a telegram as in a letter and I am
writeing this to let you know I am thinking of you and
praying for good luck.

Lick him good hon and don't wait no longer than you
have to and don't forget to wire me as soon as its over.
Give him that little old left of yours on the nose hon and
don't be afraid of spoiling his good looks because he
couldn't be no homlier than he is. But don't let him spoil
my baby's pretty face. You won't will you hon.

Well hon I would give anything to be there and see it,
but I guess you love Haley better than me or you wouldn't
let him keep me away. But when your champ hon we can
do as we please and tell Haley to go to the devil.

Well hon I will send you a telegram Saturday and I almost forgot to tell you I will need some more money, a
couple hundred say and you will have to wire it to me as
soon as you get this. You will won't you hon.

I will send you a telegram Saturday and remember hon
I am pulling for you.

Well good-by sweetheart and good luck.

Grace.

"They're all alike," said Midge. "Money, money,
money."

Tommy Haley, shining from his ablutions, came in from the adjoining room.

"Thought you'd be layin' down," he said.

"I'm goin' to," said Midge, unbuttoning his orange shoes.

"I'll call you at six and you can eat up here without no bugs to pester you. I got to go down and give them birds their tickets."

"Did you hear from Goldberg?" asked Midge.

"Didn't I tell you? Sure; fifteen weeks at five hundred, if we win. And we can get a guarantee o' twelve thousand, with privileges either in New York or Milwaukee."

"Who with?"

"Anybody that'll stand up in front of you. You don't care who it is, do you?"

"Not me. I'll make 'em all look like a monkey."

"Well you better lay down aw'ile."

"Oh, say, wire two hundred to Grace for me, will you? Right away; the New York address."

"Two hundred! You just sent her three hundred last Sunday."

"Well, what the hell do you care?"

"All right, all right. Don't get sore about it. Anything else?"

"That's all," said Midge, and dropped onto the bed.

"And I want the deed done before I come back," said Grace as she rose from the table. "You won't fall down on me, will you, hon?"

"Leave it to me," said Midge. "And don't spend no more than you have to."

Grace smiled a farewell and left the café. Midge continued to sip his coffee and read his paper.

They were in Chicago and they were in the middle

of Midge's first week in vaudeville. He had come straight north to reap the rewards of his glorious victory over the broken down Dutchman. A fortnight had been spent in learning his act, which consisted of a gymnastic exhibition and a ten minutes' monologue on the various excellences of Midge Kelly. And now he was twice daily turning 'em away from the Madison Theater.

His breakfast over and his paper read, Midge sauntered into the lobby and asked for his key. He then beckoned to a bell-boy, who had been hoping for that very honor.

"Find Haley, Tommy Haley," said Midge. "Tell him to come up to my room."

"Yes, sir, Mr. Kelly," said the boy, and proceeded to break all his former records for diligence.

Midge was looking out of his seventh-story window when Tommy answered the summons.

"What'll it be?" inquired his manager.

There was a pause before Midge replied.

"Haley," he said, "twenty-five per cent's a whole lot o' money."

"I guess I got it comin', ain't I?" said Tommy.

"I don't see how you figger it. I don't see where you're worth it to me."

"Well," said Tommy, "I didn't expect nothin' like this. I thought you was satisfied with the bargain. I don't want to beat nobody out o' nothin', but I don't see where you could have got anybody else that would of did all I done for you."

"Sure, that's all right," said the champion. "You done a lot for me in Philly. And you got good money for it, didn't you?"

"I ain't makin' no holler. Still and all, the big money's still ahead of us yet. And if it hadn't of been for me, you wouldn't of never got within grabbin' distance."

"Oh, I guess I could of went along all right," said Midge. "Who was it that hung that left on the Dutchman's jaw, me or you?"

"Yes, but you wouldn't been in the ring with the Dutchman if it wasn't for how I handled you."

"Well, this won't get us nowheres. The idear is that you ain't worth no twenty-five per cent now and it don't make no diff'rence what come off a year or two ago."

"Don't it?" said Tommy. "I'd say it made a whole lot of difference."

"Well, I say it don't and I guess that settles it."

"Look here, Midge," Tommy said, "I thought I was fair with you, but if you don't think so, I'm willin' to hear what you think is fair. I don't want nobody callin' me a Sherlock. Let's go down to business and sign up a contrac'. What's your figger?"

"I ain't namin' no figger," Midge replied. "I'm sayin' that twenty-five's too much. Now what are you willin' to take?"

"How about twenty?"

"Twenty's too much," said Kelly.

"What ain't too much?" asked Tommy.

"Well, Haley, I might as well give it to you straight. They ain't nothin' that ain't too much."

"You mean you don't want me at no figger?"

"That's the idear."

There was a minute's silence. Then Tommy Haley walked toward the door.

"Midge," he said, in a choking voice, "you're makin' a big mistake, boy. You can't throw down your best friends and get away with it. That damn woman will ruin you."

Midge sprang from his seat.

"You shut your mouth!" he stormed. "Get out o' here before they have to carry you out. You been spongin' off o' me long enough. Say one more word about the girl or about anything else and you'll get what the Dutchman got. Now get out!"

And Tommy Haley, having a very vivid memory of the Dutchman's face as he fell, got out.

Grace came in later, dropped her numerous bundles on the lounge and perched herself on the arm of Midge's chair.

"Well?" she said.

"Well," said Midge, "I got rid of him."

"Good boy!" said Grace. "And now I think you might give me that twenty-five per cent."

"Besides the seventy-five you're already gettin'?" said Midge.

"Don't be no grouch, hon. You don't look pretty when you're grouchy."

"It ain't my business to look pretty," Midge replied.

"Wait till you see how I look with the stuff I bought this mornin'!"

Midge glanced at the bundles on the lounge.

"There's Haley's twenty-five per cent," he said, "and then some."

The champion did not remain long without a manager. Haley's successor was none other than Jerome Harris, who saw in Midge a better meal ticket than his popular-priced musical show had been.

The contract, giving Mr. Harris twenty-five per cent of Midge's earnings, was signed in Detroit the week after Tommy Haley had heard his dismissal read. It had taken Midge just six days to learn that a popular actor cannot get on without the ministrations of a man who thinks, talks, and means business. At first Grace objected to the new member of the firm, but when Mr. Harris had demanded and secured from the vaudeville people a one-hundred dollar increase in Midge's weekly stipend, she was convinced that the champion had acted for the best.

"You and my missus will have some great old times," Harris told Grace. "I'd of wired her to join us here, only I seen the Kid's bookin' takes us to Milwaukee next week, and that's where she is."

But when they were introduced in the Milwaukee hotel, Grace admitted to herself that her feeling for Mrs. Harris could hardly be called love at first sight. Midge, on the contrary, gave his new manager's wife the many times over and seemed loath to end the feast of his eyes.

"Some doll," he said to Grace when they were alone.

"Doll is right," the lady replied, "and sawdust where her brains ought to be."

"I'm li'ble to steal that baby," said Midge, and he smiled as he noted the effect of his words on his audience's face.

On Tuesday of the Milwaukee week the champion successfully defended his title in a bout that the newspapers never reported. Midge was alone in his room that morning when a visitor entered without knocking. The visitor was Lou Hersch.

Midge turned white at sight of him.

"What do you want?" he demanded.

"I guess you know," said Lou Hersch. "Your wife's starvin' to death and your baby's starvin' to death and I'm starvin' to death. And you're dirty with money."

"Listen," said Midge, "if it wasn't for you, I wouldn't never saw your sister. And, if you ain't man enough to hold a job, what's that to me? The best thing you can do is keep away from me."

"You give me a piece o' money and I'll go."

Midge's reply to the ultimatum was a straight right to his brother-in-law's narrow chest.

"Take that home to your sister."

And after Lou Hersch had picked himself up and slunk away, Midge thought: "It's lucky I didn't give him my left or I'd of croaked him. And if I'd hit him in the stomach, I'd of broke his spine."

There was a party after each evening performance during the Milwaukee engagement. The wine flowed freely and Midge had more of it than Tommy Haley ever would have permitted him. Mr. Harris offered no objection, which was possibly just as well for his own physical comfort.

In the dancing between drinks, Midge had his new manager's wife for a partner as often as Grace. The latter's face as she floundered round in the arms of the portly Harris, belied her frequent protestations that she was having the time of her life.

Several times that week, Midge thought Grace was on the point of starting the quarrel he hoped to have. But it was not until Friday night that she accommodated. He and Mrs. Harris had disappeared after the matinee and when Grace saw him again at the close of the night show, she came to the point at once.

"What are you tryin' to pull off?" she demanded.

"It's none o' your business, is it?" said Midge.

"You bet it's my business; mine and Harris's. You cut it short or you'll find out."

"Listen," said Midge, "have you got a mortgage on me or somethin'? You talk like we was married."

"We're goin' to be, too. And to-morrow's as good a time as any."

"Just about," Midge said. "You got as much chanct o' marryin' me to-morrow as the next day or next year and that ain't no chanct at all."

"We'll find out," said Grace.

"You're the one that's got somethin' to find out."

"What do you mean?"

"I mean I'm married already."

"You lie!"

"You think so, do you? Well, s'pose you go to this here address and get acquainted with my missus."

Midge scrawled a number on a piece of paper and handed it to her. She stared at it unseeingly.

"Well," said Midge, "I ain't kiddin' you. You go there and ask for Mrs. Michael Kelly, and if you don't find her, I'll marry you to-morrow before breakfast."

Still Grace stared at the scrap of paper. To Midge it seemed an age before she spoke again.

"You lied to me all this w'ile."

"You never ast me was I married. What's more, what the hell diff'rence did it make to you? You got a split, didn't you? Better'n fifty-fifty."

He started away.

"Where you goin'?"

"I'm goin' to meet Harris and his wife."

"I'm goin' with you. You're not goin' to shake me now."

"Yes, I am, too," said Midge quietly. "When I leave town to-morrow night, you're going to stay here. And if I see where you're goin' to make a fuss, I'll put you in a hospital where they'll keep you quiet. You can get your stuff to-morrow mornin' and I'll slip you a hundred bucks. And then I don't want to see no more o' you. And don't try and tag along now or I'll have to add another K. O. to the old record."

When Grace returned to the hotel that night, she discovered that Midge and the Harrises had moved to another. And when Midge left town the following night, he was again without a manager, and Mr. Harris was without a wife.

Three days prior to Midge Kelly's ten-round bout with Young Milton in New York City, the sporting editor of the *News* assigned Joe Morgan to write two or three thousand words about the champion to run with a picture lay-out for Sunday.

Joe Morgan dropped in at Midge's training quarters Friday afternoon. Midge, he learned, was doing road work, but Midge's manager, Wallie Adams, stood ready and willing to supply reams of dope about the greatest fighter of the age.

"Let's hear what you've got," said Joe, "and then I'll try to fix up something."

So Wallie stepped on the accelerator of his imagination and shot away.

"Just a kid; that's all he is; a regular boy. Get what I mean? Don't know the meanin' o' bad habits. Never tasted liquor in his life and would prob'bly get sick if he smelled it. Clean livin' put him up where he's at. Get what I mean? And modest and unassumin' as a school girl. He's so quiet you wouldn't never know he was round. And he'd go to jail before he'd talk about himself.

"No job at all to get him in shape, 'cause he's always that way. The only trouble we have with him is gettin' him to light into these poor bums they match him up with. He's scared he'll hurt somebody. Get what I mean? He's tickled to death over this match with Milton, 'cause everybody says Milton can stand the gaff. Midge'll maybe be able to cut loose a little this time. But the last two bouts he had, the guys hadn't no business in the ring with him, and he was holdin' back all the w'ile for the fear he'd kill somebody. Get what I mean?"

"Is he married?" inquired Joe.

"Say, you'd think he was married to hear him rave about them kiddies he's got. His fam'ly's up in Canada

to their summer home and Midge is wild to get up there
with 'em. He thinks more o' that wife and them kiddies
than all the money in the world. Get what I mean?"

"How many children has he?"

"I don't know, four or five, I guess. All boys and every
one of 'em a dead ringer for their dad."

"Is his father living?"

"No, the old man died when he was a kid. But he's
got a grand old mother and a kid brother out in Chi.
They're the first ones he thinks about after a match,
them and his wife and kiddies. And he don't forget
to send the old woman a thousand bucks after every
bout. He's goin' to buy her a new home as soon as they
pay him off for this match."

"How about his brother? Is he going to tackle the
game?"

"Sure, and Midge says he'll be a champion before
he's twenty years old. They're a fightin' fam'ly and all
of 'em honest and straight as a die. Get what I mean?
A fella that I can't tell you his name come to Midge in
Milwaukee onct and wanted him to throw a fight and
Midge give him such a trimmin' in the street that he
couldn't go on that night. That's the kind he is. Get
what I mean?"

Joe Morgan hung around the camp until Midge and
his trainers returned.

"One o' the boys from the *News*," said Wallie by
way of introduction. "I been givin' him your fam'ly
hist'ry."

"Did he give you good dope?" he inquired.

"He's some historian," said Joe.

"Don't call me no names," said Wallie smiling. "Call
us up if they's anything more you want. And keep your
eyes on us Monday night. Get what I mean?"

The story in Sunday's *News* was read by thousands

of lovers of the manly art. It was well written and full
of human interest. Its slight inaccuracies went unchal-
lenged, though three readers, besides Wallie Adams and
Midge Kelly, saw and recognized them. The three were
Grace, Tommy Haley, and Jerome Harris and the comments they made were not for publication.

Neither the Mrs. Kelly in Chicago nor the Mrs. Kelly
in Milwaukee knew that there was such a paper as the
New York *News.* And even if they had known of it and
that it contained two columns of reading matter about
Midge, neither mother nor wife could have bought it.
For the *News* on Sunday is a nickel a copy.

Joe Morgan could have written more accurately, no
doubt, if instead of Wallie Adams, he had interviewed
Ellen Kelly and Connie Kelly and Emma Kelly and Lou
Hersch and Grace and Jerome Harris and Tommy
Haley and Hap Collins and two or three Milwaukee
bartenders.

But a story built on their evidence would never have
passed the sporting editor.

"Suppose you can prove it," that gentleman would
have said. "It wouldn't get us anything but abuse to
print it. The people don't want to see him knocked.
He's champion."

A DAY WITH CONRAD GREEN

CONRAD GREEN woke up depressed and, for a moment, could not think why. Then he remembered. Herman Plant was dead; Herman Plant, who had been his confidential secretary ever since he had begun producing; who had been much more than a secretary—his champion, votary, shield, bodyguard, tool, occasional lackey, and the butt of his heavy jokes and nasty temper. For forty-five dollars a week.

Herman Plant was dead, and this Lewis, recommended by Ezra Peebles, a fellow entrepreneur, had not, yesterday, made a good first impression. Lewis was apparently impervious to hints. You had to tell him things right out, and when he did understand he looked at you as if you were a boob. And insisted on a salary of sixty dollars right at the start. Perhaps Peebles, who, Green knew, hated him almost enough to make it fifty-fifty, was doing him another dirty trick dressed up as a favor.

After ten o'clock, and still Green had not had enough sleep. It had been nearly three when his young wife and he had left the Bryant-Walkers's. Mrs. Green, the former Marjorie Manning of the Vanities chorus, had driven home to Long Island, while he had stayed in the rooms he always kept at the Ambassador.

Marjorie had wanted to leave a good deal earlier; through no lack of effort on her part she had been almost entirely ignored by her aristocratic host and hostess and most of the guests. She had confided to her

390

husband more than once that she was sick of the whole such-and-such bunch of so-and-so's. As far as she was concerned, they could all go to hell and stay there! But Green had been rushed by the pretty and stage-struck Joyce Brainard, wife of the international polo star, and had successfully combated his own wife's importunities till the Brainards themselves had gone.

Yes, he could have used a little more sleep, but the memory of the party cheered him. Mrs. Brainard, excited by his theatrical aura and several highballs, had been almost affectionate. She had promised to come to his office some time and talk over a stage career which both knew was impossible so long as Brainard lived. But, best of all, Mr. and Mrs. Green would be listed in the papers as among those present at the Bryant-Walkers's, along with the Vanderbecks, the Suttons, and the Schuylers, and that would just about be the death of Peebles and other social sycophants of "show business." He would order all the papers now and look for his name. No; he was late and must get to his office. No telling what a mess things were in without Herman Plant. And, by the way, he mustn't forget Plant's funeral this afternoon.

He bathed, telephoned for his breakfast and his favorite barber, dressed in a symphony of purple and gray, and set out for Broadway, pretending not to hear the "There's Conrad Green!" spoken in awed tones by two flappers and a Westchester realtor whom he passed en route.

Green let himself into his private office, an office of luxurious, exotic furnishings, its walls adorned with expensive landscapes and a Zuloaga portrait of his wife. He took off his twenty-five dollar velour hat, approved of himself in the large mirror, sat down at his desk, and rang for Miss Jackson.

"All the morning papers," he ordered, "and tell Lewis to come in."

"I'll have to send out for the papers," said Miss Jackson, a tired-looking woman of forty-five or fifty.

"What do you mean, send out? I thought we had an arrangement with that boy to leave them every morning."

"We did. But the boy says he can't leave them any more till we've paid up to date."

"What do we owe?"

"Sixty-five dollars."

"Sixty-five dollars! He's crazy! Haven't you been paying him by the week?"

"No. You told me not to."

"I told you nothing of the kind! Sixty-five dollars! He's trying to rob us!"

"I don't believe so, Mr. Green," said Miss Jackson. "He showed me his book. It's more than thirty weeks since he began, and you know we've never paid him."

"But hell! There isn't sixty-five dollars' worth of newspapers ever been printed! Tell him to sue us! And now send out for the papers and do it quick! After this we'll get them down at the corner every morning and pay for them. Tell Lewis to bring me the mail."

Miss Jackson left him, and presently the new secretray came in. He was a man under thirty, whom one would have taken for a high-school teacher rather than a theatrical general's aide-de-camp.

"Good-morning, Mr. Green," he said.

His employer disregarded the greeting.

"Anything in the mail?" he asked.

"Not much of importance. I've already answered most of it. Here are a few things from your clipping bureau and a sort of dunning letter from some jeweler in Philadelphia."

"What did you open that for?" demanded Green, crossly. "Wasn't it marked personal?"

"Look here, Mr. Green," said Lewis quietly: "I was told you had a habit of being rough with your employees. I want to warn you that I am not used to that sort of treatment and don't intend to get used to it. If you are decent with me, I'll work for you. Otherwise I'll resign."

"I don't know what you're talking about, Lewis. I didn't mean to be rough. It's just my way of speaking. Let's forget it and I'll try not to give you any more cause to complain."

"All right, Mr. Green. You told me to open all your mail except the letters with that one little mark on them—"

"Yes, I know. Now let's have the clippings."

Lewis laid them on the desk.

"I threw away about ten of them that were all the same—the announcement that you had signed Bonnie Blue for next season. There's one there that speaks of a possible partnership between you and Sam Stein—"

"What a nerve he's got, giving out a statement like that. Fine chance of me mixing myself up with a crook like Stein! Peebles says he's a full stepbrother to the James boys. So is Peebles himself, for that matter. What's this long one about?"

"It's about that young composer, Casper Ettelson. It's by Deems Taylor of the *World*. There's just a mention of you down at the bottom."

"Read it to me, will you? I've overstrained my eyes lately."

The dead Herman Plant had first heard of that recent eye strain twenty years ago. It amounted to almost total blindness where words of over two syllables were concerned.

"So far," Lewis read, "Ettelson has not had a book worthy of his imaginative, whimsical music. How we would revel in an Ettelson score with a Barrie libretto and a Conrad Green production."

"Who is this Barrie?" asked Green.

"I suppose it's James M. Barrie," replied Lewis, "the man who wrote *Peter Pan*."

"I thought that was written by a fella over in England," said Green.

"I guess he does live in England. He was born in Scotland. I don't know where he is now."

"Well, find out if he's in New York, and, if he is, get a hold of him. Maybe he'll do a couple of scenes for our next show. Come in, Miss Jackson. Oh, the papers!"

Miss Jackson handed them to him and went out. Green turned first to the society page of the *Herald Tribune*. His eye trouble was not so severe as to prevent his finding that page. And he could read his name when it was there to be read.

Three paragraphs were devoted to the Bryant-Walker affair, two of them being lists of names. And Mr. and Mrs. Conrad Green were left out.

"——!" commented Green, and grabbed the other papers. The *World* and *Times* were searched with the same hideous result. And the others did not mention the party at all.

"——!" repeated Green. "I'll get somebody for this!" Then to Lewis: "Here! Take this telegram. Send it to the managing editors of all the morning papers; you'll find their names pasted on Plant's desk. Now: 'Ask your society editor why my name was not on list of guests at Bryant-Walker dinner Wednesday night. Makes no difference to me, as am not seeking and do not need publicity, but it looks like conspiracy, and thought you ought to be informed, as have always been good friend of your paper, as well as steady advertiser.' I guess that's enough."

"If you'll pardon a suggestion," said Lewis, "I'm afraid a telegram like this would just be laughed at."

"You send the telegram; I'm not going to have a bunch of cheap reporters make a fool of me!"

"I don't believe you can blame the reporters. There probably weren't reporters there. The list of guests is generally given out by the people who give the party."

"But listen—" Green paused and thought. "All right. Don't send the telegram. But if the Bryant-Walkers are ashamed of me, why the hell did they invite me? I certainly didn't want to go and they weren't under obligations to me. I never—"

As if it had been waiting for its cue, the telephone rang at this instant, and Kate, the switchboard girl, announced that the Bryant-Walkers's secretary was on the wire.

"I am speaking for Mrs. Bryant-Walker," said a female voice. "She is chairman of the committee on entertainment for the Women's Progress Bazaar. The bazaar is to open on the third of next month and wind up on the evening of the fifth with a sort of vaudeville entertainment. She wanted me to ask you—"

Green hung up with an oath.

"That's the answer!" he said. "The damn grafters!"

Miss Jackson came in again.

"Mr. Robert Blair is waiting to see you."

"Who is he?"

"You know. He tried to write some things for one of the shows last year."

"Oh, yes. Say, did you send flowers to Plant's house?"

"I did," replied Miss Jackson. "I sent some beautiful roses."

"How much?"

"Forty-five dollars," said Miss Jackson.

"Forty-five dollars for roses! And the man hated flowers even when he was alive! Well, send in this Blair."

Robert Blair was an ambitious young free lance who had long been trying to write for the stage, but with little success.

"Sit down, Blair," said Green. "What's on your mind?"

"Well, Mr. Green, my stuff didn't seem to suit you last year, but this time I think I've got a scene that can't miss."

"All right. If you want to leave it here, I'll read it over."

"I haven't written it out. I thought I'd tell you the idea first."

"Well, go ahead, but cut it short; I've got a lot of things to do today. Got to go to old Plant's funeral for one thing."

"I bet you miss him, don't you?" said Blair, sympathetically.

"Miss him! I should say I do! A lovable character and" —with a glance at Lewis—"the best secretary I'll ever have. But let's hear your scene."

"Well," said Blair, "it may not sound like much the way I tell it, but I think it'll work out great. Well, the police get a report that a woman has been murdered in her home, and they go there and find her husband, who is acting very nervous. They give him the third degree, and he finally breaks down and admits he killed her. They ask him why, and he tells them he is very fond of beans, and on the preceding evening he came home to dinner and asked her what there was to eat, and she told him she had lamb chops, mashed potatoes, spinach, and apple pie. So he says, 'No beans?' and she says, 'No beans.' So he shoots her dead. Of course, the scene between the husband and wife is acted out on the stage. Then—"

"It's no good!" said Conrad Green. "In the first place, it takes too many people, all those policemen and everybody."

"Why, all you need is two policemen and the man and his wife. And wait till I tell you the rest of it."

"I don't like it; it's no good. Come back again when you've got something."

When Blair had gone Green turned to Lewis.

"That's all for just now," he said, "but on your way out tell Miss Jackson to get a hold of Martin and say I want him to drop in here as soon as he can."

"What Martin?" asked Lewis.

"She'll know—Joe Martin, the man that writes most of our librettos."

Alone, Conrad Green crossed the room to his safe, opened it, and took out a box on which was inscribed the name of a Philadelphia jeweler. From the box he removed a beautiful rope of matched pearls and was gazing at them in admiration when Miss Jackson came in; whereupon he hastily replaced them in their case and closed the safe.

"That man is here again," said Miss Jackson, "That man Hawley from *Gay New York*."

"Tell him I'm not in."

"I did, but he says he saw you come in and he's going to wait till you'll talk to him. Really, Mr. Green, I think it would be best in the long run to see him. He's awfully persistent."

"All right; send him in," said Green, impatiently, "though I have no idea what he can possibly want of me."

Mr. Hawley, dapper and eternally smiling, insisted on shaking hands with his unwilling host, who had again sat down at his desk.

"I think," he said, "we've met before."

"Not that I know of," Green replied shortly.

"Well, it makes no difference, but I'm sure you've read our little paper, *Gay New York*."

"No," said Green. "All I have time to read is manuscripts."

"You don't know what you're missing," said Hawley. "It's really a growing paper, with a big New York circulation, and a circulation that is important from your standpoint."

"Are you soliciting subscriptions?" asked Green.

"No. Advertising."

"Well, frankly, Mr. Hawley, I don't believe I need any advertising. I believe that even the advertising I put in the regular daily papers is a waste of money."

"Just the same," said Hawley, "I think you'd be making a mistake not to take a page in *Gay New York*. It's only a matter of fifteen hundred dollars."

"Fifteen hundred dollars! That's a joke! Nobody's going to hold *me* up!"

"Nobody's trying to, Mr. Green. But I might as well tell you that one of our reporters came in with a story the other day—well, it was about a little gambling affair in which some of the losers sort of forgot to settle, and—well, my partner was all for printing it, but I said I had always felt friendly toward you and why not give you a chance to state your side of it?"

"I don't know what you're talking about. If your reporter has got my name mixed up in a gambling story he's crazy."

"No. He's perfectly sane and very, very careful. We

make a specialty of careful reporters and we're always sure of our facts."

Conrad Green was silent for a long, long time. Then he said:

"I tell you, I don't know what gambling business you refer to, and, furthermore, fifteen hundred dollars is a hell of a price for a page in a paper like yours. But still, as you say, you've got the kind of circulation that might do me good. So if you'll cut down the price——"

"I'm sorry, Mr. Green, but we never do that."

"Well, then, of course you'll have to give me a few days to get my ad fixed up. Say you come back here next Monday afternoon."

"That's perfectly satisfactory, Mr. Green," said Hawley, "and I assure you that you're not making a mistake. And now I won't keep you any longer from your work."

He extended his hand, but it was ignored, and he went out, his smile a little broader than when he had come in. Green remained at his desk, staring straight ahead of him and making semi-audible references to certain kinds of dogs as well as personages referred to in the Old and New Testaments. He was interrupted by the entrance of Lewis.

"Mr. Green," said the new secretary, "I have found a check for forty-five dollars, made out to Herman Plant. I imagine it is for his final week's pay. Would you like to have me change it and make it out to his widow?"

"Yes," said Green. "But no; wait a minute. Tear it up and I'll make out my personal check to her and add something to it."

"All right," said Lewis, and left.

"Forty-five dollars' worth of flowers," said Green to himself, and smiled for the first time that morning.

He looked at his watch and got up and put on his beautiful hat.

"I'm going to lunch," he told Miss Jackson on his way through the outer office. "If Peebles or anybody important calls up, tell them I'll be here all afternoon."

"You're not forgetting Mr. Plant's funeral?"

"Oh, that's right. Well, I'll be here from one-thirty to about three."

A head waiter at the Astor bowed to him obsequiously and escorted him to a table near a window, while the occupants of several other tables gazed at him spellbound and whispered, "Conrad Green."

A luncheon of clams, sweetbreads, spinach, strawberry ice cream, and small coffee seemed to satisfy him. He signed his check and then tipped his own waiter and the head waiter a dollar apiece, the two tips falling just short of the cost of the meal.

Joe Martin, his chief librettist, was waiting when he got back to his office.

"Oh, hello, Joe!" he said, cordially. "Come right inside. I think I've got something for you."

Martin followed him in and sat down without waiting for an invitation. Green seated himself at his desk and drew out his cigarette case.

"Have one, Joe?"

"Not that kind!" said Martin, lighting one of his own. "You've got rotten taste in everything but gals."

"And librettists," replied Green, smiling.

"But here's what I wanted to talk about. I couldn't sleep last night, and I just laid there and an idea came to me for a comedy scene. I'll give you the bare idea and you can work it out. It'll take a girl and one of the comics, maybe Fraser, and a couple of other men that can play.

"Well, the idea is that the comic is married to the girl. In the first place, I'd better mention that the comic is crazy about beans. Well, one night the comic—no, wait a minute. The police get word that the comic's wife has been murdered and two policemen come to the comic's apartment to investigate. They examine the corpse and find out she's been shot through the head. They ask the comic if he knows who did it and he says no, but they keep after him, and finally he breaks down and admits that he did it himself.

"But he says, 'Gentlemen, if you'll let me explain the circumstances, I don't believe you'll arrest me.' So they tell him to explain, and he says that he came home from work and he was very hungry and he asked his wife what they were going to have for dinner. So she tells him—clams and sweetbreads and spinach and strawberry ice cream and coffee. So he asks her if she isn't going to have any beans and she says no, and he shoots her. What do you think you could do with that idea?"

"Listen, Connie," said Martin: "You've only got half the scene, and you've got that half wrong. In the second place, it was played a whole season in the Music Box and it was written by Bert Kalmar and Harry Ruby. Otherwise I can do a whole lot with it."

"Are you sure you're right?"

"I certainly am!"

"Why, that damn little thief! He told me it was his!"

"Who?" asked Martin.

"Why, that Blair, that tried to butt in here last year. I'll fix him!"

"I thought you said it was your own idea."

"Hell, no! Do you think I'd be stealing stuff, especially if it was a year old?"

"Well," said Martin, "when you get another inspiration like this, give me a ring and I'll come around. Now I've got to hurry up to the old Stadium and see what the old Babe does in the first inning."

"I'm sorry, Joe. I thought it was perfectly all right."

"Never mind! You didn't waste much of my time. But after this you'd better leave the ideas to me. So long!"

"Good-by, Joe; and thanks for coming in."

Martin went and Green pressed the button for Miss Jackson.

"Miss Jackson, don't ever let that young Blair in here again. He's a faker!"

"All right, Mr. Green. But don't you think it's about time you were starting for the funeral? It's twenty minutes of three."

"Yes. But let's see: where is Plant's house?"

"It's up on One Hundred and Sixtieth street, just off Broadway."

"My God! Imagine living there! Wait a minute, Miss Jackson. Send Lewis here."

"Lewis," he said, when the new secretary appeared, "I ate something this noon that disagreed with me. I wanted to go up to Plant's funeral, but I really think it would be dangerous to try it. Will you go up there, let them know who you are, and kind of represent me? Miss Jackson will give you the address."

"Yes, sir," said Lewis, and went out.

Almost immediately the sanctum door opened again and the beautiful Marjorie Green, née Manning, entered unannounced. Green's face registered not altogether pleasant surprise.

"Why, hello, dear!" he said. "I didn't know you were coming to town today."

"I never told you I wasn't," his wife replied.

They exchanged the usual connubial salutations.

"I supposed you noticed," said Mrs. Green, "that our names were not on the list of guests at the party."

"No; I haven't had time to look at the papers. But what's the difference?"

"No difference at all, of course. But do you know

what I think? I think we were invited just because those people want to get something out of you, for some benefit or something."

"A fine chance! I hope they try it!"

"However, that's not what I came to talk about."

"Well, dear, what is it?"

"I thought maybe you'd remember something."

"What, honey?"

"Why—oh, well, there's no use talking about it if you've forgotten."

Green's forehead wrinkled in deep thought; then suddenly his face brightened.

"Of course I haven't forgotten! It's your birthday!"

"You just thought of it now!"

"No such a thing! I've been thinking of it for weeks!"

"I don't believe you! If you had been, you'd have said something, and"—his wife was on the verge of tears—"you'd have given me some little thing, just any little thing."

Once more Green frowned, and once more brightened up.

"I'll prove it to you," he said, and walked rapidly to the safe.

In a moment he had placed in her hands the jewel box from Philadelphia. In another moment she had opened it, gasped at the beauty of its contents, and thrown her arms around his neck.

"Oh, dearest!" she cried. "Can you ever forgive me for doubting you?"

She put the pearls to her mouth as if she would eat them.

"But haven't you been terribly extravagant?"

"I don't consider anything too extravagant for you."

"You're the best husband a girl ever had!"

"I'm glad you're pleased," said Green.

"Pleased! I'm overwhelmed. And to think I imagined you'd forgotten! But I'm not going to break up your whole day. I know you want to get out to poor old Plant's funeral. So I'll run along. And maybe you'll take me to dinner somewhere tonight."

"I certainly will! You be at the Ambassador about six-thirty and we'll have a little birthday party. But don't you want to leave the pearls here now?"

"I should say not! They're going to stay with me for-ever! Anyone that tries to take them will do it over my dead body!"

"Well, good-by then, dear."

"Till half past six."

Green, alone again, kicked shut the door of his safe and returned to his desk, saying in loud tones things which are not ordinarily considered appropriate to the birthday of a loved one. The hubbub must have been audible to Miss Jackson ouside, but perhaps she was accustomed to it. It ceased at another unannounced en-trance, that of a girl even more beautiful than the one who had just gone out. She looked at Green and laughed.

"My God! You look happy!" she said.

"Rose!"

"Yes, it's Rose. But what's the matter with you?"

"I've had a bad day."

"But isn't it better now?"

"I didn't think you were coming till tomorrow."

"But aren't you glad I came today?"

"You bet I am!" said Green. "And if you'll come here and kiss me I'll be all the gladder."

"No. Let's get our business transacted first."

"What business?"

"You know perfectly well! Last time I saw you you insisted that I must give up everybody else but you. And

I promised you it would be all off between Harry and I if— Well, you know. There was a little matter of some pearls."

"I meant everything I said."

"Well, where are they?"

"They're all bought and all ready for you. But I bought them in Philadelphia and for some damn reason they haven't got here yet."

"Got here yet! Were they so heavy you couldn't bring them with you?"

"Honest, dear, they'll be here day after tomorrow at the latest."

" 'Honest' is a good word for you to use! Do you think I'm dumb? Or is it that you're so used to lying that you can't help it?"

"If you'll let me explain—"

"Explain hell! We made a bargain and you haven't kept your end of it. And now—"

"But listen—"

"I'll listen to nothing! You know where to reach me and when you've kept your promise you can call me up. Till then— Well, Harry isn't such bad company."

"Wait a minute, Rose!"

"You've heard all I've got to say. Good-by!"

And she was gone before he could intercept her.

Conrad Green sat as if stunned. For fifteen minutes he was so silent and motionless that one might have thought him dead. Then he shivered as if with cold and said aloud:

"I'm not going to worry about them any more. To hell with all of them!"

He drew the telephone to him and took off the receiver.

"Get me Mrs. Bryant-Walker."

And after a pause:

"Is this Mrs. Bryant-Walker? No, I want to speak to her personally. This is Conrad Green. Oh, hello, Mrs. Walker. Your secretary called me up this morning, but we were cut off. She was saying something about a benefit. Why, yes, certainly, I'll be glad to. As many of them as you want. If you'll just leave it all in my hands I'll guarantee you a pretty good entertainment. It's no bother at all. It's a pleasure. Thank you. Good-by."

Lewis came in.

"Well, Lewis, did you get to the funeral?"

"Yes, Mr. Green, and I saw Mrs. Plant and explained the circumstances to her. She said you had always been very kind to her husband. She said that during the week of his illness he talked of you nearly all the time and expressed confidence that if he died you would attend his funeral. So she wished you had been there."

"Good God! So do I!" said Conrad Green.

THE LOVE NEST

"I'LL TELL you what I'm going to do with you, Mr. Bartlett," said the great man. "I'm going to take you right out to my home and have you meet the wife and family; stay to dinner and all night. We've got plenty of room and extra pajamas, if you don't mind them silk. I mean that'll give you a chance to see us just as we are. I mean you can get more that way than if you sat here a whole week, asking me questions."

"But I don't want to put you to a lot of trouble," said Bartlett.

"Trouble!" The great man laughed. "There's no trouble about it. I've got a house that's like a hotel. I mean a big house with lots of servants. But anyway I'm always glad to do anything I can for a writing man, especially a man that works for Ralph Doane. I'm very fond of Ralph. I mean I like him personally besides being a great editor. I mean I've known him for years and when there's anything I can do for him, I'm glad to do it. I mean it'll be a pleasure to have you. So if you want to notify your family—"

"I haven't any family," said Bartlett.

"Well, I'm sorry for you! And I bet when you see mine, you'll wish you had one of your own. But I'm glad you can come and we'll start now so as to get there before the kiddies are put away for the night. I mean I want you to be sure and see the kiddies. I've got three."

"I've seen their pictures," said Bartlett. "You must be very proud of them. They're all girls, aren't they?"

"Yes, sir; three girls. I wouldn't have a boy. I mean I always wanted girls. I mean girls have got a lot more zip to them. I mean they're a lot zippier. But let's go! The Rolls is downstairs and if we start now we'll get there before dark. I mean I want you to see the place while it's still daylight."

The great man—Lou Gregg, president of Modern Pictures, Inc.—escorted his visitor from the magnificent office by a private door and down a private stairway to the avenue, where the glittering car with its glittering chauffeur waited.

"My wife was in town today," said Gregg as they glided northward, "and I hoped we could ride out together, but she called up about two and asked would I mind if she went on home in the Pierce. She was through with her shopping and she hates to be away from the house and the kiddies any longer than she can help. Celia's a great home girl. You'd never know she was the same girl now as the girl I married seven years ago. I mean she's different. I mean she's not the same. I mean her marriage and being a mother has developed her. Did you ever see her? I mean in pictures?"

"I think I did once," replied Bartlett. "Didn't she play the young sister in The Cad?"

"Yes, with Harold Hodgson and Marie Blythe."

"I thought I'd seen her. I remember her as very pretty and vivacious."

"She certainly was! And she is yet! I mean she's even prettier, but of course she ain't a kid, though she looks it. I mean she was only seventeen in that picture and that was ten years ago. I mean she's twenty-seven years old now. But I never met a girl with as much zip as she had in those days. It's remarkable how marriage changes them. I mean nobody would ever thought Celia Sayles would turn out to be a sit-by-the-fire. I mean she still likes a good time, but her home and kiddies come first. I mean her home and kiddies come first."

"I see what you mean," said Bartlett.

An hour's drive brought them to Ardsley-on-Hudson and the great man's home.

"A wonderful place!" Bartlett exclaimed with a heroic semblance of enthusiasm as the car turned in at an *arc de triomphe* of a gateway and approached a white house that might have been mistaken for the Yale Bowl.

"It ought to be!" said Gregg. "I mean I've spent enough on it. I mean these things cost money."

He indicated with a gesture the huge house and Urbanesque landscaping.

"But no amount of money is too much to spend on home. I mean it's a good investment if it tends to make your family proud and satisfied with their home. I mean every nickel I've spent here is like so much insurance; it insures me of a happy wife and family. And what more can a man ask!"

Bartlett didn't know, but the topic was forgotten in the business of leaving the resplendent Rolls and entering the even more resplendent reception hall.

"Forbes will take your things," said Gregg. "And, Forbes, you may tell Dennis that Mr. Bartlett will spend the night." He faced the wide stairway and raised his voice. "Sweetheart!" he called.

From above came the reply in contralto: "Hello, sweetheart!"

"Come down, sweetheart. I've brought you a visitor."

"All right, sweetheart, in just a minute."

Gregg led Bartlett into a living-room that was five laps to the mile and suggestive of an Atlantic City auction sale.

"Sit there," said the host, pointing to a balloon-stuffed easy chair, "and I'll see if we can get a drink. I've got some real old Bourbon that I'd like you to try. You know I come from Chicago and I always liked Bourbon better than Scotch. I mean I always preferred it to Scotch. Forbes," he addressed the servant, "we want a drink. You'll find a full bottle of that Bourbon in the cupboard."

"It's only half full, sir," said Forbes.

"Half full! That's funny! I mean I opened it last night and just took one drink. I mean it ought to be full."

"It's only half full," repeated Forbes, and went to fetch it.

"I'll have to investigate," Gregg told his guest. "I mean this ain't the first time lately that some of my good stuff has disappeared. When you keep so many servants, it's hard to get all honest ones. But here's Celia!"

Bartlett rose to greet the striking brunette who at this moment made an entrance so Delsarte as to be almost painful. With never a glance at him, she minced across the room to her husband and took a half interest in a convincing kiss.

"Well, sweetheart," she said when it was at last over.

"This is Mr. Bartlett, sweetheart," said her husband. "Mr. Bartlett, meet Mrs. Gregg."

Bartlett shook his hostess's proffered two fingers.

"I'm so pleased!" said Celia in a voice reminiscent of Miss Claire's imitation of Miss Barrymore.

"Mr. Bartlett," Gregg went on, "is with *Mankind,* Ralph Doane's magazine. He is going to write me up; I mean us."

"No, you mean you," said Celia. "I'm sure the public is not interested in great men's wives."

"I am sure you are mistaken, Mrs. Gregg," said Bartlett politely. "In this case at least. You are worth writing up aside from being a great man's wife."

"I'm afraid you're a flatterer, Mr. Bartlett," she returned. "I have been out of the limelight so long that I doubt if anybody remembers me. I'm no longer an artist; merely a happy wife and mother."

"And I claim, sweetheart," said Gregg, "that it takes an artist to be that."

"Oh, no, sweetheart!" said Celia. "Not when they have you for a husband!"

The exchange of hosannahs was interrupted by the arrival of Forbes with the tray.

"Will you take yours straight or in a high-ball?" Gregg inquired of his guest. "Personally I like good whisky straight. I mean mixing it with water spoils the flavor. I mean whisky like this, it seems like a crime to mix it with water."

"I'll have mine straight," said Bartlett, who would have preferred a high-ball.

While the drinks were being prepared, he observed his hostess more closely and thought how much more charming she would be if she had used finesse in improving on nature. Her cheeks, her mouth, her eyes, and lashes had been, he guessed, far above the average in beauty before she had begun experimenting with them. And her experiments had been clumsy. She was handsome in spite of her efforts to be handsomer.

"Listen, sweetheart," said her husband. "One of the servants has been helping himself to this Bourbon. I mean it was a full bottle last night and I only had one little drink out of it. And now it's less than half full. Who do you suppose has been at it?"

"How do I know, sweetheart? Maybe the groceryman or the iceman or somebody."

"But you and I and Forbes are the only ones that have a key. I mean it was locked up."

"Maybe you forgot to lock it."

"I never do. Well, anyway, Bartlett, here's a go!"

"Doesn't Mrs. Gregg indulge?" asked Bartlett.

"Only a cocktail before dinner," said Celia. "Lou objects to me drinking whisky, and I don't like it much anyway."

"I don't object to you drinking whisky, sweetheart. I just object to you drinking to excess. I mean I think it coarsens a woman to drink. I mean it makes them coarse."

"Well, there's no argument, sweetheart. As I say, I don't care whether I have it or not."

"It certainly is great Bourbon!" said Bartlett, smacking his lips and putting his glass back on the tray.

"You bet it is!" Gregg agreed. "I mean you can't buy that kind of stuff any more. I mean it's real stuff. You help yourself when you want another. Mr. Bartlett is going to stay all night, sweetheart. I told him he could get a whole lot more of a line on us that way than just interviewing me in the office. I mean I'm tongue-tied when it comes to talking about my work and my success. I mean it's better to see me out here as I am, in my home, with my family. I mean my home life speaks for itself without me saying a word."

"But, sweetheart," said his wife, "what about Mr. Latham?"

"Gosh! I forgot all about him! I must phone and see if I can call it off. That's terrible! You see," he explained to Bartlett, "I made a date to go up to Tarrytown to-night, to K. L. Latham's, the sugar people. We're going to talk over the new club. We're going to have a golf club that will make the rest of them look like a toy. I mean a real golf club! They want me to kind of run it. And I was to go up there tonight and talk it over. I'll phone and see if I can postpone it."

"Oh, don't postpone it on my account!" urged Bartlett. "I can come out again some other time, or I can see you in town."

"I don't see how you *can* postpone it, sweetheart," said Celia. "Didn't he say old Mr. King was coming over from White Plains? They'll be mad at you if you don't go."

"I'm afraid they would resent it, sweetheart. Well, I'll tell you. You can entertain Mr. Bartlett and I'll go up there right after dinner and come back as soon as I can. And Bartlett and I can talk when I get back. I mean we can talk when I get back. How is that?"

"That suits me," said Bartlett.

"I'll be as entertaining as I can," said Celia, "but I'm afraid that isn't very entertaining. However, if I'm too much of a bore, there's plenty to read."

"No danger of my being bored," said Bartlett.

"Well, that's all fixed then," said the relieved host. "I hope you'll excuse me running away. But I don't see how I can get out of it. I mean with old King coming over from White Plains. I mean he's an old man. But listen, sweetheart—where are the kiddies? Mr. Bartlett wants to see them."

"Yes, indeed!" agreed the visitor.

"Of course you'd say so!" Celia said. "But we *are* proud of them! I suppose all parents are the same. They all think their own children are the only children in the world. Isn't that so, Mr. Bartlett? Or haven't you any children?"

"I'm sorry to say I'm not married."

"Oh, you poor thing! We pity him, don't we, sweetheart? But why aren't you, Mr. Bartlett? Don't tell me you're a woman hater!"

"Not now, anyway," said the gallant Bartlett.

"Do you get that, sweetheart? He's paying **you** a pretty compliment."

"I heard it, sweetheart. And now I'm sure he's a flatterer. But I must hurry and get the children before Hortense puts them to bed."

"Well," said Gregg when his wife had left the room, "would you say she's changed?"

"A little, and for the better. She's more than fulfilled her early promise."

"I think so," said Gregg. "I mean I think she was a beautiful girl and now she's an even more beautiful woman. I mean wifehood and maternity have given her a kind of a—well, you know—I mean a kind of a pose. I mean a pose. How about another drink?"

They were emptying their glasses when Celia returned with two of her little girls.

"The baby's in bed and I was afraid to ask Hortense to get her up again. But you'll see her in the morning. This is Norma and this is Grace. Girls, this Mr. Bartlett."

The girls received this news calmly.

"Well, girls," said Bartlett.

"What do you think of them, Bartlett?" demanded their father. "I mean what do you think of them?"

"They're great!" replied the guest with creditable warmth.

"I mean aren't they pretty?"

"I should say they are!"

"There, girls! Why don't you thank Mr. Bartlett?"

"Thanks," murmured Norma.

"How old are you, Norma?" asked Bartlett.

"Six," said Norma.

"Well," said Bartlett. "And how old is Grace?"

"Four," replied Norma.

"Well," said Bartlett. "And how old is baby sister?"

"One and a half," answered Norma.

"Well," said Bartlett.

As this seemed to be final, "Come, girls," said their

mother. "Kiss daddy good night and I'll take you back to Hortense."

"I'll take them," said Gregg. "I'm going up-stairs.anyway. And you can show Bartlett around. I mean before it gets any darker."

"Good night, girls," said Bartlett, and the children murmured a good night.

"I'll come and see you before you're asleep," Celia told them. And after Gregg had led them out, "Do you really think they're pretty?" she asked Bartlett.

"I certainly do. Especially Norma. She's the image of you," said Bartlett.

"She looks a little like I used to," Celia admitted. "But I hope she doesn't look like me now. I'm too old looking."

"You look remarkably young!" said Bartlett. "No one would believe you were the mother of three children."

"Oh, Mr. Bartlett! But I mustn't forget I'm to 'show you around.' Lou is so proud of our home!"

"And with reason," said Bartlett.

"It *is* wonderful! I call it our love nest. Quite a big nest, don't you think? Mother says it's too big to be cosy; she says she can't think of it as a home. But I always say a place is whatever one makes of it. A woman can be happy in a tent if they love each other. And miserable in a royal palace without love. Don't you think so, Mr. Bartlett?"

"Yes, indeed."

"Is this really such wonderful Bourbon? I think I'll just take a sip of it and see what it's like. It can't hurt me if it's so good. Do you think so, Mr. Bartlett?"

"I don't believe so."

"Well then, I'm going to taste it and if it hurts me it's your fault."

Celia poured a whisky glass two-thirds full and drained it at a gulp.

"It *is* good, isn't it?" she said. "Of course I'm not much of a judge as I don't care for whisky and Lou won't let me drink it. But he's raved so about this Bourbon that I did want to see what it was like. You won't tell on me, will you, Mr. Bartlett?"

"Not I!"

"I wonder how it would be in a high-ball. Let's you and I have just one. But I'm forgetting I'm supposed to show you the place. We won't have time to drink a high-ball and see the place too before Lou comes down. Are you so crazy to see the place?"

"Not very."

"Well, then, what do you say if we have a high-ball? And it'll be a secret between you and I."

They drank in silence and Celia pressed a button by the door.

"You may take the bottle and tray," she told Forbes. "And now," she said to Bartlett, "we'll go out on the porch and see as much as we can see. You'll have to guess the rest."

Gregg, having changed his shirt and collar, joined them.

"Well," he said to Bartlett, "have you seen everything?"

"I guess I have, Mr. Gregg," lied the guest readily. "It's a wonderful place!"

"We like it. I mean it suits us. I mean it's my idear of a real home. And Celia calls it her love nest."

"So she told me," said Bartlett.

"She'll always be sentimental," said her husband.

He put his hand on her shoulder, but she drew away.

"I must run up and dress," she said.

"Dress!" exclaimed Bartlett, who had been dazzled by her flowered green chiffon.

"Oh, I'm not going to really dress," she said. "But I couldn't wear this thing for dinner!"

"Perhaps you'd like to clean up a little, Bartlett," said Gregg. "I mean Forbes will show you your room if you want to go up."

"It might be best," said Bartlett.

Celia, in a black lace dinner gown, was rather quiet during the elaborate meal. Three or four times when Gregg addressed her, she seemed to be thinking of something else and had to ask, "What did you say, sweetheart?" Her face was red and Bartlett imagined that she had "sneaked" a drink or two besides the two helpings of Bourbon and the cocktail that had preceded dinner.

"Well, I'll leave you," said Gregg when they were in the living-room once more. "I mean the sooner I get started, the sooner I'll be back. Sweetheart, try and keep your guest awake and don't let him die of thirst. *Au revoir,* Bartlett. I'm sorry, but it can't be helped. There's a fresh bottle of the Bourbon, so go to it. I mean help yourself. It's too bad you have to drink alone."

"It *is* too bad, Mr. Bartlett," said Celia when Gregg had gone.

"What's too bad?" asked Bartlett.

"That you have to drink alone. I feel like I wasn't being a good hostess to let you do it. In fact, I refuse to let you do it. I'll join you in just a little wee sip."

"But it's so soon after dinner!"

"It's never too soon! I'm going to have a drink myself and if you don't join me, you're a quitter."

She mixed two life-sized high-balls and handed one to her guest.

"Now we'll turn on the radio and see if we can't stir things up. There! No, no! Who cares about the old base-ball! Now! This is better! Let's dance."

"I'm sorry, Mrs. Gregg, but I don't dance."

"Well, you're an old cheese! To make me dance alone! 'All alone, yes, I'm all alone.'"

There was no affectation in her voice now and Bartlett was amazed at her unlabored grace as she glided around the big room.

"But it's no fun alone," she complained. "Let's shut the damn thing off and talk."

"I love to watch you dance," said Bartlett.

"Yes, but I'm no Pavlowa," said Celia as she silenced the radio. "And besides, it's time for a drink."

"I've still got more than half of mine."

"Well, you had that wine at dinner, so I'll have to catch up with you."

She poured herself another high-ball and went at the task of "catching up."

"The trouble with you, Mr.—now isn't that a scream! I can't think of your name."

"Bartlett."

"The trouble with you, Barker—do you know what's the trouble with you? You're too sober. See? You're too damn sober! That's the whole trouble, see? If you weren't so sober, we'd be better off. See? What I can't understand is how you can be so sober and me so high."

"You're not used to it."

"Not used to it! That's the cat's pajamas! Say, I'm like this half the time, see? If I wasn't, I'd die!"

"What does your husband say?"

"He don't say because he don't know. See, Barker? There's nights when he's out and there's a few nights when I'm out myself. And there's other nights when we're both in and I pretend I'm sleepy and I go upstairs. See? But I don't go to bed. See? I have a little party all by myself. See? If I didn't, I'd die!"

"What do you mean, you'd die?"

"You're dumb, Barker! You may be sober, but you're dumb! Did you fall for all that apple sauce about the happy home and the contented wife? Listen, Barker— I'd give anything in the world to be out of this mess. I'd give anything to never see him again."

"Don't you love him any more? Doesn't he love you? Or what?"

"Love! I never did love him! I didn't know what love was! And all his love is for himself!"

"How did you happen to get married?"

"I was a kid; that's the answer. A kid and ambitious. See? He was a director then and he got stuck on me and I thought he'd make me a star. See, Barker? I married him to get myself a chance. And now look at me!"

"I'd say you were fairly well off."

"Well off, am I? I'd change places with the scum of the earth just to be free! See, Barker? And I could have been a star without any help if I'd only realized it. I had the looks and I had the talent. I've got it yet. I could be a Swanson and get myself a marquis; maybe a prince! And look what I did get! A self-satisfied, self-centered——! I thought he'd *make* me! See, Barker? Well, he's made me all right; he's made me a chronic mother and it's a wonder I've got any looks left.

"I fought at first. I told him marriage didn't mean giving up my art, my life work. But it was no use. He wanted a beautiful wife and beautiful children for his beautiful home. Just to show us off. See? I'm part of his chattels. See, Barker? I'm just like his big diamond or his cars or his horses. And he wouldn't stand for his wife 'lowering' herself to act in pictures. Just as if pictures hadn't made him!

"You go back to your magazine tomorrow and write about our love nest. See, Barker? And be sure and don't get mixed and call it a baby ranch. Babies! You thought little Norma was pretty. Well, she is. And what is it going to get her? A rich —— of a husband that treats her like a ——! That's what it'll get her if I don't interfere. I hope I don't last long enough to see her grow up, but if I do, I'm going to advise her to run away from home and live her own life. And *be* somebody! Not a *thing* like I am! See, Barker?"

"Did you ever think of a divorce?"

"Did I ever think of one! Listen—but there's no chance. I've got nothing on him, and no matter what he had on me, he'd never let the world know it. He'd keep me here and torture me like he does now, only worse. But I haven't done anything wrong, see? The men I might care for, they're all scared of him and his money and power. See, Barker? And the others are just as bad as him. Like fat old Morris, the hotel man, that everybody thinks he's a model husband. The reason he don't step out more is because he's too stingy. But I could have him if I wanted him. Every time he gets near enough to me, he squeezes my hand. I guess he thinks it's a nickel, the tight old ——! But come on, Barker. Let's have a drink. I'm running down."

"I think it's about time you were running up—upstairs," said Bartlett. "If I were you, I'd try to be in bed and asleep when Gregg gets home."

"You're all right, Barker. And after this drink I'm going to do just as you say. Only I thought of it before you did, see? I think of it lots of nights. And tonight you can help me out by telling him I had a bad headache."

Left alone, Bartlett thought a while, then read, and finally dozed off. He was dozing when Gregg returned.

"Well, well, Bartlett," said the great man, "did Celia desert you?"

"It was perfectly all right, Mr. Gregg. She had a headache and I told her to go to bed."

"She's had a lot of headaches lately; reads too much, I guess. Well, I'm sorry I had this date. It was about a new golf club and I had to be there. I mean I'm going to be president of it. I see you consoled yourself with some of the Bourbon. I mean the bottle doesn't look as full as it did."

"I hope you'll forgive me for helping myself so generously," said Bartlett. "I don't get stuff like that every day!"

"Well, what do you say if we turn in? We can talk on the way to town tomorrow. Though I guess you won't have much to ask me. I guess you know all about us. I mean you know all about us now."

"Yes, indeed, Mr. Gregg. I've got plenty of material if I can just handle it."

Celia had not put in an appearance when Gregg and his guest were ready to leave the house next day.

"She always sleeps late," said Gregg. "I mean she never wakes up very early. But she's later than usual this morning. Sweetheart!" he called up the stairs.

"Yes, sweetheart," came the reply.

"Mr. Bartlett's leaving now. I mean he's going."

"Oh, good-by, Mr. Bartlett. Please forgive me for not being down to see you off."

"You're forgiven, Mrs. Gregg. And thanks for your hospitality."

"Good-by, sweetheart!"

"Good-by, sweetheart!"

THE GOLDEN HONEYMOON

MOTHER says that when I start talking I never know
when to stop. But I tell her the only time I get a chance
is when she ain't around, so I have to make the most
of it. I guess the fact is neither one of us would be welcome in a Quaker meeting, but as I tell Mother, what
did God give us tongues for if He didn't want we should
use them? Only she says He didn't give them to us to
say the same thing over and over again, like I do, and
repeat myself. But I say:

"Well, Mother," I say, "when people is like you and I
and been married fifty years, do you expect everything
I say will be something you ain't heard me say before?
But it may be new to others, as they ain't nobody else
lived with me as long as you have."

So she says:

"You can bet they ain't, as they couldn't nobody else
stand you that long."

"Well," I tell her, "you look pretty healthy."

"Maybe I do," she will say, "but I looked even health-
ier before I married you."

You can't get ahead of Mother.

Yes, sir, we was married just fifty years ago the
seventeenth day of last December and my daughter and
son-in-law was over from Trenton to help us celebrate
the Golden Wedding. My son-in-law is John H. Kramer,
the real estate man. He made $12,000 one year and is
pretty well thought of around Trenton; a good, steady,
hard worker. The Rotarians was after him a long time

to join, but he kept telling them his home was his club. But Edie finally made him join. That's my daughter.

Well, anyway, they come over to help us celebrate the Golden Wedding and it was pretty crimpy weather and the furnace don't seem to heat up no more like it used to and Mother made the remark that she hoped this winter wouldn't be as cold as the last, referring to the winter previous. So Edie said if she was us, and nothing to keep us home, she certainly wouldn't spend no more winters up here and why didn't we just shut off the water and close up the house and go down to Tampa, Florida? You know we was there four winters ago and staid five weeks, but it cost us over three hundred and fifty dollars for hotel bill alone. So Mother said we wasn't going no place to be robbed. So my son-in-law spoke up and said that Tampa wasn't the only place in the South, and besides we didn't have to stop at no high price hotel but could rent us a couple rooms and board out somewheres, and he had heard that St. Petersburg, Florida, was *the* spot and if we said the word he would write down there and make inquiries.

Well, to make a long story short, we decided to do it and Edie said it would be our Golden Honeymoon and for a present my son-in-law paid the difference between a section and a compartment so as we could have a compartment and have more privatecy. In a compartment you have an upper and lower berth just like the regular sleeper, but it is a shut in room by itself and got a wash bowl. The car we went in was all compartments and no regular berths at all. It was all compartments.

We went to Trenton the night before and staid at my daughter and son-in-law and we left Trenton the next afternoon at 3.23 p.m.

This was the twelfth day of January. Mother set facing the front of the train, as it makes her giddy to ride backwards. I set facing her, which does not affect me. We reached North Philadelphia at 4.03 p.m. and we reached West Philadelphia at 4.14, but did not go into Broad Street. We reached Baltimore at 6.30 and Washington, D.C., at 7.25. Our train laid over in Washington two hours till another train come along to pick us up and I got out and strolled up the platform and into the Union Station. When I come back, our car had been switched on to another track, but I remembered the name of it, the La Belle, as I had once visited my aunt out in Oconomowoc, Wisconsin, where there was a lake of that name, so I had no difficulty in getting located. But Mother had nearly fretted herself sick for fear I would be left.

"Well," I said, "I would of followed you on the next train."

"You could of," said Mother, and she pointed out that she had the money.

"Well," I said, "we are in Washington and I could of borrowed from the United States Treasury. I would of pretended I was an Englishman."

Mother caught the point and laughed heartily.

Our train pulled out of Washington at 9.40 p.m. and Mother and I turned in early, I taking the upper. During the night we passed through the green fields of old Virginia, though it was too dark to tell if they was green or what color. When we got up in the morning, we was at Fayetteville, North Carolina. We had breakfast in the dining car and after breakfast I got in conversation with the man in the next compartment to ours. He was from Lebanon, New Hampshire, and a man about eighty years of age. His wife was with him, and two unmarried daughters and I made the remark that I should think the four of them would be crowded in one compartment, but he said they had made the trip every winter for fifteen years and knowed how to keep out of each other's way. He said they was bound for Tarpon Springs.

We reached Charleston, South Carolina, at 12.50 p.m. and arrived at Savannah, Georgia, at 4.20. We reached Jacksonville, Florida, at 8.45 p.m. and had an hour and a quarter to lay over there, but Mother made a fuss about me getting off the train, so we had the darky make up our berths and retired before we left Jacksonville. I didn't sleep good as the train done a lot of hemming and hawing, and Mother never sleeps good on a train as she says she is always worrying that I will fall out. She says she would rather have the upper herself, as then she would not have to worry about me, but I tell her I can't take the risk of having it get out that I allowed my wife to sleep in an upper berth. It would make talk.

We was up in the morning in time to see our friends from New Hampshire get off at Tarpon Springs, which we reached at 6.53 a.m.

Several of our fellow passengers got off at Clearwater and some at Belleair, where the train backs right up to the door of the mammoth hotel. Belleair is the winter headquarters for the golf dudes and everybody that got off there had their bag of sticks, as many as ten and twelve in a bag. Women and all. When I was a young man we called it shinny and only needed one club to play with and about one game of it would of been a-plenty for some of these dudes, the way we played it.

The train pulled into St. Petersburg at 8.20 and when we got off the train you would think they was a riot, what with all the darkies barking for the different hotels.

I said to Mother, I said:

"It is a good thing we have got a place picked out to

go to and don't have to choose a hotel, as it would be hard to choose amongst them if everyone of them is the best."

She laughed.

We found a jitney and I give him the address of the room my son-in-law had got for us and soon we was there and introduced ourselves to the lady that owns the house, a young widow about forty-eight years of age. She showed us our room, which was light and airy with a comfortable bed and bureau and washstand. It was twelve dollars a week, but the location was good, only three blocks from Williams Park.

St. Pete is what folks calls the town, though they also call it the Sunshine City, as they claim they's no other place in the country where they's fewer days when Old Sol don't smile down on Mother Earth, and one of the newspapers gives away all their copies free every day when the sun don't shine. They claim to of only give them away some sixty-odd times in the last eleven years. Another nickname they have got for the town is "the Poor Man's Palm Beach," but I guess they's men that comes there that could borrow as much from the bank as some of the Willie boys over to the other Palm Beach.

During our stay we paid a visit to the Lewis Tent City, which is the headquarters for the Tin-Can Tourists. But maybe you ain't heard about them. Well, they are an organization that takes their vacation trips by auto and carries everything with them. That is, they bring along their tents to sleep in and cook in and they don't patronize no hotels or cafeterias, but they have got to be bona fide auto campers or they can't belong to the organization.

They tell me they's over 200,000 members to it and they call themselves the Tin-Canners on account of most of their food being put up in tin cans. One couple we seen in the Tent City was a couple from Brady, Texas, named Mr. and Mrs. Pence, which the old man is over eighty years of age and they had come in their auto all the way from home, a distance of 1,641 miles. They took five weeks for the trip, Mr. Pence driving the entire distance.

The Tin-Canners hails from every State in the Union and in the summer time they visit places like New England and the Great Lakes region, but in the winter the most of them comes to Florida and scatters all over the State. While we was down there, they was a national convention of them at Gainesville, Florida, and they elected a Fredonia, New York, man as their president. His title is Royal Tin-Can Opener of the World. They have got a song wrote up which everybody has got to learn it before they are a member:

"The tin can forever! Hurrah, boys! Hurrah!
   Up with the tin can! Down with the foe!
 We will rally round the campfire, we'll rally once again,
   Shouting, 'We auto camp forever!'"

That is something like it. And the members has also got to have a tin can fastened on to the front of their machine.

I asked Mother how she would like to travel around that way and she said:

"Fine, but not with an old rattle brain like you driving."

"Well," I said, "I am eight years younger than this Mr. Pence who drove here from Texas."

"Yes," she said, "but he is old enough to not be skittish."

You can't get ahead of Mother.

Well, one of the first things we done in St. Petersburg was to go to the Chamber of Commerce and register our names and where we was from as they's great rivalry amongst the different States in regards to the number of their citizens visiting in town and of course our little State don't stand much of a show, but still every little bit helps, as the fella says. All and all, the man told us, they was eleven thousand names registered, Ohio leading with some fifteen hundred-odd and New York State next with twelve hundred. Then come Michigan, Pennsylvania and so on down, with one man each from Cuba and Nevada.

The first night we was there, they was a meeting of the New York-New Jersey Society at the Congregational Church and a man from Ogdensburg, New York State, made the talk. His subject was Rainbow Chasing. He is a Rotarian and a very convicting speaker, though I forget his name.

Our first business, of course, was to find a place to eat and after trying several places we run on to a cafeteria on Central Avenue that suited us up and down. We eat pretty near all our meals there and it averaged about two dollars per day for the two of us, but the food was well cooked and everything nice and clean. A man don't mind paying the price if things is clean and well cooked.

On the third day of February, which is Mother's birthday, we spread ourselves and eat supper at the Poinsettia Hotel and they charged us seventy-five cents for a sirloin steak that wasn't hardly big enough for one.

I said to Mother: "Well," I said, "I guess it's a good thing every day ain't your birthday or we would be in the poorhouse."

"No," says Mother, "because if every day was my birthday, I would be old enough by this time to of been in my grave long ago."

You can't get ahead of Mother.

In the hotel they had a card room where they was

several men and ladies playing five hundred and this new fangled whist bridge. We also seen a place where they was dancing, so I asked Mother would she like to trip the light fantastic toe and she said no, she was too old to squirm like you have got to do now days. We watched some of the young folks at it awhile till Mother got disgusted and said we would have to see a good movie to take the taste out of our mouth. Mother is a great movie heroyne and we go twice a week here at home.

But I want to tell you about the Park. The second day we was there we visited the Park, which is a good deal like the one in Tampa, only bigger, and they's more fun goes on here every day than you could shake a stick at. In the middle they's a big bandstand and chairs for the folks to set and listen to the concerts, which they give you music for all tastes, from "Dixie" up to classical pieces like "Hearts and Flowers."

Then all around they's places marked off for different sports and games—chess and checkers and dominoes for folks that enjoys those kind of games, and roque and horse-shoes for the nimbler ones. I used to pitch a pretty fair shoe myself, but ain't done much of it in the last twenty years.

Well, anyway, we bought a membership ticket in the club which costs one dollar for the season, and they tell me that up to a couple years ago it was fifty cents, but they had to raise it to keep out the riffraff.

Well, Mother and I put in a great day watching the pitchers and she wanted I should get in the game, but I told her I was all out of practice and would make a fool of myself, though I seen several men pitching who I guess I could take their measure without no practice. However, they was some good pitchers, too, and one boy from Akron, Ohio, who could certainly throw a pretty shoe. They told me it looked like he would win the championship of the United States in the February tournament. We come away a few days before they held that and I never did hear if he win. I forget his name, but he was a clean cut young fella and he has got a brother in Cleveland that's a Rotarian.

Well, we just stood around and watched the different games for two or three days and finally I set down in a checker game with a man named Weaver from Danville, Illinois. He was a pretty fair checker player, but he wasn't no match for me, and I hope that don't sound like bragging. But I always could hold my own on a checker-board and the folks around here will tell you the same thing. I played with this Weaver pretty near all morning for two or three mornings and he beat me one game and the only other time it looked like he had a chance, the noon whistle blowed and we had to quit and go to dinner.

While I was playing checkers, Mother would set and listen to the band, as she loves music, classical or no matter what kind, but anyway she was setting there one day and between selections the woman next to her opened up a conversation. She was a woman about Mother's own age, seventy or seventy-one, and finally she asked Mother's name and Mother told her her name and where she was from and Mother asked her the same question, and who do you think the woman was?

Well, sir, it was the wife of Frank M. Hartsell, the man who was engaged to Mother till I stepped in and cut him out, fifty-two years ago!

Yes, sir!

You can imagine Mother's surprise! And Mrs. Hartsell was surprised, too, when Mother told her she had once been friends with her husband, though Mother didn't say how close friends they had been, or that Mother and

I was the cause of Hartsell going out West. But that's what we was. Hartsell left his town a month after the engagement was broke off and ain't never been back since. He had went out to Michigan and become a veterinary, and that is where he had settled down, in Hillsdale, Michigan, and finally married his wife.

Well, Mother screwed up her courage to ask if Frank was still living and Mrs. Hartsell took her over to where they was pitching horse-shoes and there was old Frank, waiting his turn. And he knowed Mother as soon as he seen her, though it was over fifty years. He said he knowed her by her eyes.

"Why, it's Lucy Frost!" he says, and he throwed down his shoes and quit the game.

Then they come over and hunted me up and I will confess I wouldn't of knowed him. Him and I is the same age to the month, but he seems to show it more, some way. He is balder for one thing. And his beard is all white, where mine has still got a streak of brown in it. The very first thing I said to him, I said:

"Well, Frank, that beard of yours makes me feel like I was back north. It looks like a regular blizzard."

"Well," he said, "I guess yourn would be just as white if you had it dry cleaned."

But Mother wouldn't stand that.

"Is that so!" she said to Frank. "Well, Charley ain't had no tobacco in his mouth for over ten years!"

And I ain't!

Well, I excused myself from the checker game and it was pretty close to noon, so we decided to all have dinner together and they was nothing for it only we must try their cafeteria on Third Avenue. It was a little more expensive than ours and not near as good, I thought. I and Mother had about the same dinner we had been having every day and our bill was $1.10.

Frank's check was $1.20 for he and his wife. The same meal wouldn't of cost them more than a dollar at our place.

After dinner we made them come up to our house and we all set in the parlor, which the young woman had give us the use of to entertain company. We begun talking over old times and Mother said she was a-scared Mrs. Hartsell would find it tiresome listening to we three talk over old times, but as it turned out they wasn't much chance for nobody else to talk with Mrs. Hartsell in the company. I have heard lots of women that could go it, but Hartsell's wife takes the cake of all the women I ever seen. She told us the family history of everybody in the State of Michigan and bragged for a half hour about her son, who she said is in the drug business in Grand Rapids, and a Rotarian.

When I and Hartsell could get a word in edgeways we joked one another back and forth and I chafed him about being a horse doctor.

"Well, Frank," I said, "you look pretty prosperous, so I suppose they's been plenty of glanders around Hillsdale."

"Well," he said, "I've managed to make more than a fair living. But I've worked pretty hard."

"Yes," I said, "and I suppose you get called out all hours of the night to attend births and so on."

Mother made me shut up.

Well, I thought they wouldn't never go home and I and Mother was in misery trying to keep awake, as the both of us generally always takes a nap after dinner. Finally they went, after we had made an engagement to meet them in the Park the next morning, and Mrs. Hartsell also invited us to come to their place the next night and play five hundred. But she had forgot that they was a meeting of the Michigan Society that evening, so it was not till two evenings later that we had our first card game.

Hartsell and his wife lived in a house on Third Avenue North and had a private setting room besides their bedroom. Mrs. Hartsell couldn't quit talking about their private setting room like it was something wonderful. We played cards with them, with Mother and Hartsell partners against his wife and I. Mrs. Hartsell is a miserable card player and we certainly got the worst of it.

After the game she brought out a dish of oranges and we had to pretend it was just what we wanted, though oranges down there is like a young man's whiskers; you enjoy them at first, but they get to be a pesky nuisance.

We played cards again the next night at our place with the same partners and I and Mrs. Hartsell was beat again. Mother and Hartsell was full of compliments for each other on what a good team they made, but the both of them knowed well enough where the secret of their success laid. I guess all and all we must of played ten different evenings and they was only one night when Mrs. Hartsell and I come out ahead. And that one night wasn't no fault of hern.

When we had been down there about two weeks, we spent one evening as their guest in the Congregational Church, at a social give by the Michigan Society. A talk was made by a man named Bitting of Detroit, Michigan, on How I was Cured of Story Telling. He is a big man in the Rotarians and give a witty talk.

A woman named Mrs. Oxford rendered some selections which Mrs. Hartsell said was grand opera music, but whatever they was my daughter Edie could of give her cards and spades and not made such a hullaballoo about it neither.

Then they was a ventriloquist from Grand Rapids and a young woman about forty-five years of age that mimicked different kinds of birds. I whispered to Mother that they all sounded like a chicken, but she nudged me to shut up.

After the show we stopped in a drugstore and I set up the refreshments and it was pretty close to ten o'clock before we finally turned in. Mother and I would of preferred tending the movies, but Mother said we mustn't offend Mrs. Hartsell, though I asked her had we came to Florida to enjoy ourselves or to just not offend an old chatter-box from Michigan.

I felt sorry for Hartsell one morning. The women folks both had an engagement down to the chiropodist's and I run across Hartsell in the Park and he foolishly offered to play me checkers.

It was him that suggested it, not me, and I guess he repented himself before we had played one game. But he was too stubborn to give up and set there while I beat him game after game and the worst part of it was that a crowd of folks had got in the habit of watching me play and there they all was, looking on, and finally they seen what a fool Frank was making of himself, and they began to chafe him and pass remarks. Like one of them said:

"Who ever told you you was a checker player!"

And:

"You might maybe be good for tiddle-de-winks, but not checkers!"

I almost felt like letting him beat me a couple games. But the crowd would of knowed it was a put up job.

Well, the women folks joined us in the Park and I wasn't going to mention our little game, but Hartsell told about it himself and admitted he wasn't no match for me.

"Well," said Mrs. Hartsell, "checkers ain't much of a game anyway, is it?" She said: "It's more of a children's game, ain't it? At least, I know my boy's children used to play it a good deal."

"Yes, ma'am," I said. "It's a children's game the way your husband plays it, too."

Mother wanted to smooth things over, so she said:

"Maybe they's other games where Frank can beat you."

"Yes," said Mrs. Hartsell, "and I bet he could beat you pitching horse-shoes."

"Well," I said, "I would give him a chance to try, only I ain't pitched a shoe in over sixteen years."

"Well," said Hartsell, "I ain't played checkers in twenty years."

"You ain't never played it," I said.

"Anyway," says Frank, "Lucy and I is your master at five hundred."

Well, I could of told him why that was, but had decency enough to hold my tongue.

It had got so now that he wanted to play cards every night and when I or Mother wanted to go to a movie, any one of us would have to pretend we had a headache and then trust to goodness that they wouldn't see us sneak into the theater. I don't mind playing cards when my partner keeps their mind on the game, but you take a woman like Hartsell's wife and how can they play cards when they have got to stop every couple seconds and brag about their son in Grand Rapids?

Well, the New York-New Jersey Society announced that they was going to give a social evening too and I said to Mother, I said:

"Well, that is one evening when we will have an excuse not to play five hundred."

"Yes," she said, "but we will have to ask Frank and his wife to go to the social with us as they asked us to go to the Michigan social."

"Well," I said, "I had rather stay home than drag that Chatter-box everywheres we go."

So Mother said:

"You are getting too cranky. Maybe she does talk a little too much but she is good hearted. And Frank is always good company."

So I said:

"I suppose if he is such good company you wished you had of married him."

Mother laughed and said I sounded like I was jealous. Jealous of a cow doctor!

Anyway we had to drag them along to the social and I will say that we give them a much better entertainment than they had given us.

Judge Lane of Paterson made a fine talk on business conditions and a Mrs. Newell of Westfield imitated birds, only you could really tell what they was the way she done it. Two young women from Red Bank sung a choral selection and we clapped them back and they gave us "Home to Our Mountains" and Mother and Mrs. Hartsell both had tears in their eyes. And Hartsell, too.

Well, some way or another the chairman got wind that I was there and asked me to make a talk and I wasn't even going to get up, but Mother made me, so I got up and said:

"Ladies and gentlemen," I said. "I didn't expect to be called on for a speech on an occasion like this or no other occasion as I do not set myself up as a speech maker, so will have to do the best I can, which I often say is the best anybody can do."

Then I told them the story about Pat and the motorcycle, using the brogue, and it seemed to tickle them and I told them one or two other stories, but altogether I wasn't on my feet more than twenty or twenty-five minutes and you ought to of heard the clapping and hollering when I set down. Even Mrs. Hartsell admitted that I am quite a speechifier and said if I ever went to Grand Rapids, Michigan, her son would make me talk to the Rotarians.

When it was over, Hartsell wanted we should go to their house and play cards, but his wife reminded him that it was after 9.30 p.m., rather a late hour to start a card game, but he had went crazy on the subject of cards, probably because he didn't have to play partners with his wife. Anyway, we got rid of them and went home to bed.

It was the next morning, when we met over to the Park, that Mrs. Hartsell made the remark that she wasn't getting no exercise so I suggested that why didn't she take part in the roque game.

She said she had not played a game of roque in twenty years, but if Mother would play she would play. Well, at first Mother wouldn't hear of it, but finally consented, more to please Mrs. Hartsell than anything else.

Well, they had a game with a Mrs. Ryan from Eagle, Nebraska, and a young Mrs. Morse from Rutland, Vermont, who Mother had met down to the chiropodist's. Well, Mother couldn't hit a flea and they all laughed at her and I couldn't help from laughing at her myself and finally she quit and said her back was too lame to stoop over. So they got another lady and kept on playing and soon Mrs. Hartsell was the one everybody was laughing at, as she had a long shot to hit the black ball, and as she made the effort her teeth fell out on to the court. I never seen a woman so flustered in my life. And I never heard so much laughing, only Mrs. Hartsell didn't join in and she was madder than a hornet and wouldn't play no more, so the game broke up.

Mrs. Hartsell went home without speaking to nobody, but Hartsell stayed around and finally he said to me, he said:

"Well, I played you checkers the other day and you beat me bad and now what do you say if you and me play a game of horse-shoes?"

I told him I hadn't pitched a shoe in sixteen years, but Mother said:

"Go ahead and play. You used to be good at it and maybe it will come back to you."

Well, to make a long story short, I give in. I oughtn't to of never tried it, as I hadn't pitched a shoe in sixteen years, and I only done it to humor Hartsell.

Before we started, Mother patted me on the back and told me to do my best, so we started in and I seen right off that I was in for it, as I hadn't pitched a shoe in sixteen years and didn't have my distance. And besides, the plating had wore off the shoes so that they was points right where they stuck into my thumb and I hadn't throwed more than two or three times when my thumb was raw and it pretty near killed me to hang on to the shoe, let alone pitch it.

Well, Hartsell throws the awkwardest shoe I ever seen pitched and to see him pitch you wouldn't think he would ever come nowheres near, but he is also the luckiest pitcher I ever seen and he made some pitches where the shoe lit five and six feet short and then schoonered up and was a ringer. They's no use trying to beat that kind of luck.

They was a pretty fair size crowd watching us and four or five other ladies besides Mother, and it seems like, when Hartsell pitches, he has got to chew and it kept the ladies on the anxious seat as he don't seem to care which way he is facing when he leaves go.

You would think a man as old as him would of learnt more manners.

Well, to make a long story short, I was just beginning to get my distance when I had to give up on account of my thumb, which I showed it to Hartsell and he seen I couldn't go on, as it was raw and bleeding. Even if I could of stood it to go on myself, Mother wouldn't of allowed it after she seen my thumb. So anyway I quit and Hartsell said the score was nineteen to six, but I don't know what it was. Or don't care, neither.

Well, Mother and I went home and I said I hoped we was through with the Hartsells as I was sick and tired of them, but it seemed like she had promised we would go over to their house that evening for another game of their everlasting cards.

Well, my thumb was giving me considerable pain and I felt kind of out of sorts and I guess maybe I forgot myself, but anyway, when we was about through play-ing Hartsell made the remark that he wouldn't never lose a game of cards if he could always have Mother for a partner.

So I said:

"Well, you had a chance fifty years ago to always have her for a partner, but you wasn't man enough to keep her."

I was sorry the minute I had said it and Hartsell didn't know what to say and for once his wife couldn't say nothing. Mother tried to smooth things over by making the remark that I must of had something stronger than tea or I wouldn't talk so silly. But Mrs. Hartsell had froze up like an iceberg and hardly said good night to us and I bet her and Frank put in a pleasant hour after we was gone.

As we was leaving, Mother said to him: "Never mind

Charley's nonsense, Frank. He is just mad because you beat him all hollow pitching horse-shoes and playing cards."

She said that to make up for my slip, but at the same time she certainly riled me. I tried to keep ahold of myself, but as soon as we was out of the house she had to open up the subject and begun to scold me for the break I had made.

Well, I wasn't in no mood to be scolded. So I said:

"I guess he is such a wonderful pitcher and card player that you wished you had married him."

"Well," she said, "at least he ain't a baby to give up pitching because his thumb has got a few scratches."

"And how about you," I said, "making a fool of yourself on the roque court and then pretending your back is lame and you can't play no more!"

"Yes," she said, "but when you hurt your thumb I didn't laugh at you, and why did you laugh at me when I sprained my back?"

"Who could help from laughing!" I said.

"Well," she said, "Frank Hartsell didn't laugh."

"Well," I said, "why didn't you marry him?"

"Well," said Mother, "I almost wished I had!"

"And I wished so, too!" I said.

"I'll remember that!" said Mother, and that's the last word she said to me for two days.

We seen the Hartsells the next day in the Park and I was willing to apologize, but they just nodded to us. And a couple days later we heard they had left for Orlando, where they have got relatives.

I wished they had went there in the first place.

Mother and I made it up setting on a bench.

"Listen, Charley," she said. "This is our Golden Honeymoon and we don't want the whole thing spoilt with a silly old quarrel."

"Well," I said, "did you mean that about wishing you had married Hartsell?"

"Of course not," she said, "that is, if you didn't mean that you wished I had, too."

So I said:

"I was just tired and all wrought up. I thank God you chose me instead of him as they's no other woman in the world who I could of lived with all these years."

"How about Mrs. Hartsell?" says Mother.

"Good gracious!" I said. "Imagine being married to a woman that plays five hundred like she does and drops her teeth on the roque court!"

"Well," said Mother, "it wouldn't be no worse than being married to a man that expectorates towards ladies and is such a fool in a checker game."

So I put my arm around her shoulder and she stroked my hand and I guess we got kind of spoony.

They was two days left of our stay in St. Petersburg and the next to the last day Mother introduced me to a Mrs. Kendall from Kingston, Rhode Island, who she had met at the chiropodist's.

Mrs. Kendall made us acquainted with her husband, who is in the grocery business. They have got two sons and five grandchildren and one great-grandchild. One of their sons lives in Providence and is way up in the Elks as well as a Rotarian.

We found them very congenial people and we played cards with them the last two nights we was there. They was both experts and I only wished we had met them sooner instead of running into the Hartsells. But the Kendalls will be there again next winter and we will see more of them, that is, if we decide to make the trip again.

We left the Sunshine City on the eleventh day of February, at 11 a.m. This give us a day trip through

Florida and we seen all the country we had passed through at night on the way down.

We reached Jacksonville at 7 p.m. and pulled out of there at 8.10 p.m. We reached Fayetteville, North Carolina, at nine o'clock the following morning, and reached Washington, D. C., at 6.30 p.m., laying over there half an hour.

We reached Trenton at 11.01 p.m. and had wired ahead to my daughter and son-in-law and they met us at the train and we went to their house and they put us up for the night. John would of made us stay up all night, telling about our trip, but Edie said we must be tired and made us go to bed. That's my daughter.

The next day we took our train for home and arrived safe and sound, having been gone just one month and a day.

Here comes Mother, so I guess I better shut up.

SOME LIKE THEM COLD

N. Y., Aug. 3

DEAR MISS GILLESPIE: How about our bet now as you bet me I would forget all about you the minute I hit the big town and would never write you a letter. Well girlie it looks like you lose so pay me. Seriously we will call all bets off as I am not the kind that bet on a sure thing and it sure was a sure thing that I would not forget a girlie like you and all that is worrying me is whether it may not be the other way round and you are wondering who this fresh guy is that is writeing you this letter. I bet you are so will try and refreshen your memory.

Well girlie I am the handsome young man that was wondering round the Lasalle st. station Monday and "happened" to sit down beside of a mighty pretty girlie who was waiting to meet her sister from Toledo and the train was late and I am glad of it because if it had not of been that little girlie and I would never of met. So for once I was a lucky guy but still I guess it was time I had some luck as it was certainly tough luck for you and I to both be liveing in Chi all that time and never get together till a half hour before I was leaveing town for good.

Still "better late than never" you know and maybe we can make up for lost time though it looks like we would have to do our makeing up at long distants unless you make good on your threat and come to N. Y. I wish you would do that little thing girlie as it looks like that was the only way we would get a chance to play round to-

443

gether as it looks like they was little or no chance of me comeing back to Chi as my whole future is in the big town. N. Y. is the only spot and specially for a man that expects to make my liveing in the song writeing game as here is the Mecca for that line of work and no matter how good a man may be they don't get no recognition unless they live in N. Y.

Well girlie you asked me to tell you all about my trip. Well I remember you saying that you would give anything to be makeing it yourself but as far as the trip itself was conserned you ought to be thankfull you did not have to make it as you would of sweat your head off. I know I did specially wile going through Ind. Monday p.m. but Monday night was the worst of all trying to sleep and finely I give it up and just layed there with the prespiration rolling off of me though I was laying on top of the covers and nothing on but my underwear.

Yesterday was not so bad as it rained most of the a.m. comeing through N. Y. state and in the p.m. we road along side of the Hudson all p.m. Some river girlie and just looking at it makes a man forget all about the heat and everything else except a certain girlie who I seen for the first time Monday and then only for a half hour but she is the kind of a girlie that a man don't need to see her only once and they would be no danger of forgetting her. There I guess I better lay off that subject or you will think I am a "fresh guy."

Well that is about all to tell you about the trip only they was one amuseing incidence that come off yesterday which I will tell you. Well they was a dame got on the train at Toledo Monday and had the birth opp. mine but I did not see nothing of her that night as I was out smokeing till late and she hit the hay early but yesterday a.m. she come in the dinner and sit at the same table with me and tried to make me and it was so raw that the dinge waiter seen it and give me the wink and of course I paid no tension and I waited till she got through so as they would be no danger of her folling me out but she stopped on the way out to get a tooth pick and when I come out she was out on the platform with it so I tried to brush right by but she spoke up and asked me what time it was and I told her and she said she guessed her watch was slow so I said maybe it just seemed slow on acct. of the company it was in.

I don't know if she got what I was driveing at or not but any way she give up trying to make me and got off at Albany. She was a good looker but I have no time for gals that tries to make strangers on a train.

Well if I don't quit you will think I am writeing a book but will expect a long letter in answer to this letter and we will see if you can keep your promise like I have kept mine. Don't dissapoint me girlie as I am all alone in a large city and hearing from you will keep me from getting homesick for old Chi though I never thought so much of the old town till I found out you lived there. Don't think that is kidding girlie as I mean it.

You can address me at this hotel as it looks like I will be here right along as it is on 47th st. right off of old Broadway and handy to everything and am only paying $21 per wk. for my rm. and could of got one for $16 but without bath but am glad to pay the differents as am lost without my bath in the a.m. and sometimes at night too.

Tomorrow I expect to commence fighting the "battle of Broadway" and will let you know how I come out that is if you answer this letter. In the mean wile girlie au reservoir and don't do nothing I would not do.

> Your new friend (?)
> Chas. F. Lewis.

Chicago, Ill., Aug. 6

My Dear Mr. Lewis: Well, that certainly was a "surprise party" getting your letter and you are certainly a "wonder man" to keep your word as I am afraid most men of your sex are gay deceivers but maybe you are "different." Any way it sure was a surprise and will gladly pay the bet if you will just tell me what it was we bet. Hope it was not money as I am a "working girl" but if it was not more than a dollar or two will try to dig it up even if I have to "beg, borrow or steal."

Suppose you will think me a "case" to make a bet and then forget what it was, but you must remember, Mr. Man, that I had just met you and was "dazzled." Joking aside I was rather "fussed" and will tell you why. Well, Mr. Lewis, I suppose you see lots of girls like the one you told me about that you saw on the train who tried to "get acquainted" but I want to assure you that I am not one of those kind and sincerely hope you will believe me when I tell you that you was the first man I ever spoke to meeting them like that and my friends and the people who know me would simply faint if they knew I ever spoke to a man without a "proper introduction."

Believe me, Mr. Lewis, I am not that kind and I don't know now why I did it only that you was so "different" looking if you know what I mean and not at all like the kind of men that usually try to force their attentions on every pretty girl they see. Lots of times I act on impulse and let my feelings run away from me and sometimes I do things on the impulse of the moment which I regret them later on, and that is what I did this time, but hope you won't give me cause to regret it and I know you won't as I know you are not that kind of a man a specially after what you told me about the girl on the train. But any way as I say, I was in a "daze" so can't remember what it was we bet, but will try and pay it if it does not "break" me.

Sis's train got in about ten minutes after yours had gone and when she saw me what do you think was the first thing she said? Well, Mr. Lewis, she said: "Why Mibs (That is a pet name some of my friends have given me) what has happened to you? I never seen you have as much color." So I passed it off with some remark about the heat and changed the subject as I certainly was not going to tell her that I had just been talking to a man who I had never met or she would of dropped dead from the shock. Either that or she would not of believed me as it would be hard for a person who knows me well to imagine me doing a thing like that as I have quite a reputation for "squelching" men who try to act fresh. I don't mean anything personal by that, Mr. Lewis, as am a good judge of character and could tell without you telling me that you are not that kind.

Well, Sis and I have been on the "go" ever since she arrived as I took yesterday and today off so I could show her the "sights" though she says she would be perfectly satisfied to just sit in the apartment and listen to me "rattle on." Am afraid I am a great talker, Mr. Lewis, but Sis says it is as good as a show to hear me talk as I tell things in such a different way as I cannot help from seeing the humorous side of everything and she says she never gets tired of listening to me, but of course she is my sister and thinks the world of me, but she really does laugh like she enjoyed my craziness.

Maybe I told you that I have a tiny little apartment which a girl friend of mine and I have together and it is hardly big enough to turn round in, but still it is "home" and I am a great home girl and hardly ever care to go out evenings except occasionally to the theater or dance.

But even if our "nest" is small we are proud of it and Sis complimented us on how cozy it is and how "homey" it looks and she said she did not see how we could afford to have everything so nice and Edith (my girl friend) said: "Mibs deserves all the credit for that. I never knew a girl who could make a little money go a long ways like she can." Well, of course she is my best friend and always saying nice things about me, but I do try and I hope I get results. Have always said that good taste and being careful is a whole lot more important than lots of money though it is nice to have it.

You must write and tell me how you are getting along in the "battle of Broadway" (I laughed when I read that) and whether the publishers like your songs though I know they will. Am crazy to hear them and hear you play the piano as I love good jazz music even better than classical, though I suppose it is terrible to say such a thing. But I usually say just what I think though sometimes I wish afterwards I had not of. But still I believe it is better for a girl to be her own self and natural instead of always acting. But am afraid I will never have a chance to hear you play unless you come back to Chi and pay us a visit as my "threat" to come to New York was just a "threat" and I don't see any hope of ever getting there unless some rich New Yorker should fall in love with me and take me there to live. Fine chance for poor little me, eh Mr. Lewis?

Well, I guess I have "rattled on" long enough and you will think I am writing a book unless I quit and besides, Sis has asked me as a special favor to make her a pie for dinner. Maybe you don't know it, Mr. Man, but I am quite famous for my pie and pastry, but I don't suppose a "genius" is interested in common things like that.

Well, be sure and write soon and tell me what N. Y. is like and all about it and don't forget the little girlie

who was "bad" and spoke to a strange man in the station
and have been blushing over it ever since.

Your friend (?)
Mabelle Gillespie.

N. Y., Aug. 10

DEAR GIRLIE: I bet you will think I am a fresh guy
commenceing that way but Miss Gillespie is too cold
and a man can not do nothing cold in this kind of
weather specially in this man's town which is the hottest
place I ever been in and I guess maybe the reason why
New Yorkers is so bad is because they think they are
all ready in H—— and can not go no worse place no
matter how they behave themselves. Honest girlie I
certainly envy you being where there is a breeze off the
old Lake and Chi may be dirty but I never heard of
nobody dying because they was dirty but four people
died here yesterday on acct. of the heat and I seen two
different women flop right on Broadway and had to be
taken away in the ambulance and it could not of been
because they was dressed too warm because it would be
impossible for the women here to leave off any more
cloths.

Well have not had much luck yet in the battle of
Broadway as all the heads of the big music publishers is
out of town on their vacation and the big boys is the only
ones I will do business with as it would be silly for a
man with the stuff I have got to waste my time on somebody that is just on the staff and have not got the final
say. But I did play a couple of my numbers for the
people up to Levy's and Goebel's and they went crazy
over them in both places. So it looks like all I have to
do is wait for the big boys to get back and then play my
numbers for them and I will be all set. What I want is to

get taken on the staff of one of the big firms as that gives a man the inside and they will plug your numbers more if you are on the staff. In the mean wile have not got nothing to worry me but am just seeing the sights of the big town as have saved up enough money to play round for a wile and any way a man that can play piano like I can don't never have to worry about starveing. Can certainly make the old music box talk girlie and am always good for a $75 or $100 job.

Well have been here a week now and on the go every minute and I thought I would be lonesome down here but no chance of that as I have been treated fine by the people I have met and have sure met a bunch of them. One of the boys liveing in the hotel is a vaudeville actor and he is a member of the Friars club and took me over there to dinner the other night and some way another the bunch got wise that I could play piano so of course I had to sit down and give them some of my numbers and everybody went crazy over them. One of the boys I met there was Paul Sears the song writer but he just writes the lyrics and has wrote a bunch of hits and when he heard some of my melodies he called me over to one side and said he would like to work with me on some numbers. How is that girlie as he is one of the biggest hit writers in N. Y.

N. Y. has got some mighty pretty girlies and I guess it would not be hard to get acquainted with them and in fact several of them has tried to make me since I been here but I always figure that a girl must be something wrong with her if she tries to make a man that she don't know nothing about so I pass them all up. But I did meet a couple of pips that a man here in the hotel went up on Riverside Drive to see them and insisted on me going along and they got on some way that I could make a piano talk so they was nothing but I must play for them so I sit down and played some of my own stuff and they went crazy over it.

One of the girls wanted I should come up and see her again, and I said I might but I think I better keep away as she acted like she wanted to vamp me and I am not the kind that likes to play round with a gal just for their company and dance with them etc. but when I see the right gal that will be a different thing and she won't have to beg me to come and see her as I will camp right on her trail till she says yes. And it won't be none of these N. Y. fly by nights neither. They are all right to look at but a man would be a sucker to get serious with them as they might take you up and next thing you know you would have a wife on your hands that don't know a dish rag from a waffle iron.

Well girlie will quit and call it a day as it is too hot to write any more and I guess I will turn on the cold water and lay in the tub a wile and then turn in. Don't forget to write to

Your friend,
Chas. F. Lewis.

Chicago, Ill., Aug. 13

Dear Mr. Man: Hope you won't think me a "silly Billy" for starting my letter that way but "Mr. Lewis" is so formal and "Charles" is too much the other way and any way I would not dare call a man by their first name after only knowing them only two weeks. Though I may as well confess that Charles is my favorite name for a man and have always been crazy about it as it was my father's name. Poor old dad, he died of cancer three years ago, but left enough insurance so that mother and we girls were well provided for and do not have to do anything to support ourselves though I have been earn-ing my own living for two years to make things easier for mother and also because I simply can't bear to be doing nothing as I feel like a "drone." So I flew away from the "home nest" though mother felt bad about it as I was her favorite and she always said I was such a comfort to her as when I was in the house she never had to worry about how things would go.

But there I go gossiping about my domestic affairs just like you would be interested in them though I don't see how you could be though personly I always like to know all about my friends, but I know men are different so will try and not bore you any longer. Poor Man, I certainly feel sorry for you if New York is as hot as all that. I guess it has been very hot in Chi, too, at least everybody has been complaining about how terrible it is. Suppose you will wonder why I say "I guess" and you will think I ought to know if it is hot. Well, sir, the reason I say "I guess" is because I don't feel the heat like others do or at least I don't let myself feel it. That sounds crazy I know, but don't you think there is a good deal in mental suggestion and not letting yourself feel things? I believe that if a person simply won't allow themselves to be affected by disagreeable things; why such things won't bother them near as much. I know it works with me and that is the reason why I am never cross when things go wrong and "keep smiling" no matter what happens and as far as the heat is concerned, why I just don't let myself feel it and my friends say I don't even look hot no matter if the weather is boiling and Edith, my girl friend, often says that I am like a breeze and it cools her off just to have me come in the room. Poor Edie suffers terribly during the hot weather and says it almost makes her mad at me to see how cool and unruffled I look when everybody else is perspiring and have red faces etc.

I laughed when I read what you said about New York being so hot that people thought it was the "other place." I can appreciate a joke, Mr. Man, and that one did not go "over my head." Am still laughing at some of the things you said in the station though they probably struck me funnier than they would most girls as I always see the funny side and sometimes something is said and I laugh and the others wonder what I am laughing at as they cannot see anything in it themselves, but it is just the way I look at things so of course I cannot explain to them why I laughed and they think I am crazy. But I had rather part with almost anything rather than my sense of humour as it helps me over a great many rough spots.

Sis has gone back home though I would of liked to of kept her here much longer, but she had to go though she said she would of liked nothing better than to stay with me and just listen to me "rattle on." She always says it is just like a show to hear me talk as I always put things in such a funny way and for weeks after she has been visiting me she thinks of some of the things I said and laughs over them. Since she left Edith and I have been pretty quiet though poor Edie wants to be on the "go" all the time and tries to make me go out with her every evening to the pictures and scolds me when I say I had rather stay home and read and calls me a "book worm." Well, it is true that I had rather stay home with a good book than go to some crazy old picture and the last two nights I have been reading myself to sleep with Robert W. Service's poems. Don't you love Service or don't you care for "highbrow" writings?

Personly there is nothing I love more than to just sit and read a good book or sit and listen to somebody play the piano, I mean if they can really play and I really believe I like popular music better than the classical though I suppose that is a terrible thing to confess, but I love all kinds of music but a specially the piano when it is played by somebody who can really play.

Am glad you have not "fallen" for the "ladies" who have tried to make your acquaintance in New York. You are right in thinking there must be something wrong with girls who try to "pick up" strange men as no girl with self respect would do such a thing and when I say that, Mr. Man, I know you will think it is a funny thing for me to say on account of the way our friendship started, but I mean it and I assure you that was the first time I ever done such a thing in my life and would never of thought of doing it had I not known you were the right kind of a man as I flatter myself that I am a good judge of character and can tell pretty well what a person is like by just looking at them and I assure you I had made up my mind what kind of a man you were before I allowed myself to answer your opening remark. Otherwise I am the last girl in the world that would allow myself to speak to a person without being introduced to them.

When you write again you must tell me all about the girl on Riverside Drive and what she looks like and if you went to see her again and all about her. Suppose you will think I am a little old "curiosity shop" for asking all those questions and will wonder why I want to know. Well, sir, I won't tell you why, so there, but I insist on you answering all questions and will scold you if you don't. Maybe you will think that the reason why I am so curious is because I am "jealous" of the lady in question. Well, sir, I won't tell you whether I am or not, but will keep you "guessing." Now, don't you wish you knew?

Must close or you will think I am going to "rattle on" forever or maybe you have all ready become disgusted and torn my letter up. If so all I can say is poor little me

—she was a nice little girl and meant well, but the man did not appreciate her.

There! Will stop or you will think I am crazy if you do not all ready.

Yours (?)
Mabelle.

N. Y., Aug. 20

Dear Girlie: Well girlie I suppose you thought I was never going to answer your letter but have been busier than a one armed paper hanger the last week as have been working on a number with Paul Sears who is one of the best lyric writers in N. Y. and has turned out as many hits as Berlin or Davis or any of them. And believe me girlie he has turned out another hit this time that is he and I have done it together. It is all done now and we are just waiting for the best chance to place it but will not place it nowheres unless we get the right kind of a deal but maybe will publish it ourselves.

The song is bound to go over big as Sears has wrote a great lyric and I have give it a great tune or at least every body that has heard it goes crazy over it and it looks like it would go over bigger than any song since Mammy and would not be surprised to see it come out the hit of the year. If it is handled right we will make a bbl. of money and Sears says it is a cinch we will clean up as much as $25000 apiece which is pretty fair for one song but this one is not like the most of them but has got a great lyric and I have wrote a melody that will knock them out of their seats. I only wish you could hear it girlie and hear it the way I play it. I had to play it over and over about 50 times at the Friars last night.

I will copy down the lyric of the chorus so you can see what it is like and get the idea of the song though of course you can't tell much about it unless you hear it played and sang. The title of the song is "When They're Like You" and here is the chorus:

> Some like them hot, some like them cold.
> Some like them when they're not too darn old.
> Some like them fat, some like them lean.
> Some like them only at sweet sixteen.
> Some like them dark, some like them light.
> Some like them in the park, late at night.
> Some like them fickle, some like them true,
> But the time I like them is when they're like you.

How is that for a lyric and I only wish I could play my melody for you as you would go nuts over it but will send you a copy as soon as the song is published and you can get some of your friends to play it over for you and I know you will like it though it is a different melody when I play it or when somebody else plays it.

Well girlie you will see how busy I have been and am libel to keep right on being busy as we are not going to let the grass grow under our feet but as soon as we have got this number placed we will get busy on another one as a couple like that will put me on Easy st. even if they don't go as big as we expect but even 25 grand is a big bunch of money and if a man could only turn out one hit a year and make that much out of it I would be on Easy st. and no more hammering on the old music box in some cabaret.

Who ever we take the song to we will make them come across with one grand for advance royaltys and that will keep me going till I can turn out another one. So the future looks bright and rosey to yours truly and I am certainly glad I come to the big town though sorry I did not do it a whole lot quicker.

This is a great old town girlie and when you have lived here a wile you wonder how you ever stood for a burg like Chi which is just a hick town along side of this besides being dirty etc. and a man is a sucker to stay there all their life specially a man in my line of work as N. Y. is the Mecca for a man that has got the musical gift. I figure that all the time I spent in Chi I was just wasteing my time and never really started to live till I come down here and I have to laugh when I think of the boys out there that is trying to make a liveing in the song writeing game and most of them starve to death all their life and the first week I am down here I meet a man like Sears and the next thing you know we have turned out a song that will make us a fortune.

Well girlie you asked me to tell you about the girlie up on the Drive that tried to make me and asked me to come and see her again. Well I can assure you you have no reasons to be jealous in that quarter as I have not been back to see her as I figure it is wasteing my time to play round with a dame like she that wants to go out somewheres every night and if you married her she would want a house on 5th ave. with a dozen servants so I have passed her up as that is not my idea of home.

What I want when I get married is a real home where a man can stay home and work and maybe have a few of his friends in once in a wile and entertain them or go to a good musical show once in a wile and have a wife that is in sympathy with you and not nag at you all the wile but be a real help mate. The girlie up on the Drive would run me ragged and have me in the poor house inside of a year even if I was makeing 25 grand out of one song. Besides she wears a make up that you would have to blast to find out what her face looks like. So I have not been back there and don't intend to see her again so what is the use of me telling you about her. And the only other girlie I have met is a sister of Paul Sears who I met up to his house wile we was working on the song but she don't hardly count as she has not got no use for the boys but treats them like dirt and Paul says she is the coldest proposition he ever seen.

Well I don't know no more to write and besides have got a date to go out to Paul's place for dinner and play some of my stuff for him so as he can see if he wants to set words to some more of my melodies. Well don't do nothing I would not do and have as good a time as you can in old Chi and will let you know how we come along with the song.

Chas. F. Lewis.

Chicago, Ill., Aug. 23

DEAR MR. MAN: I am thrilled to death over the song and think the words awfully pretty and am crazy to hear the music which I know must be great. It must be wonderful to have the gift of writing songs and then hear people play and sing them and just think of making $25,000 in such a short time. My, how rich you will be and I certainly congratulate you though am afraid when you are rich and famous you will have no time for insignificant little me or will you be an exception and remember your "old" friends even when you are up in the world? I sincerely hope so.

Will look forward to receiving a copy of the song and will you be sure and put your name on it? I am all ready very conceited just to think that I know a man that writes songs and makes all that money.

Seriously I wish you success with your next song and I laughed when I read your remark about being busier than a one armed paper hanger. I don't see how you think up all those comparisons and crazy things to say. The next time one of the girls asks me to go out with them I am going to tell them I can't go because I am busier than a one armed paper hanger and then they will think I made it up and say: "The girl is clever."

Seriously I am glad you did not go back to see the girl on the Drive and am also glad you don't like girls who makes themselves up so much as I think it is disgusting and would rather go round looking like a ghost than put artificial color on my face. Fortunately I have a complexion that does not need "fixing" but even if my coloring was not what it is I would never think of lowering myself to "fix" it. But I must tell you a joke that happened just the other day when Edith and I were out at lunch and there was another girl in the restaurant whom Edie knew and she introduced her to me and I noticed how this girl kept staring at me and finally she begged my pardon and asked if she could ask me a personal question and I said yes and she asked me if my complexion was really "mine." I assured her it was and she said: "Well, I thought so because I did not think anybody could put it on so artistically. I certainly envy you." Edie and I both laughed.

Well, if that girl envies me my complexion, why I envy you living in New York. Chicago is rather dirty though I don't let that part of it bother me as I bathe and change my clothing so often that the dirt does not have time to "settle." Edie often says she cannot see how I always keep so clean looking and says I always look like I had just stepped out of a band box. She also calls me a fish (jokingly) because I spend so much time in the water. But seriously I do love to bathe and never feel so happy as when I have just "cleaned up" and put on fresh clothing.

Edie has just gone out to see a picture and was cross at me because I would not go with her. I told her I was going to write a letter and she wanted to know to whom and I told her and she said: "You write to him so often that a person would almost think you was in love with him." I just laughed and turned it off, but she does say the most embarrassing things and I would be angry if it was anybody but she that said them.

Seriously I had much rather sit here and write letters or read or just sit and dream than go out to some crazy old picture show except once in awhile I do like to go to the theater and see a good play and a specially a musical play if the music is catchy. But as a rule I am contented to just stay home and feel cozy and lots of evenings Edie and I sit here without saying hardly a word to each other though she would love to talk but she knows I had rather be quiet and she often says it is just like living with a deaf and dumb mute to live with me because I make so little noise round the apartment. I guess I was born to be a home body as I so seldom care to go "gadding."

Though I do love to have company once in awhile, just a few congenial friends whom I can talk to and feel at home with and play cards or have some music. My friends love to drop in here, too, as they say Edie and I always give them such nice things to eat. Though poor Edie has not much to do with it, I am afraid, as she hates anything connected with cooking which is one of the things I love best of anything and I often say that when I begin keeping house in my own home I will insist on doing most of my own work as I would take so much more interest in it than a servant, though I would want somebody to help me a little if I could afford it as I often think a woman that does all her own work is liable to get so tired that she loses interest in the bigger things of life like books and music. Though after all what bigger thing is there than home making a specially for a woman?

I am sitting in the dearest old chair that I bought

yesterday at a little store on the North Side. That is my one extravagance, buying furniture and things for the house, but I always say it is economy in the long run as I will always have them and have use for them and when I can pick them up at a bargain I would be silly not to. Though heaven knows I will never be "poor" in regards to furniture and rugs and things like that as mother's house in Toledo is full of lovely things which she says she is going to give to Sis and myself as soon as we have real homes of our own. She is going to give me the first choice as I am her favorite. She has the loveliest old things that you could not buy now for love or money including lovely old rugs and a piano which Sis wanted to have a player attachment put on it but I said it would be an insult to the piano so we did not get one. I am funny about things like that, a specially old furniture and feel towards them like people whom I love.

Poor mother, I am afraid she won't live much longer to enjoy her lovely old things as she has been suffering for years from stomach trouble and the doctor says it has been worse lately instead of better and her heart is weak besides. I am going home to see her a few days this fall as it may be the last time. She is very cheerful and always says she is ready to go now as she has had enough joy out of life and all she would like would be to see her girls settled down in their own homes before she goes.

There I go, talking about my domestic affairs again and I will bet you are bored to death though personly I am never bored when my friends tell me about themselves. But I won't "rattle on" any longer, but will say good night and don't forget to write and tell me how you come out with the song and thanks for sending me the words to it. Will you write a song about me some time? I would be thrilled to death! But I am afraid I am not the kind of girl that inspires men to write songs about them, but am just a quiet "mouse" that loves home and am not giddy enough to be the heroine of a song.

Well, Mr. Man, good night and don't wait so long before writing again to

Yours (?)
Mabelle.

N. Y., Sept. 8

DEAR GIRLIE: Well girlie have not got your last letter with me so cannot answer what was in it as I have forgotten if there was anything I was supposed to answer and besides have only a little time to write as I have a date to go out on a party with the Sears. We are going to the Georgie White show and afterwards somewheres for supper. Sears is the boy who wrote the lyric to my song and it is him and his sister I am going on the party with. The sister is a cold fish that has no use for men but she is show crazy and insists on Paul takeing her to 3 or 4 of them a week.

Paul wants me to give up my room here and come and live with them as they have plenty of room and I am running a little low on money but don't know if I will do it or not as am afraid I would freeze to death in the same house with a girl like the sister as she is ice cold but she don't hang round the house much as she is always takeing trips or going to shows or somewheres.

So far we have not had no luck with the song. All the publishers we have showed it to has went crazy over it but they won't make the right kind of a deal with us and if they don't loosen up and give us a decent royalty rate we are libel to put the song out ourselves and show them up. The man up to Goebel's told us the song was O. K. and he liked it but it was more of a production number

than anything else and ought to go in a show like the
Follies but they won't be in N. Y. much longer and what
we ought to do is hold it till next spring.

Mean wile I am working on some new numbers and
also have taken a position with the orchestra at the
Wilton and am going to work there starting next week.
They pay good money $60 and it will keep me going.

Well girlie that is about all the news. I believe you
said your father was sick and hope he is better and also
hope you are getting along O. K. and take care of yourself. When you have nothing else to do write to your
friend,

Chas. F. Lewis.

Chicago, Ill., Sept. 11

DEAR MR. LEWIS: Your short note reached me yesterday
and must say I was puzzled when I read it. It sounded
like you was mad at me though I cannot think of any
reason why you should be. If there was something I said
in my last letter that offended you I wish you would tell
me what it was and I will ask your pardon though I
cannot remember anything I could of said that you
could take offense at. But if there was something, why I
assure you, Mr. Lewis, that I did not mean anything
by it. I certainly did not intend to offend you in any
way.

Perhaps it is nothing I wrote you, but you are worried
on account of the publishers not treating you fair in
regards to your song and that is why your letter
sounded so distant. If that is the case I hope that by
this time matters have rectified themselves and the
future looks brighter. But any way, Mr. Lewis, don't
allow yourself to worry over business cares as they will

all come right in the end and I always think it is silly for people to worry themselves sick over temporary troubles, but the best way is to "keep smiling" and look for the "silver lining" in the cloud. That is the way I always do and no matter what happens, I manage to smile and my girl friend, Edie, calls me Sunny because I always look on the bright side.

Remember also, Mr. Lewis, that $60 is a salary that a great many men would like to be getting and are living on less than that and supporting a wife and family on it. I always say that a person can get along on whatever amount they make if they manage things in the right way.

So if it is business troubles, Mr. Lewis, I say don't worry, but look on the bright side. But if it is something I wrote in my last letter that offended you I wish you would tell me what it was so I can apologize as I assure you I meant nothing and would not say anything to hurt you for the world.

Please let me hear from you soon as I will not feel comfortable until I know I am not to blame for the sudden change.

Sincerely,
Mabelle Gillespie.

N. Y. Sept. 24

DEAR MISS GILLESPIE: Just a few lines to tell you the big news or at least it is big news to me. I am engaged to be married to Paul Sears' sister and we are going to be married early next month and live in Atlantic City where the orchestra I have been playing with has got an engagement in one of the big cabarets.

I know this will be a surprise to you as it was even a

surprise to me as I did not think I would ever have the nerve to ask the girlie the big question as she was always so cold and acted like I was just in the way. But she said she supposed she would have to marry somebody some time and she did not dislike me as much as most of the other men her brother brought round and she would marry me with the understanding that she would not have to be a slave and work round the house and also I would have to take her to a show or somewheres every night and if I could not take her myself she would "run wild" alone. Atlantic City will be O. K. for that as a lot of new shows opens down there and she will be able to see them before they get to the big town. As for her being a slave, I would hate to think of marrying a girl and then have them spend their lives in druggery round the house. We are going to live in a hotel till we find something better but will be in no hurry to start house keeping as we will have to buy all new furniture.

Betsy is some doll when she is all fixed up and believe me she knows how to fix herself up. I don't know what she uses but it is weather proof and I have been out in a rain storm with her and we both got drowned but her face stayed on. I would almost think it was real only she tells me different.

Well girlie I may write to you again once in a wile as Betsy says she don't give a damn if I write to all the girls in the world just so I don't make her read the answers but that is all I can think of to say now except good bye and good luck and may the right man come along soon and he will be a lucky man getting a girl that is such a good cook and got all that furniture etc.

But just let me give you a word of advice before I close and that is don't never speak to strange men who you don't know nothing about as they may get you wrong and think you are trying to make them. It just happened that I knew better so you was lucky in my case but the luck might not last.

Your friend,
Chas. F. Lewis.

Chicago, Ill., Sept. 27

MY DEAR MR. LEWIS: Thanks for your advice and also thank your fiance for her generosity in allowing you to continue your correspondence with her "rivals," but personly I have no desire to take advantage of that generosity as I have something better to do than read letters from a man like you, a specially as I have a man friend who is not so generous as Miss Sears and would strongly object to my continuing a correspondence with another man. It is at his request that I am writing this note to tell you not to expect to hear from me again.

Allow me to congratulate you on your engagement to Miss Sears and I am sure she is to be congratulated too, though if I met the lady I would be tempted to ask her to tell me her secret, namely how she is going to "run wild" on $60.

Sincerely,
Mabelle Gillespie.

A CADDY'S DIARY

I AM 16 of age and am a caddy at the Pleasant View Golf Club but only temporary as I expect to soon land a job some wheres as asst pro as my game is good enough now to be a pro but to young looking. My pal Joe Bean also says I have not got enough swell head to make a good pro but suppose that will come in time, Joe is a wise cracker.

But first will put down how I come to be writeing this diary, we have got a member name Mr Colby who writes articles in the newspapers and I hope for his sakes that he is a better writer then he plays golf but any way I cadded for him a good many times last yr and today he was out for the first time this yr and I cadded for him and we got talking about this in that and something was mentioned in regards to the golf articles by Alex Laird that comes out every Sun in the paper Mr Colby writes his articles for so I asked Mr Colby did he know how much Laird got paid for the articles and he said he did not know but supposed that Laird had to split 50-50 with who ever wrote the articles for him. So I said don't he write the articles himself and Mr Colby said why no he guessed not. Laird may be a master mind in regards to golf he said, but that is no sign he can write about it as very few men can write decent let alone a pro. Writeing is a nag.

How do you learn it I asked him.

Well he said read what other people writes and study

467

them and write things yourself, and maybe you will get on to the nag and maybe you wont.

Well Mr Colby I said do you think I could get on to it?

Why he said smileing I did not know that was your ambition to be a writer.

Not exactly was my reply, but I am going to be a golf pro myself and maybe some day I will get good enough so as the papers will want I should write them articles and if I can learn to write them myself why I will not have to hire another writer and split with them.

Well said Mr Colby smileing you have certainly got the right temperament for a pro, they are all big hearted fellows.

But listen Mr Colby I said if I want to learn it would not do me no good to copy down what other writers have wrote, what I would have to do would be write things out of my own head.

That is true said Mr Colby.

Well I said what could I write about?

Well said Mr Colby why dont you keep a diary and every night after your supper set down and write what happened that day and write who you cadded for and what they done only leave me out of it. And you can write down what people say and what you think and etc., it will be the best kind of practice for you, and once in a wile you can bring me your writeings and I will tell you the truth if they are good or rotten.

So that is how I come to be writeing this diary is so as I can get some practice writeing and maybe if I keep at it long enough I can get on to the nag.

We been haveing Apr. showers for a couple days and nobody out on the course so they has been nothing happen that I could write down in my diary but dont want to leave it go to long or will never learn the trick so will try and write a few lines about a caddys life and some of our members and etc.

Well I and Joe Bean is the 2 oldest caddys in the club and I been cadding now for 5 yrs and quit school 3 yrs ago tho my mother did not like it for me to quit but my father said he can read and write and figure so what is the use in keeping him there any longer as greek and latin dont get you no credit at the grocer, so they lied about my age to the trunce officer and I been cadding every yr from March till Nov and the rest of the winter I work around Heismans store in the village.

Dureing the time I am cadding I genally always manage to play at lease 9 holes a day myself on wk days and some times 18 and am never more then 2 or 3 over par figures on our course but it is a cinch.

I played the engineers course 1 day last summer in 75 which is some golf and some of our members who has been playing 20 yrs would give their right eye to play as good as myself.

I use to play around with our pro Jack Andrews till I got so as I could beat him pretty near every time we played and now he wont play with me no more, he is not a very good player for a pro but they claim he is a good teacher. Personly I think golf teachers is a joke tho I am glad people is suckers enough to fall for it as I expect to make my liveing that way. We have got a member Mr Dunham who must of took 500 lessons in the past 3 yrs and when he starts to shoot he trys to remember all the junk Andrews has learned him and he gets dizzy and they is no telling where the ball will go and about the safest place to stand when he is shooting is between he and the hole.

I dont beleive the club pays Andrews much salery but of course he makes pretty fair money giveing lessons but his best graft is a 3 some which he plays 2 and 3 times a wk with Mr Perdue and Mr Lewis and he gives Mr Lewis a stroke a hole and they genally break some wheres near even but Mr Perdue made a 83 one time so he thinks that is his game so he insists on playing Jack even, well they always play for $5.00 a hole and Andrews makes $20.00 to $30.00 per round and if he wanted to cut loose and play his best he could make $50.00 to $60.00 per round but a couple of wallops like that and Mr Perdue might get cured so Jack figures a small stedy income is safer.

I have got a pal name Joe Bean and we pal around together as he is about my age and he says some comical things and some times will wisper some thing comical to me wile we are cadding and it is all I can do to help from laughing out loud, that is one of the first things a caddy has got to learn is never laugh out loud only when a member makes a joke. How ever on the days when theys ladies on the course I dont get a chance to caddy with Joe because for some reason another the woman folks dont like Joe to caddy for them wile on the other hand they are always after me tho I am no Othello for looks or do I seek their flavors, in fact it is just the opp and I try to keep in the back ground when the fair sex appears on the seen as cadding for ladies means you will get just so much money and no more as theys no chance of them loosning up. As Joe says the rule against tipping is the only rule the woman folks keeps.

Theys one lady how ever who I like to caddy for as she looks like Lillian Gish and it is a pleasure to just look at her and I would caddy for her for nothing tho it is hard to keep your eye on the ball when you are cadding for this lady, her name is Mrs Doane.

This was a long day and am pretty well wore out but must not get behind in my writeing practice. I and Joe carried all day for Mr Thomas and Mr Blake. Mr Thomas is the vice president of one of the big banks down town and he always slips you a $1.00 extra per round but beleive me you earn it cadding for Mr Thomas, there is just 16 clubs in his bag includeing 5 wood clubs tho he has not used the wood in 3 yrs but says he has got to have them along in case his irons goes wrong on him. I dont know how bad his irons will have to get before he will think they have went wrong on him but personly if I made some of the tee shots he made today I would certainly considder some kind of a change of weppons.

Mr Thomas is one of the kind of players that when it has took him more than 6 shots to get on the green he will turn to you and say how many have I had caddy and then you are suppose to pretend like you was thinking a minute and then say 4, then he will say to the man he is playing with well I did not know if I had shot 4 or 5 but the caddy says it is 4. You see in this way it is not him that is cheating but the caddy but he makes it up to the caddy afterwards with a $1.00 tip.

Mr Blake gives Mr Thomas a stroke a hole and they play a $10.00 nassua and niether one of them wins much money from the other one but even if they did why $10.00 is chickens food to men like they. But the way they crab and squak about different things you would think their last $1.00 was at stake. Mr Thomas started out this a.m. with a 8 and a 7 and of course that spoilt

the day for him and me to. Theys lots of men that if
they dont make a good score on the first 2 holes they
will founder all the rest of the way around and raze H
with their caddy and if I was laying out a golf course I
would make the first 2 holes so darn easy that you could
not help from getting a 4 or better on them and in that
way everybody would start off good natured and it
would be a few holes at lease before they begun to turn
sour.

Mr Thomas was beat both in the a.m. and p.m. in
spite of my help as Mr Blake is a pretty fair counter
himself and I heard him say he got a 88 in the p.m.
which is about a 94 but any way it was good enough to
win. Mr Blakes regular game is about a 90 takeing his
own figures and he is one of these cocky guys that takes
his own game serious and snears at men that cant break
100 and if you was to ask him if he had ever been over
100 himself he would say not since the first yr he begun
to play. Well I have watched a lot of those guys like
he and I will tell you how they keep from going over 100
namely by doing just what he done this a.m. when he
come to the 13th hole. Well he missed his tee shot and
dubbed along and finely he got in a trap on his 4th shot
and I seen him take 6 wallops in the trap and when he
had took the 6th one his ball was worse off then when he
started so he picked it up and marked a X down on his
score card. Well if he had of played out the hole why the
best he could of got was a 11 by holeing his next niblick
shot but he would of probly got about a 20 which would
of made him around 108 as he admitted takeing a 88
for the other 17 holes. But I bet if you was to ask him
what score he had made he would say O I was terrible
and I picked up on one hole but if I had of played them
all out I guess I would of had about a 92.

These is the kind of men that laughs themselfs horse

when they hear of some dub takeing 10 strokes for a hole but if they was made to play out every hole and mark down their real score their card would be decorated with many a big casino.

Well as I say I had a hard day and was pretty sore along towards the finish but still I had to laugh at Joe Bean on the 15th hole which is a par 3 and you can get there with a fair drive and personly I am genally hole high with a midiron, but Mr Thomas topped his tee shot and dubbed a couple with his mashie and was still quiet a ways off the green and he stood studing the situation a minute and said to Mr Blake well I wonder what I better take here. So Joe Bean was standing by me and he said under his breath take my advice and quit you old rascal.

Mon. Apr. 17

Yesterday was Sun and I was to wore out last night to write as I cadded 45 holes. I cadded for Mr Colby in the a.m. and Mr Langley in the p.m. Mr Thomas thinks golf is wrong on the sabath tho as Joe Bean says it is wrong any day the way he plays it.

This a.m. they was nobody on the course and I played 18 holes by myself and had a 5 for a 76 on the 18th hole but the wind got a hold of my drive and it went out of bounds. This p.m. they was 3 of us had a game of rummy started but Miss Rennie and Mrs Thomas come out to play and asked for me to caddy for them, they are both terrible.

Mrs Thomas is Mr Thomas wife and she is big and fat and shakes like jell and she always says she plays golf just to make her skinny and she dont care how rotten she plays as long as she is getting the exercise, well maybe so but when we find her ball in a bad lie she aint never sure it is hers till she picks it up and smells it and when she puts it back beleive me she don't cram it down no gopher hole.

Miss Rennie is a good looker and young and they say she is engaged to Chas Crane, he is one of our members and is the best player in the club and dont cheat hardly at all and he has got a job in the bank where Mr Thomas is the vice president. Well I have cadded for Miss Rennie when she was playing with Mr Crane and I have cadded for her when she was playing alone or with another lady and I often think if Mr Crane could hear her talk when he was not around he would not be so stuck on her. You would be surprised at some of the words that falls from those fare lips.

Well the 2 ladies played for 2 bits a hole and Miss Rennie was haveing a terrible time wile Mrs Thomas was shot with luck on the greens and sunk 3 or 4 putts that was murder. Well Miss Rennie used some expressions which was best not repeated but towards the last the luck changed around and it was Miss Rennie that was sinking the long ones and when they got to the 18th tee Mrs Thomas was only 1 up.

Well we had started pretty late and when we left the 17th green Miss Rennie made the remark that we would have to hurry to get the last hole played, well it was her honor and she got the best drive she made all day about 120 yds down the fair way. Well Mrs Thomas got nervous and looked up and missed her ball a ft and then done the same thing right over and when she finely hit it she only knocked it about 20 yds and this made her lay 3. Well her 4th went wild and lit over in the rough in the apple trees. It was a cinch Miss Rennie would win the hole unless she dropped dead.

Well we all went over to hunt for Mrs Thomas ball but we would of been lucky to find it even in day light but now you could not hardly see under the trees, so

Miss Rennie said drop another ball and we will not count no penalty. Well it is some job any time to make a woman give up hunting for a lost ball and all the more so when it is going to cost her 2 bits to play the hole out so there we stayed for at lease 10 minutes till it was so dark we could not see each other let alone a lost ball and finely Mrs Thomas said well it looks like we could not finish, how do we stand? Just like she did not know how they stood.

You had me one down up to this hole said Miss Rennic.

Well that is finishing pretty close said Mrs Thomas.

I will have to give Miss Rennie credit that what ever word she thought of for this occasion she did not say it out loud but when she was paying me she said I might of give you a quarter tip only I have to give Mrs Thomas a quarter she dont deserve so you dont get it.

Fat chance I would of had any way.

Thurs. Apr. 20

Well we been haveing some more bad weather but today the weather was all right but that was the only thing that was all right. This p.m. I cadded double for Mr Thomas and Chas Crane the club champion who is stuck on Miss Rennie. It was a 4 some with he and Mr Thomas against Mr Blake and Jack Andrews the pro, they was only playing best ball so it was really just a match between Mr Crane and Jack Andrews and Mr Crane win by 1 up. Joe Bean cadded for Jack and Mr Blake. Mr Thomas was terrible and I put in a swell p.m. lugging that heavy bag of his besides Mr Cranes bag.

Mr Thomas did not go off of the course as much as usual but he kept hitting behind the ball and he run me ragged replaceing his divots but still I had to laugh when we was playing the 4th hole which you have to drive over a ravine and every time Mr Thomas misses his tee shot on this hole why he makes a squak about the ravine and says it ought not to be there and etc.

Today he had a terrible time getting over it and afterwards he said to Jack Andrews this is a joke hole and ought to be changed. So Joe Bean wispered to me that if Mr Thomas kept on playing like he was the whole course would be changed.

Then a little wile later when we come to the long 9th hole Mr Thomas got a fair tee shot but then he whiffed twice missing the ball by a ft and the 3d time he hit it but it only went a little ways and Joe Bean said that is 3 trys and no gain, he will have to punt.

But I must write down about my tough luck, well we finely got through the 18 holes and Mr Thomas reached down in his pocket for the money to pay me and he genally pays for Mr Crane to when they play together as Mr Crane is just a employ in the bank and dont have much money but this time all Mr Thomas had was a $20.00 bill so he said to Mr Crane I guess you will have to pay the boy Charley so Charley dug down and got the money to pay me and he paid just what it was and not a dime over, where if Mr Thomas had of had the change I would of got a $1.00 extra at lease and maybe I was not sore and Joe Bean to because of course Andrews never gives you nothing and Mr Blake dont tip his caddy unless he wins.

They are a fine bunch of tight wads said Joe and I said well Crane is all right only he just has not got no money.

He aint all right no more than the rest of them said Joe.

Well at lease he dont cheat on his score I said.

And you know why that is said Joe, neither does Jack Andrews cheat on his score but that is because they play to good. Players like Crane and Andrews that goes around in 80 or better cant cheat on their score because they make the most of the holes in around 4 strokes and the 4 strokes includes their tee shot and a couple of putts which everybody is right there to watch them when they make them and count them right along with them. So if they make a 4 and claim a 3 why people would just laugh in their face and say how did the ball get from the fair way on to the green, did it fly? But the boys that takes 7 and 8 strokes to a hole can shave their score and you know they are shaveing it but you have to let them get away with it because you cant prove nothing. But that is one of the penaltys for being a good player, you cant cheat.

To hear Joe tell it pretty near everybody are born crooks, well maybe he is right.

Wed. Apr. 26

Today Mrs Doane was out for the first time this yr and asked for me to caddy for her and you bet I was on the job. Well how are you Dick she said, she always calls me by name. She asked me what had I been doing all winter and was I glad to see her and etc.

She said she had been down south all winter and played golf pretty near every day and would I watch her and notice how much she had improved.

Well to tell the truth she was no better then last yr and wont never be no better and I guess she is just to pretty to be a golf player but of course when she asked me did I think her game was improved I had to reply yes indeed as I would not hurt her feelings and she laughed like my reply pleased her. She played with Mr and Mrs Carter and I carried the 2 ladies bags wile Joe Bean cadded for Mr Carter. Mrs Carter is a ugly dame with things on her face and it must make Mr Carter feel sore when he looks at Mrs Doane to think he married Mrs Carter but I suppose they could not all marry the same one and besides Mrs Doane would not be a sucker enough to marry a man like he who drinks all the time and is pretty near always stood, tho Mr Doane who she did marry aint such a H of a man himself tho dirty with money.

They all gave me the laugh on the 3d hole when Mrs Doane was makeing her 2d shot and the ball was in the fair way but laid kind of bad and she just ticked it and then she asked me if winter rules was in force and I said yes so we teed her ball up so as she could get a good shot at it and they gave me the laugh for saying winter rules was in force.

You have got the caddys bribed Mr Carter said to her.

But she just smiled and put her hand on my sholder and said Dick is my pal. That is enough of a bribe to just have her touch you and I would caddy all day for her and never ask for a cent only to have her smile at me and call me her pal.

Sat. Apr. 29

Today they had the first club tournament of the yr and they have a monthly tournament every month and today was the first one, it is a handicap tournament and everybody plays in it and they have prizes for low net score and low gross score and etc. I cadded for Mr Thomas today and will tell what happened.

They played a 4 some and besides Mr Thomas we had Mr Blake and Mr Carter and Mr Dunham. Mr Dunham is the worst man player in the club and the other men would not play with him a specialy on a Saturday only him and Mr Blake is partners together in business. Mr Dunham has got the highest handicap in the club which is 50 but it would have to be 150 for him to win a prize. Mr Blake and Mr Carter has got a handicap of about 15 a piece I think and Mr Thomas is 30, the first prize for the low net score for the day was a dozen golf balls and the second low score a ½ dozen golf balls and etc.

Well we had a great battle and Mr Colby ought to been along to write it up or some good writer. Mr Carter and Mr Dunham played partners against Mr Thomas and Mr Blake which ment that Mr Carter was playing Thomas and Blakes best ball, well Mr Dunham took the honor and the first ball he hit went strate off to the right and over the fence outside of the grounds, well he done the same thing 3 times. Well when he finely did hit one in the course why Mr Carter said why not let us not count them 3 first shots of Mr Dunham as they was just practice. Like H we wont count them said Mr Thomas we must count every shot and keep our scores correct for the tournament.

All right said Mr Carter.

Well we got down to the green and Mr Dunham had about 11 and Mr Carter sunk a long putt for a par 5, Mr Blake all ready had 5 strokes and so did Mr Thomas and when Mr Carter sunk his putt why Mr Thomas picked his ball up and said Carter wins the hole and I and Blake will take 6s. Like H you will said Mr Carter, this is a tournament and we must play every hole out and keep our scores correct. So Mr Dunham putted and went down in 13 and Mr Blake got a 6 and Mr Thomas missed 2 easy putts and took a 8 and maybe he was not boiling.

Well it was still their honor and Mr Dunham had one of his dizzy spells on the 2d tee and he missed the ball twice before he hit it and then Mr Carter drove the green which is only a midiron shot and then Mr Thomas stepped up and missed the ball just like Mr Dunham.

He was wild and yelled at Mr Dunham no man could play golf playing with a man like you, you would spoil anybodys game.

Your game was all ready spoiled said Mr Dunham, it turned sour on the 1st green.

You would turn anybody sour said Mr Thomas.

Well Mr Thomas finely took a 8 for the hole which is a par 3 and it certainly looked bad for him winning a prize when he started out with 2 8s, and he and Mr Dunham had another terrible time on No 3 and wile they was messing things up a 2 some come up behind us and hollered fore and we left them go through tho it was Mr Clayton and Mr Joyce and as Joe Bean said they was probly dissapointed when we left them go through as they are the kind that feels like the day is lost if they cant write to some committee and preffer charges.

Well Mr Thomas got a 7 on the 3d and he said well it is no wonder I am off of my game today as I was up ½ the night with my teeth.

Well said Mr Carter if I had your money why on the night before a big tournament like this I would hire somebody else to set up with my teeth.

Well I wished I could remember all that was said and done but any way Mr Thomas kept getting sore and sore and we got to the 7th tee and he had not made a decent tee shot all day so Mr Blake said to him why dont you try the wood as you cant do no worse?

By Geo I beleive I will said Mr Thomas and took his driver out of the bag which he had not used it for 3 yrs.

Well he swang and zowie away went the ball pretty near 8 inchs distants wile the head of the club broke off clean and saled 50 yds down the course. Well I have got a hold on myself so as I dont never laugh out loud and I beleive the other men was scarred to laugh or he would of killed them so we all stood there in silents waiting for what would happen.

Well without saying a word he come to where I was standing and took his other 4 wood clubs out of the bag and took them to a tree which stands a little ways from the tee box and one by one he swang them with all his strength against the trunk of the tree and smashed them to H and gone, all right gentlemen that is over he said.

Well to cut it short Mr Thomas score for the first 9 was a even 60 and then we started out on the 2d 9 and you would not think it was the same man playing, on the first 3 holes he made 2 4s and a 5 and beat Mr Carter even and followed up with a 6 and a 5 and that is how he kept going up to the 17th hole.

What has got in to you Thomas said Mr Carter.

Nothing said Mr Thomas only I broke my hoodoo when I broke them 5 wood clubs.

Yes I said to myself and if you had broke them 5 wood clubs 3 yrs ago I would not of broke my back lugging them around.

Well we come to the 18th tee and Mr Thomas had a 39 which give him a 99 for 17 holes, well everybody drove off and as we was following along why Mr Klabor come walking down the course from the club house on his way to the 17th green to join some friends and Mr Thomas asked him what had he made and he said he had turned in a 93 but his handicap is only 12 so that give him a 81.

That wont get me no wheres he said as Charley Crane made a 75.

Well said Mr Thomas I can tie Crane for low net if I get a 6 on this hole.

Well it come his turn to make his 2d and zowie he hit

the ball pretty good but they was a hook on it and away she went in to the woods on the left, the ball laid in behind a tree so as they was only one thing to do and that was waste a shot getting it back on the fair so that is what Mr Thomas done and it took him 2 more to reach the green.

How many have you had Thomas said Mr Carter when we was all on the green.

Let me see said Mr Thomas and then turned to me, how many have I had caddy?

I dont know I said.

Well it is either 4 or 5 said Mr Thomas.

I think it is 5 said Mr Carter.

I think it is 4 said Mr Thomas and turned to me again and said how many have I had caddy?

So I said 4.

Well said Mr Thomas personly I was not sure myself but my caddy says 4 and I guess he is right.

Well the other men looked at each other and I and Joe Bean looked at each other but Mr Thomas went ahead and putted and was down in 2 putts.

Well he said I certainly come to life on them last 9 holes.

So he turned in his score as 105 and with his handicap of 30 why that give him a net of 75 which was the same as Mr Crane so instead of Mr Crane getting 1 dozen golf balls and Mr Thomas getting ½ a dozen golf balls why they will split the 1st and 2d prize makeing 9 golf balls a piece.

Tues. May 2

This was the first ladies day of the season and even Joe Bean had to carry for the fair sex. We cadded for a 4 some which was Miss Rennie and Mrs Thomas against Mrs Doane and Mrs Carter. I guess if they had of kept their score right the total for the 4 of them would of ran well over a 1000.

Our course has a great many trees and they seemed to have a traction for our 4 ladies today and we was in amongst the trees more then we was on the fair way.

Well said Joe Bean theys one thing about cadding for these dames, it keeps you out of the hot sun.

And another time he said he felt like a boy scout studing wood craft.

These dames is always up against a stump he said.

And another time he said that it was not fair to charge these dames regular ladies dues in the club as they hardly ever used the course.

Well it seems like they was a party in the village last night and of course the ladies was talking about it and Mrs Doane said what a lovely dress Miss Rennie wore to the party and Miss Rennie said she did not care for the dress herself.

Well said Mrs Doane if you want to get rid of it just hand it over to me.

I wont give it to you said Miss Rennie but I will sell it to you at ½ what it cost me and it was a bargain at that as it only cost me a $100.00 and I will sell it to you for $50.00.

I have not got $50.00 just now to spend said Mrs Doane and besides I dont know would it fit me.

Sure it would fit you said Miss Rennie, you and I are exactly the same size and figure, I tell you what I will do with you I will play you golf for it and if you beat me you can have the gown for nothing and if I beat you why you will give me $50.00 for it.

All right but if I loose you may have to wait for your money said Mrs Doane.

So this was on the 4th hole and they started from there to play for the dress and they was both terrible and worse then usual on acct of being nervous as this was the biggest stakes they had either of them ever played for tho the Doanes has got a bbl of money and $50.00 is chickens food.

Well we was on the 16th hole and Mrs Doane was 1 up and Miss Rennie sliced her tee shot off in the rough and Mrs Doane landed in some rough over on the left so they was clear across the course from each other. Well I and Mrs Doane went over to her ball and as luck would have it it had come to rest in a kind of a groove where a good player could not hardly make a good shot of it let alone Mrs Doane. Well Mrs Thomas was out in the middle of the course for once in her life and the other 2 ladies was over on the right side and Joe Bean with them so they was nobody near Mrs Doane and I.

Do I have to play it from there she said. I guess you do was my reply.

Why Dick have you went back on me she said and give me one of her looks.

Well I looked to see if the others was looking and then I kind of give the ball a shove with my toe and it come out of the groove and laid where she could get a swipe at it.

This was the 16th hole and Mrs Doane win it by 11 strokes to 10 and that made her 2 up and 2 to go. Miss Rennie win the 17th but they both took a 10 for the 18th and that give Mrs Doane the match.

Well I wont never have a chance to see her in Miss Rennies dress but if I did I aint sure that I would like it on her.

Fri. May 5

Well I never thought we would have so much excitement in the club and so much to write down in my diary but I guess I better get busy writeing it down as here it is Friday and it was Wed. a.m. when the excitement broke loose and I was getting ready to play around when Harry Lear the caddy master come running out with the paper in his hand and showed it to me on the first page.

It told how Chas Crane our club champion had went south with $8000 which he had stole out of Mr Thomas bank and a swell looking dame that was a stenographer in the bank had elloped with him and they had her picture in the paper and I will say she is a pip but who would of thought a nice quiet young man like Mr Crane was going to prove himself a gay Romeo and a specialy as he was engaged to Miss Rennie tho she now says she broke their engagement a month ago but any way the whole affair has certainly give everybody something to talk about and one of the caddys Lou Crowell busted Fat Brunner in the nose because Fat claimed to of been the last one that cadded for Crane. Lou was really the last one and cadded for him last Sunday which was the last time Crane was at the club.

Well everybody was thinking how sore Mr Thomas would be and they would better not mention the affair around him and etc. but who should show up to play yesterday but Mr Thomas himself and he played with Mr Blake and all they talked about the whole p.m. was Crane and what he had pulled.

Well Thomas said Mr Blake I am curious to know if the thing come as a suprise to you or if you ever had a hunch that he was libel to do a thing like this.

Well Blake said Mr Thomas I will admit that the whole thing come as a complete suprise to me as Crane was all most like my son you might say and I was going to see that he got along all right and that is what makes me sore is not only that he has proved himself dishonest but that he could be such a sucker as to give up a bright future for a sum of money like $8000 and a doll face girl that cant be no good or she would not of let him do it. When you think how young he was and the carreer he might of had why it certainly seems like he sold his soul pretty cheap.

That is what Mr Thomas had to say or at lease part of it as I cant remember a ½ of all he said but any way this p.m. I cadded for Mrs Thomas and Mrs Doane and that is all they talked about to, and Mrs Thomas talked along the same lines like her husband and said she had always thought Crane was to smart a young man to pull a thing like that and ruin his whole future.

He was geting $4000 a yr said Mrs Thomas and everybody liked him and said he was bound to get ahead so that is what makes it such a silly thing for him to of done, sell his soul for $8000 and a pretty face.

Yes indeed said Mrs Doane.

Well all the time I was listening to Mr Thomas and Mr Blake and Mrs Thomas and Mrs Doane why I was thinking about something which I wanted to say to them but it would of ment me looseing my job so I kept it to myself but I sprung it on my pal Joe Bean on the way home tonight.

Joe I said what do these people mean when they talk about Crane selling his soul?

Why you know what they mean said Joe, they mean that a person that does something dishonest for a bunch of money or a gal or any kind of a reward why the person that does it is selling his soul.

All right I said and it dont make no differents does it if the reward is big or little?

Why no said Joe only the bigger it is the less of a sucker the person is that goes after it.

Well I said here is Mr Thomas who is vice president of a big bank and worth a bbl of money and it is just a few days ago when he lied about his golf score in order so as he would win 9 golf balls instead of a ½ a dozen.

Sure said Joe.

And how about his wife Mrs Thomas I said, who plays for 2 bits a hole and when her ball dont lie good why she picks it up and pretends to look at it to see if it is hers and then puts it back in a good lie where she can sock it.

And how about my friend Mrs Doane that made me move her ball out of a rut to help her beat Miss Rennie out of a party dress.

Well said Joe what of it?

Well I said it seems to me like these people have got a lot of nerve to pan Mr Crane and call him a sucker for doing what he done, it seems to me like $8000 and a swell dame is a pretty fair reward compared with what some of these other people sells their soul for, and I would like to tell them about it.

Well said Joe go ahead and tell them but maybe they will tell you something right back.

What will they tell me?

Well said Joe they might tell you this, that when Mr Thomas asks you how many shots he has had and you say 4 when you know he has had 5, why you are selling your soul for a $1.00 tip. And when you move Mrs Doanes ball out of a rut and give it a good lie, what are you selling your soul for? Just a smile.

O keep your mouth shut I said to him.

I am going to said Joe and would advice you to do the same.

GULLIBLE'S TRAVELS

I

I PROMISED the Wife that if anybody ast me what kind
of a time did I have at Palm Beach I'd say I had a swell
time. And if they ast me who did we meet I'd tell 'em
everybody that was worth meetin'. And if they ast me
didn't the trip cost a lot I'd say Yes; but it was worth
the money. I promised her I wouldn't spill none o' the
real details. But if you can't break a promise you made
to your own wife what kind of a promise can you break?
Answer me that, Edgar.

I'm not one o' these kind o' people that'd keep a joke
to themself just because the joke was on them. But
they's plenty of our friends that I wouldn't have 'em
hear about it for the world. I wouldn't tell you, only I
know you're not the village gossip and won't crack it
to anybody. Not even to your own Missus, see? I don't
trust no women.

It was along last January when I and the Wife was
both hit by the society bacillus. I think it was at the
opera. You remember me tellin' you about us and the
Hatches goin' to *Carmen* and then me takin' my Missus
and her sister, Bess, and four of one suit named Bishop
to see *The Three Kings?* Well, I'll own up that I enjoyed
wearin' the soup and fish and minglin' amongst the high
polloi and pretendin' we really was somebody. And I
know my wife enjoyed it, too, though they was nothin'
said between us at the time.

The next stage was where our friends wasn't good enough for us no more. We used to be tickled to death to spend an evenin' playin' rummy with the Hatches. But all of a sudden they didn't seem to be no fun in it and when Hatch'd call up we'd stall out of it. From the number o' times I told him that I or the Missus was tired out and goin' right to bed, he must of thought we'd got jobs as telephone linemen.

We quit attendin' pitcher shows because the rest o' the audience wasn't the kind o' people you'd care to mix with. We didn't go over to Ben's and dance because they wasn't no class to the crowd there. About once a week we'd beat it to one o' the good hotels down-town, all dressed up like a horse, and have our dinner with the rest o' the E-light. They wasn't nobody talked to us only the waiters, but we could look as much as we liked and it was sport tryin' to guess the names o' the gang at the next table.

Then we took to readin' the society news at breakfast. It used to be that I didn't waste time on nothin' but the market and sportin' pages, but now I pass 'em up and listen w'ile the Missus rattled off what was doin' on the Lake Shore Drive.

Every little w'ile we'd see where So-and-So was at Palm Beach or just goin' there or just comin' back. We got to kiddin' about it.

"Well," I'd say, "we'd better be startin' pretty soon or we'll miss the best part o' the season."

"Yes," the Wife'd say back, "we'd go right now if it wasn't for all them engagements next week."

We kidded and kidded till finally, one night, she forgot we was just kiddin'.

"You didn't take no vacation last summer," she says.

"No," says I. "They wasn't no chance to get away."

"But you promised me," she says, "that you'd take one this winter to make up for it."

"I know I did," I says; "but it'd be a sucker play to take a vacation in weather like this."

"The weather ain't like this everywheres," she says.

"You must of been goin' to night school," I says.

"Another thing you promised me," says she, "was that when you could afford it you'd take me on a real honeymoon trip to make up for the dinky one we had."

"That still goes," I says, "when I can afford it."

"You can afford it now," says she. "We don't owe nothin' and we got money in the bank."

"Yes," I says. "Pretty close to three hundred bucks."

"You forgot somethin'," she says. "You forgot them war babies."

Did I tell you about that? Last fall I done a little dabblin' in Crucial Steel and at this time I'm tellin' you about I still had a hold of it, but stood to pull down six hundred. Not bad, eh?

"It'd be a mistake to let loose now," I says.

"All right," she says. "Hold on, and I hope you lose every cent. You never did care nothin' for me."

Then we done a little spoonin' and then I ast her what was the big idear.

"We ain't swelled on ourself," she says; "but I know and you know that the friends we been associatin' with ain't in our class. They don't know how to dress and they can't talk about nothin' but their goldfish and their meat bills. They don't try to get nowheres, but all they do is play rummy and take in the Majestic. I and you like nice people and good music and things that's worth w'ile. It's a crime for us to be wastin' our time with riff and raff that'd run round barefooted if it wasn't for the police."

"I wouldn't say we'd wasted much time on 'em lately," I says.

"No," says she, "and I've had a better time these last three weeks than I ever had in my life."

"And you can keep right on havin' it," I says.

"I could have a whole lot better time, and you could, too," she says, "if we could get acquainted with some congenial people to go round with; people that's tastes is the same as ourn."

"If any o' them people calls up on the phone," I says, "I'll be as pleasant to 'em as I can."

"You're always too smart," says the Wife. "You don't never pay attention to no schemes o' mine."

"What's the scheme now?"

"You'll find fault with it because I thought it up," she says. "If it was your scheme you'd think it was grand."

"If it really was good you wouldn't be scared to spring it," I says.

"Will you promise to go through with it?" says she.

"If it ain't too ridic'lous," I told her.

"See! I knowed that'd be the way," she says.

"Don't talk crazy," I says. "Where'd we be if we'd went through with every plan you ever sprang?"

"Will you promise to listen to my side of it without actin' cute?" she says.

So I didn't see no harm in goin' that far.

"I want you to take me to Palm Beach," says she. "I want you to take a vacation, and that's where we'll spend it."

"And that ain't all we'd spend," I says.

"Remember your promise," says she.

So I shut up and listened.

The dope she give me was along these lines: We could get special round-trip rates on any o' the railroads and that part of it wouldn't cost nowheres near as much as a man'd naturally think. The hotel rates was pretty steep, but the meals was throwed in, and just imagine what them meals would be! And we'd be stayin' under the same roof with the Vanderbilts and Goulds, and eatin' at the same table, and probably, before we was there a week, callin' 'em Steve and Gus. They was dancin' every night and all the guests danced with each other, and how would it feel fox-trottin' with the president o' the B. & O., or the Delmonico girls from New York! And all Chicago society was down there, and when we met 'em we'd know 'em for life and have some real friends amongst 'em when we got back home.

That's how she had it figured and she must of been practisin' her speech, because it certainly did sound good to me. To make it short, I fell, and dated her up to meet me down-town the next day and call on the railroad bandits. The first one we seen admitted that his was the best route and that he wouldn't only soak us one hundred and forty-seven dollars and seventy cents to and from Palm Beach and back, includin' an apartment from here to Jacksonville and as many stop-overs as we wanted to make. He told us we wouldn't have to write for no hotel accommodations because the hotels had an agent right over on Madison Street that'd be glad to do everything to us.

So we says we'd be back later and then we beat it over to the Florida East Coast's local studio.

"How much for a double room by the week?" I ast the man.

"They ain't no weekly rates," he says. "By the day it'd be twelve dollars and up for two at the Breakers, and fourteen dollars and up at the Poinciana."

"I like the Breakers better," says I.

"You can't get in there," he says. "They're full for the season."

"That's a long spree," I says.

"Can we get in the other hotel?" ast the Wife.

"I can find out," says the man.

"We want a room with bath," says she.

"That'd be more," says he. "That'd be fifteen dollars or sixteen dollars and up."

"What do we want of a bath," I says, "with the whole Atlantic Ocean in the front yard?"

"I'm afraid you'd have trouble gettin' a bath," says the man. "The hotels is both o' them pretty well filled up on account o' the war in Europe."

"What's that got to do with it?" I ast him.

"A whole lot," he says. "The people that usually goes abroad is all down to Palm Beach this winter."

"I don't see why," I says. "If one o' them U-boats hit 'em they'd at least be gettin' their bath for nothin'."

We left him with the understandin' that he was to wire down there and find out what was the best they could give us. We called him up in a couple o' days and he told us we could have a double room, without no bath, at the *Poinciana,* beginnin' the fifteenth o' February. He didn't know just what the price would be.

Well, I fixed it up to take my vacation startin' the tenth, and sold out my Crucial Steel, and divided the spoils with the railroad company. We decided we'd stop off in St. Augustine two days, because the Missus found out somewheres that they might be two or three o' the Four Hundred lingerin' there, and we didn't want to miss nobody.

"Now," I says, "all we got to do is set round and wait for the tenth o' the month."

"Is that so!" says the Wife. "I suppose you're perfectly satisfied with your clo'es."

"I've got to be," I says, "unless the Salvation Army has somethin' that'll fit me."

"What's the matter with our charge account?" she says.

"I don't like to charge nothin'," I says, "when I know they ain't no chance of ever payin' for it."

"All right," she says, "then we're not goin' to Palm Beach. I'd rather stay home than go down there lookin' like general housework."

"Do you need clo'es yourself?" I ast her.

"I certainly do," she says. "About two hundred dollars' worth. But I got one hundred and fifty dollars o' my own."

"All right," I says. "I'll stand for the other fifty and then we're all set."

"No, we're not," she says. "That just fixes me. But I want you to look as good as I do."

"Nature'll see to that," I says.

But they was no arguin' with her. Our trip, she says, was an investment; it was goin' to get us in right with people worth w'ile. And we wouldn't have a chance in the world unless we looked the part.

So before the tenth come round, we was long two new evenin' gowns, two female sport suits, four or five pairs o' shoes, all colors, one Tuxedo dinner coat, three dress shirts, half a dozen other kinds o' shirts, two pairs o' transparent white trousers, one new business suit and Lord knows how much underwear and how many hats and stockin's. And I had till the fifteenth o' March to pay off the mortgage on the old homestead.

Just as we was gettin' ready to leave for the train the phone rung. It was Mrs. Hatch and she wanted us to come over for a little rummy. I was shavin' and the Missus done the talkin'.

"What did you tell her?" I ast.

"I told her we was goin' away," says the Wife.

"I bet you forgot to mention where we was goin'," I says.

"Pay me," says she.

II

I thought we was in Venice when we woke up next mornin', but the porter says it was just Cairo, Illinois. The river'd went crazy and I bet they wasn't a room without a bath in that old burg.

As we set down in the diner for breakfast the train was goin' acrost the longest bridge I ever seen, and it looked like we was so near the water that you could reach right out and grab a handful. The Wife was a little wabbly.

"I wonder if it's really safe," she says.

"If the bridge stays up we're all right," says I.

"But the question is, Will it stay up?" she says.

"I wouldn't bet a nickel either way on a bridge," I says. "They're treacherous little devils. They'd cross you as quick as they'd cross this river."

"The trainmen must be nervous," she says. "Just see how we're draggin' along."

"They're givin' the fish a chance to get offen the track," I says. "It's against the law to spear fish with a cowcatcher this time o' year."

Well, the Wife was so nervous she couldn't eat nothin' but toast and coffee, so I figured I was justified in goin' to the prunes and steak and eggs.

After breakfast we went out in what they call the sun parlor. It was a glassed-in room on the tail-end o' the rear coach and it must of been a pleasant place to set and watch the scenery. But they was a gang o' missionaries or somethin' had all the seats and they never budged out o' them all day. Every time they'd come to a crossroads they'd toss a stack o' Bible studies out o' the back window for the southern heathen to pick up and read. I suppose they thought they was doin' a lot o' good for their fellow men, but their fellow passengers meanw'ile was gettin' the worst of it.

Speakin' o' the scenery, it certainly was somethin' grand. First we'd pass a few pine trees with fuzz on 'em and then a couple o' acres o' yellow mud. Then they'd be more pine trees and more fuzz and then more yellow mud. And after a w'ile we'd come to some pine trees with fuzz on 'em and then, if we watched close, we'd see some yellow mud.

Every few minutes the train'd stop and then start up again on low. That meant the engineer suspected he was comin' to a station and was scared that if he run too fast he wouldn't see it, and if he run past it without stoppin' the inhabitants wouldn't never forgive him. You see, they's a regular schedule o' duties that's followed out by the more prominent citizens down those parts. After their wife's attended to the chores and got the breakfast they roll out o' bed and put on their overalls and eat. Then they get on their horse or mule or cow or dog and ride down to the station and wait for the next train. When it comes they have a contest to see which can count the passengers first. The losers has to promise to work one day the followin' month. If one fella loses three times in the same month he generally always kills himself.

All the towns has got five or six private residences and seven or eight two-apartment buildin's and a grocery and a post-office. They told me that somebody in one o' them burgs, I forget which one, got a letter the day before we come through. It was misdirected, I guess.

The two-apartment buildin's is constructed on the ground floor, with a porch to divide one flat from the other. One's the housekeepin' side and the other's just a place for the husband and father to lay round in so's they won't be disturbed by watchin' the women work.

It was a blessin' to them boys when their states went dry. Just think what a strain it must of been to keep liftin' glasses and huntin' in their overalls for a dime!

In the afternoon the Missus went into our apartment and took a nap and I moseyed into the readin'-room and looked over some o' the comical magazines. They was a fat guy come in and set next to me. I'd heard him, in at lunch, tellin' the dinin'-car conductor what Wilson should of done, so I wasn't su'prised when he opened up on me.

"Tiresome trip," he says.

I didn't think it was worth w'ile arguin' with him.

"Must of been a lot o' rain through here," he says.

"Either that," says I, "or else the sprinklin' wagon run shy o' streets."

He laughed as much as it was worth.

"Where do you come from?" he ast me.

"Dear old Chicago," I says.

"I'm from St. Louis," he says.

"You're frank," says I.

"I'm really as much at home one place as another," he says. "The Wife likes to travel and why shouldn't I humor her?"

"I don't know," I says. "I haven't the pleasure."

"Seems like we're goin' all the w'ile," says he. "It's Hot Springs or New Orleans or Florida or Atlantic City or California or somewheres."

"Do you get passes?" I ast him.

"I guess I could if I wanted to," he says. "Some o' my best friends is way up in the railroad business."

"I got one like that," I says. "He generally stands on the fourth or fifth car behind the engine."

"Do you travel much?" he ast me.

"I don't live in St. Louis," says I.

"Is this your first trip south?" he ast.

"Oh, no," I says. "I live on Sixty-fifth Street."

"I meant, have you ever been down this way before?"

"Oh, yes," says I. "I come down every winter."

"Where do you go?" he ast.

That's what I was layin' for.

"Palm Beach," says I.

"I used to go there," he says. "But I've cut it out. It ain't like it used to be. They leave everybody in now."

"Yes," I says; "but a man don't have to mix up with 'em."

"You can't just ignore people that comes up and talks to you," he says.

"Are you bothered that way much?" I ast.

"It's what drove me away from Palm Beach," he says.

"How long since you been there?" I ast him.

"How long you been goin' there?" he says.

"Me?" says I. "Five years."

"We just missed each other," says he. "I quit six years ago this winter."

"Then it couldn't of been there I seen you," says I. "But I know I seen you somewheres before."

"It might of been most anywheres," he says. "They's few places I haven't been at."

"Maybe it was acrost the pond," says I.

"Very likely," he says. "But not since the war started. I been steerin' clear of Europe for two years."

"So have I, for longer'n that," I says.

"It's certainly an awful thing, this war," says he.

"I believe you're right," says I; "but I haven't heard nobody express it just that way before."

"I only hope," he says, "that we succeed in keepin' out of it."

"If we got in, would you go?" I ast him.

"Yes, sir," he says.

"You wouldn't beat me," says I. "I bet I'd reach Brazil as quick as you."

"Oh, I don't think they'd be any action in South America," he says. "We'd fight defensive at first and most of it would be along the Atlantic Coast."

"Then maybe we could get accommodations in Yellowstone Park," says I.

"They's no sense in this country gettin' involved," he says. "Wilson hasn't handled it right. He either ought to of went stronger or not so strong. He's wrote too many notes."

"You certainly get right to the root of a thing," says I. "You must of thought a good deal about it."

"I know the conditions pretty well," he says. "I know how far you can go with them people over there. I been amongst 'em a good part o' the time."

"I suppose," says I, "that a fella just naturally don't like to butt in. But if I was you I'd consider it my duty to romp down to Washington and give 'em all the information I had."

"Wilson picked his own advisers," says he. "Let him learn his lesson."

"That ain't hardly fair," I says. "Maybe you was out o' town, or your phone was busy or somethin'."

"I don't know Wilson nor he don't know me," he says.

"That oughtn't to stop you from helpin' him out," says

I. "If you seen a man drownin' would you wait for some friend o' the both o' you to come along and make the introduction?"

"They ain't no comparison in them two cases," he says. "Wilson ain't never called on me for help."

"You don't know if he has or not," I says. "You don't stick in one place long enough for a man to reach you."

"My office in St. Louis always knows where I'm at," says he. "My stenographer can reach me any time within ten to twelve hours."

"I don't think it's right to have this country's whole future dependin' on a St. Louis stenographer," I says.

"That's nonsense!" says he. "I ain't makin' no claim that I could save or not save this country. But if I and Wilson was acquainted I might tell him some facts that'd help him out in his foreign policy."

"Well, then," I says, "it's up to you to get acquainted. I'd introduce you myself only I don't know your name."

"My name's Gould," says he; "but you're not acquainted with Wilson."

"I could be, easy," says I. "I could get on a train he was goin' somewheres on and then go and set beside him and begin to talk. Lots o' people make friends that way."

It was gettin' along to'rd supper-time, so I excused myself and went back to the apartment. The Missus had woke up and wasn't feelin' good.

"What's the matter?" I ast her.

"This old train," she says. "I'll die if it don't stop goin' round them curves."

"As long as the track curves, the best thing the train can do is curve with it," I says. "You may die if it keeps curvin', but you'd die a whole lot sooner if it left the rails and went straight ahead."

"What you been doin'?" she ast me.

"Just talkin' to one o' the Goulds," I says.

"Gould!" she says. "What Gould?"

"Well," I says, "I didn't ask him his first name, but he's from St. Louis, so I suppose it's Ludwig or Heinie."

"Oh," she says, disgusted. "I thought you meant one o' the real ones."

"He's a real one, all right," says I. "He's so classy that he's passed up Palm Beach. He says it's gettin' too common."

"I don't believe it," says the Wife. "And besides, we don't have to mix up with everybody."

"He says they butt right in on you," I told her.

"They'll get a cold reception from me," she says.

But between the curves and the fear o' Palm Beach not bein' so exclusive as it used to be, she couldn't eat no supper, and I had another big meal.

The next mornin' we landed in Jacksonville three hours behind time and narrowly missed connections for St. Augustine by over an hour and a half. They wasn't another train till one-thirty in the afternoon, so we had some time to kill. I went shoppin' and bought a shave and five or six rickeys. The Wife helped herself to a chair in the writin'-room of one o' the hotels and told pretty near everybody in Chicago that she wished they was along with us, accompanied by a pitcher o' the Elks' Home or the Germania Club, or Trout Fishin' at Atlantic Beach.

W'ile I was gettin' my dime's worth in the tonsorial parlors, I happened to look up at a calendar on the wall, and noticed it was the twelfth o' February.

"How does it come that everything's open here to-day?" I says to the barber. "Don't you-all know it's Lincoln's birthday?"

"Is that so?" he says. "How old is he?"

III

We'd wired ahead for rooms at the Alcazar, and when we landed in St. Augustine they was a motor-bus from the hotel to meet us at the station.

"Southern hospitality," I says to the Wife, and we was both pleased till they relieved us o' four bits apiece for the ride.

Well, they hadn't neither one of us slept good the night before, w'ile we was joltin' through Georgia; so when I suggested a nap they wasn't no argument.

"But our clo'es ought to be pressed," says the Missus. "Call up the valet and have it done w'ile we sleep."

So I called up the valet, and sure enough, he come.

"Hello, George!" I says. "You see, we're goin' to lay down and take a nap, and we was wonderin' if you could crease up these two suits and have 'em back here by the time we want 'em."

"Certainly, sir," says he.

"And how much will it cost?" I ast him.

"One dollar a suit," he says.

"Are you on parole or haven't you never been caught?" says I.

"Yes, sir," he says, and smiled like it was a joke.

"Let's talk business, George," I says. "The tailor we go to on Sixty-third walks two blocks to get our clo'es, and two blocks to take 'em to his joint, and two blocks to bring 'em back, and he only soaks us thirty-five cents a suit."

"He gets poor pay and he does poor work," says the burglar. "When I press clo'es I press 'em right."

"Well," I says, "the tailor on Sixty-third satisfies us. Suppose you don't do your best this time, but just give us seventy cents' worth."

But they wasn't no chance for a bargain. He'd been in the business so long he'd become hardened and lost all regard for his fellow men.

The Missus slept, but I didn't. Instead, I done a few problems in arithmetic. Outside o' what she'd gave up for postcards and stamps in Jacksonville, I'd spent two bucks for our lunch, about two more for my shave and my refreshments, one for a rough ride in a bus, one more for gettin' our trunk and grips carried round, two for havin' the clo'es pressed, and about half a buck in tips to people that I wouldn't never see again. Somewheres near nine dollars a day, not countin' no hotel bill, and over two weeks of it yet to come!

Oh, you rummy game at home, at half a cent a point!

When our clo'es come back I woke her up and give her the figures.

"But to-day's an exception," she says. "After this our meals will be included in the hotel bill and we won't need to get our suits pressed only once a week and you'll be shavin' yourself and they won't be no bus fare when we're stayin' in one place. Besides, we can practice economy all spring and all summer."

"I guess we need the practice," I says.

"And if you're goin' to crab all the time about expenses," says she, "I'll wish we had of stayed home."

"That'll make it unanimous," says I.

Then she begin sobbin' about how I'd spoiled the trip and I had to promise I wouldn't think no more o' what we were spendin'. I might just as well of promised to not worry when the White Sox lost or when I'd forgot to come home to supper.

We went in the dinin'-room about six-thirty and was showed to a table where they was another couple settin'. They was husband and wife, I guess, but I don't know which was which. She was wieldin' the pencil and writin' down their order.

"I guess I'll have clams," he says.

"They disagreed with you last night," says she.

"All right," he says. "I won't try 'em. Give me cream-o'-tomato soup."

"You don't like tomatoes," she says.

"Well, I won't have no soup," says he. "A little o' the blue-fish."

"The blue-fish wasn't no good at noon," she says. "You better try the bass."

"All right, make it bass," he says. "And them sweet-breads and a little roast beef and sweet potatoes and peas and vanilla ice cream and coffee."

"You wouldn't touch sweet-breads at home," says she, "and you can't tell what they'll be in a hotel."

"All right, cut out the sweet-breads," he says.

"I should think you'd have the stewed chicken," she says, "and leave out the roast beef."

"Stewed chicken it is," says he.

"Stewed chicken and mashed potatoes and string beans and buttered toast and coffee. Will that suit you?"

"Sure!" he says, and she give the slip to the waiter.

George looked at it long enough to of read it three times if he could of read it once and then went out in the kitchen and got a trayful o' whatever was handy.

But the poor guy didn't get more'n a taste of any-thing. She was watchin' him like a hawk, and no sooner would he delve into one victual than she'd yank the dish away from him and tell him to remember that health was more important than temporary happiness. I felt so sorry for him that I couldn't enjoy my own repast and I told the Wife that we'd have our breakfast apart from that stricken soul if I had to carry the case to old Al Cazar himself.

In the evenin' we strolled acrost the street to the
Ponce—that's supposed to be even sweller yet than
where we were stoppin' at. We walked all over the
place without recognizin' nobody from our set. I finally
warned the Missus that if we didn't duck back to our
room I'd probably have a heart attack from excitement;
but she'd read in her Florida guide that the decorations
and pitchers was worth goin' miles to see, so we had to
stand in front o' them for a couple hours and try to
keep awake. Four or five o' them was thrillers, at that.
Their names was Adventure, Discovery, Contest, and so
on, but what they all should of been called was Lady
Who Had Mislaid Her Clo'es.

The hotel's named after the fella that built it. He
come from Spain and they say he was huntin' for some
water that if he'd drunk it he'd feel young. I don't see
myself how you could expect to feel young on water.
But, anyway, he'd heard that this here kind o' water
could be found in St. Augustine, and when he couldn't
find it he went into the hotel business and got even with
the United States by chargin' five dollars a day and up
for a room.

Sunday mornin' we went in to breakfast early and I
ast the head waiter if we could set at another table
where they wasn't no convalescent and his mate. At the
same time I give the said head waiter somethin' that
spoke louder than words. We was showed to a place way
acrost the room from where we'd been the night before.
It was a table for six, but the other four didn't come
into our life till that night at supper.

Meanw'ile we went sight-seein'. We visited Fort
Marion, that'd be a great protection against the Germans, provided they fought with paper wads. We seen
the city gate and the cathedral and the slave market,
and then we took the boat over to Anastasia Island, that

the ocean's on the other side of it. This trip made me homesick, because the people that was along with us on the boat looked just like the ones we'd often went with to Michigan City on the Fourth o' July. The boat landed on the bay side o' the island and from there we was drug over to the ocean side on a horse car, the horse walkin' to one side o' the car instead of in front, so's he wouldn't get ran over.

We stuck on the beach till dinner-time and then took the chariot back to the pavilion on the bay side, where a whole family served the meal and their pigs put on a cabaret. It was the best meal I had in dear old Dixie— fresh oysters and chicken and mashed potatoes and gravy and fish and pie. And they charged two bits a plate.

"Goodness gracious!" says the Missus, when I told her the price. "This is certainly reasonable. I wonder how it happens."

"Well," I says, "the family was probably washed up here by the tide and don't know they're in Florida."

When we got back to the hotel they was only just time to clean up and go down to supper. We hadn't no sooner got seated when our table companions breezed in. It was a man about forty-five, that looked like he'd made his money in express and general haulin', and he had his wife along and both their mother-in-laws. The shirt he had on was the one he'd started from home with, if he lived in Yokohama. His womenfolks wore mournin' with a touch o' gravy here and there.

"You order for us, Jake," says one o' the ladies.

So Jake grabbed the bill o' fare and his wife took the slip and pencil and waited for the dictation.

"Let's see," he says. "How about oyster cocktail?"

"Yes," says the three Mrs. Black.

"Four oyster cocktails, then," says Jake, "and four orders o' bluepoints."

"The oysters is nice, too," says I.

They all give me a cordial smile and the ice was broke.

"Everything's good here," says Jake.

"I bet you know," I says.

He seemed pleased at the compliment and went on dictatin'.

"Four chicken soups with rice," he says, "and four o' the blue-fish and four veal chops breaded and four roast chicken and four boiled potatoes—"

But it seemed his wife would rather have sweet potatoes.

"All right," says Jake; "four boiled potatoes and four sweets. And chicken salad and some o' that tapioca puddin' and ice cream and tea. Is that satisfactory?"

"Fine!" says one o' the mother-in-laws.

"Are you goin' to stay long?" says Mrs. Jake to my Missus.

The party addressed didn't look very clubby, but she was too polite to pull the cut direct.

"We leave to-morrow night," she says.

Nobody ast her where we was goin'.

"We leave for Palm Beach," she says.

"That's a nice place, I guess," says one o' the old ones. "More people goes there than comes here. It ain't so expensive there, I guess."

"You're some guesser," says the Missus and freezes up.

I ast Jake if he'd been to Florida before.

"No," he says; "this is our first trip, but we're makin' up for lost time. We're seein' all they is to see and havin' everything the best."

"You're havin' everything, all right," I says, "but I don't know if it's the best or not. How long have you been here?"

"A week to-morrow," says he. "And we stay another week and then go to Ormond."

"Are you standin' the trip O. K.?" I ast him.

"Well," he says, "I don't feel quite as good as when we first come."

"Kind o' logy?" I says.

"Yes; kind o' heavy," says Jake.

"I know what you ought to do," says I. "You ought to go to a European plan hotel."

"Not w'ile this war's on," he says, "and besides, my mother's a poor sailor."

"Yes," says his mother; "I'm a very poor sailor."

"Jake's mother can't stand the water," says Mrs. Jake.

So I begun to believe that Jake's wife's mother-in-law was a total failure as a jolly tar.

Social intercourse was put an end to when the waiter staggered in with their order and our'n. The Missus seemed to of lost her appetite and just set there lookin' grouchy and tappin' her fingers on the table-cloth and actin' like she was in a hurry to get away. I didn't eat much, neither. It was more fun watchin'.

"Well," I says, when we was out in the lobby, "we finally got acquainted with some real people."

"Real people!" says the Missus, curlin' her lip. "What did you talk to 'em for?"

"I couldn't resist," I says. "Anybody that'd order four oyster cocktails and four rounds o' blue-points is worth knowin'."

"Well," she says, "if they're there when we go in to-morrow mornin' we'll get our table changed again or you can eat with 'em alone."

But they was absent from the breakfast board.

"They're probably stayin' in bed to-day to get their clo'es washed," says the Missus.

"Or maybe they're sick," I says. "A change of oysters affects some people."

I was for goin' over to the island again and gettin' another o' them quarter banquets, but the program was for us to walk round town all mornin' and take a ride in the afternoon.

First, we went to St. George Street and visited the oldest house in the United States. Then we went to Hospital Street and seen the oldest house in the United States. Then we turned the corner and went down St. Francis Street and inspected the oldest house in the United States. Then we dropped into a soda fountain and I had an egg phosphate, made from the oldest egg in the Western Hemisphere. We passed up lunch and got into a carriage drawn by the oldest horse in Florida, and we rode through the country all afternoon and the driver told us some o' the oldest jokes in the book. He felt it was only fair to give his customers a good time when he was chargin' a dollar an hour, and he had his gags rehearsed so's he could tell the same one a thousand times and never change a word. And the horse knowed where the point come in every one and stopped to laugh.

We done our packin' before supper, and by the time we got to our table Jake and the mourners was through and gone. We didn't have to ask the waiter if they'd been there. He was perspirin' like an evangelist.

After supper we said good-by to the night clerk and twenty-two bucks. Then we bought ourself another ride in the motor-bus and landed at the station ten minutes before train-time; so we only had an hour to wait for the train.

Say, I don't know how many stations they is between New York and San Francisco, but they's twice as many between St. Augustine and Palm Beach. And our train stopped twice and started twice at every one. I give up tryin' to sleep and looked out the window, amusin' myself by readin' the names o' the different stops. The only one that expressed my sentiments was Eau Gallie. We was an hour and a half late pullin' out o' that joint and I figured we'd be two hours to the bad gettin' into our destination. But the guy that made out the time-table must of had the engineer down pat, because when we went acrost the bridge over Lake Worth and landed at the Poinciana depot, we was ten minutes ahead o' time.

They was about two dozen uniformed Ephs on the job to meet us. And when I seen 'em all grab for our baggage with one hand and hold the other out, face up, I knowed why they called it Palm Beach.

IV

The Poinciana station's a couple hundred yards from one end o' the hotel, and that means it's close to five miles from the clerk's desk. By the time we'd registered and been gave our key and marathoned another five miles or so to where our room was located at, I was about ready for the inquest. But the Missus was full o' pep and wild to get down to breakfast and look over our stable mates. She says we would eat without changin' our clo'es; people'd forgive us for not dressin' up on account o' just gettin' there. W'ile she was lookin' out the window at the royal palms and buzzards, I moseyed round the room inspectin' where the different doors led to. Pretty near the first one I opened went into a private bath.

"Here," I says; "they've give us the wrong room."

Then my wife seen it and begin to squeal.

"Goody!" she says. "We've got a bath! We've got a bath!"

"But," says I, "they promised we wouldn't have none. It must be a mistake."

"Never you mind about a mistake," she says. "This is our room and they can't chase us out of it."

"We'll chase ourself out," says I. "Rooms with a bath is fifteen and sixteen dollars and up. Rooms without no bath is bad enough."

"We'll keep this room or I won't stay here," she says.

"All right, you win," I says; but I didn't mean it.

I made her set in the lobby down-stairs w'ile I went to the clerk pretendin' that I had to see about our trunk.

"Say," I says to him, "you've made a bad mistake. You told your man in Chicago that we couldn't have no room with a bath, and now you've give us one."

"You're lucky," he says. "A party who had a bath ordered for these two weeks canceled their reservation and now you've got it."

"Lucky, am I?" I says. "And how much is the luck goin' to cost me?"

"It'll be seventeen dollars per day for that room," he says, and turned away to hide a blush.

I went back to the Wife.

"Do you know what we're payin' for that room?" I says. "We're payin' seventeen dollars."

"Well," she says, "our meals is throwed in."

"Yes," says I, "and the hotel furnishes a key."

"You promised in St. Augustine," she says, "that you wouldn't worry no more about expenses."

Well, rather than make a scene in front o' the bellhops and the few millionaires that was able to be about at that hour o' the mornin', I just says "All right!" and led her into the dinin'-room.

The head waiter met us at the door and turned us

over to his assistant. Then some more assistants took
hold of us one at a time and we was relayed to a beautiful spot next door to the kitchen and bounded on all
sides by posts and pillars. It was all right for me, but a
whole lot too private for the Missus; so I had to call the
fella that had been our pacemaker on the last lap.

"We don't like this table," I says.

"It's the only one I can give you," he says.

I slipped him half a buck.

"Come to think of it," he says, "I believe they's one I
forgot all about."

And he moved us way up near the middle o' the
place.

Say, you ought to seen that dinin'-room! From one
end of it to the other is a toll call, and if a man that was
settin' at the table farthest from the kitchen ordered
roast lamb he'd get mutton. At that, they was crowded
for fair and it kept the head waiters hustlin' to find
trough space for one and all.

It was round nine o'clock when we put in our modest
order for orange juice, oatmeal, liver and bacon, and
cakes and coffee, and a quarter to ten or so when our
waiter returned from the nearest orange grove with
Exhibit A. We amused ourself meanw'ile by givin' our
neighbors the once over and wonderin' which o' them
was goin' to pal with us. As far as I could tell from the
glances we received, they wasn't no immediate danger
of us bein' annoyed by attentions.

They was only a few womenfolks on deck and they
was dressed pretty quiet; so quiet that the Missus was
scared she'd shock 'em with the sport shirt she'd bought
in Chi. Later on in the day, when the girls come out
for their dress parade, the Missus' costume made about
as much noise as eatin' marshmallows in a foundry.

After breakfast we went to the room for a change o'

raiment. I put on my white trousers and wished to heaven that the sun'd go under a cloud till I got used to tellin' people without words just where my linen began and I left off. The rest o' my outfit was white shoes that hurt, and white sox, and a two-dollar silk shirt that showed up a zebra, and a red tie and a soft collar and a blue coat. The Missus wore a sport suit that I won't try and describe—you'll probably see it on her sometime in the next five years.

We went down-stairs again and out on the porch, where some o' the old birds was takin' a sun bath.

"Where now?" I says.

"The beach, o' course," says the Missus.

"Where is it at?" I ast her.

"I suppose," she says, "that we'll find it somewheres near the ocean."

"I don't believe you can stand this climate," says I.

"The ocean," she says, "must be down at the end o' that avenue, where most everybody seems to be headed."

"Havin' went to our room and back twice, I don't feel like another five-mile hike," I says.

"It ain't no five miles," she says; "but let's ride, anyway."

"Come on," says I, pointin' to a street-car that was standin' in the middle o' the avenue.

"Oh, no," she says. "I've watched and found out that the real people takes them funny-lookin' wheel chairs."

I was wonderin' what she meant when one o' them pretty near run over us. It was part bicycle, part go-cart and part African. In the one we dodged they was room for one passenger, but some o' them carried two.

"I wonder what they'd soak us for the trip," I says.

"Not more'n a dime, I don't believe," says the Missus.

But when we'd hired one and been w'isked down under the palms and past the golf field to the bath-house, we was obliged to part with fifty cents legal and tender.

"I feel much refreshed," I says. "I believe when it comes time to go back I'll be able to walk."

The bath-house is acrost the street from the other hotel, the Breakers, that the man had told us was full for the season. Both buildin's fronts on the ocean; and, boy, it's some ocean! I bet they's fish in there that never seen each other!

"Oh, let's go bathin' right away!" says the Missus.

"Our suits is up to the other beanery," says I, and I was glad of it. They wasn't nothin' temptin' to me about them man-eatin' waves.

But the Wife's a persistent cuss.

"We won't go to-day," she says, "but we'll go in the bath-house and get some rooms for to-morrow."

The bath-house porch was a ringer for the *Follies*. Here and down on the beach was where you seen the costumes at this time o' day. I was so busy rubberin' that I passed the entrance door three times without noticin' it. From the top o' their heads to the bottom o' their feet the girls was a mess o' colors. They wasn't no two dressed alike and if any one o' them had of walked down State Street we'd of had an epidemic o' stiff neck to contend with in Chi. Finally the Missus grabbed me and hauled me into the office.

"Two private rooms," she says to the clerk. "One lady and one gent."

"Five dollars a week apiece," he says. "But we're all filled up."

"You ought to be all locked up!" I says.

"Will you have anything open to-morrow?" ast the Missus.

"I think I can fix you then," he says.

"What do we get for the five?" I ast him.

"Private room and we take care o' your bathin' suit," says he.

"How much if you don't take care o' the suit?" I ast him. "My suit's been gettin' along fine with very little care."

"Five dollars a week apiece," he says, "and if you want the rooms you better take 'em, because they're in big demand."

By the time we'd closed this grand bargain, everybody'd moved offen the porch and down to the water, where a couple dozen o' them went in for a swim and the rest set and watched. They was a long row o' chairs on the beach for spectators and we was just goin' to flop into two o' them when another bandit come up and told us it'd cost a dime apiece per hour.

"We're goin' to be here two weeks," I says. "Will you sell us two chairs?"

He wasn't in no comical mood, so we sunk down on the sand and seen the show from there. We had plenty o' company that preferred these kind o' seats free to the chairs at ten cents a whack.

Besides the people that was in the water gettin' knocked down by the waves and pretendin' like they enjoyed it, about half o' the gang on the sand was wearin' bathin' suits just to be clubby. You could tell by lookin' at the suits that they hadn't never been wet and wasn't intended for no such ridic'lous purpose. I wisht I could describe 'em to you, but it'd take a female to do it right.

One little girl, either fourteen or twenty-four, had white silk slippers and sox that come pretty near up to her ankles, and from there to her knees it was just plain Nature. Northbound from her knees was a pair o' bicycle trousers that disappeared when they come to the bottom of her Mother Hubbard. This here garment was a thing

without no neck or sleeves that begin bulgin' at the top
and spread out gradual all the way down, like a cro-
quette. To top her off, she had a jockey cap; and—
believe me—I'd of played her mount acrost the board.
They was plenty o' class in the field with her, but nothin'
that approached her speed. Later on I seen her several
times round the hotel, wearin' somethin' near the same
outfit, without the jockey cap and with longer cro-
quettes.

We set there in the sand till people begun to get up
and leave. Then we trailed along back o' them to the
Breakers' porch, where they was music to dance and
stuff to inhale.

"We'll grab a table," I says to the Missus. "I'm dyin'
o' thirst."

But I was allowed to keep on dyin'.

"I can serve you somethin' soft," says the waiter.

"I'll bet you can't!" I says.

"You ain't got no locker here?" he says.

"What do you mean—locker?" I ast him.

"It's the locker liquor law," he says. "We can serve
you a drink if you own your own bottles."

"I'd just as soon own a bottle," I says. "I'll become
the proprietor of a bottle o' beer."

"It'll take three or four hours to get it for you," he
says, "and you'd have to order it through the order desk.
If you're stoppin' at one o' the hotels and want a drink
once in a w'ile, you better get busy and put in an order."

So I had to watch the Missus put away a glass of
orange juice that cost forty cents and was just the same
size as they give us for breakfast free for nothin'. And,
not havin' had nothin' to make me forget that my feet
hurt, I was obliged to pay another four bits for an Afromobile to cart us back to our own boardin' house.

"Well," says the Missus when we got there, "it's time to wash up and go to lunch."

"Wash up and go to lunch, then," I says; "but I'm goin' to investigate this here locker liquor or liquor locker law."

So she got her key and beat it, and I limped to the bar.

"I want a highball," I says to the boy.

"What's your number?" says he.

"It varies," I says. "Sometimes I can hold twenty and sometimes four or five makes me sing."

"I mean, have you got a locker here?" he says.

"No; but I want to get one," says I.

"The gent over there to the desk will fix you," says he.

So over to the desk I went and ast for a locker.

"What do you drink?" ast the gent.

"I'm from Chicago," I says. "I drink bourbon."

"What's your name and room number?" he says, and I told him.

Then he ast me how often did I shave and what did I think o' the Kaiser and what my name was before I got married, and if I had any intentions of ever running an elevator. Finally he says I was all right.

"I'll order you some bourbon," he says. "Anything else?"

I was goin' to say no, but I happened to remember that the Wife generally always wants a bronix before dinner. So I had to also put in a bid for a bottle o' gin and bottles o' the Vermouth brothers, Tony and Pierre. It wasn't till later that I appreciated what a grand law this here law was. When I got my drinks I paid ten cents apiece for 'em for service, besides payin' for the bottles o' stuff to drink. And, besides that, about every

third highball or bronix I ordered, the waiter'd bring
back word that I was just out of ingredients and then
they'd be another delay w'ile they sent to the garage
for more. If they had that law all over the country they'd
soon be an end o' drinkin', because everybody'd get so
mad they'd kill each other.

My cross-examination had took quite a long time, but
when I got to my room the Wife wasn't back from
lunch yet and I had to cover the Marathon route all
over again and look her up. We only had the one key to
the room, and o' course couldn't expect no more'n that
at the price.

The Missus had bought one o' the daily programs
they get out and she knowed just what we had to do the
rest o' the day.

"For the next couple hours," she says, "we can suit
ourself."

"All right," says I. "It suits me to take off my shoes
and lay down."

"I'll rest, too," she says; "but at half past four we have
to be in the Cocoanut Grove for tea and dancin'. And
then we come back to the room and dress for dinner.
Then we eat and then we set around till the evenin'
dance starts. Then we dance till we're ready for bed."

"Who do we dance all these dances with?" I ast her.

"With whoever we get acquainted with," she says.

"All right," says I; "but let's be careful."

Well, we took our nap and then we followed schedule
and had our tea in the Cocoanut Grove. You know how
I love tea! My feet was still achin' and the Missus
couldn't talk me into no dance.

When we'd set there an hour and was saturated with
tea, the Wife says it was time to go up and change into
our Tuxedos. I was all in when we reached the room and
willin' to even pass up supper and nestle in the hay, but

I was informed that the biggest part o' the day's doin's was yet to come. So from six o'clock till after seven I wrestled with studs, and hooks and eyes that didn't act like they'd ever met before and wasn't anxious to get acquainted, and then down we went again to the dinin'-room.

"How about a little bronix before the feed?" I says.

"It would taste good," says the Missus.

So I called Eph and give him the order. In somethin' less than half an hour he come back empty-handed.

"You ain't got no cocktail stuff," he says.

"I certainly have," says I. "I ordered it early this afternoon."

"Where at?" he ast me.

"Over in the bar," I says.

"Oh, the regular bar!" he says. "That don't count. You got to have stuff at the service bar to get it served in here."

"I ain't as thirsty as I thought I was," says I.

"Me, neither," says the Missus.

So we went ahead and ordered our meal, and w'ile we was waitin' for it a young couple come and took the other two chairs at our table. They didn't have to announce through a megaphone that they was honey-mooners. It was wrote all over 'em. They was reachin' under the table for each other's hand every other minute, and when they wasn't doin' that they was smilin' at each other or gigglin' at nothin'. You couldn't feel that good and be payin' seventeen dollars a day for room and board unless you was just married or somethin'.

I thought at first their company'd be fun, but after a few meals it got like the southern cookin' and begun to undermine the health.

The conversation between they and us was what you could call limited. It took place the next day at lunch.

The young husband thought he was about to take a bite o' the entry, which happened to be roast mutton with sirup; but he couldn't help from lookin' at her at the same time and his empty fork started for his face prongs up.

"Look out for your eye," I says.

He dropped the fork and they both blushed till you could see it right through the sunburn. Then they give me a Mexican look and our acquaintance was at an end.

This first night, when we was through eatin', we wandered out in the lobby and took seats where we could watch the passin' show. The men was all dressed like me, except I was up to date and had on a mushroom shirt, w'ile they was sportin' the old-fashioned concrete bosom. The women's dresses begun at the top with a belt, and some o' them stopped at the mezzanine floor, w'ile others went clear down to the basement and helped keep the rugs clean. They was one that must of thought it was the Fourth o' July. From the top of her head to where the top of her bathin' suit had left off, she was a red, red rose. From there to the top of her gown was white, and her gown, what they was of it—was blue.

"My!" says the Missus. "What stunnin' gowns!"

"Yes," I says; "and you could have one just like 'em if you'd take the shade offen the piano lamp at home and cut it down to the right size."

Round ten o'clock we wandered in the Palm Garden, where the dancin' had been renewed. The Wife wanted to plunge right in the mazes o' the foxy trot.

"I'll take some courage first," says I. And then was when I found out that it cost you ten cents extra besides the tip to pay for a drink that you already owned in fee simple.

Well, I guess we must of danced about six dances together and had that many quarrels before she was ready to go to bed. And oh, how grand that old hay-pile felt when I finally bounced into it!

The next day we went to the ocean at the legal hour —half past eleven. I never had so much fun in my life. The surf was runnin' high, I heard 'em say; and I don't know which I'd rather do, go bathin' in the ocean at Palm Beach when the surf is runnin' high, or have a dentist get one o' my molars ready for a big inlay at a big outlay. Once in a w'ile I managed to not get throwed on my head when a wave hit me. As for swimmin', you had just as much chance as if you was at State and Madison at the noon hour. And before I'd been in a minute they was enough salt in my different features to keep the Blackstone hotel runnin' all through the onion season.

The Missus enjoyed it just as much as me. She tried to pretend at first, and when she got floored she'd give a squeal that was supposed to mean heavenly bliss. But after she'd been bruised from head to feet and her hair looked and felt like spinach with French dressin', and she'd drank all she could hold o' the Gulf Stream, she didn't resist none when I drug her in to shore and staggered with her up to our private rooms at five a week per each.

Without consultin' her, I went to the desk at the Casino and told 'em they could have them rooms back.

"All right," says the clerk, and turned our keys over to the next in line.

"How about a refund?" I ast him; but he was waitin' on somebody else.

After that we done our bathin' in the tub. But we was down to the beach every morning at eleven-thirty to watch the rest o' them get batted round.

· And at half past twelve every day we'd follow the crowd to the Breakers' porch and dance together, the

Missus and I. Then it'd be back to the other hostelry, sometimes limpin' and sometimes in an Afromobile, and a drink or two in the Palm Garden before lunch. And after lunch we'd lay down; or we'd pay some Eph two or three dollars to pedal us through the windin' jungle trail, that was every bit as wild as the Art Institute; or we'd ferry acrost Lake Worth to West Palm Beach and take in a movie, or we'd stand in front o' the portable Fifth Avenue stores w'ile the Missus wished she could have this dress or that hat, or somethin' else that she wouldn't of looked at if she'd been home and in her right mind. But always at half past four we had to live up to the rules and be in the Cocoanut Grove for tea and some more foxy trottin'. And then it was dress for dinner, eat dinner, watch the parade and wind up the glorious day with more dancin'.

I bet you any amount you name that the Castles in their whole life haven't danced together as much as I and the Missus did at Palm Beach. I'd of gave five dollars if even one o' the waiters had took her offen my hands for one dance. But I knowed that if I made the offer public they'd of been a really serious quarrel between us instead o' just the minor brawls occasioned by steppin' on each other's feet.

She made a discovery one night. She found out that they was a place called the Beach Club where most o' the real people disappeared to every evenin' after dinner. She says we would have to go there too.

"But I ain't a member," I says.

"Then find out how you get to be one," she says.

So to the Beach Club I went and made inquiries.

"You'll have to be introduced by a guy that already belongs," says the man at the door.

"Who belongs?" I ast him.

"Hundreds o' people," he says. "Who do you know?"

"Two waiters, two barkeepers and one elevator boy," I says.

He laughed, but his laugh didn't get me no membership card and I had to dance three or four extra times the next day to square myself with the Missus.

She made another discovery and it cost me six bucks. She found out that, though the meals in the regular dinin'-room was included in the triflin' rates per day, the real people had at least two o' their meals in the garden grill and paid extra for 'em. We tried it for one meal and I must say I enjoyed it—all but the check.

"We can't keep up that clip," I says to her.

"We could," says she, "if you wasn't spendin' so much on your locker."

"The locker's a matter o' life and death," I says. "They ain't no man in the world that could dance as much with their own wife as I do and live without liquid stimulus."

When we'd been there four days she got to be on speakin' terms with the ladies' maid that hung round the lobby and helped put the costumes back on when they slipped off. From this here maid the Missus learned who was who, and the information was relayed to me as soon as they was a chance. We'd be settin' on the porch when I'd feel an elbow in my ribs all of a sudden. I'd look up at who was passin' and then try and pretend I was excited.

"Who is it?" I'd whisper.

"That's Mrs. Vandeventer," the Wife'd say. "Her husband's the biggest street-car conductor in Philadelphia."

Or somebody'd set beside us at the beach or in the Palm Garden and my ribs would be all battered up before the Missus was calm enough to tip me off.

"The Vincents," she'd say; "the canned prune people."

It was a little bit thrillin' at first to be rubbin' elbows

with all them celeb's; but it got so finally that I could walk out o' the dinin'-room right behind Scotti, the opera singer, without forgettin' that my feet hurt.

The Washington's Birthday Ball brought 'em all together at once, and the Missus pointed out eight and nine at a time and got me so mixed up that I didn't know Pat Vanderbilt from Maggie Rockefeller. The only one you couldn't make no mistake about was a Russian count that you couldn't pronounce. He was buyin' bay mules or somethin' for the Russian government, and he was in ambush.

"They say he can't hardly speak a word of English," says the Missus.

"If I knowed the word for barber shop in Russia," says I, "I'd tell him they was one in this hotel."

v

In our mail box the next mornin' they was a notice that our first week was up and all we owed was one hundred and forty-six dollars and fifty cents. The bill for room and meals was one hundred and nineteen dollars. the rest was for gettin' clo'es pressed and keepin' the locker damp.

I didn't have no appetite for breakfast. I told the Wife I'd wait up in the room and for her to come when she got through. When she blew in I had my speech prepared.

"Look here," I says; "this is our eighth day in Palm Beach society. You're on speakin' terms with a maid and I've got acquainted with half a dozen o' the male hired help. It's cost us about a hundred and sixty-five dollars, includin' them private rooms down to the Casino and our Afromobile trips, and this and that. You know a whole lot o' swell people by sight, but you can't talk to 'em. It'd be just as much satisfaction and hundreds o' dollars cheaper to look up their names in the telephone directory at home; then phone to 'em and, when you got 'em, tell 'em it was the wrong number. That way, you'd get 'em to speak to you at least.

"As for sport," I says, "we don't play golf and we don't play tennis and we don't swim. We go through the same program o' doin' nothin' every day. We dance, but we don't never change partners. For twelve dollars I could buy a phonograph up home and I and you could trot round the livin'-room all evenin' without no danger o' havin' some o' them fancy birds cave our shins in. And we could have twice as much liquid refreshments up there at about a twentieth the cost.

"That Gould I met on the train comin' down," I says, "was a even bigger liar than I give him credit for. He says that when he was here people pestered him to death by comin' up and speakin' to him. We ain't had to dodge nobody or hike behind a cocoanut tree to remain exclusive. He says Palm Beach was too common for him. What he should of said was that it was too lonesome. If they was just one white man here that'd listen to my stuff I wouldn't have no kick. But it ain't no pleasure tellin' stories to the Ephs. They laugh whether it's good or not, and then want a dime for laughin'.

"As for our clo'es," I says, "they would be all right for a couple o' days' stay. But the dames round here, and the men, too, has somethin' different to put on for every mornin', afternoon, and night. You've wore your two evenin' gowns so much that I just have to snap my finger at the hooks and they go and grab the right eyes.

"The meals would be grand," I says, "if the cook didn't keep gettin' mixed up and puttin' puddin' sauce on the meat and gravy on the pie.

"I'm glad we've been to Palm Beach," I says. "I wouldn't of missed it for nothin'. But the ocean won't be no different to-morrow than it was yesterday, and the same for the daily program. It don't even rain here, to give us a little variety.

"Now what do you say," I says, "to us just settlin' this bill, and whatever we owe since then, and beatin' it out o' here just as fast as we can go?"

The Missus didn't say nothin' for a w'ile. She was too busy cryin'. She knowed that what I'd said was the truth, but she wouldn't give up without a struggle.

"Just three more days," she says finally. "If we don't meet somebody worth meetin' in the next three days I'll go wherever you want to take me."

"All right," I says; "three more days it is. What's a little matter o' sixty dollars?"

Well, in them next two days and a half she done some desperate flirtin', but as it was all with women I didn't get jealous. She picked out some o' the E-light o' Chicago and tried every trick she could think up. She told 'em their noses was shiny and offered 'em her powder. She stepped on their white shoes just so's to get a chance to beg their pardon. She told 'em their clo'es was unhooked, and then unhooked 'em so's she could hook 'em up again. She tried to loan 'em her finger-nail tools. When she seen one fannin' herself she'd say: "Excuse me, Mrs. So-and-So; but we got the coolest room in the hotel, and I'd be glad to have you go up there and quit perspirin'." But not a rise did she get.

Not till the afternoon o' the third day o' grace. And I don't know if I ought to tell you this or not—only I'm sure you won't spill it nowheres.

We'd went up in our room after lunch. I was tired out and she was discouraged. We'd set round for over an hour, not sayin' or doin' nothin'.

I wanted to talk about the chance of us gettin' away the next mornin', but I didn't dast bring up the subject.

The Missus complained of it bein' hot and opened the door to leave the breeze go through. She was settin' in a chair near the doorway, pretendin' to read the *Palm Beach News*. All of a sudden she jumped up and kind o' hissed at me.

"What's the matter?" I says, springin' from the lounge.

"Come here!" she says, and went out the door into the hall.

I got there as fast as I could, thinkin' it was a rat or a fire. But the Missus just pointed to a lady walkin' away from us, six or seven doors down.

"It's Mrs. Potter," she says; "*the* Mrs. Potter from Chicago!"

"Oh!" I says, puttin' all the excitement I could into my voice.

And I was just startin' back into the room when I seen Mrs. Potter stop and turn round and come to'rd us. She stopped again maybe twenty feet from where the Missus was standin'.

"Are you on this floor?" she says.

The Missus shook like a leaf.

"Yes," says she, so low you couldn't hardly hear her.

"Please see that they's some towels put in 559," says *the* Mrs. Potter from Chicago.

VI

About five o'clock the Wife quieted down and I thought it was safe to talk to her. "I've been readin' in the guide about a pretty river trip," I says. "We can start from here on the boat to-morrow mornin'. They run to Fort Pierce to-morrow and stay there to-morrow night. The next day they go from Fort Pierce to Rockledge, and the day after that from Rockledge to Daytona. The fare's only five dollars apiece. And we can catch a north-bound train at Daytona."

"All right, I don't care," says the Missus.

So I left her and went down-stairs and acrost the street to ask Mr. Foster. Ask Mr. Foster happened to be a girl. She sold me the boat tickets and promised she would reserve a room with bath for us at Fort Pierce, where we was to spend the followin' night. I bet she knowed all the w'ile that rooms with a bath in Fort Pierce is scarcer than toes on a sturgeon.

I went back to the room and helped with the packin' in an advisory capacity. Neither one of us had the heart to dress for dinner. We ordered somethin' sent up and got soaked an extra dollar for service. But we was past carin' for a little thing like that.

At nine o'clock next mornin' the good ship *Constitution* stopped at the Poinciana dock w'ile we piled aboard. One bellhop was down to see us off and it cost me a quarter to get that much attention. Mrs. Potter must of overslept herself.

The boat was loaded to the guards and I ain't braggin' when I say that we was the best-lookin' people aboard. And as for manners, why, say, old Bill Sykes could of passed off for Henry Chesterfield in that gang! Each one o' them occupied three o' the deck chairs and sprayed orange juice all over their neighbors. We could of talked to plenty o' people here, all right; they were as clubby a gang as I ever seen. But I was afraid if I said somethin' they'd have to answer; and, with their mouths as full o' citrus fruit as they was, the results might of been fatal to my light suit.

We went up the lake to a canal and then through it

to Indian River. The boat run aground every few minutes and had to be pried loose. About twelve o'clock a cullud gemman come up on deck and told us lunch was ready. At half past one he served it at a long family table in the cabin. As far as I was concerned, he might as well of left it on the stove. Even if you could of bit into the food, a glimpse of your fellow diners would of strangled your appetite.

After the repast I called the Missus aside.

"Somethin' tells me we're not goin' to live through three days o' this," I says. "What about takin' the train from Fort Pierce and beatin' it for Jacksonville, and then home?"

"But that'd get us to Chicago too quick," says she. "We told people how long we was goin' to be gone and if we got back ahead o' time they'd think they was somethin' queer."

"They's too much queer on this boat," I says. "But you're goin' to have your own way from now on."

We landed in Fort Pierce about six. It was only two or three blocks to the hotel, but when they laid out that part o' town they overlooked some o' the modern conveniences, includin' sidewalks. We staggered through the sand with our grips and sure had worked up a hunger by the time we reached Ye Inn.

"Got reservations for us here?" I ast the clerk.

"Yes," he says, and led us to 'em in person.

The room he showed us didn't have no bath, or even a chair that you could set on w'ile you pulled off your socks.

"Where's the bath?" I ast him.

"This way," he says, and I followed him down the hall, outdoors and up an alley.

Finally we come to a bathroom complete in all details, except that it didn't have no door. I went back to the room, got the Missus and went down to supper. Well, sir, I wish you could of been present at that supper. The choice o' meats was calves' liver and onions or calves' liver and onions. And I bet if them calves had of been still livin' yet they could of gave us some personal reminiscences about Garfield.

The Missus give the banquet one look and then laughed for the first time in several days.

"The guy that named this burg got the capitals mixed," I says. "It should of been Port Fierce."

And she laughed still heartier. Takin' advantage, I says:

"How about the train from here to Jacksonville?"

"You win!" says she. "We can't get home too soon to suit me."

VII

The mornin' we landed in Chicago it was about eight above and a wind was comin' offen the Lake a mile a minute. But it didn't feaze us.

"Lord!" says the Missus. "Ain't it grand to be home!"

"You said somethin'," says I. "But wouldn't it of been grander if we hadn't never left?"

"I don't know about that," she says. "I think we both of us learned a lesson."

"Yes," I says; "and the tuition wasn't only a matter o' close to seven hundred bucks!"

"Oh," says she, "we'll get that back easy!"

"How?" I ast her. "Do you expect some tips on the market from Mrs. Potter and the rest o' your new friends?"

"No," she says. "We'll win it. We'll win it in the rummy game with the Hatches."

CARMEN

WE WAS playin' rummy over to Hatch's, and Hatch must of fell in a bed of four-leaf clovers on his way home the night before, because he plays rummy like he does everything else; but this night I refer to you couldn't beat him, and besides him havin' all the luck my Missus played like she'd been bought off, so when we come to settle up we was plain seven and a half out. You know who paid it. So Hatch says:

"They must be some game you can play."

"No," I says, "not and beat you. I can run two blocks w'ile you're stoopin over to start, but if we was runnin' a foot race between each other, and suppose I was leadin' by eighty yards, a flivver'd prob'ly come up and hit you in the back and bump you over the finishin' line ahead o' me."

So Mrs. Hatch thinks I'm sore on account o' the seven-fifty, so she says:

"It don't seem fair for us to have all the luck."

"Sure it's fair!" I says. "If you didn't have the luck, what would you have?"

"I know," she says; "but I don't never feel right winnin' money at cards."

"I don't blame you," I says.

"I know," she says; "but it seems like we should ought to give it back or else stand treat, either one."

"Jim's too old to change all his habits," I says.

"Oh, well," says Mrs. Hatch, "I guess if I told him

to loosen up he'd loosen up. I ain't lived with him all these years for nothin'."

"You'd be a sucker if you did," I says.

So they all laughed, and when they'd quieted down Mrs. Hatch says:

"I don't suppose you'd feel like takin' the money back?"

"Not without a gun," I says. "Jim's pretty husky."

So that give them another good laugh; but finally she says:

"What do you say, Jim, to us takin' the money they lose to us and gettin' four tickets to some show?"

Jim managed to stay conscious, but he couldn't answer nothin'; so my Missus says:

"That'd be grand of you to do it, but don't think you got to."

Well, of course, Mrs. Hatch knowed all the w'ile she didn't have to, but from what my Missus says she could tell that if they really give us the invitation we wouldn't start no fight. So they talked it over beween themself w'ile I and Hatch went out in the kitchen and split a pint o' beer, and Hatch done the pourin' and his best friend couldn't say he give himself the worst of it. So when we come back my Missus and Mrs. Hatch had it all framed that the Hatches was goin' to take us to a show, and the next thing was what show would it be. So Hatch found the afternoon paper, that somebody'd left on the streetcar, and read us off a list o' the shows that was in town. I spoke for the Columbia, but the Missus give me the sign to stay out; so they argued back and forth and finally Mrs. Hatch says:

"Let's see that paper a minute."

"What for?" says Hatch. "I didn't hold nothin' out on you."

But he give her the paper and she run through the list herself, and then she says:

"You did, too, hold out on us. You didn't say nothin' about the Auditorium."

"What could I say about it?" says Hatch. "I never was inside."

"It's time you was then," says Mrs. Hatch.

"What's playin' there?" I says.

"Grand op'ra," says Mrs. Hatch.

"Oh!" says my Missus. "Wouldn't that be wonderful?"

"What do you say?" says Mrs. Hatch to me.

"I think it'd be grand for you girls," I says. "I and Jim could leave you there and go down on Madison and see Charley Chaplin, and then come back after you."

"Nothin' doin'!" says Mrs. Hatch. "We'll pick a show that everybody wants to see."

Well, if I hadn't of looked at my Missus then we'd of been O. K. But my eyes happened to light on where she was settin' and she was chewin' her lips so's she wouldn't cry. That finished me. "I was just kiddin'," I says to Mrs. Hatch. "They ain't nothin' I'd like better than grand op'ra."

"Nothin' except gettin' trimmed in a rummy game," says Hatch, but he didn't get no rise.

Well, the Missus let loose of her lips so's she could smile and her and Mrs. Hatch got all excited, and I and Hatch pretended like we was excited too. So Hatch ast what night could we go, and Mrs. Hatch says that depended on what did we want to hear, because they changed the bill every day. So her and the Missus looked at the paper again and found out where Friday night was goin' to be a big special night and the bill was a musical show called *Carmen,* and all the stars was goin' to sing, includin' Mooratory and Alda and Genevieve

Farr'r, that was in the movies a w'ile till they found out she could sing, and some fella they called Daddy, but I don't know his real name. So the girls both says Friday night was the best, but Hatch says he would have to go to lodge that evenin'.

"Lodge!" says Mrs. Hatch. "What do you care about lodge when you got a chance to see Genevieve Farr'r in *Carmen?*"

"Chance!" says Hatch. "If that's what you call a chance, I got a chance to buy a thousand shares o' Bethlehem Steel. Who's goin' to pay for my chance?"

"All right," says Mrs. Hatch, "go to your old lodge and spoil everything!"

So this time it was her that choked up and made like she was goin' to blubber. So Hatch changed his mind all of a sudden and decided to disappoint the brother Owls. So all of us was satisfied except fifty per cent., and I and the Missus beat it home, and on the way she says how nice Mrs. Hatch was to give us this treat.

"Yes," I says, "but if you hadn't of had a regular epidemic o' discardin' deuces and treys Hatch would of treated us to groceries for a week." I says: "I always thought they was only twelve pitcher cards in the deck till I seen them hands you saved up to-night."

"You lose as much as I did," she says.

"Yes," I says, "and I always will as long as you forget to fetch your purse along."

So they wasn't no comeback to that, so we went on home without no more dialogue.

Well, Mrs. Hatch called up the next night and says Jim had the tickets boughten and we was to be sure and be ready at seven o'clock Friday night because the show started at eight. So when I was down-town Friday the Missus sent my evenin' dress suit over to Katzes' and had it pressed up and when I come home it was laid out on the bed like a corpse.

"What's that for?" I says.

"For the op'ra," she says. "Everybody wears them to the op'ra."

"Did you ask the Hatches what was they goin' to wear?" I says.

"No," says she. "They know what to wear without me tellin' them. They ain't goin' to the Auditorium in their nightgown."

So I clumb into the soup and fish, and the Missus spent about a hour puttin' on a dress that she could have left off without nobody knowin' the difference, and she didn't have time for no supper at all, and I just managed to surround a piece o' steak as big as your eye and spill some gravy on my clo'es when the bell rung and there was the Hatches.

Well, Hatch didn't have no more evenin' dress suit on than a kewpie. I could see his pants under his over-coat and they was the same old bay pants he'd wore the day he got mad at his kid and christened him Kenneth. And his shoes was a last year's edition o' the kind that's supposed to give your feet a chance, and if his feet had of been the kind that takes chances they was two or three places where they could of got away without much trouble.

I could tell from the expression on Mrs. Hatch's face when she seen our make-up that we'd crossed her. She looked about as comf'table as a Belgium.

"Oh," she says. "I didn't think you'd dress up."

"We thought you would," says my Frau.

"We!" I says. "Where do you get that 'we'?"

"If it ain't too late we'll run in and change," says my Missus.

"Not me," I says. "I didn't go to all this trouble and expense for a splash o' gravy. When this here uniform retires it'll be to make room for pajamas."

"Come on!" says Hatch. "What's the difference? You can pretend like you ain't with us."

"It don't really make no difference," says Mrs. Hatch.

And maybe it didn't. But we all stood within whisperin' distance of each other on the car goin' in, and if you had a dollar for every word that was talked among us you couldn't mail a postcard from Hammond to Gary. When we got off at Congress my Missus tried to thaw out the party.

"The prices is awful high, aren't they?" she says.

"Outrageous," says Mrs. Hatch.

Well, even if the prices was awful high, they didn't have nothin' on our seats. If I was in trainin' to be a steeple jack I'd go to grand op'ra every night and leave Hatch buy my ticket. And where he took us I'd of been more at home in overalls and a sport shirt.

"How do you like Denver?" says I to the Missus, but she'd sank for the third time.

"We're safe here," I says to Hatch. "Them French guns can't never reach us. We'd ought to brought more bumbs."

"What did the seats cost?" I says to Hatch.

"One-fifty," he says.

"Very reasonable," says I. "One o' them aviators wouldn't take you more than half this height for a five-spot."

The Hatches had their overcoats off by this time and I got a look at their full costume. Hatch had went without his vest durin' the hot months and when it was alongside his coat and pants it looked like two different families. He had a pink shirt with prune-colored horizontal bars, and a tie to match his neck, and a collar that would of took care of him and I both, and them shoes I told you about, and burlap hosiery. They wasn't nothin' the matter with Mrs. Hatch except she must of thought that, instead o' dressin' for the op'ra, she was gettin' ready for Kenneth's bath.

And there was my Missus, just within the law, and me all spicked and spanned with my soup and fish and gravy!

Well, we all set there and tried to get the focus till about a half-hour after the show was billed to commence, and finally a Lilliputhian with a match in his hand come out and started up the orchestry and they played a few o' the hits and then the lights was turned out and up went the curtain.

Well, sir, you'd be surprised at how good we could hear and see after we got used to it. But the hearin' didn't do us no good—that is, the words part of it. All the actors had been smuggled in from Europe and they wasn't none o' them that could talk English. So all their songs was gave in different languages and I wouldn't of never knew what was goin' on only for Hatch havin' all the nerve in the world.

After the first act a lady that was settin' in front of us dropped somethin' and Hatch stooped over and picked it up, and it was one o' these here books they call a liberetto, and it's got all the words they're singin' on the stage wrote out in English.

So the lady begin lookin' all over for it and Hatch was goin' to give it back because he thought it was a shoe catalogue, but he happened to see at the top of it where it says "Price 25 Cents," so he tossed it in his lap and stuck his hat over it. And the lady kept lookin' and lookin' and finally she turned round and looked Hatch

right in the eye, but he dropped down inside his collar
and left her wear herself out. So when she'd gave up I
says somethin' about I'd like to have a drink.

"Let's go," says Hatch.

"No," I says. "I don't want it bad enough to go back
to town after it. I thought maybe we could get it sent
up to the room."

"I'm goin' alone then," says Hatch.

"You're liable to miss the second act," I says.

"I'd never miss it," says Hatch.

"All right," says I. "I hope you have good weather."

So he slipped me the book to keep for him and beat
it. So I seen the lady had forgot us, and I opened up the
book and that's how I come to find out what the show
was about. I read her all through, the part that was in
English, before the curtain went up again, so when the
second act begin I knowed what had came off and what
was comin' off, and Hatch and Mrs. Hatch hadn't no
idear if the show was comical or dry. My Missus hadn't,
neither, till we got home and I told her the plot.

Carmen ain't no regular musical show where a couple
o' Yids comes out and pulls a few lines o' dialogue and
then a girl and a he-flirt sings a song that ain't got
nothin' to do with it. *Carmen's* a regular play, only instead o' them sayin' the lines, they sing them, and in
for'n languages so's the actors can pick up some loose
change offen the sale o' the liberettos. The music was
wrote by George S. Busy, and it must of kept him that
way about two mont's. The words was either throwed
together by the stage carpenter or else took down by a
stenographer outdoors durin' a drizzle. Anyway, they
ain't nobody claims them. Every oncet in three or four
pages they forget themself and rhyme. You got to read
each verse over two or three times before you learn what

they're hintin' at, but the management gives you plenty o' time to do it between acts and still sneak a couple o' hours' sleep.

The first act opens up somewheres in Spain, about the corner o' Chicago Avenue and Wells. On one side o' the stage they's a pill mill where the employees is all girls, or was girls a few years ago. On the other side they's a soldiers' garage where they keep the militia in case of a strike. In the back o' the stage they's a bridge, but it ain't over no water or no railroad tracks or nothin'. It's prob'ly somethin' the cat dragged in.

Well, the soldiers stands out in front o' the garage hittin' up some barber shops, and pretty soon a girl blows in from the hero's home town, Janesville or somewheres. She runs a few steps every little w'ile and then stops, like the rails was slippery. The soldiers sings at her and she tells them she's came to look for Don Joss that run the chop-suey dump up to Janesville, but when they shet down on him servin' beer he quit and joined the army. So the soldiers never heard o' the bird, but they all ask her if they won't do just as good, but she says nothin' doin' and skids off the stage. She ain't no sooner gone when the Chinaman from Janesville and some more soldiers and some alley rats comes in to help out the singin'. The book says that this new gang o' soldiers was sent on to relieve the others, but if anything happened to wear out the first ones it must of took place at rehearsal. Well, one o' the boys tells Joss about the girl askin' for him and he says: "Oh, yes; that must be the little Michaels girl from up in Wisconsin."

So pretty soon the whistle blows for noon and the girls comes out o' the pill mill smokin' up the mornin' receipts and a crowd o' the unemployed comes in to shoot the snipes. So the soldiers notices that Genevieve Farr'r ain't on yet, so they ask where she's at, and that's

her cue. She puts on a song number and a Spanish
dance, and then she slips her bouquet to the Chink,
though he ain't sang a note since the whistle blowed.
But now it's one o'clock and Genevieve and the rest o'
the girls beats it back to the coffin factory and the vags
chases down to the Loop to get the last home edition and
look at the want ads to see if they's any jobs open with
fair pay and nothin' to do. And the soldiers mosey into
the garage for a well-earned rest and that leaves Don all
alone on the stage.

But he ain't no more than started on his next song
when back comes the Michaels girl. It oozes out here
that she's in love with the Joss party, but she stalls and
pretends like his mother'd sent her to get the receipt for
makin' eggs *fo yung*. And she says his mother ast her to
kiss him and she slips him a dime, so he leaves her kiss
him on the scalp and he asks her if she can stay in town
that evenin' and see a nickel show, but they's a important meetin' o' the Maccabees at Janesville that night,
so away she goes to catch the two-ten and Don starts in
on another song number, but the rest o' the company
don't like his stuff and he ain't hardly past the vamp
when they's a riot.

It seems like Genevieve and one o' the chorus girls
has quarreled over a second-hand stick o' gum and the
chorus girl got the gum, but Genevieve relieved her of
part of a earlobe, so they pinch Genevieve and leave Joss
to watch her till the wagon comes, but the wagon's
went out to the night desk sergeant's house with a case o'
quarts and before it gets round to pick up Genevieve
she's bunked the Chink into settin' her free. So she
makes a getaway, tellin' Don to meet her later on at
Lily and Pat's place acrost the Indiana line. So that
winds up the first act.

Well, the next act's out to Lily and Pat's, and it ain't no Y. M. C. A. headquarters, but it's a hang-out for dips and policemans. They's a cabaret and Genevieve's one o' the performers, but she forgets the words to her first song and winds up with tra-la-la, and she could of forgot the whole song as far as I'm concerned, because it wasn't nothin' you'd want to buy and take along home.

Finally Pat comes in and says it's one o'clock and he's got to close up, but they won't none o' them make a move, and pretty soon they's a live one blows into the joint and he's Eskimo Bill, one o' the butchers out to the Yards. He's got paid that day and he ain't never goin' home. He sings a song and it's the hit o' the show. Then he buys a drink and starts flirtin' with Genevieve, but Pat chases everybody but the performers and a couple o' dips that ain't got nowheres else to sleep. The dips or stick-up guys, or whatever they are, tries to get Genevieve to go along with them in the car w'ile they pull off somethin', but she's still expectin' the Chinaman. So they pass her up and blow, and along comes Don and she lets him in, and it seems like he'd been in jail for two mont's, or ever since the end o' the first act. So he asks her how everything has been goin' down to the pill mill and she tells him that she's quit and became a entertainer. So he says, "What can you do?" And she beats time with a pair o' chopsticks and dances the Chinese Blues.

After a w'ile they's a bugle call somewhere outdoors and Don says that means he's got to go back to the garage. So she gets sore and tries to bean him with a Spanish onion. Then he reaches inside his coat and pulls out the bouquet she give him in Atto First to show her he ain't changed his clo'es, and then the sheriff comes in and tries to coax him with a razor to go back to his job. They fight like it was the first time either o' them ever tried it and the sheriff's leadin' on points when Genevieve hollers for the dips, who dashes in with their gats pulled and it's good night, Mister Sheriff! They put him in moth balls and they ask Joss to join their tong. He says all right and they're all pretty well lit by this time and they've reached the singin' stage, and Pat can't get them to go home and he's scared some o' the Hammond people'll put in a complaint, so he has the curtain rang down.

Then they's a relapse of it don't say how long, and Don and Genevieve and the yeggs and their lady friends is all out in the country somewheres attendin' a Bohunk Sokol Verein picnic and Don starts whinin' about his old lady that he'd left up to Janesville.

"I wisht I was back there," he says.

"You got nothin' on me," says Genevieve. "Only Janesville ain't far enough. I wisht you was back in Hongkong."

So w'ile they're flatterin' each other back and forth, a couple o' the girls is monkeyin' with the pasteboards and tellin' their fortunes, and one o' them turns up a two-spot and that's a sign they're goin' to sing a duet. So it comes true and then Genevieve horns into the game and they play three-handed rummy, singin' all the w'ile to bother each other, but finally the fellas that's runnin' the picnic says it's time for the fat man's one-legged race and everybody goes offen the stage. So the Michaels girl comes on and is gettin' by pretty good with a song when she's scared by the noise o' the gun that's fired to start the race for the bay-window championship. So she trips back to her dressin'-room and then Don and Eskimo Bill put on a little slap-stick stuff.

When they first meet they're pals, but as soon as they get wise that the both o' them's bugs over the same girl their relations to'rds each other becomes strange. Here's the talk they spill:

"Where do you tend bar?" says Don.

"You got me guessed wrong," says Bill. "I work out to the Yards."

"Got anything on the hip?" says Don.

"You took the words out o' my mouth," says Bill. "I'm drier than St. Petersgrad."

"Stick round a w'ile and maybe we can scare up somethin'," says Don.

"I'll stick all right," says Bill. "They's a Jane in your party that's knocked me dead."

"What's her name?" says Don.

"Carmen," says Bill, Carmen bein' the girl's name in the show that Genevieve was takin' that part.

"Carmen!" says Joss. "Get offen that stuff! I and Carmen's just like two pavin' bricks."

"I should worry!" says Bill. "I ain't goin' to run away from no rat-eater."

"You're a rat-eater yourself, you rat-eater!" says Don.

"I'll rat-eat you!" says Bill.

And they go to it with a carvin' set, but they couldn't neither one o' them handle their utensils.

Don may of been all right slicin' toad-stools for the suey and Bill prob'ly could of massacreed a flock o' sheep with one stab, but they was all up in the air when it come to stickin' each other. They'd of did it better with dice.

Pretty soon the other actors can't stand it no longer and they come on yellin' "Fake!" So Don and Bill fold up their razors and Bill invites the whole bunch to come out and go through the Yards some mornin' and then he beats it, and the Michaels girl ain't did nothin' for fifteen minutes, so the management shoots her out for another song and she sings to Don about how he should ought to go home on account of his old lady bein' sick, so he asks Genevieve if she cares if he goes back to Janesville.

"Sure, I care," says Genevieve. "Go ahead!"

So the act winds up with everybody satisfied.

The last act's outside the Yards on the Halsted Street end. Bill's ast the entire company to come in and watch him croak a steer. The scene opens up with the crowd buyin' perfume and smellin' salts from the guys that's got the concessions. Pretty soon Eskimo Bill and Carmen drive in, all dressed up like a horse. Don's came in from Wisconsin and is hidin' in the bunch. He's sore at Carmen for not meetin' him on the Elevated platform.

He lays low till everybody's went inside, only Carmen. Then he braces her. He tells her his old lady's died and left him the laundry, and he wants her to go in with him and do the ironin'.

"Not me!" she says.

"What do you mean—'Not me'?" says Don.

"I and Bill's goin' to run a kosher market," she says.

Just about now you can hear noises behind the scenes like the cattle's gettin' theirs, so Carmen don't want to miss none of it, so she makes a break for the gate.

"Where you goin'?" says Joss.

"I want to see the butcherin'," she says.

"Stick round and I'll show you how it's done," says Joss.

So he pulls his knife and makes a pass at her, just foolin'. He misses her as far as from here to Des Moines. But she don't know he's kiddin' and she's scared to death. Yes, sir, she topples over as dead as the Federal League.

It was prob'ly her heart.

So now the whole crowd comes dashin' out because they's been a report that the place is infested with the hoof and mouth disease. They tell Don about it, but he's all excited over Carmen dyin'. He's delirious and gets himself mixed up with a Irish policeman.

"I yield me prisoner," he says.

Then the house doctor says the curtain's got to come down to prevent the epidemic from spreadin' to the audience. So the show's over and the company's quarantined.

Well, Hatch was out all durin' the second act and part o' the third, and when he finally come back he didn't have to tell nobody where he'd been. And he dozed off the minute he hit his seat. I was for lettin' him sleep so's the rest o' the audience'd think we had one o' the op'ra bass singers in our party. But Mrs. Hatch wasn't lookin' for no publicity, on account of her costume, so she reached over and prodded him with a hatpin every time he begin a new aria.

Goin' out, I says to him:

"How'd you like it?"

"Pretty good," he says, "only they was too much gin in the last one."

"I mean the op'ra," I says.

"Don't ask him!" says Mrs. Hatch. "He didn't hear half of it and he didn't understand none of it."

"Oh, I wouldn't say that," says I. "Jim here ain't no boob, and they wasn't nothin' hard about it to understand."

"Not if you know the plot," says Mrs. Hatch.

"And somethin' about music," says my Missus.

"And got a little knowledge o' French," says Mrs. Hatch.

"Was that French they was singin'?" says Hatch. "I thought it was Wop or ostrich."

"That shows you up," says his Frau.

Well, when we got on the car for home they wasn't only one vacant seat and, o' course, Hatch had to have that. So I and my Missus and Mrs. Hatch clubbed together on the straps and I got a earful o' the real dope.

"What do you think o' Farr'r's costumes?" says Mrs. Hatch.

"Heavenly!" says my Missus. "Specially the one in the second act. It was all colors o' the rainbow."

"Hatch is right in style then," I says.

"And her actin' is perfect," says Mrs. Hatch.

"Her voice too," says the Wife.

"I liked her actin' better," says Mrs. H. "I thought her voice yodeled in the up-stairs registers."

"What do you suppose killed her?" I says.

"She was stabbed by her lover," says the Missus.

"You wasn't lookin'," I says. "He never touched her. It was prob'ly tobacco heart."

"He stabs her in the book," says Mrs. Hatch.

"It never went through the bindin'," I says.

"And wasn't Mooratory grand?" says the Wife.

"Splendid!" says Mrs. Hatch. "His actin' and singin' was both grand."

"I preferred his actin'," I says. "I thought his voice hissed in the down-stairs radiators."

This give them a good laugh, but they was soon at it again.

"And how sweet Alda was!" my Missus remarks.

"Which was her?" I ast them.

"The good girl," says Mrs. Hatch. "The girl that sung that beautiful aria in Atto Three."

"Atto girl!" I says. "I liked her too; the little Michaels girl. She came from Janesville."

"She did!" says Mrs. Hatch. "How do you know?"

So I thought I'd kid them along.

"My uncle told me," I says. "He used to be post-master up there."

"What uncle was that?" says my wife.

"He ain't really my uncle," I says. "We all used to call him our uncle just like all these here singers calls the one o' them Daddy."

"They was a lady in back o' me," says Mrs. Hatch, "that says Daddy didn't appear tonight."

"Prob'ly the Missus' night out," I says.

"How'd you like the Tor'ador?" says Mrs. Hatch.

"I thought she moaned in the chimney," says I.

"It wasn't no 'she'," says the Missus. "We're talkin' about the bull-fighter."

"I didn't see no bull-fight," I says.

"It come off behind the scenes," says the Missus.

"When was you behind the scenes?" I says.

"I wasn't never," says my Missus. "But that's where it's supposed to come off."

"Well," I says, "you can take it from me that it wasn't pulled. Do you think the mayor'd stand for that stuff when he won't even leave them stage a box fight? You two girls has got a fine idear o' this here op'ra!"

"You know all about it, I guess," says the Missus. "You talk French so good!"

"I talk as much French as you do," I says. "But not nowheres near as much English, if you could call it that."

That kept her quiet, but Mrs. Hatch buzzed all the way home, and she was scared to death that the motor-man wouldn't know where she'd been spendin' the evenin'. And if there was anybody in the car besides me that knowed *Carmen* it must of been a joke to them hearin' her chatter. It wasn't no joke to me though. Hatch's berth was way off from us and they didn't no-body suspect him o' bein' in our party. I was standin'

right up there with her where people couldn't help seein'
that we was together.

I didn't want them to think she was my wife. So I
kept smilin' at her. And when it finally come time to get
off I hollered out loud at Hatch and says:

"All right, Hatch! Here's our street. Your Missus'll
keep you awake the rest o' the way with her liberetto."

"It can't hurt no more than them hatpins," he says.

Well, when the paper come the next mornin' my Missus had to grab it up and turn right away to the place
where the op'ras is wrote up. Under the article they was
a list o' the ladies and gents in the boxes and what they
wore, but it didn't say nothin' about what the gents
wore, only the ladies. Prob'ly the ladies happened to
have the most comical costumes that night, but I bet if
the reporters could of saw Hatch they would of gave
him a page to himself.

"Is your name there?" I says to the Missus.

"O' course not," she says. "They wasn't none o' them
reporters tall enough to see us. You got to set in a box
to be mentioned."

"Well," I says, "you don't care nothin' about bein'
mentioned, do you?"

"O' course not," she says; but I could tell from how
she said it that she wouldn't run down-town and horse-
whip the editor if he made a mistake and printed about
she and her costume; her costume wouldn't of et up all
the space he had neither.

"How much does box seats cost?" I ast her.

"About six or seven dollars," she says.

"Well," I says, "let's I and you show Hatch up."

"What do you mean?" she says.

"I mean we should ought to return the compliment,"
says I. "We should ought to give them a party right
back."

"We'd be broke for six weeks," she says.

"Oh, we'd do it with their money like they done it with ours," I says.

"Yes," she says; "but if you can ever win enough from the Hatches to buy four box seats to the op'ra I'd rather spend the money on a dress."

"Who said anything about four box seats?" I ast her.

"You did," she says.

"You're delirious!" I says. "Two box seats will be a plenty."

"Who's to set in them?" ast the Missus.

"Who do you think?" I says. "I and you is to set in them."

"But what about the Hatches?" she says.

"They'll set up where they was," says I. "Hatch picked out the seats before, and if he hadn't of wanted that altitude he'd of bought somewheres else."

"Yes," says the Missus, "but Mrs. Hatch won't think we're very polite to plant our guests in the Alps and we set down in a box."

"But they won't know where we're settin'," I says. "We'll tell them we couldn't get four seats together, so for them to set where they was the last time and we're goin' elsewheres."

"It don't seem fair," says my wife.

"I should worry about bein' fair with Hatch," I says. "If he's ever left with more than a dime's worth o' cards you got to look under the table for his hand."

"It don't seem fair," says the Missus.

"You should worry!" I says.

So we ast them over the followin' night and it looked for a minute like we was goin' to clean up. But after that one minute my Missus began collectin' pitcher cards again and every card Hatch drawed seemed like it was made to his measure. Well, sir, when we was through the lucky stiff was eight dollars to the good and Mrs. Hatch had about broke even.

"Do you suppose you can get them same seats?" I says.

"What seats?" says Hatch.

"For the op'ra," I says.

"You won't get me to no more op'ra," says Hatch. "I don't never go to the same show twicet."

"It ain't the same show, you goof!" I says. "They change the bill every day."

"They ain't goin' to change this eight-dollar bill o' mine," he says.

"You're a fine stiff!" I says.

"Call me anything you want to," says Hatch, "as long as you don't go over eight bucks' worth."

"Jim don't enjoy op'ra," says Mrs. Hatch.

"He don't enjoy nothin' that's more than a nickel," I says. "But as long as he's goin' to welsh on us I hope he lavishes the eight-spot where it'll do him some good."

"I'll do what I want to with it," says Hatch.

"Sure you will!" I says. "You'll bury it. But what you should ought to do is buy two suits o' clo'es."

So I went out in the kitchen and split a pint one way.

But don't think for a minute that I and the Missus ain't goin' to hear no more op'ra just because of a cheap stiff like him welshin'. I don't have to win in no rummy game before I spend.

We're goin' next Tuesday night, I and the Missus, and we're goin' to set somewheres near Congress Street. The show's *Armour's Do Re Me*, a new one that's bein' gave for the first time. It's prob'ly named after some soap.

MISCELLANEOUS

SYMPTOMS OF BEING 35

On reaching my dottage I ain't makeing no complaints to the management and I'm willing to accomodate with a few rules which has enabled me to reach the age of 35 annums and which if stuck to faithful will bring you the same results

THE OTHER night one of my friends whose name is Legion got me on the telephone some way another and wanted I should come over and call, but that is all I done the last 3 or 4 times I had went over there and it costs a lot of money even in a 4 bit limit. So I said no that I was busy on a book which I had promised my publisher I would write it.

"What is it about" says Legion.

So I told him "How it feels to be 35."

"That guy must think you got a good memory" says Legion and hung up on me.

Well friends 35 is how young I am no matter how old I look, but I am so use to haveing smart Alex make wise cracks when I tell them my age that it don't have no more effect on me now than the 6 day bicycle race. Only I can't figure why they think I would lie about it like I was trying to pose as a boy chess marvel or something. When a man has got a legal wife and 4 and no one hundredths children what does he care if he is 35 or double that amt. Besides which they claim that 35 is about the average of all the grown ups in the world. If I was above the average would I keep it a secret? Don't be silly.

And don't judge a person by their hair gents. Many a man that can remember the first Ford has got more foliage on their egg than myself and also I know several ball players in the big league to-day that is anywheres from 5 to 30 yrs. younger than the present writer that when the fish applauds them for makeing a 2 handed catch with 1 hand, you wonder why they don't take off their cap. Personly I am not sensitive about my plummage. When my features got to the decision that one of them would half to retract all I done was thank God they picked the forehead and not the chin. The only hardship connected with pyorrhea of the scalp is trying to act supprised when the barber says you are looseing your hair.

But I guess it ain't only the loss of a few ebony ringlets that makes me look senile. It seems like I was over estimated long before I begin to molt. For inst. I can recall when I was 16 and had a thatch on my dome like a virtuoso and I used to pal around with a boy who we will call Geo. Dougan because that was his name and Geo. was going on 21. Well this was in Niles, Mich., in the days when they sold 6% beer in vases and for $.20 you could get enough to patrol 4th St. serenading true music lovers of the opposing sex. In them hellcyon days 1 of the few things that was vs. the law was selling it to minors and 2 or 3 of the retail mchts. around town was pretty strick and time and again I and Geo. would be out shopping and go in a store and order 2 vats and Dave or Punk or who ever it happened to be would set one up for me to knock over and then give Geo. a wise cracking smile and ask him would he like a bottle of white pop. Incidentally I had a taste of that lucius ambrosia at a ball game once and if the penalty for selling honest old beer to minors was a $100 fine why 2 to

14 yrs. in a meat grinder would be mild for a guy that sells white pop on the theory that its a drink.

Well Geo. would say "Aw come on Dave I am older than him." But you couldn't fool Dave and the result was that we would half to take our custom down to Pigeon's where everybody that had a dime was the same age and the only minors was the boys that tried to start a charge acct.

I must hand it to Geo. for one thing. No matter how sore it made him to get turned down he never told them the truth about me. And they wouldn't of believed him if he had of. No more than you birds believe me now.

But now in regards to this book: When the publisher asked me to write it up I said I didn't see how more than only a few people would be interested because they was only a few that is this old. So he told me that as a matter of fact pretty near everybody in the world that can read is either 35 or a few mos. one way or the other and if I didn't think that was so to go and look it up in a book. So I looked up in the encyclopedia and they was nothing in there like he said but I found out a whole lot of other things that was news to me and maybe the reader don't know them neither so I will write them down.

In the 1st. place it says that most people dies when they are 1 yr. old and the 1st. 10 yrs. is the most fatalist. But if they's a 100 thousand people that can manage to get to be 10 yrs. old why then 749 of them is pretty libel to die the next yr. After that the older you get the longer you live up to when you are 59 and then you can just about count on liveing 14 and seven-tenths yrs. more. In other wds. if you ain't one of the 749 that crokes between 10 and 11 why you are safe till about June of the yr. when you are 73. So a person is a sucker to try and take care of themself at my age and from now on I am going to be a loose fish and run wild.

Out in Benton Harbor, Mich. however, near where I use to live, they have got a sex that calls themselfs the Holy Terrors or something that claims you live as long as you are good and as soon as you do wrong you die. But I notice that they all wear a beard so as the encyclopedia can't tell if they are 73 or 21.

Another thing it says in the book is that figures compiled in Norway and Sweden shows the death rate amongst bachelors is a lot more than amongst married men even includeing murder. So anybody that is between 11 and 73 yrs. old and got a wife is practically death proof especially if you are a Swede.

But all that is either here or there. The idear is to tell how it feels to be my age and I may as well get to it. Well in the 1st. place I am speaking for myself only. I don't know how the other 35 yr. olders feels about it and don't care. Probably the most of them don't feel near as old as the writer. Laughter is supposed to keep a man young but if its forced laughter it works the opp. When a guy is named Ring W. and is expected to split their sides when ever somebody asks if your middle name is Worm which is an average of 365 times per annum over a period of 35 annums, why it can't help from telling on you. Or it don't lighten the wgt. of the yrs. none to half to snicker every time they say Ring give me a ring or Ring why ain't you a ring master in Ringling Bros. And yet a number of birds has asked me if that was my real name or did I assume it. They would probably ask the kaiser if he moved to Holland to be near the tulips.

I suppose that on the morning of their 21st birthday the right kind of a American citizen wakes up full of excitement and says to themself "Now I am of age and can vote and everything." And when they come to what I often call the 35th. mile stone they are even more smoked up with the thought that now they are eligible to be President and go around all day stoop shouldered with the new responsibility.

Well I don't recall how I woke up the day I was 21 if at all but my last birthday is still green and sour in my memory. I spent the most of it in Mineola signing mortgages and if I thought of the White House it was just to wonder if it would do any good to write and tell President Wilson about the Long Island R. R.

At the present writeing I have got so use to being 35 that I don't know if it feels any different from 34 or 33. But I can at lease state that being 35 don't feel nothing like being under 30. For inst. when the telephone rings now days I am scared to death that its somebody asking us to go somewheres for dinner or somewheres. Six yrs. ago I was afraid it wasn't. At 29 home was like they say on the vaudeville stage, a place to go when all the other joints was closed up. At 35 its a place you never leave without a loud squawk.

A man don't appreciate their home till you are up around par for 9 holes. Under 30 you think of it as a dump where you can't pick out what you want to eat like roast Vt. turkey or a filet mignon or some of that prune fed muskrat a la Biltmore. If Kathleen decides in the a.m. that you are going to crave spare ribs at night why you can either crave spare ribs at night or put on a hunger strike that won't get you no more sympathy than the hiccups.

In them ribald days home is just a kind of a pest where you half to choke down breakfast or they will think something ails you and talk about sending for a Dr. And 1 or 2 evenings per wk. when you can't think of no reason to go out, its where you half to set around and wait for 9 o'clock so as you begin to talk about going to bed and sometimes things gets so desperate that you half to read a book or something.

But at 35 you spell it with a big H. Its where you can take off your shoes. Its where you can have more soup. Its where you don't half to say nothing when they's nothing to say. Its where they don't wait till the meal is all over and then give you a eye dropper full of coffee raw. Its where you don't half to listen. Its where they don't smear everything with cheese dressing. Its where you can pan everybody without it going no further. Its where they know you like doughnuts and what you think about a banana.

When you was 29 you didn't care for the band to play Home sweet Home. It was old stuff and a rotten tune any way. Now you hope they won't play it neither. Its a pretty tune but it makes you bust out crying.

Bud Kelland that lives over to Port Washington wrote a piece for a magazine a wile ago where he said in it that it kind of shocked him to find out that young people didn't act like he was one of them no more. Well he ain't but it took the old gaffer a long time to find it out. Here he is pretty near 39 and I guess the old Methuselum wants folks to hide I Mary Mac Lane when he comes in the rm.

Well it was 5 or 6 yrs. ago when I realized that I was past my nonages as they say. It come to me all of a sudden that the only compliments I had for a long wile was what a pretty tie you got or something. Nothing about my natural charms no more. It was an egg's age since anybody had called me to 1 side and whispered "I got a T. L. for you. Gertie thinks your ears is immense."

I seen then that I wasn't no longer a larva and I guess maybe it hurt at first. But its like falling hair or the telephone service or anything else. When you have lived with it a wile you don't mind. Which is just as well because they ain't a wk. passes when you wouldn't get touched on the raw if they was any raw left.

Like for inst. a few wks. back I was up in Boston where I got a young and beautiful sister in law. When it come time to part from she and her husband she kissed me 6 times which was suppose to be once for me and once apiece for the Mrs. and 4 kiddies. Well I thought it was pretty nice and got kind of excited about it till I looked at her husband to see how he took it. He took it without batting an eye. To him it was like as if she was kissing an old cab horse on a bet for the benefit of the Red Cross. And when I had left and they was alone together, instead of lepping at her throat with a terrible curse he probably says "Janey, you're a good game gal," and she gave him a kiss that meant something.

Now an incidence like this would of spoilt my whole trip if I didn't look at it in a sensible way which is to say to yourself, "Well if I wasn't in the Sears and yellow I wouldn't of got them 6 kisses. And 6 kisses is ½ a dozen kisses in any language."

Or for inst. out on the golf course. Suppose I and Grant Rice is playing with some young whipper snapper like say Jack Wheeler and they's only 1 caddy for the 3 of us. "Take them two" says Jack pointing to my and Grant's bags but the caddy has all ready took them any way as soon as he found out which ones belonged to which. Or when one of my young brother in laws is around the house and I come in the rm. and they are setting in the easy chair, why they jump up like food shot from guns and say "Here take this chair."

All and all when you get hardened to it they's many advantages in reaching your dottage. When they's 7 passengers for a 7 passenger car its never you that has to take one of them little torture seats. When your brother in law is here on a visit and the Mrs. thinks it would be nice to have a fire in the fire place, you ain't the one that has got to ruin his clothes. Yes friends the benefits is many fold but if them ½ dozen kisses and a few stray others pretty near as good was all, why you could still think to yourself Youth may get good service, but 35 ain't makeing no complaints to the management neither.

As for the gen. symptoms of 35 and vicinity as I have found them and not speaking for nobody only myself you understand, the following points may interest science:

1. The patient sometimes finds himself and one lady the only people left at the table and all the others is danceing. They seems to be nothing for it but to get up and dance. You start and the music stops and the young buddies on the flr. claps their hands for a encore. The patient claps his hands too but not very loud and he hopes to high heaven the leader will take it in a jokeing way.

2. For some reason another its necessary to find some old papers and in going through the trunk the patient runs acrost a bunch of souvenirs and keep sakes like a note a gal wrote him in high school, a picture of himself in a dirty football suit, a program of the 1907 May festival in South Bend and etc. "Why keep this junk" he says and dumps them all in the waste basket.

3. The case develops nausea in the presents of all story tellers except maybe Irvin Cobb and Riley Wilson and Bert Williams. Any others has to work pretty fast to get him cornered. Violent chills attends the sound of those saddest wds. of tongue or pen "I don't know if you heard this one or not but it struck me funny. It seems they was a woman went in a drygoods store in Detroit to buy some towels. Stop me if you heard it before." You couldn't stop them with big Bertha. The

best funny storys is Balzac's because they are in a book and you don't half to buy it. But when you get up vs. one of these here voluntary stag entertainers you either got to listen and laugh or they put you down as a dumb bell.

4. The invalid goes to a ball game and along comes the last ½ of the 14th. innings and the score is 1 and 1 and the 1st. guy up makes a base hit. The patient happens to look at his watch and it says 11 minutes to 6 and if he leaves the park right away he can make the 6:27 home where as if he waits a few min. he will half to take the 6:54. Without no hesitation he leaves the park right away and makes the 6:27.

5. The subject is woke up at 3 a.m. by the fire whistle. He sniffles but can't smell no smoke. He thinks well it ain't our house and goes back to sleep.

6. He sets down after breakfast to read the paper. The mail man comes and brings him 3 letters. One of them looks like it was a gal's writeing. He reads the paper.

7. He buys a magazine in April and reads the first instalment of a misery serial. The instalment winds up with the servants finding their master's body in bed and his head in the ash tray. Everything pts. to the young wife. Our patient forgets to buy the May number.

8. Somebody calls up and says they are giveing a party Thursday night for Mabel Normand and can you come. Our hero says he is sorry but he will be in Washington on business. He hasn't no more business in Washington than Gov. Cox.

9. They's a show in town that you got to see like Frank Craven or *Mecca*. "It's a dandy night" says the Mrs. "Shall we drive in or take the train?" "We will take the train" says our hero.

These is a few of the symptoms as I have observed

them and as I say I am speaking for just myself and maybe I am a peculiar case. They may not be another 35 yr. older in the world that is affected the same way and in fact I know several suffers about that age which I am as different than as day and night. Take Jess Willard for inst. He was somewheres around 35 in July 1919 and Dempsey knocked him down 7 times in one rd. He wouldn't do that to me, not 7 times he wouldn't. Or look at Ty Cobb. Do you think they would get me to play center field and manage a ball club for $30,000? Or would Jim Thorpe's brother in law look on him as too frail to hobble down in the basement and get a few sticks of wood?

On the other hand they might be 2 or 3 brother eagles in the mediocer 30s that is even more mildewed than me, but I am afraid they's a whole lot more of them feels like a colt. They take care of themselfs. When they get up in the a.m. they take a cold plunge and then hang by their eye teeth on a hook in the closet while they count 50 in Squinch. And noons when they come back from their lunch of hot milk and ferns, they roll over on the office rug 10 times without bending their shin.

I can't compete with these babies. I slice a few golf balls in season but bet. Nov. and May the only exercise I get or want to get is twice a wk. when I take the buttons out of shirt A and stick them in shirt B.

They's still another crowd yet that renews their youth by going back every yr. to commencement or a class reunion or something. Well I don't know if I want to renew my youth or not. Leave bad enough alone is my slogum. And in the 2d. place I don't half to go nowheres to a class reunion. I could hold it in the bath tub. I was the only one that graduated when I did as it was in March of my freshman yr. and they didn't seem to be haveing no commencement exercises for nobody else. I guess I must have been one of these here infantile proteges like that 11 mos. old junior they got up to Columbia.

No book of this kind would be complete without shooting a few wds. of unwanted advice at my youngers and betters. For inst. John D. tells the boys how to build up a fortune and John Jones tells them how to rise from a white wings to a steeple jack. So it looks like it was up to me to tell them how to get to be what I am, 35 yrs. old.

Well my lads they's 4 rules that I made and have stuck to them and I think you will find they'll bring you the same results. The 1st. rule is don't die the 1st. yr. The 2d. rule is don't be one of the 749 that dies when they are 11. The 3d. rule is don't pick a quarrel with a man like Dempsey. And the 4th. and last rule is marry a girl like Sue.

In explanations of that last rule I will say that the one I married ain't Sue but the name don't make no differents if she is the right kind of a gal. And the reason I say that is because its customary in these intimate capital I talks to throw in a paragraph of blurb about the little woman. What ever success a man has had he has got to pretend he owes it to Her. So if they's any glory to be gleaned out of my success in reaching 35 and looking even older why she can have it.

A GENERAL COMMENTARY

ON NEWSPAPERS

FROM everywheres comes the cry to save white paper and in my letters only recently I all ready mentioned about the props. of all the big newspapers in the country held a meeting in New York City and disgust the shortage and promised they wouldn't use no more of it then was nessary but from all as I can see the papers is still comeing out daily and Sun. as big as life and all the paper they been saveing wouldn't make a night gown for a cigarette and a outsider might think they had give their promise as a practical joke and with no intentions of carrying them out. But a friend of mine that knows some of the big editors personly claims that they would be tickled to death to live up to the agreement only they haven't no idear in regards to how to go at it in other words they don't know what they could leave out of the papers without the subscribers getting sore.

Maybe the genial editor of this paper is in the same pretty pass and would welcome a few suggestions from a person like I who has give the matter a good deal of thought and have got my finger on the public pulse at all times you might say.

In the first place gents I would cut out the news from foreign countries. They's a paper laying here along side of me which has got ½ a col. on Page 1 about Egypt being give a constitution and another ½ a col. about 115 million gals. of whisky being released from bondige and throwed on the market in England. Well, if the item about Egypt had of been left out the most of us would

564

have thought that Egypt always did have a constitution but even the few that knowed better could of stood it a few more months to go on thinking Egypt didn't have no constitution at lease till the white paper shortage is over. As for the other item it is like rubbing salt in a raw wound and if the papers wants to spend ½ a col. lacerating their readers on a exposed nerve why they can holler their heads off about the paper famine and not get no sympathy from thinking men.

I don't know of no case where printing the news acrost from the old pond ever done any good where as they's plenty of times it has cost a lot of trouble like back in 1914 for inst. when the papers all came out 1 day and said the Belgiums had started a big war and all the big Europe countries was messed up in it and they kept printing about it till finely we got into it ourselfs where as if the news had of been suppressed in the 1st place I wouldn't of knew they was a war or where to go to get into it. And if we hadn't of got into it I could've kept it a secret of haveing 4 vertical children and 2 flat feet.

2. You can pick up the paper everyday and find where President Hoover is mentioned in it about a average of 10 times. Well, it looks to me like most of your subscribers knows by this time that the President's last name is Hoover and they's no sense following up the word President with the word Hoover every time you got to mention him and as they's suppose to be 1200 words in a col. why every paper could save a col. in 120 days by just saying President done so and so or President said this and that and the other thing instead of President Hoover said it or done it etc.

3. Cut out the death notices. When a man dies their family usually finds out about it without looking in no paper and as for his friends why I don't know nobody

that reads the death notices every day and finds out if any of their friends has died on them but if they got a friend that they think they's any chance of him dying on short notice why they will give his house a ring a couple of times a day and say is So and So still alive or dead or neutral. People that dies suddenly with or without help usually eats up a couple of paragraphs in the news section so all and all the mortician col. could be cut out bodily and everybody have just as good a time.

4. Pretty near every paper nowadays has got a page or 2 of comical that they call them strips which is supposed to make their peal to the readers resibles and cheer them up. The strips the way they have got them now is divided up in panels usually 4 or 5 of them in 1 strip. But as far as I can see all the cackles is crammed into the last panel so why not cut out the other 3 or 4 and just leave the comical one where Pat beans Abie with a crow bar and says Bam.

5. Finelly gents I would cut out the advertising cols. You can't never make me believe that a person don't know they need something without waiting till they see it in the ads. Or you can't make me believe that when I need a certain thing the ads. is going to make me buy something else. For inst. what do I do when I need a hair cut why I go to a barber shop and make my wants known either by word or token to the nearest vacant barber and they won't no amt. of advertising make me go in a animal store and buy a pet wolf for my children instead of go in a barber shop and buy a hair cut for myself. Or take when a female subscriber needs a new shoe why her toes knows without her seeing the word mentioned in the advertising cols. and if she is a stranger in the city why she can find out by walking up to a policeman and saying where can I get a new shoe. Or if it's a pt. of gin she wants instead of a shoe why she

can substitute the word pt. of gin for the word shoe and say where can I get a pt. of gin.

The advertising cols. crowds out more live news such as "Babe Ruth took a foot bath last night" then any one feature in a newspaper and personly I have penned many a comical line that never seen print because it had to make way for a eulogy of somebody's embalming fluid that nobody will ever know if all they claim for it is true or not.

Cut out the ads gents and all so the other items which I have mentioned and 1st thing you know people will be throwing white paper around like it was 200 proof Scotch.

ON CHAIN LETTERS

I DON'T suppose a person gets so old but that they feel a kind of thrill when the mail man comes and brings them a letter that you can see from the outside that it ain't a bill or circular or ad. of some kind but looks like a real letter and in a strange writeing and you set there and finger it over and look at it from different angles and wonder who can it be from and etc. and finely you open it up and it may be just another mash note from some poor little gal that don't know you are married and got 4 kiddies and loseing your hair, but just the same the letter gives you a thrill before you open it up because they was a element of mystery connected with same.

Anyway that is how I felt in regards to letters up to the end of this last summer, and I was always on tender hooks when the mail man came along wondering what would he bring for me but since along about the 1 of September I have lost all interest in same and even when they hand me a letter marked personal and wrote in a hand writing which I ain't never seen before, why my pulse still goes around under 80 and my forehead stays cool because I know just what that letter is going to say:

> *Good luck.*
> *Copy this and send to nine people whom you wish good luck. The chain was started by an American officer and should go three times around the world.*
> *Don't break the chain for whoever does will have bad luck. But do it in 24 hrs. and count nine days and you will have good fortune.*

Then comes the signature of the party that sent it to you and sometimes they's a whole lot of other names of people that is mixed up in the plot and once in a wile they's a name of somebody you know but most of the time they are all strangers and will remain such.

Well friends as I say this business has been going on since about the 1 of September and up to date I ain't said nothing and have kept my mouth shut and took things as they come in the hopes the storm would blow over like the nullo fad in bridge whist but it begins to look now like this thing is libel to develop into a permanent plague unlest somebody steps forward and puts the quietus on it and wile I don't pretend to have influence enough with the gen. public to influence them one way or the other still and all I feel like I wouldn't be doing my duty was I to remain in silents and not state my stand in regards to the matter of these here endless letter chains.

Well then friends anybody that wants one of these here letters to go one time around the world to say nothing of three times around the world is going about it in the wrong way when they mail one of them to me because as far as one of these letters is conserned I am what you might call a terminus. When one of these letters reaches my house the conductor may as well get up and holler this is as far as we go, all out and don't forget your packages and umbrellas.

Now I don't want anybody to get the idear that I am wishing myself bad luck or anybody else, but after several years experience I have come to the conclusion that the only way to get good luck is work hard, try and keep in the fair way, and don't overbid your hand.

You know them dimes that John D. Rockefeller scatters around Cleveland and Tarrytown like they was so much platinum.

Well do you think he got hold of them dimes by forwarding somebody else's mail within 24 hours and then setting around and wishing nine days was up?

No, friends, he got them dimes by staying on the job wile other guys was makeing sure of their luck by sending a army officer's mail three times around the world.

Outside of believing that it is bad luck to bet vs. the Yankees I ain't got no superstitions and will take this opportunity of warning my friends that I ain't going to be no party to a endless chain letter not even if it was started by Gen. Pershing and even was I in sympathy with this great movement I couldn't hardly carry our provisions of same as it would take me a lot longer than 24 hours to think of nine people to who I wish good luck.

All jokeing to 1 side what happens to people like I that is defiant in regards to the letters? It will be noticed that the letters warns people to not break the chains for whoever does will have bad luck.

Well friends without no kidding I have received at least 12 of the letters since the summer and just as fast as I have received them I have forwarded them towards the ash can or in other words I have flied right in the face of danger no lest than 12 times and what is the result.

The only time I been to the race track I knocked the bookies for a ghoul beating them for no lest than $40.00 smackers. As near as I can remember I am at least $8.00 bucks ahead of the bridge game and may be $1.25 winner in the poker though playing mostly with women and deuces both wild. I ain't had a Dr. in the house though measles and whooping cough is run amuck all over Long Island. And I ain't even been looked at by a traffic policeman.

I suppose my superstitious friends will say wait a wile, give the jinx time to work. Well friends I don't expect the kind of luck I been haveing to last forever and I wouldn't be surprised if sometime next March I will get mixed up in a bridge game with some of them sharps like Mr. Kerwin from Detroit or maybe Mr. Culbertson himself and maybe lose a $1.40.

But until that happens I ain't going to change my habits in regards to these letter chains and in closeing will say once more that if you want them to go three times around the world or even 1 time send them elsewheres but don't send them to me.

ON CONVERSATION

THE OTHER night I happened to be comeing back from Wilmington, Del. to wherever I was going and was setting in the smokeing compartment or whatever they now call the wash room and overheard a conversation between two fellows who we will call Mr. Butler and Mr. Hawkes. Both of them seemed to be from the same town and I only wished I could repeat the conversation verbatim but the best I can do is report it from memory. The fellows evidently had not met for some three to fifteen years as the judges say.

"Well," said Mr. Hawkes, "if this isn't Dick Butler!"

"Well," said Mr. Butler, "if it isn't Dale Hawkes."

"Well, Dick," said Hawkes, "I never expected to meet you on this train."

"No," replied Butler. "I genally always take Number 28. I just took this train this evening because I had to be in Wilmington today."

"Where are you headed for?" asked Hawkes.

"Well, I am going to the big town," said Butler.

"So am I, and I am certainly glad we happened to be in the same car."

"I am glad too, but it is funny we happened to be in the same car."

It seemed funny to both of them but they successfully concealed it so far as facial expression was conserned. After a pause Hawkes spoke again:

"How long since you been back in Lansing?"

"Me?" replied Butler. "I ain't been back there for 12 years."

"I ain't been back there either myself for ten years. How long since you been back there?"

"I ain't been back there for twelve years."

"I ain't been back there myself for ten years. Where are you headed for?"

"New York," replied Butler. "I have got to get there about once a year. Where are you going?"

"Me?" asked Hawkes. "I am going to New York too. I have got to go down there every little wile for the firm."

"Do you have to go there very often?"

"Me? Every little wile. How often do you have to go there?"

"About once a year. How often do you get back to Lansing?"

"Last time I was there was ten years ago. How long since you was back?"

"About twelve years ago. Lot of changes there since we left there."

"That's the way I figured it. It makes a man seem kind of old to go back there and not see nobody you know."

"You said something. I go along the streets there now and don't see nobody I know."

"How long since you was there?"

"Me?" said Hawkes. "I only get back there about once every ten years. By the way what become of old man Kelsey?"

"Who do you mean, Kelsey?"

"Yes, what become of him?"

"Old Kelsey? Why he has been dead for ten years."

"Oh, I didn't know that. And what become of his daughter? I mean Eleanor."

"Why Eleanor married a man named Forster or Jennings or something like that from Flint."

"Yes, but I mean the other daughter, Louise."

"Oh, she's married."

"Where are you going now?"

"I am headed for New York on business for the firm."

"I have to go there about once a year myself—for the firm."

"Do you get back to Lansing very often?"

"About once in ten or twelve years. I hardly know anybody there now. It seems funny to go down the street and not know nobody."

"That's the way I always feel. It seems like it was not

my old home town at all. I go up and down the street and don't know anybody and nobody speaks to you. I guess I know more people in New York now than I do in Lansing."

"Do you get to New York often?"

"Only about once a year. I have to go there for the firm."

"New York isn't the same town it used to be neither."

"No, it is changeing all the time. Just like Lansing. I guess they all change."

"I don't know much about Lansing any more. I only get there about once in ten or twelve years."

"What are you reading there?"

"Oh, it is just a little article in *Asia*. They's a good many interesting articles in *Asia*."

"I only seen a couple copies of it. This thing I am reading is a little article on 'Application' in the *American*."

"Well, go ahead and read and don't let me disturb you."

"Well I just wanted to finish it up. Go ahead and finish what you're reading yourself."

"All right. We will talk things over later. It is funny we happened to get on the same car."

MEN AND WOMEN

SAY IT WITH OIL

THE EDITOR of this hardy perennial asked me would I write a article on my impressions in regards to wives.

"Well," I says, "I have only got the one wife, and wile I admit she has made quite an impression, still and all it seems to me like you ought to get a hold of a husband with more experience."

So he says:

"Yes, I know you have only got one yourself, but you must be acquainted with a whole lot of them."

"I suppose I am," I said, blushing furiously; "I guess I am personly acquainted with practally every A-No. 1 wife around N. Y. City except Nina Wilcox Putnam."

The Editor jumped as if stang by a bee.

"That is almost uncanny you mentioning her name," he said. "She is the lady who has wrote up a article in regards to husbands, and what I am asking you to write is a kind of a reply to what she wrote. Because I would not be loyal to my sex was I to print her scatheing arrangement of the male gender and not give no space to our defense."

"All right," I said; "but I can't conduct no defense without knowing what is the charges, so before I reply to her article I would better see it first."

So he showed me the article, and I read it, and you can read it for yourselfs as it is printed elsewheres in this issue[1] under the dainty *nom de plume* of "Say It with Bricks," only I suppose the proof-readers has kind

---

[1] *The American Magazine*, November, 1922.

of fixed it up since I seen it, as it struck me that the lady in question has studied husbands at the expense of grammar and spelling.

But before dealing with her article, and wile still cool, I would like to state the cold facts which the gen. public is well aware of same, but for one reason and another don't care to confess it even to themselfs. One fact is that a man defending husbands vs. wives, or men vs. women has got about as much chance as a traffic policeman trying to stop a mad dog by blowing 2 whistles. Another fact is that, with all the recent jokeing about give us equal rights and etc. the wives has got the husbands licked to a pulp and has had them licked for hundreds of yrs., and same can be proved by consulting the works of any writer young or old that touches on the subject.

We will take for inst. the dictionary, and what does it say about a husband? The 1st. definition is a husbandman, which don't mean nothing. The 2d. definition is a frugal person, an economist. The 3d. definition is a man who has a wife. In other wds. Mr. Webster realized that his book wouldn't have no sale unless it tickled the womenfolks, so before he dast come out and say that a husband is a man with a wife, he had to call him a tightwad.

Now what is the definition of a wife? Well, he says she is the lawful consort of a man, and it don't require no Shylock Holmes to figure out that what he meant to say, but was scared to say, was, *awful* consort.

Back toward the end of the same book you will run across the wd. uxoricide which means the murder of a wife by her husband. But nowheres in the book will you find a wd. that means the murder of a husband by a wife. Unless it's the wd. congratulations.

In this connection it might be well to point out the

fine bunch of equal rights with which the happy pair embarks on the matrimonial seas. If either one of them ain't satisfied with the other, why they have got equal rights to shoot. But if it's the wife that gets bumped off, the husband has got exclusive rights to a seat in the electric chair, or strap hanging by his Adam's apple, or spending the rest of his life in a bird cage. If, however, the husband was the target, why the worst that can happen to mother is that she will half to poll the jury with kisses, which can't be such a hardship even granting that statistics is accurate, and that 10 out of every 12 good men and true is kindly disposed toward eating-tobacco.

But to return to the writers, why you can't find more than a couple of them great or small but what has came out in print or in speeches before the Rotary Club to the effect that their success and everybody else's was due to their wives or sweethearts. They know a whole lot better, but don't dast say so. The prominent exceptions to this rule is Francis Bacon and Rudyard Kipling. Mr. Bacon made the remark that "he that hath wife and children hath given hostages to fortune, for they are impediments to great enterprises, either of virtue or mischief." And Mr. Kipling wrote one about a good man married being a good man marred, and another one to the effect that he travels the fastest who travels alone.

Some nerve these two babies had, but where did it land them? Mr. Bacon is quite dead and Mr. Kipling wasn't even invited to Princess Mary's wedding.

The writers of the present day has learnt better than take chances like that, and you can't read a story or tend the theater now days without getting a fresh sample of log rolling in favor of the squalling sex. Like for inst. take the play *To the Ladies* where Marc Connelly and

Geo. Kaufman has their leading female character say a line something like "No man that wasn't married ever made a name for himself." Well they was a whole lot of us guys in the audience with our wives, and when the line was sprang why we just kind of giggled and smirked as much as to say "How true that is." Where as if we had of dared to be nasty we would of rose up on our legs and said "What about H. L. Mencken and Tris Speaker and Geo. Ade?"

Even the authors of the marriage ceremony has woke up to the situation and agreed to rewrite same and fix themselfs right with the ladies by leaving out the wd. obey. This is just another public recognition of how bad we are licked. As a matter of fact the obey rule got obsolete along about the same time as 1st. bounce is out. And another thing the boys is going to eliminate is the giving of a woman in marriage, because the gals don't like to have it even hinted that anybody has got the right to give them away like they was a cut glass gold fish bowl or a pen wiper. So instead of "Who giveth this dame to this guy," why from now on they are going to can those lines and substitute a hymn or anthem which will probably be some song like "O what a gal was Mary."

So much for Man's position in the Standing of the Clubs and the fat chance I or any other male has got to defend ourself vs. attacks by Mrs. Putnam or any other member of her lodge. But when I undertake to do a job why I am one of these here he-blooded Americans that never quits till they are counted out which can't possibly happen till I been in the arena 10 seconds. In this case however I expect to last longer than that for one little reason. The wife I have got don't read my stuff. Incidently that just about describes her. But any way the knowledge that she don't read my stuff gives me courage to say a few wds. about wives and what they are that I wouldn't dast say if I thought she was going to read it.

Well then here is some of my idears about wives as I have studied them at home and abroad.

Wives is people that thinks you ought to eat at 8 o'clock, one o'clock, and 7 o'clock. If you express yourself as having an appetite for turkey at midnight they think you are crazy.

Wives is people that always wants to go home when you don't and vice versa.

Wives is people that ain't never satisfied as they are always too fat or too thin. Of all the wives I ever talked to I never run acrost one yet that was just right.

Wives is people that thinks 2 ash trays should ought to be plenty for a 12 rm. house.

Wives is people that asks you what time the 12:55 train gets to New York. "At 1:37," you tell them. "How do you know?" they ask.

Wives is people that sets on the right side of the front seat in their husband's costly motor and when he turns down a street to the left they tell him he ought to of kept straight ahead.

They are people that you ask them to go to a ball game and they act tickled to death. So along about the 7th. innings you look at them and they are fast asleep and you remind them with a delicate punch in the ribs that they are supposed to be excited. "Oh, yes," they say. "I love it." So you ask them what is the score and they say "St. Louis is ahead ain't they?" "Well," you say, "I don't know if St. Louis is ahead or ain't ahead, but the game you are watching is between Boston and New York."

That reminds me of one time I took the little woman

(I can't always remember her first name) to a game in old Chi and it was Cleveland vs. the White Sox and it was a close game something like 2 to 1 in favor of somebody and along come the 8th. innings, and Mother, which is how I sometimes think of her, was sleeping pretty and all of a sudden they was a big jam down around 1st. base between a citizen named Tris Speaker, mentioned before in this article and now mentioned again, and Chick Gandil of blessed memory. As they was taking the shirtless remains of Chick off of the field I nudged Mamma in the jaw and said: "Did you see that? It looked to me like Graney took a wallop at him for good measure." "Who is ahead?" says the little gal.

Wives is people who you make an outlay of $50, so as they can set somewheres in New Jersey during the so-called Dempsey-Carpentier fight and when it is over, you meet them and ask them how they liked it and they say Oh, they was thrilled. "Did you see that last punch?" you ask them. "No," they say. "I was watching Irma Goldberg." Who of course is worth watching even at $50.

They are people who you get invited out somewheres with them and you ask them if they think you ought to shave and they say no, you look all right. But when you get to wherever you are going they ask everybody to please forgive Lute as he didn't have time to shave.

They are people that kid you because when the morning paper comes the first thing you look at is the sporting sheet. You leave the paper home and buy another one to read on the way down-town. When you get home that evening, in trying to make conversation you remark that it was kind of sad, the Kaiser's wife dying in exile. "I didn't know she was dead," says Ma. "Well," you tell her, "it was in the morning paper." "I didn't notice it," she says. "It must of been on the front page."

They are people that never have nothing that is fit to wear.

They are people that think when the telephone bell rings it is against the law to not answer it.

They are people whose watch is always a ¼ of a hr. off either one way or the other. But they wouldn't have no idear what time it was any way as this daylight savings gets them all balled up.

The above observations is made without resentment as I have no complaint vs. wives in gen. or anybody's wife in particular. Personly I get along fine with whatever her name is and am perfectly satisfied with my home, which I often call my castle. I also refer to it sometimes as jail, but only in a joking way.

But here I am in jail and supposed to be defending my sex vs. the opponents and as I said before what a fat chance. However I promised the old boy that I would answer Mrs. Putnam's article, and a promise is a promise especially when you get paid for it.

So will point out in the beginning that Mrs. Putnam denies all through her article that it is a article and she certainly hit the nail on the hammer that time. What it reads like to me is pure fiction. Like for inst. she gives you the impression that whenever she seen her husbands before she married them, they always had on a dress suit. Well friends I think you will find the fact is that when a kid is 16 or 17 yrs. of age he gets a dress suit and by the time he is 19 yrs. of age he couldn't get it on with a shoe horn, and from that age to when he gets married he don't have no more dress suit than Robinson Crusoe and he wouldn't never have no more dress suit as long as he lived if she didn't insist on him joining the Rotarians.

The lady's complaint is that after being used to him in nothing but dress suits wile he was doing the alleged courting, why it is a kind of a blow to see him walking around the rm. in his shaving uniform with his suspenders drapped over his hips. In reply to that will say that the lady shouldn't ought to of had no trouble picking out a husband with something on his hip besides suspenders.

Another complaint is how much noise a husband makes with his tooth brush. Well if a man is at all musical they's no instrument he won't attempt to play on and besides what good is brushing your teeth if you are going to keep it a secret.

And another complaint is that husbands prefers toothpicks to any other form of dessert. I don't think this is entirely fair because they's some desserts that you get in hotels and restaurants that a person would really relish more than a toothpick, whereas they's desserts that is served in some private homes than whom a person would not only rather have toothpicks but sulphur matches if necessary.

The lady says it is husbands that is always delaying the game and when they are told that dinner is ready dear, why it is then and then only that they start to wash their hands and brush their hair. Our reply to that is that when the little woman says dinner is ready you can generally always figure on anywheres from 10 minutes to a ½ hr. before they's anything on the table but flies.

As for husbands causing the missing of the first act, judgeing from the most of the plays I seen lately she should ought to be grateful for that and if he is even slower and makes her miss the whole show she ought to kiss him.

Now then along toward the finish of her story the lady says something which I will half to quote as it is such a pretty sentiment namely, "Any complaint you can make about husbands and marriage would be a true one. And only one thing about them (meaning husbands) has got me buffaloed. Would I be willing to do without them? And the answer to that is 'No.' "

Well friends it is hard to bear ill will toward a writer that kind of softens her tirade with such a neat little compliment as that and it looks to me like it would be no more than gentlemanly on my part to reply to same in kind. For inst.

"Pretty near any complaint you make about wives, why it is true though they will probably resent it. But I often ask myself the question could I get along without them? And the answer to that is that I got along without none for twenty-five yrs. and never felt better in my life. Believe you me."

MARRIAGE MADE EASY

Every once in so often old Doc Crane breaks loose with a article in regards to one thing another, and one time he asked a lot of questions about one thing another, and unless a man could answer them all without looking it up in the seed catalogue, why you was supposed to be a moron poor and simple, and the questions the Doc asked was so tough that a whole lot of our smartest Alex took just one look and then went to the county cuckoo cage and gave themselfs up and couldn't get out to vote.

Well it didn't do so much harm to get all them people out of the way, but since the Doc has came acrost with 20 rules on how to be a happy marriage and they are even tougher than the cuckoo test, but it wouldn't make no differents to me as I have all ready got the proposition mastered without no doctor's prescription, but still and all this country is full of young upstarts that may of been just getting ready to assume the connubial yokel and all of a sudden they run acrost the Doc's dope and say it can't be done and they decide to remain celebrates and then what is to become of them 2 grand American institutions, the home and the rent for same.

So in order to perpetrate same by not allowing our young singletons to discourage themselfs with the Doc's dope, I have wrote out a set of 10 simple rules instead of 20 tough ones witch means it won't only take ½ as long to be a happy marriage and twice as easy.

1.

The marital twain should ought to be opp. sex if possible and somewheres near the other one's age. For inst. when a man of 15 gets marred to a gal of 45 why it may pan out all right for the time being but don't never forget that when a groom is nearing the century mark and wants to know where they's a clean bath towel, why he can't find out without leaveing Thurston the magician into the secret.

2.

The ideal marred life is for the 2 belligerents to live in the same town so as when they feel like a brawl they won't be no toll charges.

3.

The bride should ought to have at lease as much money as the groom and a salary of her own so as when she feels like she has got to buy something she don't want she will know that it's her money being throwed away. All women hates to feel like they was spongeing off of their husbands but the most of them is such a good actress that you wouldn't never guess how it hurts them.

4.

If the union is crowned with a offspring, the offspring should be crowned at intervals by the father. Otherwise the mother should have exclusive rights as care taker as even a baby don't like to change horses in the middle of the night and wile the old adage says that everybody ought to have 8 hrs. sleep, why it amounts to the same thing if a couple splits 16 hrs. between them, the husband getting the winners share of 80 per cent. and ½ the picture rights.

5.

As Doc Crane says, it ain't right to find fault with the other on no grounds and the best way is to pertend like you are tickled to death with everything she does. Like for inst. if you are ½ way home on the train and she shreaks that she has forgot her pocket book, lean over and give her a good loud kiss.

6.

Both partys should try and talk about subjects that the other is interested in it. They ain't no husband cares a d—mn if the wash woman that is comeing next wk. goes to a different church than the one that was here last wk. and they's very few wifes cares the same amt. whether Max Baer is going to be the next heavyweight champion, so the idear is that when supper is over and the loveing pair sets down in the liveing rm. to wait till its polite to go to bed, the husband should ought to in-

sist that they won't be no conversation unlest its about
the wash woman and the wife should ought to insist
that they won't be no conversation unlest its about the
next heavyweight champ and if the both of them insist
hard enough they won't be no conversation at all witch
boarders on the ideal.

7.

In most familys its too cold to set up late but when the
partys retires the wife wants to go right to sleep like a
horse or something wile the husband wants to read, but
the wife can't sleep if he reads a wile. This can be overcome by a unselfish spirit on both sides. Let the wife
keep saying, "I don't want you to not read on my acct."
and keep turning the light on and the husband keep saying, "I don't want you to not sleep on my acct. or you
will crab about it all day tomorrow" and every time she
turns the light on he turns it off and in this way its
morning before you know it and both sides a winner.

8.

Marred life is a job just the same as like a telegraph
operator or a embalmer and every employ is entitled to
2 wks. vacation per annum and if the husband takes a
2 wks. vacation trip every summer and vice versa, why
they will get so as they won't miss their regular jobs ½
as much as if they was on it all the wile. For inst. I knew
a couple where the husband use to go South for a mo.
every Winter and one time he didn't come home at all
and all of his relic's friends was feeling sorry for her
where as she didn't know he was still missing till one
night in August when a bat got in the house and she
screamed and nobody told her to shut up.

9.

Doc Crane advises marred couples to not both get mad at the same time, the old spoil sport. That was the trouble with Sharkey and Schmeling over in Long's Island because Schmeling didn't lose his temper though the boys tell me he had even more reason than the saps that paid $55 for a ringside seat. They's no fun playing tennis unlest the guy on the other side of the net has got a racket and the same goes for a connubial quarl and my advice is for the husband to call up home just before he leaves the office and ask the spouse if she is feeling brutal this evening and if she ain't she better be, because by the time he gets the right number they won't be nobody half to wait till dog days to see him froth at the mouth.

10.

Finely, try and forget once in a wile that you are marred and go out somewheres together for a good time. Don't go to a dance or a card party or a good show or the opera, but pick out something that the both of you can enjoy, like for inst. a 3 cushion billiard match or a cock fight or to watch the high school football five practice. Remember always that you swore at each other at the altar that each was taking the other from bad to worse and may the best man win.

LOVE LETTERS MADE EASY

I just got hold of a book which I only wished I'd ran acrost it about 20 years ago, and it would have saved me from a whole lot of trouble and mistakes and etc. which anybody is libel to make through ignorants when if they only knew that they was a book of this kind to refer to it and study it and master what is in it, why they's no telling what a differents it would make in a man's life and adventures. So I am going to tell my readers a little about the book in the hopes that some of them is still young enough yet to get the full benefits from it and that it will prove as good a boom to them as I feel it would have proved to me had I not ran acrost it too late.

Well, friends, the name of the book is "Love Letters Made Easy," and it is the works of a lady of the fair sex and it tells all the secrets of love making by U. S. mail and the gal has wrote out some sample love letters which takes the 2 opponents through all the stages from the time they met till matters has went beyond recall and I don't know no better investment which I could recommend to my young readers than buy this here book and study it like they would their Bible and fashion their love letters along the same lines as those printed in the book.

The man's name in the book is Edgar Dale and the gal's name is Margaret Merton and they meet at a dance and the next day he sends her some pamphlets about playground associations which shows they must have had some pretty hot conversation at the dance. She writes and thanks him for the pamphlets and he writes back and says he is a traveling man and has got to go out on the road and will she write to a poor lonesome chap. Pretty soon they break down a few barriers and begin calling each other Edgar and Margie and the next thing you know he starts a letter to her my dear young Butterfly. Personly I would give anything if I knew 20 yrs. ago just which letter to start calling my gal a young Butterfly in it.

Well in the butterfly letter he pretends like he is fond of nature includeing birds, so she starts her next letter dear Birdsman and winds up by telling him they's nothing she enjoys like a cold shower. After that of course they ain't no more restraint between them, and the climax comes when she opens up a letter to him by saying the top of the morning to you dear man. The author leaves you where they are engaged and makeing plans for the wedding and she don't give you no samples of the letters they wrote after they had been married a few yrs. but I can furnish some of those kind myself though I am afraid they ain't no butterfly nor birdman in them.

As I say, the sample letters comes too late to be any use to this old dowager but the first chapter of the book contains plenty meat for married and single men alike as it tells how to send messages three different ways and by that I don't mean night letters and day letters and etc., but what it tells is how to express your ideas by postage stamps and flowers and gems which you send them to whoever you want to send them to and the party that gets them will know what you means without you committing yourself in black and white. Like for inst. in regards to postage stamps. I always been in the habit of sticking one right side up in the upper right hand corner of the envelope which don't mean nothing, but it seems they's a different meaning to all the other ways you fix them and from now on people that gets a letter from me would pay better tension to how the stamp is stuck on and if they notice that and understand it they won't half to read what I got wrote inside the letter.

Like for inst., if the stamp is upside down on the left hand corner means write no more and in the bottom corner at the left which means I seek your acquaintance. Straight up and down in the left corner says good-by sweetheart and if the stamp is along side of the line which you have wrote the name of the person who you are writeing to, it means accept my love.

So for example that in the next few days I get a letter from some firm mentioning that I ain't paid the Jan. bill, why instead of me wasteing my time quarreling with them I will just set down and address them a envelope and stick a stamp on the right corner upside down, meaning write no more or maybe put it upside down in the left corner, meaning I love you and they will either get scared and lay off of me or else the next letter I get from them won't be no dun but will be a mush letter. Then I can write back and put the stamp upside down on the line with their name, meaning I am engaged and the whole affair will come to a end before they's anybody hurt.

Or suppose I was to receive a letter from the Ku Klux Klan saying they are libel to suspend me for not paying my dues, I will send them back a envelope with the stamp cross ways in the upper right hand corner which means I wish your friendship and that will show them I ain't sore at them but if they don't quit sending me them kind of letters I will quit the klan.

LARGE COFFEE

Note: Readers of the daily papers will recall a paragraph printed earlier this week to the effect that the body of a Mr. Lardner was found in a New York hotel room by a house officer who had broken in after the chambermaids had reported that they had rapped on the door every day for over a fortnight and had received no response, and were disposed to believe that the occupant of the room would need a clean towel if living, and perhaps two of them if dead. The occupant was in the last-named condition or worse. Dressed as usual in pajamas, he was sprawled out on the floor, his head crushed in by a blow from some blunt instrument, probably another hotel. At the time the item appeared, there was mention of the discovery of a diary. It now develops that one really was unearthed and turned over to the police, who used parts of it as curl papers for Grover Whalen. We have acquired the mechanical rights to the balance and herewith publish extracts from it as a human document of particular interest to men and women who, like the writer thereof, have been battered and broken by an insensate world.

Friday, May 31

Today I registered and was assigned this room, 657, which is to be my home through most of the summer. At a conference of my wife and children, it was decided that I ought to contribute something to their support and they recommended that I do a little writing for the magazines or newspapers. I told them this would be impossible in our hut on Long Island unless they and the neighbors agreed to become hermits so that my mind would not be constantly distracted by the knowledge that other people were having fun. It is my plan to visit the family one day in the middle of each week, not at the week-end when there seems to be a tendency to drink cocktails and expect you to sit by, look on and like it. The hotel is giving me a rate of $4.00 a day, really a bargain because the room has a window. You can look right into other people's rooms on the courtyard if they don't keep their shades down. O diary, I hope it's a hot summer. (Editors' Note: Did he get his hope?)

Sunday, June 2

I spent so much thought yesterday and this morning on what I would have sent up for breakfast that when I sat down at the typewriter, my mind was too tired to work. I spoke of this over the telephone (my only means of communication with the outside world) to a friend and he advised me to make a selection of a few nourishing and inoffensive victuals, commit them to memory and order them every morning. I then asked him what to do about the coffee problem, which is something of a problem to me. You see, when you drink lots of coffee you can kind of kid yourself into believing it's something else, so for breakfast I always want four cups. What I mean is enough coffee to fill one cup four times. Yesterday morning I said to the order clerk, "Two orders of coffee," and the result was two small pots of coffee, each containing enough for two cups. But the set-up, as I believe they call it, was for two people; there were two cereal dishes, two plates for my bacon and eggs and two cups for my coffee. This lay-out congested the table, leaving no space for my shoe tree. So this morning I said, "Two orders of coffee, but served for one person." The result was a small pot of coffee, containing enough for two cups. Well, my friend said I would have to work this out for myself; the only advice he could give me was ridiculous—that I give up coffee. This evening I will try to think of a solution and also select a permanent breakfast so there will be no more brain fag or waste of time.

Friday, June 7

The breakfast I have picked out for the summer consists of orange juice, corn flakes, medium hard boiled eggs, and buttered toast. Boiled eggs are preferable to other kinds because they don't bring you two plates for them even if your coffee order makes them believe you are two people. I selected toast instead of plain rolls or sweet rolls because the sweet ones are too filling and messy, and the plain ones are made in Bethlehem, Pa. The toast is also immune, but you have to say something when the order clerk insists. The coffee situation is just as baffling as a week ago. One morning I said, "I am living alone, but I drink four cups of coffee." I got a large pot of coffee and four cups. Another morning I said, "Double coffee, served for one." I got a large pot of coffee, two cups, and two orders of tooth-proof toast. Yesterday I asked the waiter how much a large pot of coffee cost. He said it was sixty cents. So this morning I said to the order clerk, "One orange juice, one corn flakes, one medium hard boiled eggs, one buttered toast, and sixty cents worth of coffee." "Coffee," she replied, "is only thirty cents a pot." "But I want twice as much as that." "Oh, all right. You want two orders." "Yes, but I'm not two people." I got one small pot of coffee.

Monday, July 8

It is the hottest summer in history. Everybody on our court is free and easy. Formality and modesty have been thrown to the winds, if there are any. A business woman who looks like Tom Heeney and has a red splotch under her left shoulder blade is occupying the room just opposite. She is out all day and goes to bed at eight and reads the Brooklyn telephone directory. The electric light in my bathroom wouldn't work today and I wanted to shave on account of the waiters. I told the floor clerk to send me the electrician. Pretty soon a plumber came and turned on everything but the light. "I don't see anything wrong," he said. "The light won't turn on," I said. "Oh," said he. "You want the electrician." The electrician came. I said, "The light won't turn on in the bathroom and I know the bulb isn't burned out because I tried another bulb and it wouldn't work." So the electrician tried another bulb and found it wouldn't work. "It must be something else," he said. He found the trouble and fixed it. This may have no bearing on the case, but I want to tell all.

I have been getting my large pot of coffee every morning, but never with less than two cups and nearly always with two egg cups, two dishes for cereal, and two orders of toast.

Double coffee, large coffee, enough coffee for four cups, sixty cents worth of coffee, enough coffee for two people served for one person. I have thought I might ask Percy Hammond to come and room with me, but that would only mean six or eight cups on the same-sized table. An assistant manager called me up at twenty minutes to three this morning and said somebody had just complained that I was using a typewriter. What the hell does Mrs. Heeney think I moved in here for, to be near Gimbel Brothers?

Thursday, August 22

Yesterday morning I got what I wanted and I called right back and asked for the order clerk. "Are you the only order clerk?" "Oh, no." "Well, are you the one that just took the order for 657?" "Yes. Was it wrong?" "No. It was right. Now listen, I'm not trying to start a flirtation, but what is your name?" "If there's any complaint, I'll connect you with the superintendent." "There's no complaint, but I want your name so I can give you my order every morning." "Well, my name is Foley." "Thanks, Miss Foley. And when I call you tomorrow and other mornings, please do as you just did—send me a large pot of coffee and only one cup."

Every day the paper says cooler tomorrow. They ought to put that with the rest of the comics. A mystifying combination of tenants has taken the room across the court. There are two young women and a man. They can't be going to stay in town very long because the women apparently haven't brought anything but nightgowns and when the man isn't in B.V.D.'s he's out of them. I feel as if some time I would almost have to shout at them, "Don't you want a fourth for bridge?"

Monday, September 2

The worst has happened. Miss Foley "isn't here any more." My house was built on sand. I've got to start all over again and work up from the bottom.

And I'm pretty sure that late tonight I will lean out the window and holler, "Hey! Don't you want a fourth for strip bridge?"

A WORLD'S SERIOUS

ADVANCE NOTICE

Sept. 30.—All though they have been world serious
practally every yr. for the last 20 yrs. this next world
serious which is supposed to open up Wed. p.m. at the
Polo grounds is the most important world serious in history as far as I and my family are conserned and even
more important to us than the famous world serious of
1919 which was win by the Cincinnati Reds greatly to
their surprise.

Maybe I would better exclaim myself before going
any further. Well, a few days previous to the serious
of 1919 I was approached by a young lady who I soon
recognized as my wife, and any way this woman says
would I buy her a fur coat as the winter was comeing on
and we was going to spend it in Connecticut which is
not genally considered one of the tropics.

"But don't do it," she says, "unless you have got the
money to spare because of course I can get along without it. In fact," she added bursting into teers, "I am so
used to getting along without this, that, and the other
thing that maybe it would be best for you not to buy
me that coat after all as the sight of a luxury of any kind
might prove my undoing."

"Listen," was my reply, "as far as I am concerned you
don't half to prove your undoing. But listen you are in
a position to know that I can't spare the money to buy
you one stoat leave alone enough of the little codgers
skins to make a coat for a growed up girl like you. But
if I can get a hold of any body that is sucker enough to

595

bet on Cincinnati in this world serious, why I will borrow from some good pal and cover their bet and will try and make the bet big enough so as the winnings will buy you the handsomest muleskin coat in New England."

Well friends I found the sucker and got a hold of enough money to cover his bet and not only that but give him odds of 6 to 5 and that is why we did not go out much in Greenwich that winter and not for lack of invitations as certain smart Alex has let fall.

I might also mention at this junction that they was a similar agreement at that serious between Eddie Collins the capt. of the White Sox and his Mrs. only of course Eddie did not make no bet, but if his team win, why he should buy the madam a personal sedan whereas if his team lost, why she would half to walk all winter. Luckily the Collinses live in Lansdowne, Pa., where you can't walk far.

Well friends I do not know what is the automobile situation in the Collins family at the present writeing as have not saw them of late but the fur coat situation in my family is practically the same like it was in 1919 only as I hinted in the opening paragraph of this intimate article, it is a d-a-m sight worse.

Because this yr. they won't be no chance for the little woman to offset her paucity of outdoor raps by spending the winter in the house. She is going to need furs even there.

Therefore as I say this comeing serious is the most important of all as far as we are conserned for Mother ain't the same gal when she is cold and after all is said and done what is home with mother in her tantrums?

So I and my little ones is hopeing and praying that the boys on who I have staked my winters happiness this yr. will not have no meetings in no hotel rooms between now and Wednesday but will go into this serious determined to do their best which I once said was the best anybody could do and the man who heard me say it said "You are dead right Lardner" and if these boys do their best, why it looks to me like as if the serious should ought to be well over by Sunday night and the little woman's new fur coat delivered to our little home some time Monday and maybe we will get invited out somewheres that night and they will be a blizzard.

THE FIRST DAY

Oct. 5.—Well friends you can imagine my surprise and horror when I found out last night that the impression had got around some way another that as soon as this serious was over I was planning to buy a expensive fur coat for my Mrs. and put a lot of money into same and buy a coat that would probably run up into hundreds and hundreds of dollars.

Well I did not mean to give no such kind of a impression and I certainly hope that my little article was not read that way by everybody a specially around my little home because in the first place I am not a sucker enough to invest hundreds and hundreds of dollars in a garment which the chances are that the Mrs. will not wear it more than a couple times all winter as the way it looks now we are libel to have the most openest winter in history and if women folks should walk along the st. in expensive fur coats in the kind of weather which it looks like we are going to have why they would only be laughed at and any way I believe a couple can have a whole lot better time in winter staying home and reading a good book or maybe have a few friends to play bridge.

Further and more I met a man at supper last night that has been in the fur business all his life and ain't did nothing you might say only deal in furs and this man says that they are a great many furs in this world which is reasonable priced that has got as much warmth in them as high price furs and looks a great deal better. For inst. he says that a man is a sucker to invest thousands and thousands of dollars in expensive furs like Erminie, Muleskin, squirrel skin, and kerensky when for a hundred dollars or not even that much, why a man can buy a owl skin or horse skin or weasel skin garment that looks like big dough and practically prostrates people with the heat when they wear them.

So I hope my readers will put a quietus on the silly rumor that I am planning to plunge in the fur market. I will see that my Mrs. is dressed in as warm a style as she has been accustomed to but neither her or I is the kind that likes to make a big show and go up and down 5th ave sweltering in a $700 hogskin garment in order so as people will turn around and gap at us. Live and let live is my slocum.

So much for the fur coat episode and let us hear no more about it and will now go on with my article which I must apologize for it not being very good and the reason is on account of being very nervous after our little ride from the polo grounds to park row. It was my intentions to make this trip in the subway but while walking across the field after the game I run into Izzy Kaplan the photographer and he says would I like to ride down in a car which him and his friends had hired so I and Grantland Rice got in and we hadn't no sooner than started when one of our fellow passengers says that we ought to been with them coming up.

"We made the trip from park row in 24 minutes," he

says, "and our driver said he was going to beat that record on the return trip."

So we asked what had held them back comeing up and one of them said that the driver had kept peeling and eating bananas all the way and that he did not drive so good when both his hands was off the wheel. Besides that, they had ran into a guy and had to wait till the ambulance come and picked him up.

Well friends I will not try and describe our flight only to say that we did not beat the record but tied it and the lack of bananas didn't prevent our hero from driving with his hands off the wheel as he used the last named to shake his fists at pedestrians and other riff raff that don't know enough to keep off the public highways during the rush hour.

Most of the things I was going to mention in this article was scared out of me during our little jaunt. One of them however was the man from Toronto that stood in line with his wife from 8 p.m. Tuesday night till the gates opened Wednesday morning so as to be sure of good seats. According to officials of the club, they could of got the same seats if they had not showed up till a couple hours before the game, but if they had of done that, why the lady would not of had no chance to brag when she got back home. The way it is, why she can say to her friend, "Charley may not be much for looks, but he certainly showed me the night life of New York."

Dividing interest with this couple was a couple of heel and toe pedestrians that done their base circling stunt just before the start of the game. One of them was the same guy that done it before the first game last fall, but this time he was accompanied by a lady hoofer and it is not too much to say that the lady was dressed practically as though for her bath. Casey Stengel expressed the general sentiment in the following words, "If that is just her walking costume I would hate to see her made up for tennis."

THE SECOND DAY

Oct. 6.—No doubt my readers has been tipped off by this time that the 2d game of the big serious was called on acct. of darkness but a great many of them may not know that the umpires and club owners was called a lot of different names which I will not repeat here but suffice it to say that none of them was honey, dearie, and etc.

The boys that had paid $5.50 and up to see a ball game did not seem to think it was dark enough for the umps to step in and stop it. Personly I will not express no opinion as some of my best friends is umpires, but will merely state that I started out of the press box the instant it was over and by the aid of a powerful candle which I generally always carry to world serious games when Shawkey and Barnes is scheduled to pitch, why I was able to find my way down to the field where I run plum into A. D. Lasker who had forgot to light his headlights. Will further state that nobody who I passed on the way out to 8th avenue had yet put on their pajamas or made any other preparations that would indicate the fall of night and even when I got down to park's row, pretty near a hr. after the game's untimely end, I was still able to grope my way to the office by feeling along the sides of buildings and was seated right here at my typewriter writing this article before the hoot owls and nightingales begun to emit their nocturnal squawk.

However, one of our fellow passengers on the bus down town was Billy Evans, an umpire himself, and

while he admitted that he had not saw none of the outfielders signaling to each other with flares, still and all
he says the polo grounds is a terrible hard place for the
athletes, and a specially the batters, to see a ball when
they's the slightest twinge of darkness. As far as that is
concerned there is 2 or 3 of the boys on each of the contending clubs that dont seem able to see the ball any too
good even at high noon.

Anyway it means we are going to have a extra ball
game to play over and some of we boys who predicted a
short serious is being made to look like a monkey. Personly I was never so ashamed of myself since I picked
Willard.

The general opinion amongst the writing boys to-
night was that the game being a tie is a big help to one
of the two teams but I forget which. It certainly aint no
help to me and the only thing I liked about the day was
the weather, which it would make a person sick to even
talk about a fur coat in such weather, and it goes to show
what a sucker a man would be to squander thousands
and thousands of dollars in a costly fur garment and
then may be have a whole winter of just such days like
yesterday.

Personly I seen a girlie on the street last night wearing a linen duster and you have no idear how good they
look on some people and keep you plenty warm too if
you move around and dont stand still.

Well friends, I prophesied in these columns earlier in
the week that Bob Shawkey would be a whole lot better
this fall than he was last fall and that prophecy certainly
come true, but the boy has still got the habit of pitching
bad in the first innings and if I was running the Yank
ball club here is what I would do. When it was Bob's
turn to pitch, why just before the game started I would
call Bob to one side and I would say, "well Bob it's the

second innings all ready." If he believed it, why they would be nothing to prevent him from stepping right in and pitching his best from the start.

Jess Barnes pitched better than Bob at the start and not so good at finish. The way Jess pitched to Ruth did not seem to rouse unanimous enthusiasm amongst the bugs in the grandstand. Slow balls is what Jess feeds the Babe and the reason for same is because Babe dont hit slow balls out of the ball park. If Jess did not feed the Babe slow balls when he knows he cant hit slow balls so good, why that would make Jess a ½ wit and when he does feed the Babe slow balls, why it shows he is thinking. That is why the crowd hoots him for pitching slow balls, because the average baseball bug hates to see anybody think. It makes them jealous.

Well friends today is another day and may the best team win as I often say to Mother which is what I call the little woman when I am in a hurry and cant think of her name.

THE THIRD DAY

Oct. 7.—Amongst the inmates of our heavily mortgaged home in Great Neck is 3 members of what is sometimes referred to as the feline tribe born the 11th day of last April and christened respectully Barney, Blackie, and Ringer.

These 3 little ones is motherless, as the lady cat who bore them, aptly named Robin Hood, took sick one June day and was give away by Fred to a friend to whom he kindly refrained from mentioning her illness.

These 3 little members of the feline tribe is the cutest and best behaved kitties in all catdom, their conduct having always been above reproaches outside of a tendency on the part of Ringer to bite strangers knuckles. Nowhere on Long Island is a more loveable trio of grimalkins and how it pierces my old heart to think that some day next week these 3 little fellows must be shot down like a dog so as their fur can be fashioned into a warm winter coat for she who their antics has so often caused to screek with laughter. Yes boys the 3 little kittens is practically doomed you might say and all because today's game at the polo grounds was not called on account of darkness long before it started though they was no time during the afternoon when the Yanks could see.

I probably never would of heard of a cat skin coat was it not for an accidental introduction last night to a man who has did nothing all his life but sell and wear fur coats and who told me that no finer or more warmer garment can be fashioned than is made from the skin of a milk fed kitty.

"Listen," was the way he put it. "You would be a even worse sucker than you are if you was to squander thousands on thousands of dollars on the fur of a muskrat or a mule when you have right in your own asylum the makings of the most satisfactory and handsome coat that money can buy."

"Yes," was my reply, "but the fur of 3 kittens would make a mighty small coat."

"Small coats is the rage," was his reply, "and I personally seen some of the best dressed women in New York strolling up and down 10th avenue during the last cold snap with cat skin garments no bigger than a guest towel."

So while I said a few paragraphs ago that the result of this ball game spelled the doom of our little kitties, why as a matter of fact I have just about made up my mind to not buy no costly furs even if the Yankees does come through and bring me out on the right side of the public ledger. Whatever I win in bets on this serious I will freely give to charity.

I would try and describe the game to you in intimate detail was it not played in such darkness that I was only able to see a few incidence. Of these few occured in the 3rd innings and consisted of Whitey Witt getting caught asleep off of first base by a snap throw from one of the Smith brothers.

The dean of Cleveland baseball experts explained this incidence by saying that Whitey thought he was still with the Athletics. It is more likely however that Whitey was deceived by the darkness into believing it was his bedtime.

The next incidence come in the innings when the Babe tried to go from first to third on a wallop by Bob Meusel that got away from Frisch. Frankie pegged the ball to Heine Groh who stood in Babe's path to third but it was so dark that Babe crashed right smack into him and secured a rolling fall. For a minute it looked like they would be fisticuffs between the 2 famous athletes but Heine suddenly remembered the advice given him by his first school teacher, "never be a bully," and the fight was over before it begun.

Fifteen minutes before the start of the game the official announcer come up to the press box and said that McQuillan was going to pitch for the Giants. A minute later he come around again and said to make it Scott instead of McQuillan. McQuillan thus broke Fred Toney's record for the length of time spent in a world serious ball game.

I will close this article by making a apology to the boys to who I have give tickets for games no 1 and 3 and whose seats is in section 24 which is as far north as you can get without falling out of the grandstand. The gents who sold me these seats thought I was a close friend of the Meusel boys and might want to set out there myself and kid with them.

THE END

Oct. 9.—Well boys it looks like it was all over and the only complaint I have got to make is that the traffic regulations was not handled right.

The next time the Yankees takes part in world serious they should ought to have a traffic policeman stationed between 1st and 2nd base and another traffic policeman stationed between home and 1st.

The former should tell the boys when it is O.K. to run to 2nd. And the latter must inform them that when a ground ball is hit to the infield in a world serious the general theory which has never been disapproved is to run on high speed to 1st base which is the base towards the right field from the home plate.

The lack of a adequate stop and go system is what lost this serious on the part of the Yanks. The final game of the serious was marked by the only incedence of brains exhibited by the Yanks during the whole serious.

In the 2nd innings with two boys on the bases and one out Joe Bush passed Arthur Nehf to 1st base so as to get the head of the batting order up and not confuse the official scorers. This bit of thinking probably was responsible for nothing.

I will not try and dilate on the rest of the serious only to say that Charles A. Hughes and Eddie Batchelor of Detroit spent this a.m. at the Bronx Soo to try and see more animals. It is hard to satisfy the boys from Detroit.

All as I know what to write about on a occasion like this kind is little incedence that come off. The 1st incedence that calls to mine is in regards to Tommy Rice of the *Brooklyn Eagle*. Tommy wrote 7,000 words in regards to the 1st game of the serious and page by page it blew out of the window in the costly appartment building in which Brooklyn experts lives, there is no telling what the loss to the world is on account of not being able to read Tommy's story to say nothing about the readers of the *Eagle*.

Now boys I suppose they is a few interested in whether the little woman is going to get a costly fur coat. The other day I wrote a story to the general effects that we was going to kill our cats and use their fur to make the costly garment. This story was not appreciated in the heavily mortgaged home. After a long argument the master of the house compromised and decided to not doom the little members of the finny tribe to death. Instead of that we are going to use a idea furnished by the same Eddie Batchelor, of Detroit, mentioned a few thousands words ago. Eddie's idears is to start a chain letter to all our friends and readers asking them to look around the old homestead and find their family albums and take the plush off of the covers and send it to the undersigned and make a plush coat which everybody tells me is the most fashionable fur on the green footstool. The little woman can wear plush and a specially the red pigment but black and tan plush covers will be welcomed and this man tells me theys nothing more attractive than a black and red and tan blocked coat made out of plush albums.

I was going to say further in regards to the plush albums but Harry Frazee has just butted in with the story of his life. It seems like when Harry was a young man in Peoria his father said to him if you don't be wild and go into the theatrical business and stay around Peoria you will be as big a man as your uncle. So Harry looked at his uncle who was getting $125 per month staring at books.

"Well," says Harry, "I can get more than that catching runaway horses." So he is now catching runaway horses and selling them to the New York club.

As I now sit here and write I am surrounded by a corpse of experts just as ignorant as me and they don't seem to be none of them able to tell who is going to pitch tomorrow. Personally I think it will be Col. Ruppert and Huston.

ON POLITICS

DISARMAMENT IN 1921

Washington, D. C., Nov. 12.—Well, I don't suppose it will surprise nobody to find out that I am in Washington for the disarmament conference as it is getting so that they can't put on no event of worldwide interest without they have me there and if you look it up you will find that I have been behind the scenes at every real big occasion that has came off in the world in the last five years, except the tennis match between Mrs. Mallory and Miss Lenglen—and what a flop that was.

Anyway here I am a good five hours from Long's Island but no chance to get lonesome as this old town is full of celebritys and it seems like every time I turn around H. G. Wells or M. Briand or somebody hollers: "Hay Ring."

Wells and some of the other visiting firemen is stopping at private homes but personally I always prefer a hotel where a person can get their pants pressed nights and look like something in the morning and besides if you stay at somebody's house that don't know you very well you are libel to set down to meal after meal of cheese omelet and sliced bananas.

Of course, the paper Wells is working for done a smart thing when they stuck him in a private home. Hotel grub runs into real money even when you only put on the feed bag 3 times every 24 hours but imagine having an Englishman knocking 7 meals per day at your expense.

I am stopping at the Willard which is the same hotel

where the French delegation is at but so far I ain't ran
acrost many of them in the lobby and the bell captain
says the most of them spends their time in their room
looking curiously at the bath tub.

Another thing that got them puzzled is a concoction
that the waiter sticks in front of them as soon as they
set down in the dining-rm. This is a glass that has got
a piece of ice floating in a liquid that ain't red or white
or no color of at all but when you tip the glass a little
and ice hits against the side of it and tinkles so maybe
it is some kind of a musical instrument.

There may be some of my readers that is dumb
enough to not know what this conference is all about.
Well friends it has been called together to see if they
ain't some way of stopping war and that is what the
league of nations was supposed to do but the league has
been to bat five or six times and ain't even got a foul.

So the idear is to find a substitute for the league and
a lot of the boys figures that the disarmament scheme
will do the business so the object of this meeting is to
get all the different nations to quit building war ships
and making ammunitions and etc. and it looks now
like they would all agree to the proposition provided
they's an understanding that it don't include they
themselfs.

They's no question but what the United States would
be tickled to death to see all the ships sank and all the
guns and bombs and brick bats throwed in the ash can.

That would leave every nation in the same position,
namely without nothing to fight with except their fists.
And we have got Dempsey.

Jokeing to one side this country goes into the conference in dead earnest and fully prepared to cripple ourself from a fighting standpoint provided the other nations does the same and as a evidents of good faith

President Harding is planning a public bonfire at which he will burn his niblick.

The main idear of course is to persuade everybody to quit having a big navy. Rifles can do a whole lot of damage in a neighborhood brawl but you can't hide behind a tree in Omaha and snipe guys on Main st., Tokyo. So if war ships was done away with they wouldn't be no danger of another real war breaking out till the next time Germany and France gets mad at each other which ain't libel to happen for a long wile, say six months.

So all this conference has got to do is make everybody give up their navy and some nations is expected to agree while others will take a lot of coaxing. Like for inst. Switzerland will probably make a big squawk wile on the other hand Spain is already counted in the yes column as they are really the pioneers in this enterprise. They quit having a navy in 1898.

However, we won't never know what the Swiss delegation has to say as the sessions of the conference is going to be held in secret and the public is barred. The American delegation would like to have everything open and above the boards but the foreigners won't stand for it. This same explanations is given out in England and France, only over there it's America that insists on secrecy.

Well, whoever it is that insists on it they can have it, as I know a whole lot better ways of spending my time in Washington, but as far as I am concerned suppose they did let me in their old meeting wile the Japs or Swedes was airing their views. Why I could set right in their lap and hear it all and it would still be a secret from me unless they sell librettos.

Seriously speaking, I am for secret sessions if secret session is going to accomplish what the boys has set out to accomplish. They's nobody in this country or anywheres else that is pulling harder for war to be stopped than this native son of Berrien county, Mich. Because I have got a little male quartette in my home which in 20 yrs. from now they will all be draft age at once and it ain't on the cards that the whole four of them will be lucky like their dear old dad and have falling arches.

Washington, Nov. 13.—Well friends, they put on the murder scene in this play the minute the curtain went up.

The audience was expecting to set around a couple hours and listen to comical dialogue between Yvonne and Perkins, the English butler, but instead of that the leading man come right down front and knocked everybody's eye out with the speech that is generally always supposed to wind up act 3.

I don't know what lines is left in Mr. Hughes's part, but they will certainly half to be risque to keep the rest of the show from dragging. About the only thing that could get another thrill out of the customers would be to have some Germans delegate get up on the rostrum Tuesday morning and say here is what we owe you.

Even William Bryan got excited over Mr. Hughes's opening remarks, and they say this was the first time William ever stood up to cheer a speech. They has been many other speeches that he felt like cheering, but he was already standing up.

Personaly I half to take the newspapers word for what Chas. really said as up to date they hasn't nobody came around and forced a press badge on me and it begins to look like the conference would be held out doors as far as I am concerned, probably on the municipal golf links.

But as near as I can make out, Mr. Hughes's idea is a ten year naval holiday and if anybody feels like scrapping they can scrap their ships. In the next ten years no nation will be allowed to build a boat, and if a war should come up between now and 1931, they won't be no shipyards for the boys to enlist in and many a patriot's mother will breathe a sigh of relief as there won't be no danger of her boy smashing his thumb with a hammer. During the holiday the other stores will be open from 8 to 5:30.

On the face of it, the American scheme looks to be open and above the boards, but a man that is suspicious by nature might figure that they was a special reason for Mr. Hughes setting a time limit like ten years. Prohibition is libel to be over about that time and we can build better ships when we ain't all stewed.

As the next session of the conference is scheduled for Tuesday morning they won't be nothing for the delegates to do tomorrow, so tomorrow is one day when the Chinese delegates will be on a equal footing with the rest of the boys. The chinks is planning to spend a day looking over the laundry situation in Washington as this conference is libel to last a long wile.

The Japs or somebody paid the Chinamens R. R. fare over here and give them a nickel a day to live on, which is supposed to be all a Chinaman needs, but they aint got a Chinaman's chance of living in a Washington hotel on that amount of money or even twice that sum.

So it looks like they would either half to open up a laundry or a chop suey joint or else go home, which would be tough luck after getting invited to attend the conference, and they have also got permission to talk all they want provided they talk in the official language of the conference, which is English and French.

Washington is interested now in what reply Japan and England will make in regards to the proposition of destroying all them pretty boats. When you come to think of it, it is a kind of heart rendering for a navy man to have to blow up a ship which he has become attached to and learned to think of it as his own and it looks to me like it would be a good idea to reward the commanders some way for their sacrifice.

Like for inst., as soon as they had blown up their ship they could get aboard of a train and tour the country making all stops and wherever they stopped all the town gals would half to rush up and kiss them. This scheme seemed to console Lt. Hobson in 1898, only of course in them days when a gal kissed you it didn't taste so funny.

Well friends, I suppose you have read in the papers where all the famous men that is here for the conference has been besieged by invitations to parties and etc., but so far my key ain't been crowded out of my mail box.

However, they was a gal spoke to me this morning that I never seen her before in my life. I was setting in my room reading about old Yale and they come a knock at the door and I says come in, and she come in and says I have brought you some soap.

Washington, Nov. 14.—Amongst the important questions which remained unsettled at a late hour tonight was what about China and why did I bring my dinner clothes? It is libel to take at least two weeks to get a reply to either question and by that time the answer to No. 2 won't make no difference as I will be back on

Long Island where a man is admired for what he done and not just because he came from Europe and wears suspenders.

The hotel where I am stopping at seems to be in the conspiracy to keep me a secret wile in Washington as I have now been here 3 days and had 3 different rooms and every time I go to the desk they ask me would I just as leaf move to another room as somebody wants the room I am in. Maybe that is why they call it the New Willard is because they give you a new room every day.

Well, they wasn't nothing of gen. interest come off today so it looks like I would haft to try and fill up this space with a few words in regards to my personal experiences which begun when I looked out the window and seen it was raining, which meant another naval holiday for my golf sticks. Well, I shaved myself and it was worse than usual because I had to shave around a bunker which was put in the course the other day by a Philadelphia barber who I had never seen him before in my life, let alone quarrel with him.

Well, after that I wrote a couple of letters and telegrams which I thought was important so I went down to the taxi stand and told the man I want to go to the main telegraph office and the post office and the next thing you know we done a tail spin on C. street and bumped into a car load of ladies, God bless them, and it was the first time I ever seen a man driver scrimmage with a gal driver when it wasn't the gal driver's fault.

Our next bout come off on Fourteenth st. with a U. S. army car that was taking a couple of French delegates to some embassy to get a drink but the best we could do to them was put them out of bounds on the left hand sidewalk. We done a better job at the first telegraph office as they was a car already standing there with its brakes on and we used it for a bumping post. Well by this time I had give up the idear of going to the post office which is way down by the union station so I asked my driver how much I owed him and he charged me $2.40 or 80 cents a smash. I asked him if he got many tips. "I ain't had any yet" he says "I only been driving three days."

Well, I managed to walk back to the hotel without knocking nobody down and I come up to my room and as luck would have it, it was the same room I had this morning so they wasn't any unpacking to do so I figured I might as well call up the President and see about a golf game, but I couldn't find his name in the phone directory and the only name that was anything like it was a W. P. G. Harding that lives on 19th st. and I thought at first that maybe the P. might stand for President, but if it did they would probably put it in front of the W., so anyway I didn't call up the number and it begins to look like they wouldn't be any golf game between us this trip which I am sure the President will be disappointed as he likes to play golf with me. It is the same instinct that makes a good many football teams so anxious to meet Columbia.

Well, I couldn't think of nobody else to phone to so I went down to see about a ticket to some show and I finely picked out the "Merry Widow." At first I was going to Frank Tinney's show but I figured he wouldn't be funny after the taxi driver.

This is my experience for the day and as far as the conference is concerned, they wasn't no regular open meeting but they was a meeting of the American Advisory Committee which was named a couple weeks ago and is made up of 21 ladies and gents who are supposed to stick around and wait till Messrs. Hughes, Lodge, and etc., asks them for some advice. It is estimated that by the first of April they will of forgot how to talk. One of the members of this committee is Eleanor Franklin Egan, the writer, and today's meeting was for the purpose of finding out who the rest of them are, as the man that appointed them never forgets a face but can't remember names.

Washington, Nov. 15.—Another packed house seen the show at Continental Memorial Hall today and wile the performance lacked some of the zipp that Mr. Hughes put into it opening night, still the audience acted like they was pleased and I wouldn't be surprised if the piece run all Winter.

The boys finely gave me a pass this morning, and I was amongst the first to arrive in the hall but pretty soon the other newspaper men begin dropping in and several of them wore frock coats which would never be tolerated in the press stand at the World's Series. Personly I was married at night and have got just a gray business suit for day time wear.

The man setting next to me pointed out the delegates of the different Powers, as they come in and took their place at the tables which look like they had been borrowed for the occasion from the Hotel Commercial writing room. The delegate that took my eye was Mr. Schanzer from Italy, who looks like one of the apostles.

I asked my informer how an Italian come to have the name of Schanzer and he says it was because he come from Trieste. It seems a resonable explanation though personly I never was in Trieste and don't know the Schanzer boys. The delegate next to Mr. Schanzer was also quite a sight as he was a Hindu named Sastri who had just been getting a shampoo and the barber forgot to take the towel off his head.

Chairman Hughes got up and asked if anybody wanted to reply to what he had to say at Saturday's meeting and we was all in a sweat to hear from England and Japan but before they was allowed to talk a tenor leapt to his feet and sung a French translation of what Mr. Hughes had just said.

Then Mr. Balfour made the longest speech of the day and he was followed by Messrs. Kato, Schanzer, and Briand. Mr. Kato give his speech in Japanese and Mr. Schanzer spoke in what he thinks is English and of course M. Briand used French and he is the only man I ever heard talk that language that didn't seem to think it was a foot race. All the speakers were tenors except Messrs. Hughes and Briand.

Well, anyways they all said they was agreeable to the idear of cutting down the navies and if we do have a war with Japan it begins to look like it would half to be fought with souvenir post cards, I thought Mr. Balfour made a very eloquent speech.

After the five great Powers had been heard from Mr. Hughes adjourned the meeting though the delegates from Portugal and Holland set there with their tongues hanging out ready for action. I am told that the rest of the sessions is libel to be held in secret and not even newspaper men will be admitted which suits O.K. as they don't allow smoking.

In the mean wile things is beginning to perk up in a social way around the nations capital as I have been invited to attend the regular Wednesday luncheon of the Washington Rotary Club at which occasion the Chinese delegates will be the guests of honor and principal speakers and I would advice them to make their speeches long as they're no telling when they will get another chance.

Last night President Harding and I attended the Merry Widow but not together.

Washington, Nov. 16.—Wile we are waiting for the different committees to get ready with their reports it looks to me like this was a great time to open up the discussion of a subject which to my mind is pretty near as important as international disarmament, namely, dealcoholization or the neighborhood reduction of family liquor supplies. Just like the league of nations failed to prevent war, so has prohibition failed to even slow up drinking and not only that but it has made same five or six times as expensive so that nowdays the average family has quit eating all together and don't know where their next bootlegger is coming from.

Now, gentlemen and friends, I am in the same position in regards to drinking which the United States is in with respects to war, namely, I don't want nothing for myself and I haven't no intentions of invading a neighbor's home and attacking their supply, but for defensive purposes I have got to keep enough in my own home so as callers can't set around the living room and make funny cracks about how dry they are.

So it looks like it was my duty to take the leadership in regards to hootch reduction the same as it was Mr. Hughes duty to make the first suggestions about navies and with the above lines of introduction I will go ahead and present my idears as I believe the time for dreams and flowery phrases has past and the time for action has come.

Well, friends, the Japanese and England of my neighborhood on Long Island is two families who we will call the Smiths and the Browns and they are both married couples like myself and got pretty near the same tonnage of children which we leave the latter out of the present calculations as none of our kiddies has yet reached the age when people starts drinking these days, namely, eleven years of age.

Once or twice per week the Smiths and Browns comes to our house or vice versa. The ladies of these three great powers is satisfied with a couple of cocktails apiece and personly I don't touch nothing, but Smith and Brown has always got their tongues hanging out.

My motives is therefore unselfish in offering the following suggestions which I hope that Smith and Brown will give them careful consideration and talk them over with their wifes and give me their answer at the next plenary session before anybody gets too plenary.

ARTICLE 1—It is proposed that the first ten days of every month shall be a ten day hootch holiday during which no party to this agreement shall buy, manufacture, or drink liquids of more than ½ of one per cent displacement.

ARTICLE 2—Scrap all bottles which has already been opened and all or a part of their contents removed.

ARTICLE 3—At the beginning of each holiday the corkage of the three families shall of been reduced to an amount just sufficient to take care of transcients west of Pittsburgh.

ARTICLE 4—At the end of the holiday the three families may buy such new corkage as will maintain them till the next holiday and it seems only fair that the amount to be purchased by each family shall be in accordance with that family's thirst, in other words if the Browns is a thirstier family than my family, why the Browns is entitled to buy a whole lot bigger supply and on evenings when the party ain't at their house they can bring along as much of their own supply as they think necessary to the success of the evening.

Washington, Nov. 17.—While the regular delegates to the conference is still engaged in secret practice the rest of the young visitors in Washington is spending most of their time getting honored. Like for inst. the commander in chief of the French army, who my elevator boy nicknamed Marshall Fox, picked up a couple more degrees yesterday and now it looks like he had pretty near enough to start a fever. Mr. Fox got one of his new ones from Georgetown and the other from Howard University where the colored boys goes to school. Georgetown also presented him with a slight token of their esteem in the form of a sword.

"Just what I needed," was the Marshall's delighted comment. The Howard students might of give him a razor for all I know.

Marshall Fox is now practically everything which the United States can make him except a kleagle. No foreigner was ever give such a welcome as Ferdinand and he says there must be more than 110,000,000 people in this country as he has shook hands with twice that amount. He also says he wishes some American hero would visit France so as the French people could return some of the compliments that has been showered on him.

But it would be well for our heroes to remember that over there they will kiss you instead of shaking hands, but maybe the experience would be O. K. for Mr. Hughes as he is well protected on both cheeks.

The Crow Indian tribe honored General Diaz of sunny Italy by making him a member of the tribe and the chief of the tribe also give him his own name which is supposed to be the highest honor that can be bestowed on anybody though personly I named one of my kids after the old man, but he insists on being called Bill.

The Crow chief's name, which is now jointly held by General Diaz, is Plenty Crops, so when this conference has made war impossible the general can open up a chicken ranch.

The above ceremony was pulled off right here in the hotel and started with a hymn sang by two Crows Red Neck and White Faced Bear and I could not help from thinking how much more fun it would be if we was like the Indians and give ourselfs names that you can tell what we looked like by hearing them. For inst. I might have lunch with some friend of mine and he could go home and tell his wife that he just had lunch with Plenty Moles, or my Mrs. might ask me who I played poker with last night and I would say I played with Prominent Gums and Plenty Adams Apple.

After Red Neck and White Faced Bear finished their duet General Diaz was presented with a necklace of shark bones and like Marshall Fox he remarked that it was just what he needed.

Personly I went out to Robert Dawkins home on 15th street and they give me simple honors a couple times but no sword or fish bones necklace.

I am not being took into the secrets of the different committee meetings which is going on around the town, but the boys is still said to be arguing over the Far

Eastern question which as near as I can make out the
crux of the situation is that America wants the open
door to China wile Japan wants the door shut and not
even let nobody but themselfs Pekin at the Chinks.
That is what I been doing all week is thinking up that
gag, but now I have thought it up it don't read so good.

Well, they ain't no more news except that young
man from George Washington university called and
wanted to ask me a few questions and I told him to
go ahead and his first question was what did I think of
college students of the present day as compared with
college students of the last generation. I suppose everybody is crazy to know what answer I give him but if the
conference delegates is going to be so doggone secret,
why two can play at that game.

Washington, November 19.—Senator Lodge says it
looks like the boys would be out of the trenches by
Christmas and most of the correspondents seems to
think that is good news, but personly I can't afford to
lead a double life even that long at the present hotel
rates and the rest of my reports on this here disarmament conference will be wrote and sent out from Long's
Island and as far as I can see that is as good a place to
write them as any.

They's just as many different kinds of foreigners in
Great Neck as in Washington. The ones in Great Neck
is a whole lot more friendly. For inst. If you want to
interview one of the Japanese down here you have got
to go through a whole lot of red tape and then you're
lucky if you get anywheres near them, but in Great Neck

all you half to do is to go up on the front porch of any house and ring the door bell and if they's a Jap in the house he will come to the door.

Well, friends, on the eve of my departure from what has been humorously dubbed the nation's capital, I suppose they's nothing more fitting than to give a brief resume of the impressions received wile here and what do I think of the prospects for a happy ending of the conference, and etc.

Well, it seems to me like spirit of Xmas is already running amuck in Washington and all the different nations is vying with one another in self-denial and sacrifices and the great danger now is that a couple of them will go to extremes and give away something they own and personally the example set by the boys down here has had such an effect on me that the minute I get home I am going to turn my lawn mower over to the hired man and tell him to go ahead and use it like it was his.

Some people has expressed surprise at the good fellowship and harmony which has been in evidence so far, but might of guessed how it would be from the way Mr. Hughes's naval programme was received, namely, without even a suspicion of a squawk from Portugal, France, Italy, and The Netherlands, leaving England and Japan to pick flaws in same.

But joking to one side, they is bound to be some kind of navy reduction along the lines laid out by Mr. Hughes and as soon as the 3 powers conserned reaches a agreement on what ships must be destroyed and what ships can be built, why the next move will be to appoint watchmen to see that nobody gets double crossed and these watchmen will half to be wide awake young men and not suckers.

Because for inst. Suppose that Japan and England said that the U.S. would half to blow up the battleship Michigan, why if we wanted to be nasty we could paint Michigan on a scow and blow it up and have people stand around and wipe their eyes and say there goes the poor old Michigan, and if the watchmen from Japan and England didn't know their business they would wire a telegram to their govt. that the Michigan had been destroyed and in the mean wile the real Michigan might be tied right up to the wharf in Yokohama with some name like Dignity wrote on the side of it and the Japs would think it was a private yacht from N.Y. City.

Well, however the conference comes out I can assure my American readers that our delegates can be depended on to take off our hat to no country in no respect and especially personal appearance as every one of our 4 delegates has got their own frock coat and don't half to pass same around like a loving cup and I don't think they's none of the smooth faced foreigners as handsome as Mr. Underwood, wile in the matter of beards Messrs. Lodge and Hughes more than offsets Mr. Schanzer though his may have more parking space.

Mr. Briand's mustache would tickle more than Mr. Root's but Elihu's will outweigh Mr. Balfour's and Admiral Kato's combined.

Well, I must catch the old train and get back to the old town and find out what all I have missed and this trip has already made me miss seeing Yale win a football game which is something I never seen as the first part of October generally always finds me busy with the world's series. Well, anyway, friends I am going home, me and my dinner coat both and I suppose when the last named gets back in the old closet and my spring Benny asks it where it has been, it will probably say, "Oh, I been down in Washington hanging around."

THE DEMOCRATS IN 1924

For the last several days different people has been complimenting me in the following words, what terrible stuff you are writing, but one boy friend said you wrote something pretty good for the Newspaper Club Reporter so I says did I and bought a copy of same and with or without your kind indulgence will now proceed to copy same and I don't say it is good, but that is just one boy friend's opinion.

I better exclaim at the outset that this is supposed to be advice to the visiting scribes in regards to how to cover the convention and I only hope it don't come too late.

I would advise visiting reporters the 1st thing is to find out where is the convention to be held and write it down vs.: "Madison Square Garden" and memorize the location of same "Fourth ave. around 26th st." so as when you go back home and the madam says where was the convention held you can tell her it was held in Madison Square Garden, on Fourth ave., around 26th st. I learnt this lesson 4 yrs. ago when I got home from "covering" the convention in San Francisco and my Mrs. had to say something so she says where did they hold the convention and I was kind of staggered on acct. of not having no idear where had they held the convention so I says what did you say to give me time to think up something and she repeated the question and I said why they held it in the auditorium out near the presidio. This got by all right because in the 1st place she don't hardly know what state is San Francisco in and in the 2d place she was not listening as she did not give a dam where it was held but some wifes is different.

Now I don't want nobody to think I have got anything against Madison Square Garden, and, in fact, I am fond of same, as it is the only place I know of in the East where a person can be sent to "cover" a fight and not get his skull fractured by a policeman when you show them your press ticket, but, on the other hand, I could name a whole lot of nicer places to spend the convention a specially as the Garden has been host all Spring to Ringling's Circus, and certainly ain't had time to get aired out, which you wouldn't know the difference, anyway, after the delegates had been in there a couple hours.

The boys around the Newspaper Club can give you the names of these other places I refer to and you will find the most of them equipped with tables which you can write your stuff on after they been wiped off, and at this junction I would like to caution the visiting brothers vs. over writing, 200 words a day is plenty for a democrat convention and most of the time it ain't necessary to do more than send your managing editor a telegram saying see A. P. for what come off to-day. "A. P." is the nickname I got up for the Associated Press. If you send your stuff by mail it is good idear to use copy paper rather than the back of a menu card.

In the case the boys around the Neyspaper Club refuses to give the desired information, why one of the best places I know of to work is the Rendezvous (pronounced Rendezvous) on 45th street, and if it was not closed I would take you there myself.

At this writing the name of Al Smith has just been placed in nomination and those on the inside told me that the demonstration would last 2 hours. The demonstration for Mr. McAdoo yesterday only lasted 45 minutes which it looks like that means that Al is either an hour and quarter ahead of him or behind him.

They don't know or care, but if they would hurry up and nominate somebody before Saturday night I would give a demonstration that would last all Summer.

But it looks like the boys is here for the week-end including the month of August. A whole lot of them who did not hire a room with a bath is now talking to the clerk and trying to get themselfs rearranged and a good many of them is beginning to wish they had brought on their brush and comb.

They was a storm here Wednesday night and the papers reported seven people killed. One of them was a bellhop at a hotel I won't mention who died quietly when a delegate from Arkansas gave him a dime.

"Why did you give me that dime?" was his last words and some of the local talent is writing a song about it.

The outlook is beginning to look more terrible every moment, because when they finely do decide on who is going to be president, the next problem is who is to capture the honor of second place on the ticket. This honor has already been offered to me, which means they have got as far as the L's in the telephone directory, but I am proud though poor. Some of the boys has asked me what platform would I run on if nominated and I said why they are already fixing up their platform ain't they and they said yes but we want your own individual platform.

So I says all right friends I am opposed to the following propositions in every day life:

1. The matter of paper cups on Pullmans.
2. The matter of liquid soap most anywheres.
3. The matter of no hair brushes on Pullmans.
4. The length of a Democratic convention.
5. The matter of paper towels.

If nominated I will fight either for or against any or all of these propositions.

In regards to the programme for the rest of the convention, why it seems that after the demonstration for Mr. Smith gets through they are going to nominate 12 other candidates if it takes all Summer and of course it will take most of the Summer because the keyhole speech makers as Grantland Rice has aptly named them will first half to find out how to spell their names.

It now looks like the convention would be finished by the 1 of September and who won't?

They are now nominating dark horses, and I have give them the following list:

> Zev.
> Man o' War.
> Morvich.
> Black Gold.
> Black Servvant.
> Old Dobbin.
> Black Beauty.

Along with these I would name one of the four horses that acted as mounts for the four horsemens of the apocolypse. In fact there is very few blonde horses when you come to think of it.

Well any ways we got into so called convention at ten

o'clock this a.m. and the boys begin to take votes for president. They got along great till they come to the state of Missouri and it seemed like the state of Missouri wanted to be polled, as they was afraid that none of us would know who was the delegates from Missouri. Most of the delegates was women folks and they wanted their names broughten out. I can't remember them just now.

Chairman Walsh finely ruled that Missouri ought to vote the way they want to vote, and after that the convention pepped up and went along a whole lot faster.

But on the third or fourth ballot a man from Hawaii said that out of the six votes to which Hawaii is entitled to, why three of them were for Smith, four for McAdoo, three for Underwood, 7 for David, two for Brown and the balance for some good ukelele player.

Charley Goddard, a delegate-at-large from Great Neck, Long Island, was around buying silk stockings for the delegates from his old home State of Washington. He took half a vote from Mary Todd, a National Committeewoman from that State.

Martin Maloney, from the same State of Washington, nominated me a few minutes later outside of the convention, but they was no demonstration. You can't have everything.

After they took about five ballots and was no nearer a choice then when they begin, why then the smart boys decided to hold a conference. I listened in on this and can report it verbatim. We will call the delegates Mr. Woose of Texas, Mr. Capidosia from Porto Rico and Mr. Quince from Whale, Minnesota. Here was their conference:

Woose—Have you found a place to buy good liquor in New York?

Capidosia—No.

Quince—What do you think of Washington being in first place?

Woose (who is hard of hearing)—Who?

Quince—Did you know that Washington was first?

Woose—Certainly. You ain't springing nothing new. He was first in peace, first in war and first in the hearts of his country men.

Quince—Have you eat since you come to New York?

Woose (who is hard of hearing)—Who?

Quince—I said, have you eat since you come to New York?

Woose—If I wanted to eat I would of stayed home.

Capidosia—Why did not you?

If I was a democrat and if it was me that was running this convention I would see to it that the thing did not drag out over the coming week-end.

Judging from the eagerness with which the visiting firemen has started out to see New York, why if it lasts any more than five or six days the voting strength of the party will be decimated by he whom I sometimes refer to as the grim reaper, and even if the boys is obliged to keep up the pace past Friday it will be hard to get them out of bed in time to vote at the November election.

Abel Woose, the neutral delegate from Gangrene, Texas, who was one of the leading spirits at the Cleveland convention, arrived in New York yesterday in a kiddy kar and at once went to his suite at the Aquarium which he is sharing with a salt mackerel.

"Well, Mr. Woose," I inquired, "how do you like the Big Town?"

"Can a duck swim?" said Mr. Woose. "I had not no

more than got off the train when two girls smiled at me."

"Are you sure they was not laughing?" I inquired.

"You seem to feel pretty fresh," said Mr. Woose.

"Well," I says, "anybody that can feel fresh after the Cleveland convention is a hot sketch."

Mr. Woose intends to present his own name to the convention here while the other delegates is out.

Speaking about presenting names, I have been asked by some of the leaders to allow them to present my name as a dark horse.

"You are dark," said one of them, "and you look a good deal like a horse."

I laughed off this flattery but seriously I would not be surprised if they was another landslide towards me like out in San Francisco when I developed unexpected strength along the 42nd ballot and got ½ a vote.

Some folks said it was just a complimentary vote while others said it was insulting.

Be that as it may, if conditions gets to be the same here like they was in San Francisco, they's no telling what will happen, and from all appearances this is going to make San Francisco look like a meeting of the ladies guild.

A good many of the other dark horses that has been mentioned won't say whether or not they would accept the socalled honor if nominated. Personally I don't think it is just or fair to keep your admirers in the dark in regards to your intentions and if you ain't got no intentions why come out and say so and give somebody else a chance.

As far as I am concerned, while I never sought political honors, why if my friends wants to run me, I will accept on one condition, namely that Mr. Coolidge withdraw.

The boys seem to be still stalling and it looks like a dark horse was a cinch in this convention. I hereby withdraw my name from the list of candidates, but that only goes till a week from next Tuesday. If at that time they still want me I will run but only on the condition that I specified yesterday, namely that Mr. Coolidge withdraws.

Mean wile, I have got another man in mind who I will gladly present to the visiting Kiwanians. He works on a morning N. Y. newspaper who I am afraid to name because one newspaper don't like to talk about another newspaper and I work for all three at the same time. This man's name is known to the public as Bugs Baer but I happen to know his real name and where he originated and all about him.

Willy Nilly Mr. Baer's real name is Jovial Whee. He was not born but come in on a train and they was nobody there to meet it as it was kind of late. He finely conceived the cute idear of calling up a funeral director and after a while the hearse come up to the station and picked up Mr. Whee.

"Where do you want to go?" asked Ralph, which was the driver's name.

"Don't mind me," replied Mr. Whee. "My country right or wrong, but still and all, my country."

This got a big laugh from a couple of stay-out-all-night dogs. They call them owls in the Middle West.

Now I presume my readers wants to know a little bit about the history of this candidate. In the first place Mr. Whee's father was a right thinking man who believed in God's great out of doors. He believed in it so much that after living with him two years the elder Mrs. Whee would not let him indoors. The offspring of this marriage was a whole lot like other children till he reached the age of two weeks; when he finely begun to talk out loud. Never will or should anybody forget the day when he got up out of his cradle and shaved himself out of a clear sky.

"That man will be President," remarked his nurse, who was hard of hearing.

Now gentlemen and lady delegates, I present the name of Bugs Baer alias Jovial Whee to this convention in the hopes you will pay no attention to it.

Joking to one side or the other, a great many people seems to want to know who am I in favor of in the case that neither Mr. Whee or myself stampedes the convention. Well gentlemen I can't possibly vote for a man named Smith or a man named Davis because suppose they would get elected and you would go down to Washington and try to call them up, why you would look in the telephone directory and they's a hundred Smiths and Davises who you might call up by mistake and then where would you be? Leave us have a man with a odd name so as when you ask information she will say oh you mean the President.

The following is a copy of a letter wrote yesterday by Delegate Abel Woose to his wife in Gangrene, Texas, and I might state at this junction that this is the first time he has wrote to her since he left Gangrene as a neutral delegate to both conventions. It should be explained that when Mr. Woose come away from home three weeks ago he was 72 years old and is now 103 years old and if this convention runs another couple weeks he will still be older. It will be noticed that the letter follows.

DEAR MOTHER. (He calls his wife mother).

Well mother I suppose you have been wandering what has became of me. Well mother would of wrote to you sooner only have been tied up with different committee meetings and etc.

Well mother we been having a great time here and so far it don't look like we was no more than started and I was talking to-day to a man named Jefferson from Kansas and he says Woose so far they have nominated all the democrats in the United States except Ed Fleming from Chicago and Bill Lange from San Francisco. He was just joking of course but they really have nominated most everybody and it looks like none of them had a chance to get nominated and we are libel to be here till the 1 of August and yesterday they was talking about nominating a girl for vice president and I says why don't they nominate a girl for president too and then her husband would be the first gentleman of the land. Those who overheard this remark laughed hardly.

It was while I was in a barber shop and I asked the barber to give me a shave but he says I could not shave a man like you with a razor, what you need is to be gone over with a thrashing machine. Everybody laughed but he finely shaved me and charged me 25 cents.

The boys is now trying to feign up a platform and they don't know whether to put in a plank vs. the Ku Klux Klan or not say nothing about it. I asked a man today from Michigan named Erskine that if they insist on putting in a plank vs. the klan why they should also ought to express their opinion of the Elks and Kiwanis. He laughed hardly.

Well mother tomorrow is Sunday and we will get a day of rest. I will try and write you another letter and in the meantime don't forget to water the whortle berries.

ABEL WOOSE.

The convention has now took a rest over Sunday and it ain't like they didn't need it. If they was a doctor in the house his advice to the delegates would be to stay quietly in bed a few days and try and sip down a little clam juice.

Newspaper men was yesterday recalling with terror a situation that came up in 1860 when the convention met in Charleston and took plenty of ballots and finally adjourned to Baltimore and took plenty of more ballots and then nominated Mr. Stephen A. Douglas and you know what happened to him. Well any ways please don't leave us adjourn to Baltimore this time and when I say that I don't mean that I have got anything vs. Baltimore but leave us adjourn to Great Neck, where a man can get a clean shirt and see their family.

The trouble with this convention seems to be that for the first time the women is practically running it and when I say that I don't mean nothing vs. the women, but you know how they are. They never stop to realize that anybody might be in a hurry to get home. And the queer part of that is that when it gets late enough at night, they all want to get home when nobody else does.

Well any ways the most of the gals in this convention so far has all appeared in short hair, but the most of we boys wished they would cut the convention short instead of their hair.

Well a few days ago Mrs. Izetta Brown from West

Virginia got up in bobbed hair and seconded the nomination of John W. Davis. Her plea was that he was a handsome man and this country should ought to have a handsome President. I felt like getting up out of what I laughingly call my seat and asking her why did not she second the nomination of Valentino or the younger of the Barrymore boys.

The next woman to get up was a Mrs. Barrett of Virginia, who seconded the nomination of Senator Glass. Everybody applauded her and in response to same she blew kisses instead of continuing to blow glass. Women ain't got no idear of time.

Any ways most of the women delegates and alternates is from out of town and they don't seem to be in no hurry to get home but some of the rest of us is and if the gals don't stop interrupting the proceedings why I for one will try and get the 19th amendment repealed so as women will half to remain in the home and men also.

Yesterday was supposed to be a day of rest and as far as I see it ain't been no different than all the rest of the days we have been having since this convention started and my suggestion is that the next time we have a Democrat convention, make all the delegates be men or women who have got some business to tend to as we can get home some time and go to work.

Woke up in time to go to what we are laughingly calling the convention and put on my badge which says active press on it and everybody that seen it and looked at bearer laughed outright.

Madison Square Garden was surrounded by what we

sometimes call a cordon of police, and they kept questioning my rights to be there and I was tempted one time to say something derogatory to Al Smith but thought of my insurance policies and the anti-suicide clause and decided to let nature take its course.

Well I run into a newspaper man from Washington and he says he thought it would be a good idear to nominate Al and have him run for president of New York and leave the rest of the country if any to Mr. Coolidge.

Went into the convention and run acrost a delegate from my old home state, Mr. Codd of Niles, Michigan. He wanted I should go into the Indiana delegation and get introduced to the boys from down home, but I figured they was having a tough enough time as it was.

As we entered the Garden somebody from Alabama or somewheres was presenting to the convention the name of somebody named Underwood and a good many stenographers cheered as they thought it was the man that makes the typewriters. A lady journalist on my left said she thought it would be grand to have the ticket consist of Underwood and Underwood and maybe we could all get our pictures taken in front of the White House. Girls will be girls.

The boss of the press stand handed me a letter from an admirer in Kansas to the effect that I should ought to be throwed in the ash can because I was trying to make a joke out of a serious convention. Coals to Newcastle is all I can think of to say in reply.

Now a good many of my half witted friends has asked me repeatedly what do I think of the outcome of this convention and who is going to be who and etc. Well friends it looks to me like along about Friday all the visiting firemen is bound to be broke and their wives will be sending them souvenir post cards to come home and milk the cow and etc. and the next name that is mentioned after that, why he will be nominated unanimously and the boys will hustle for their uppers and tickled to death to get back home and tell the rest of the boys what a big time they had in New York. And a few of them will even remember the name of the joint where they held the convention.

At a late hour last night I went down to the Aquarium to visit Neutral Delegate at Large, Mr. Abel Woose from Gangrene, Texas.

"Well, Mr. Woose," I said, "how are you enjoying the convention?"

He was out.

ON PROHIBITION

When it was suggested that I write something about prohibition, I snapped at the idea as a starving dog goes after a deck of cards. Here was a subject that had escaped the attention of other members of the writing graft, and you don't have to be so skillful in the handling of a given theme if the theme itself is sufficiently novel.

I thought I could tear off two or three thousand words almost as fast as I could type. I forgot that even a mental contact with the Demon or anything pertaining to same always filled me with an almost overwhelming desire to abstain from work for a period of thirty-four days. So the composition of this article has been a tough job and not a siesta, and I ask my friends to bear that in mind while they are thinking what a tough job it is to read it.

I do not believe I am betraying a confidence when I say that there are, in this country, several organizations whose aim is to effect the modification or repeal of the Eighteenth Amendment.

Nearly every citizen who isn't living under an assumed name has received invitations to join one or more of these tongs. If I have been asked once, I have been asked twice. But I have consistently declined to go into them because I figure it is silly to interfere in any way with the efforts of the Drys to knock their own pet legislation for a nose dive. If they fail, it will be time for outsiders to step in.

But they won't fail. They are experienced Gummers and we should be grateful that they are not enlisted on the side of some more salutary statute such as the one which restricts husband-killers to four kinds of dessert during the week of penal servitude.

The Drys of our land are to a large extent identical with the people who have fought the good fight for purity and decency in books and plays. If their war on rum is conducted only half as shrewdly as the struggle against literary and dramatic dirt, we boy scouts need have no fear. You can hardly name one legitimate show of the past season that could possibly give offense to any 125-year-old paralytic who was unable to attend it, and parents are safe in leaving a volume of Milne or Guest on the living-room table, while the children are away at kindergarten.

With a modicum of the same energy and skill applied to the anti-alcohol campaign, the Pros will soon have it fixed so a person can't buy a drink from a horse. It were folly for an amateur to offer advice to these needle-witted strategists, but it does seem to me that if the idea is to stop tippling by homicide, bigger results could be obtained, and at less expense, through the withdrawal of artillery and snipers from the border and the free and untrammeled admittance of all the stuff the consumer wants.

The price of what is screamingly called liquor would shortly drop to a point where even actors could afford it and the consequent fatalities would outnumber those resulting from the present system by at least a hundred to one.

Moreover, this sort of war of attrition would be carried on at little or no cost to the government; the customers would have to pay for their own demise unless they died before they settled, in which case the laugh would be on the bootlegger where it belongs.

But even if the current scheme is adhered to, I believe it should be carried out with more thoroughness and zeal.

In the first place it should be under the auspices of the War Department instead of the Secretary of the Treasury. Revolvers, shotguns, small-bore rifles, and pea-shooters ought to be supplanted by long-range cannon, and bullets that can kill only one man or child at a time, replaced by high explosives, shrapnel, and all the latest delicacies in the way of gas.

Electrically charged wire should guard the Canadian border from ocean to ocean and the Mexican border from the Pacific to the Gulf. Scout planes and observation balloons should locate Canada's distilleries and direct our shell fire, and the fields of hay from which the liquor is made could be destroyed by poisoned confetti.

The entire eastern half of the Dominion to the north of us might be inundated by a company of volunteers under Capt. Gertrude Ederle, who would stand at the bottom of Niagara Falls and splash the water back as fast as it came over. Our aces could drop souvenir post cards from George Creel assuring the Canadians that we have no quarrel with them as a nation, that all we want is peace without whisky, and that this is merely a war to make the United States safe for the soda fountains. An armistice would be granted, we'd tell them, as soon as they pledged themselves to eliminate entirely the alcoholic content of the stuff they have been selling to our importers. This would mean a reduction of nearly two per cent.

Some of the war-time regulations should be in effect once more. No meat on Mondays; no heat on Tuesdays; no sweet on Wednesdays; no wheat on Thursdays; no treat on Fridays, and no eat on Saturdays. Censorship of all mail passing between us and Canada and Mexico; four-minute speeches; adoption of Belgian orphans; purling; saving fingernail parings to fill in the shell holes on the Texas and the Minnesota thoroughfares.

I do think, though, that this war should be made much more bearable and entertaining to the stay-at-homes by the adoption of a liberal policy in regard to press dispatches. I never did understand what good was accomplished by the exclusion of the names of people and places from the dull, daily stories from France in 1917 and 1918.

The theory seemed to be that if the Grand Rapids *Herald* printed the news that Hendrik Van Hooten of Holland, Michigan, was in hospital at Chalons-sur-Marne with anthrax, a German spy employed by the Grand Rapids Furniture Company would call up the Kaiser who would thus suspect that a division containing Michigan regiments was, or had been, somewhere near Châlons. Wilhelm would then confer with Ludendorff on what style of defense to use against Michigan's passing game with Van Hooten on the sidelines.

Let's cut down on caution this time; the danger of

disclosing military secrets would be more than offset by the certainty of improving the country's morale with a few human-interest stories such as:

El Paso, Tex., Aug. 2—Corporal Charley Judson of Company B, Fourth Regiment of the Eighth (Hawkeye) Division, American Prohibitionary Force, was being congratulated by his buddies tonight for shooting the left ear off a two-year-old child who was crossing the bridge from Juarez with a peculiar waddling gait. Corporal Judson said he had witnesses to prove that the fellow had been seen drinking out of a bottle; he fired at his ear instead of his heart because he just wanted to frighten him. The bottle was found to contain a little over an ounce of a liquid identified as milk. "Yeh?" said the Corporal, who has a certain dry humor. "Well, milk don't make people walk funny."

Sault St. Marie, Mich., Aug. 2—Miss Muriel Chapin of this place was scattered all over the Northern Peninsula today by a machine-gun squad in charge of Capt. Felix Lord of Houghton. The captain picked up one of the girl's lips and showed it to his colonel, H. R. King of Calumet. The lip was a pale red. "That's what fooled me," said Captain Lord. "It's just some kind of rouge, but I thought it was grenadine."

Niagara Falls, N. Y., Aug. 2—A depth bomb dropped by Lieut. Ed. Frawley of Herkimer demolished a barrel that was seen shooting the Falls late today. Frawley suspected that the barrel was full of liquor, but it developed that the contents had been John E. Gardner and wife and two children, a Buffalo family out for an outing. "This was self-defense if there ever was one!" declared Lieut. Frawley. "I acted only after assuring myself that the barrel was shooting the Falls."

Plattsburg, N. Y., Aug. 2—A bearded man on a bicycle was stopped here today by Clarence Dutton, an M. P. of the A. P. F. Dutton demanded the man's name and the man said he was Eli Kolp, a farmer residing three miles south of Plattsburg.

"Then why are you wearing a beard?" asked Dutton.

"I look funny without one," replied the bicyclist.

"You look funny with one," retorted Dutton. "You look suspicious to me. How do I know what you've got in those tires?"

"I've got nothing but some air. I'll open them and let it out."

"I'll let some into you," said Dutton, shooting him full of holes.

The bicyclist was later identified as Eli Kolp, a farmer residing three miles south of Plattsburg.

CHILDREN, SOCIETY, AND DOGS

VISITING ROYALTY

FOR THE benefit of visiting firemen I would better exclaim what this is all about as near as I am able to judge from hearsay and reading newspapers.

Well it seems that a big bunch of the riff and raff has been horning their way into New York society the last year or two and things has come to such a pass that the elite was libel to find themself time after time attending partys which people that work for a liveing was also guests at same, with the result that high mucky mucks would half to rush home early and disinfect themself. Some hostesses has forgot their social standing to such a extent that they have included Indiana and Wisconsin born folks in their invitations. It has got so that a person of breeding and refinement don't hardly dast come out of the house for the fear of being spoke to by some scum that they had met the night before by mistake, and it certainly is a terrible thing to be crouped up at home without nobody but your own wife or husband to talk to.

Well a little wile ago, along sometime last summer a select group of our best includeing the queen Kleagle of the Colonial Dames of America got together and decided that it was time for a general shake-up which they would get rid of the vermin once and for all and make society look something like it used to forty years ago when the 400 come into being. At that time a prominent butcher's granddaughter-in-law or something give a party and left the inviteing to a gent friend that had the family history of everybody in America at both ends of his tongue. He issued just a even 400 invitations and made the remark that anybody not included in his list might consider themself permanently barred from organized society. The 400 and their assigns carried along the burden until a short time back, when as I say some brother Elks and Mooses begin to horn their way in and spoil the party.

Last summer the committee of chosen people consisting almost entirely of women of the opp. sex made up their mind to change the limit from 400 to 500 so as to let in a few families that had sold out their meat markets and livery barns and turned square since the last shuffle. The queen Kleagle was sent to Paris to meet some Royalties and invite them over here and get acquainted with the reconstructed elite. The first royalty to who a invitation was extended was the grand duchess Cyril of Russia whose husband will be Czar of Russia as soon as they decide to have Czars again. This event is scheduled to take place the same fall that Utica wins the pennant in the Cotton States League. They say that the Kleagle had to slip the duchess tres beaucoup francs for steamer fare and tips. When the good ship of Paris reached New York some months later the duchess disembarked by way of the steerage gangplank and most folks said how clever she was to outwit the newspaper boys and etc., but some of the deeper thinkers suspects that the reason she disembarked by way of the steerage gangplank was, well, on account of it being right there.

Now, the committee had this scheme worked out, namely, they was to announce that a party was to be give at the Monday Opera Club in honor of the Duchess, and whoever got a invitation to this party would know that they was numbered amongst God's chillun, wile they that didn't get no invitation was quarantined from now on. Personly—but anyway I had tickets that night for a hockey game.

Well they say that the Czarina was a terrific hit with everybody but the bellhops and other employees of the hotel where she was stopping and the hit was made in spite of the fact that they ain't no danger of Her Highness running Gloria Swanson out of the picture game.

But the main point is now society in New York has been reestablished on a solid basis. If you are in the Monday Opera 500 Club you belong. If you ain't you don't. On the nights they don't have royalties or dances they probably play 500, but anyway the scheme has done what the committee expected it to do, namely, to use their own words, "to preserve dignity and good breeding, otherwise there will be a social revolution here like the French revolution." Us boys and gals should certainly ought to feel grateful and personly, it's a big load off my mind.

During Cyril's stay over here she was accompanied every place she went by detective sergeants Brown, Kelly, and Herman of the bomb squad. These boys was going along for the nominal purposes to protect her vs. attacks of the rabid reds, some of the womenfolks was catty enough to say, however, that she was not afraid of no reds but haveing a male escort all the wile appealed to her on acct. of the novelty.

The future Czarina ain't the only notoriety that is going to be a guest of the club. Already they have hooked Queen Marie of Roumania, the duchesse de Vendome, head of the Bourbons who still hopes to regain the throne of France, though it is pretty near impossible to get Bourbon over here any more, and the grand duchess Xenia of Russia, who is a sister of the last Czar and the last Czar's cousin Michael, and the

Dowager Marchioness of Milford Haven, granddaughter of Queen Victoria.

When this list has run out we can look forward to visits from the Kaiser, the Crown Prince, Count Salm of Austria, Max Oser of the Royal Swiss Yodelers, and Prince Hari Singh, and if we coax hard enough maybe we can enjoy another call from Luis Angel Firpo and lady.

TABLE MANNERS

We are now bordering on the head end of the convention season and the hotel owners in Detroit and Atlantic City where practically all the conventions is held are prepareing for some by hireing extra house detectives and putting a padlock on their soap and towels.

Well I don't belong to nothing and don't expect to tend none of the conventions already scheduled, but will take the opportunity to tell my friends and admires that I would gladly be a delegate to a convention where something would be accomplished in addition to getting boiled, namely a convention to disgust and alter the code of etiquette as now practiced and a specially the rules that govern table manners besides a couple that governs the attitude of man to what is laughingly referred to as the fair sex.

If they's enough people thinks like I do along these lines I do not see no reason why we cannot all get together either at the City of Straits or America's playground as I have dubbed them and fix up a new code with some sense to it and do away with some of the regulations which is not only silly but border on the ridiculous and is rapidly makeing residents of the earth the laughing stalk of the solar system.

Let's take table manners and I will state some of my idears in regards to needed changes and one of the first that comes to mind is the Soup Rule which has been appealed to the Soupreme Court without getting a rumble and the rules I refer to is the rules which makes it a perennial offense to tip up your soup dish so as to get all the soup.

They ain't no man or woman liveing that can pick up all their soup from a flat lie useing only a spoon and the result is that from 1/10 to a ½ an inch is always left laying in the bottom of the dish which is plane waste as the most economical Jap in the world cannot do nothing with left over soup only throw it in the ash can.

A convention of right thinking Americans would specialize on the Soup Rule and make it permissible to tip the dish to any safe and reasonable angle so as to satisfy a legal thirst for a good sound non alcoholic beverage.

The next rule that is in dire need of alterations is the rule in regards to bread and butter. According to the code in usages in exclusive Great Neck homes it is O.K. to take a whole chunk of toast and smear it with butter or any good substitute but when it comes to plain bread why then you half to break it in a couple pieces and lay the pieces on your bread and butter plate which is generally always a full arm's length away and smear them while they lay there, but you mustn't smear the both of them at once but just the piece which you pick out to start in on.

The theory in back of this rule is that maybe you won't want only the one piece and if you leave the other one unbuttered why it can be salvaged and maybe used the following week in the kid's pudding.

That is the theory and all guests recognizes it, but when they follow it out it is just like say to the house wife you are a cheap skate and further and more wile a person may get through with one buttering operation unscathed, it is too much to expect to do it twice and keep your sleeves their natural color.

The convention would give this rule the air and advocate the free and unlimited smearing of whole pieces of bread either held in the hand or laid on the table which ever makes the greatest appeal.

The convention would ask for waivers on the finger bowl which ain't proved no case and should be throwed out of court. In the first place when the hostess allows finger bowls to be passed around she as much as tells you outright that you have been fondling a chicken bone with the bare hands or that they's a relict of mushroom sauce on the lower lip.

A man with a drop of red he-blood in their veins resents this and personly my fingers has yet to sully themselfs by straying into a finger bowl and will state without bragging that I always leave the table with hands practically as clean as when I set down unlest of course they was corn or steam clams or something and in the last named case nothing short of a bath tub will relieve the situation.

Under the present regime mine hostess, without I yes or no from the guests, takes it for granted that a man can get along on a ½ demitasse of coffee and wait till a ½ after 9 for same.

The convention would compel all hostesses to find out at the start of the meal if they's any real coffee stews amongst her guests and treat them accordingly.

Personly when I get a invitation to dinner, unles it comes from some right minded hostess like Katie Hollis, for inst., why I reply with a well modulated but firm No as I do not enjoy a evening of bridge with headache for a partner.

This will maybe exclaim why I refuse so many invitations and perhaps cause many a broken heart.

Now in regards to a couple of rules governing man and woman. To state the matter briefly on acct. of the lateness of the hr. I would ask the convention to change the following rules:

1. The rule which compels a perfect gent to get up and give a lady a seat on a subway or elevated train or st. car. A great many perfect gentlemen is floor walkers and barbers, a job where you half to be on your ft. all day. A great many ladys is stenographers and very few of them does their typewriting standing up. More gentlemen than ladys deserves a seat and the rule should ought to be fixed so as when a dame gets on a car she must state the nature of her employment. If she has got a setting down job let her ride home on a strap. This amendment would be more than justice on the grounds that if it was not for men everybody would half to walk home, at least I have never heard of a traction system being built by the hands that rocks a cradle.

2. The rule which forbids a gentleman from hanging up the receiver till the lady says goodbye. All that is ever nessary for a gentleman and lady to say to each other can certainly be said in 3 minutes at the outside but the way it is now the average telephone conversation between the 2 sexes lasts from 30 minutes to a ½ hr. because the lady in question ain't got nothing else to do and hates to give in and the only party that benefits by the rule is the telephone company, and the last I heard about them, they didn't need no benefits.

OPENING REMARKS

Some weeks ago I had a few words to say in regards to formal dinner partys and what kind of a table to set for same and since then I been beseiged with letters from readers beseiging me to devote more articles to social etiquette and as more than one of these letters makes special mention of introductions I may as well devote this article to that subject.

One reader enclosed me a copy of a article on this subject by Mrs. Julia Hoyt of N.Y. city who is supposed to be the last word in decorums of all kinds but the article in question left many pts. to be cleared up at lease in the opinion of the party who sent it in and the last named wanted I should clarify these matters and also state what changes if any has been made in the code since Mrs. Hoyt's article seen print.

One pt. for inst. which the lady didn't even touch on was the matter of introduceing two people to each other when you don't know neither one's name.

This used to happen a lot more in the old days when people done their drinking standing up but they is still plenty of occasions when this embarrassing situation arises a specially in Pullman wash rooms or at a national convention of the moose.

I always kind of laugh it off and say something to the effect that you 2 boys knows each other of course and they generally tells one another what their name is which also gives me a clew.

Mrs. Hoyt gives it as a general rule that when you are makeing a plain introduction you just say "Mrs. Reed, Mrs. Wallace" unlest of course their names happens to be Mrs. Pinkney and Mrs. Welsh. But she says that when one woman is a young woman and the other one ain't so young, why the young one should ought to be presented to the older one, so if Mrs. Wallace is older than Mrs. Reed you half got to say "Mrs. Wallace, Mrs. Reed."

Now days however what with the beauty parlor and funny clothes it ain't always possible to be sure and a person would be a sucker to go ahead with the introductions without first asking the 2 dames which is the oldest.

According to Mrs. Hoyt's article when a man and woman is introduced the woman ain't required to shake hands unlest the guy sticks out his hand, but if he does so it is very rude for the woman to not grab a hold of it.

Personly however I have been introduced to many a dame that must have thought I was holding out my hand so as she could admire the callouses or something and I been humiliated so many times along these lines that now days when they's a dame being introduced to me I always pretend like I was unloosening my belt or looking through my vest pockets for a tooth pick.

It is well to remember then when the party who is makeing the introduction says "Mr. Bolling, shake hands with Mrs. Gavin," that don't neserally mean that you got to shake hands. The introducer ain't any authority to designate the mode of caress and irregardless of whatever he says you are free to put your arm around Mrs. Gavin or slap her face or ignore her entirely.

The reader who sent me Mrs. Hoyt's article marked one paragraph which she says has got her all up in the air, namely the paragraph where it says that if you are presenting your married daughter to a older man you have got to say "My daughter, Mrs. Reed."

She says that since reading the article she has had numerable occasions to introduce her daughter to old galoots and when she springs that "Mrs. Reed" they all think she is ginny as it is a notorious fact that the name of the man her daughter married is Eyclesheimer. Of course in cases like this you have to use your own judgement and as far as I am conserned I would be a whole lot more libel to think that a woman was ½ seas over if she told me her daughter's name was Mrs. Eyclesheimer.

Mrs. Hoyt's article goes on to say that when you present anybody to the President you are supposed to say "Mr. President, I have the honor to present Mr. Burke of San Francisco." But when you introduce him to a Cardinal, you must say "Your Eminence, may I present Mr. Burke?"

My reader don't think it's hardly fair to tell the President where Mr. Burke is from but to keep it a secret from the Cardinal, but personly it looks to me like this was makeing a mt. out of a mole hill because if Mr. Burke is really from San Francisco, the dialogue ain't libel to continue more than 2 or 3 hrs. before the Cardinal might of suspects same.

It is the worst kind of form to ask the introducer to say a name over when you don't catch it the first time but they's a way to get around this. Like for inst. suppose you are introduced to a pretty gal and you ain't got no idear what the man said her name was, why all as you have to do is say, "I am certainly pleased to meet you Miss Gourmand" or some such name and she will say "My name is Andrews please."

In closeing up her article Mrs. Hoyt gives a list of don'ts in introductions and amongst them she says don't ask any personal questions the moment after you have been introduced. A great many people might have different ideas in regards to what is a personal question as used in this connection and no doubt some poor hicks will draw the line too fine and refrain from asking questions which might of been regarded as too personal in the old days but would be O.K. now.

Maybe I better wind up this article of mine by giveing a couple examples of what kind of questions not to ask and what kind is perfectly permissable.

Well then we will pretend like you have just been introduced to a man named Harley. Don't say to him "Glad to meet you, Mr. Harley. Do you and your wife get along all right?" Or "Glad to know you Mr. Harley. What makes you limp?"

But do say if you feel like it, "Pleased to meet you Mr. Harley. Got anything on the hip?"

DOGS

Every little wile you hear people talking about a man that they don't nobody seem to have much use for him on acct. of him not paying his debts or beating his wife or something and everybody takes a rap at him about this and that until finely one of the party speaks up and says they must be some good in him because he likes animals.

"A man can't be all bad when he is so kind to dogs." That is what they generally always say and that is the reason you see so many men stop on the st. when they see a dog and pet it because they figure that may be somebody will be looking at them do it, and the next time they are getting panned, why who ever seen it will speak up and say:

"He can't be all bad because he likes dogs."

Well friends when you come right down to cases they's about as much sence to this as a good many other delusions that we got here in this country, like for inst. the one about nobody wanting to win the first pot and the one about the whole lot of authors not being able to do their best work unlest they are ½ pickled.

But if liking animals ain't a virtue in itself I don't see how it proves that a man has got any virtues, and personly if I had a daughter and she wanted to get marred and I asked her what kind of a bird the guy was and she said she don't know nothing about him except that one day she seen him kiss a leopard, why I would hold up my blessing till a few of the missing precincts was heard from.

But as long as our best people has got it in their skull that a friendly feeling toward dumb brutes takes the curse off of a bad egg, why I or nobody else is going to be a sucker enough to come out and admit that all the horses, rams, and oxen in the world could drop dead tomorrow morning without us batting an eye.

Pretty near everybody wants to be well thought of and if liking dogs or sheep is a help along these lines, why even if I don't like them, I wouldn't never loose a opportunity to be seen in their company and act as if I was haveing the time of my life.

But while I was raised in a kennel, you might say, and some of my most intimate childhood friends was of the canine gender, still in all I believe dogs is better in some climates than others, the same as oysters, and I don't think it should ought to be held against a man if he don't feel the same towards N.Y. dogs as he felt towards Michigan dogs, and I am free to confess that the 4 dogs who I have grew to know personly here on Long Island has failed to arouse tender yearnings any-ways near similar to those inspired by the flea bearers of my youth.

And in case they should be any tendency on the part of my readers to denounce me for failing to respond whole heartily to the wiles of the Long Island breed let me present a brief sketch of some so as true lovers of the canine tribe can judge for themselfs if the fault is all mind.

No. 1

This was the dainty boy that belonged to Gene Buck and it was a bull dog no bigger than a 2 car garage and it wouldn't harm a hair of nobody's head only other animals and people. Children were as safe with this pet as walking in the Pittsburgh freight yards and he wouldn't think of no more wronging a cat than scratching himself.

In fairness to Mr. Buck I'll state that a pal of his give him the dog as a present without no comment. Well they wasn't no trouble till Gene had the dog pretty near ½ hr. when they let him out. He was gone 10 minutes during which Gene received a couple of phone calls announcing more in anger than in sorrow the sudden deaths of 2 adjacent cats of noble berth so when the dog come back Gene spanked him and give him a terrible scolding and after that he didn't kill no more cats except when he got outdoors.

But the next day De Wolf Hopper come over to call and brought his kid which the dog thought would look better with one leg and it took 5 people to get him not to operate, so after that Gene called up the supt. of a dogs reform school and the man said he would take him and cure him of the cat habit by tying one of his victims around his neck and leaving it there for a wk. but he didn't know how to cure the taste for young Hoppers unlest De Wolf could spare the kid the wk. after they was finished with the cat.

This proposition fell through but anyway Gene sent the dog to the reformatory and is still paying board for same.

No. 2

The people that lived 3 houses from the undersigned decided to move to England where it seems like you can't take dogs no more so they asked us did we want the dog as it was very nice around children and we took it and sure enough it was O.K. in regards to children but it shared this new owners feeling towards motorcycles and every time one went past the house the dog would run out and spill the contents, and on Sundays when the traffic was heavy they would sometimes be as many as 4 or 5 motorcycle jehus standing on their heads in the middle of the road.

One of them finely took offence and told on the dog and the justice of the peace called me up and said I would have to kill it within 24 hrs. and the only way I could think of to do same was drown it in the bath tub and if you done that, why the bath tub wouldn't be no good no more because it was a good sized dog and no matter how often you pulled the stopper it would still be there.

No. 3

The next-door neighbors has a pro-German police dog that win a blue ribbon once but now it acts as body guard for the lady of the house and one day we was over there and the host says to slap his Mrs. on the arm and see what happened so I slapped her on the arm and I can still show you what happened.

When you dance with mine hostess this sweet little pet dances right along with you and watches your step and if you tred on my ladys toe he fines you a mouth full and if you and her is partners in a bridge game he lays under the table and you either bid right and play right or you get nipped.

No. 4

This is our present incumbrance which we didn't ask for him and nobody give him to us but here he is and he has got the insomonia and he has picked a spot outside my window to enjoy it but not only that but he has learnt that if you jump at a screen often enough it will finely give way and the result is that they ain't a door or window on the first floor that you couldn't drive a rhinoceros through it and all the bugs that didn't already live in the house is moveing in and bringing their family.

That is a true record of the dogs who I have met since takeing up my abode in Nassau county so when people ask me do I like dogs I say I'm crazy about them and I think they are all right in their place but it ain't Long Island.

AN INFANT INDUSTRY

OFF COLOR

No Visitors, N. Y.

You CAN count on the fingers of one thumb the present-day writers of song words who could wear becomingly the mantle of W. S. Gilbert, or even the squirrel neckpiece of Ira Gershwin. Some of them should be fitted out with rompers, the costume for which their birth, bringing-up, and education qualify them; some with sturdy boys' suits appropriate for children belonging in the third, fourth, and fifth grades. Some ought to be garbed in the nightgowns, pajamas, and lounging robes provided for rest cases at Bellevue. And a few, I am afraid, would feel at home only in strait-jackets.

This department has been laughed at for prudishness, but has not been laughed out of it. This department has reached a stage where it almost doesn't mind a song whose only faults are inanity, terrible rhyming, and glaring infractions of simple grammatical rules. Unfortunately, the "lyricists," the singers, and the whimperers are not satisfied with that comparatively harmless kind. They are polluting the once-pure air of Golly's great out-of-doors with a gas barrage of the most suggestive songs ever conceived, published, and plugged in one year.

Weeks ago in these fascinating columns, I wrote to the effect that it seemed silly for radio to bar words like God, Hell, and damn and to permit the "comedians" to get by with gags running the gamut from vulgar to vile, and the singers to use the unmistakably off-color

"Paradise" and the flagrantly immoral "As You Desire Me." In that piece, I charged Ray Perkins with unnecessary roughness, and a more or less amicable correspondence between us left him unconvinced and me pretty sad. N.B.C. asked Allie Wrubel, author of "As You Desire Me," to rewrite his refrain, cleaning it up. The rewritten version means absolutely nothing, but surely we can't complain of that. Mr. Wrubel charged me good-naturedly with responsibility for the N.B.C. edict. I hope I was guilty. But the boys in the Columbia studios didn't read my stuff that week and their singers (notably Charles Carlile, who ought to know better) still stick to the original mess. The melody, also by Mr. Wrubel, is pretty enough to deserve what it is getting: a much longer life than is usual under the radio regime.

Perhaps you wonder why I revive this tedious subject when there is so little chance of a queasy crusader making headway. There are several reasons, and one is that Mr. Wrubel and the authors of "Paradise" ought not to be the only boys criticized when scores of their fellow-geniuses are trying their worst (and with ever-increasing signs of ultimate success) to outsmut them. Another reason is that, queer as it may seem, I don't like indecency in song or story, and sex appeal employed for financial gain in this manner makes me madder than anything except fruit salad. Reason 3: A large percentage of the invisible audience is composed of old people who retain the faculty of being shocked and of children between the ages of nine and sixteen who are not morally damaged by the words Hell, damn, and God, but can't help wondering what the heck when they hear songs that glorify defiance of the seventh amendment to Moses' constitution. Reason 4: A curiosity as to whether there is such a thing as radio censorship, and if so, whether those in charge of it are morons themselves or simply don't know what is what and what is not; and whether they will take the hint lying down when their attention is called to this squawk, as it shall be. Reason 5: A curiosity as to whether the sponsors and their advertising agencies are just plain dumb or as broad as the ocean and as lewd as the sky. Reason 6: Something happened on a very recent Sunday night which rekindled the smoldering ashes of offended prudery and forced me to mention the six-letter surname of a New Testament character with such volume that even the nurse woke up.

The stations I usually play are WEAF, WOR, WJZ, and WABC. Tuning in first on WABC, I found myself listening to a risqué song. Tuning in on WJZ, I heard another one. Similar thrills were waiting on WOR and WEAF, and it was then that I lost control of my tongue and frightened poor Miss Graham out of her nap and her cap. An apology and an explanation were in order.

"Well," she said, "it's Sunday. They probably thought of that and now they're celebrating the Fourth Commandment, which begins [she whisked out the midget Bible that she carries in her hypo case]: 'Remember that thou keep holy the Sabbath Day' and ends: 'Wherefore the Lord blessed the Sabbath Day and hallowed it.'"

Now, I won't put your credulity to a test by averring that there was nothing except risqué songs on the four stations that night, but between speeches and risqué jokes, the boys and girls managed to crowd in a flock of numbers that were "questionable" in title, or in one or more lines, or in toto. I took down a few titles and print them here so that when you go Christmas shopping, you can visit your favorite music store and buy something educational to read aloud or sing to the baby. Some of them may be classified as bedtime stories, as you will see when you get them. Ready?

"I'll Never Have to Dream Again," "You're Telling Me," "Good Night, My Lady Love," "Pu-leeze! Mister Hemingway!" (a swell tune and a good idea, marred by two or three words), "You Little So-and-So," "Forbidden Love," "Let's Put Out the Lights and Go to Sleep" (just on the border. They say that in the original lyric, the last word was not "sleep"), "Love Me Tonight," "I'm Yours for Tonight," "Horses Carry Tales" (sung by what I thought was a new Negro quartet which could make "Rock of Ages" sound nasty), "Bring 'Em Back Alive," "And So to Bed" (an ingenious finishing touch), "Please," "Take Me in Your Arms," "Here Lies Love," and "What Did I Get in Return?"

Others you might buy, if the kid is bored by those I have named, are "Ain'tcha Kinda Sorry Now?" and "Thrill Me!" The latter I have not yet heard on the air, but I expect to, for it probably touches a new low for the year. A copy of this number ought to be in every right-thinking, kiddy-loving American home. Why, the refrain goes: "Thrill me with a kiss that's vicious with love delicious . . ." No, I won't spoil a sale. And I'll try hard not to feel so comstocky next time.

A CROONER

No Visitors, N. Y.

The following is For Men Only, because the main topics to be discussed are Rudy Vallée and (am I versatile!) suggestive songs. Ladies naturally shrink from the latter as comedians from a stolen joke, and my encomium of Rudy may not be enthusiastic enough to satisfy those of his adorers who can read print.

Before you gents doze off, let me remind you that the Fleischmann Yeast Hour (Thursday nights on WEAF, eight to nine) seldom runs worse than one-two-three in the week's radio derby, and twice during January was clearly entitled to first place, not only in my opinion but in that of two literate persons with whom I got acquainted by mistake.

The Hour is planned, rehearsed, and directed by Mr. Vallée. His orchestra plays popular melodies, he sings popular songs (few of which would be passed as one-hundred-per-cent O.K. by prude, grammarian, the late W. S. Gilbert, Tune Detective Sig Spaeth, or, in fact, anybody in his right mind), and he offers really worth-while entertainment by guest artists with Names: Eva Le Gallienne and Joseph Schildkraut, Beatrice Lillie, George Gershwin, Victor Moore, Frieda Inescort and Selena Royle, Sophie Tucker, Marie Dressler, June Walker and Geoffrey Kerr, Milton Berle, Gracie Allen (charge an error to the N.B.C.), Ken Murray, Colin Keith-Johnston, Fannie Brice. There is always a good balance of comedy, drama, and song, and the care Rudy takes to maintain this balance was demonstrated as recently as four Thursdays ago, when Dr. R. E. Lee was too sick to appear and Gracie Allen, a Columbia networker, batted for him and virtually stole the show. I don't mean that Gracie imitated the Doc; she was herself, and she was so funny that you didn't miss him.

Dr. Lee, if you don't know, is the only regular on Rudy's program excepting Rudy and his orchestra and James Wallington, the announcer. The Doc extols fresh yeast as a promoter of health, and on Sunday nights he pops up in Eddie Cantor's Hour and says it's all right to drink large quantities of coffee if the coffee is dated. I am not a yeast-bibber, but I tried to sell Doc Lee's coffee talk to my own doc, Dr. Tyson, and didn't get halfway to first base. Dr. Tyson is a joiner and belongs to the American Medical Association. Dr. Lee doesn't even belong to the Coffee House. My doc gave me a copy of the Association's *Journal*, and what it said— Well, Dr. Lee may have seen a copy himself. It may have been what made him sick.

Miss Graham, reading my stuff while I drink undated cocoa, remarks that I seem to have strayed from the threatened topics: Rudy and suggestive songs. Before I return to them, allow me to establish by Rudy's own words that his judgment isn't always infallible. In introducing Ken Murray, he said that the latter was to vaudeville what Charlie Chaplin was to pictures. Let's reply to that with a couple of questions: If Chaplin (Golly forbid!) were to die a natural death tonight, on what page would you find the news in tomorrow morning's paper? If Ken Murray (Golly forbid!) were, etc? Example 2: In speaking of "Lullaby of the Leaves" as one of the outstanding songs of 1932, he called attention to the blending of a beautiful tune, which it certainly is, whether the lady consulted with Brahms or not, and a great lyric, which— Well, listen:

> I'm breezing along, along with the breeze,
> I'm hearing a song, a song thru the trees,
> Ooh ooh ooh ooh ooh ooh.
> That pine melody caressing the shore
> Familiar to me, I've heard it before,
> Ooh ooh ooh ooh.

Now then, on a Thursday night not so long ago ooh ooh, I was tuned in on Rudy's program, as is customary with me and other discerning radio addicts, when suddenly it dawned on me that the young man had lost his temper; he was quite ooh ooh ooh because someone had impugned the modesty of "Let's Put Out the Lights and

Go to Sleep," *née* "Bed." The title was familiar to me or possibly I had heard it before; possibly I had heard the song itself, and blushed over it in these very columns, and here was Rudy all hot and bothered, saying it was perfectly decent, having been written by a friend of his, and that he (Rudy) was about to sing it, presumably as incontrovertible evidence of its purity, or perhaps to purge it with the hyssop of his immaculate larynx.

Mr. Vallée, let's put out the fire and go to midyear exams. (1) Did you ever sing "Paradise" before comparatively harmless words were put in where Mms and Whistles made the number charmingly suggestive, and if so, did you give a damn? (2) Arthur Ruhl, writing in *The Herald Tribune* under the name of Percy Hammond, commented as follows on your friend's spotless number: "The favorite song of the 'Music Hall Varieties' is an idyll entitled 'Let's Put Out the Lights and Go to Bed.' Sung expressively by Mr. Lahr, Mr. Richman, and the blushing Miss Damita, it leaves none of its innocent hearers in doubt about the facts of creation and recreation." And an anonymous contributor to the publication you are now reading told this story: "A frantic little niece of ours went into a music store on Broadway the other day to buy a song she had heard over the radio. (There is a touch of the pixie in her.) When she got to the counter, she hesitated. Immediately the clerk handed her 'Let's Put Out the Lights and Go to Sleep.' 'How did you know that was what I wanted?' she asked, piqued. 'You hesitated,' he said. 'They all do.'" Is alias Mr. Hammond dumb? Does the anonymous uncle sound as if he were half-witted? (3) In the middle of the refrain occur four sentimental lines beginning, as I recall them, "I'm waiting now for you to say," and ending "You never were as sweet before, dear." Considering these lines, spotted as they are, is your friend c-c-razy or is he hinting at romance? (4) Did you really go to Yale?

Anyway, Rudy, neither you nor your friend ought to be mad at Hammond or the uncle or the undersigned for hinting that "Lights" was low. The lady who runs the music store in Wellesley (that's near Boston, and a girls' school is located there ooh ooh) wrote and thanked me, at least, for my pressagentry, saying that more prospective customers than she thought existed had overwhelmed her with orders for the sheet music and pornograph records. Is the author of "Sitting in the Dark" another pal? Good night, Ohman and Arden dear.

RUNNING COMMENT

Nowheres, Calif.

These lines are being written in the middle of a desert whose violet rays are so ultra that if you try to use your receiving set between dawn and the hour when the sun goes over the mountain, you can't get anything but mad. Of course that's about all you can get in the New York district during the day, but the fact that it's usually three hours later there than here makes a disastrous difference. It means I must miss nearly a half-hour of Eddie Cantor and the same amount of Rudy, and in each case a monologue by Dr. R. E. Lee, who compels admiration by never waiting for his laughs. "You will have to be ultra amusing between five and five-thirty every Thursday and Sunday," I said to my wife (a former *Follies* girl) the other evening. "Oh, yeah?" she said.

Fortunately, the first Thursday we were here, the rays stopped interfering in time to permit us to listen to Mr. Vallée's own light-opera company sing its abbreviated *Tales of Hoffman,* and to Mr. Vallée himself vocalize the familiar "Barcarolle." As a result, I hasten to apologize for anything I ever wrote of him that may have seemed captious and I hereby vote him the Olympic and All-American, Intercollegiate and A. A. U. medals for Nerve.

Radio, I must admit, is hard to do without when a person is too old to work, too shallow-brained to read much, and too timid to try the only outdoor sport the place has to offer—horseback-riding. The proprietor swears that the horses are all desert-minded, but the undersigned, when only eleven, fell off a Michigan-minded horse of twice that age, landed on everything but his feet, and cried so hard that his sister (a former *Follies* girl) is still ashamed of him. He has never been on a horse since, except financially, and the ones he has been on that-a-way have made him cry, too. So the daylight hours occasionally drag and I feel like saying Golly darn the violet rays for coming between me and Breen and De Rose, Ann Leaf at the Organ, The Singing Lady, and the Road Report of the Motor League of South Texas.

After eight p.m. Pacific Time, I am dependent on Coast, near-Coast, and Mexican stations, and they provide a little good dance music and any quantity of after-dinner speeches, sermons, and prayers. This section of Van Loon's Geography must be largely populated by heathen and bums. There is scarcely a minute any evening when you aren't having your soul saved or at least prayed for by someone in Los Angeles, San Francisco, Salt Lake City, or Dallas, and if you don't go be bed shriven, it's because you can't be shrove.

Anyway, I have had a chance to catch up with my pan mail, as Miss Graham (a former *Follies* girl) used to call it. Of the five letters received since New Year's, three want to know why I don't, etc. A Mr. Howell Rickman, Jr., of the Asheville Rickmans, is a bit upset because I haven't mentioned Fred Hufsmith, "the best tenor on the air." Well, Junior, I have been too busy with the worst tenors on the air, and when I think of all the performers (very few of them tenors) whom I have intended to mention and haven't had time or space for, why I could just break down. Please consider Mr. Hufsmith mentioned and let me say, before it gets any later, that I like Gus Van, Fred Allen, Roy Atwell, Chico and Groucho Marx, Frank Crumit and Julia Sanderson (nearly all former *Follies* girls), the last-named pair especially when they have Irvin Cobb of the Parducar Cobbs as guest or when Frank sings songs my age, such as "Lamb, Lamb, Lamb"—which reminds me that he is my Shepherd, I shall not want.

In my humble opinion (this is one of M. Vallée's favorite expressions and I am just as sincere as he with the adjective), old Gus Van is as versatile and valuable a guy as can be got under two or five thousand dollars a week, and I hope that my admiration for him doesn't put him in bad with the desert-minded sponsors. As for Fred Allen, I claim credit for a bit of acumen in his case. He went on the air at a time when I was trying to keep up-to-date. I was going to review his first performance, but after hearing it, decided to lay off. And I postponed comment after Performance No. 2. He simply hadn't got started, and why make a sap of myself by riding him when I was sure that his originality and good comedy sense would bring him through? Was I correct? As always.

But it's three or four months now since he began clicking and I will throw caution to the winds, predicting that he is up there to stay and revealing, while he is being discussed, that his name at birth was Sullivan and he was christened Florence (possibly a former *Follies* girl). Roy Atwell is a big help to Fred's program, and if I hadn't heard him, and you were to tell me that his funniness consisted in garbling words and phrases, I would say, oh, shut up. But I have heard him and it's true and I won't say shut up or scram or anything else risqué.

Which brings us to another why-don't-you letter. This one is signed by a fellow who has forgotten his name. He says, "If you are so opposed to suggestive songs, why don't you quit listening to them?" Well, old Poison Pen, I bet you think that'll make me toss in a towel. It does kind of stagger me because it's so novel, like a comic kidding an orchestra leader or something. But I pack a mean surprise or two myself. For instance, I listen to them because they have a way of popping up on programs that are otherwise entertaining though clean, and for instance, the announcer hardly ever prefaces these programs with a warning not to listen at first, but to wait four and a half minutes till a couple of smutty new numbers have been sung, and for instance, just recently I recommended Gracie Allen to two friends, as I seem to be always doing; the two friends are of Miss Allen's sex, but as prudish as I; Miss Allen is certainly the funniest girl on the air (Miss Brice may give her some competition) and besides is the best evidence I know of that a real comic can make you laugh without making you blush. The musical part of the program (sponsored by Robert Burns Cigars) is generally harmless if you don't mind saxophonists who live in a state of doubt. But harken:

The program following this particular recommendation opened with the saxophonists (Guy Lombardo's) doing their stuff; then suddenly a singer as anonymous as my correspondent was in the midst of a refrain which that Great Genius Noel Coward wouldn't have written, though maybe he did. The title, I think, was "I'm Young and Healthy." That's all I will tell you about it and it ought to be enough.

What, three letters still unanswered? To H—— with them.

NIGHT AND DAY

Do Not Disturb, N. Y.

Nearly a year ago this department was expressing its admiration for the line "Let come what may" in the refrain of Allie Wrubel's nursery rhyme, "As You Desire Me." It struck me as perfect when it first came over the air, but in order to make sure of its perfection, I tried to improve it and asked my four spawn to do the same. Our efforts, including "Leave come what may," "Let may what come," "How come leave may," etc., were cast aside as inferior to the original, and the latter was ranked high gun (a high-gun expression) in our love nest until we heard an anthem entitled "It's Just a Little Street," or "Where Old Friends Meet," or both.

As in Mr. Wrubel's number, the stand-out line of this one occurred in the midst of the proceedings. It was, as I recall it, "Although I'm rich or poor, I still feel sure I'm welcome as the flow'rs in May." Once more I summoned the whippersnappers and conferred with them on a possible substitute for "Although" which would convey a similar meaning and add to the sublimity of the lyric. My own candidate, "What ho," was voted down as too risqué, but before that defect was discovered by a prowling helpmeet, the boys thought old daddy had again come through in a pinch, and John, the eldest, was about to lead the famous victory yell—"Old Daddy! Old Daddy!" (All respire.)

Consideration was given to "Except," suggested by

James (Jake the Barber) Lardner, and to "Suppose," which David (Winnie-the-Pooh) Lardner submitted. Both were discarded for not being in modern usage as conjunctions. Bill (Jake the Barber) Lardner was in one of his ribald moods and would offer nothing but "Hotcha," which didn't even scan. John (Winnie-the-Pooh) Lardner finally hit on a couple of likely ones— "Unless" and "Until"—and now, when the five of us get together for a sing, we frequently employ one or the other, preferably the other, as a replacement for "Although." Thus: "Unless I'm rich or poor, I still feel sure," and so on. But we do this merely for variety, not because we think we have improved on "Although."

The "Little Street" enjoyed a long radio life, a fact that ought to silence those pessimists who argue that a song can't last unless it's got something. However, it is seldom heard now, and the foregoing discussion was just a prelude to some stuff about the song "Night and Day," which continues to thrive on its own merits and because Freddie Astaire refused to believe the obituary notices of *Gay Divorce*, the show in which it is featured.

You must know that Mr. Cole Porter, lyricist of "Night and Day," shares the mantle of W. S. Gilbert with Ira Gershwin, Lorenz Hart, Irving Caesar, Irving Berlin, Joseph V. McKee, Howard Dietz, Bert Kalmar, George M. Cohan, Gus Kahn, Primo Carnera, and George Herman (Columbia Lou) Gehrig. Well, it seems to me that in this number, Mr. Porter not only makes a monkey of his contemporaries but shows up Gilbert himself as a seventh-rate Gertrude Stein, and he does it all with one couplet, held back till late in the refrain and then delivered as a final, convincing sock in the ear, an ear already flopping from the sheer magnificence of the lines that have preceded. I reprint the couplet:

Night and day under the hide of me
There's an Oh, such a hungry yearning, burning inside of
    me.

So what? Well, I have heard the song only by radio,
and those whom I have heard repeat the refrain have
sung that immortal couplet the same both times. Fortunate friends who have seen *Gay Divorce* report that
the number is generously encored and reprised, and as
a matter of course, most of the encores are pedal, not
vocal. When they are vocal, the words are not changed.

Again, so what? Well, just as the apparently perfect
lines in the Wrubel song and the "Little Street" courted
an attempt at improvement, so did this superb couplet
of Mr. Porter's, and though the attempt is as much of
a failure as the others, the fact that the song is still being sung on stage and air encourages me to publish a
few modifications to which Freddie and the radio artists
are welcome if ever they tire of the original.

This time my own kiddies were left out of the conference, most of them being away at school, taking a
course in cuts. A little niece of mine, Miss Ann (Jake
the Barber) Tobin of Niles, Mich., was the only party
consulted. We agreed that there must be no needless
trifling with the impeccable five words—"There's an
Oh, such a"—which begin the second line; they should
stand as written except where our rhythm made changes
imperative.

Well, then, here is the first variant from Little Ann's
pen, with spelling corrected by uncle:

Night and day under the rind of me
There's an Oh, such a zeal for spooning, ru'ning the mind
    of me.

And another, wherein she lapses into the patois:

Night and day under the peel o' me
There's a hert that will dree if ye think aucht but a' weel
   o' me.

And now a few by uncle himself:

1. Night and day under the fleece of me
   There's an Oh, such a flaming furneth burneth the grease
      of me.

2. Night and day under the bark of me
   There's an Oh, such a mob of microbes making a park
      of me.

3. Night and day under my dermis, dear,
   There's a spot just as hot as coffee kept in a thermos,
      dear.

4. Night and day under my cuticle
   There's a love all for you so true it never would do to kill.

5. Night and day under my tegument
   There's a voice telling me I'm he, the good little egg you
      meant.

As usual, the space is nearly all gone before I have
said anything. There may be enough left to admit that
Jack Benny was recently very funny in a Jekyll and
Hyde sketch; to express the opinion that Joe Cook, in
two trial heats, has convinced me that he is as valuable
a radio comic as any sponsor is likely to find; and to
report that Mr. John Underwood of Buffalo listened-in
on the Washington baseball opening and heard Ted
Husing speak of Maxie Bishop, Joey Kuhel, and Lukey
Sewell, and is indignant because he didn't state that
Pressy Roosevelt had thrown out the first ballie.

FUN ON THE AIR

Out to Lunch, N. Y.

Again risking the peril of being called a press agent for *Variety*, I must take today's text from that weekly pamphlet of required reading, and from a not so recent issue either, since it is impossible to exercise the horses, make three or four daily personal appearances at the dentist's, and keep everybody in gales of silent mirth without falling far behind in the cover-to-cover perusal which Mr. Silverman's publication deserves.

The subject of the piece now before me is the piteous plight of radio comics. Perhaps five of the high-salaried ones, certainly not more than six, are capable of writing their own stuff. Their pay, running from $1,500 to $5,000 a performance, is supposed to be big enough to net them living expenses after they have purchased material from experienced gag men. They claim, however, that the latter are taking advantage of the unprecedented demand and charging outrageous prices, and sometimes it may have occurred to you, as it has to me, that $2.00 a script would come under that classification. The writers argue that furnishing "fresh, new, laughable" continuities once a week or once a day is such a drain on their mental resources that they will soon be written out, and it behooves them to get as much as they can while the getting is good.

What the comics want, in order to preserve their own salaries intact, is a new deal providing for separate contracts between themselves and their sponsors and between their sponsors and the persons chosen to write the gags; otherwise there is danger that a $2,500 comic will soon be disbursing $2,700 for his material, thus losing $200 a performance and paying a Morganatic income tax.

The problem is so simple that the sponsors will doubtless be in conference all summer before they hit on the wrong solution. Meanwhile, youse other unemployed might do worse than follow my lead and experiment with this apparently lucrative gag-writing game. I have prepared a continuity suitable for a comic whose employer is trying to sell cigars, cigarettes, tires, yeast, automobiles, tea, gasoline, coffee, soap, electric refrigerators, shaving cream, aspirin, or mouth wash, and I am mailing copies to Miss Allen and Miss Brice and the Messrs. Wynn, Pearl, Cantor, Lahr, Benny, and others who are up in the big money, on the chance that they will be interested and recommend me to their sponsors when the question of next season's gag men comes up. If I had room, I would print the entire sample for the benefit of those who have not listened to as much radio comedy as I. There is space for less than a twentieth of it, but even so skinny a skeleton may give you an idea of the stuff they want.

In reading you will probably get the impression from the smooth and natural flow of the lines that conceiving and writing them was child's play. No notion could be more erroneous. When I had finished the full script, over twenty times as long as the following, I found that the drain on my mental resources had been so terrific that two glasses of 3.2 beer, one on top of the other, had no more effect on me than two glasses of 3.2 beer, one on top of the other.

(Note: The appearance of one asterisk denotes that the gag is neither original with me nor with the gag man who wrote it for the comic who sprang it. Two asterisks denote the same.)

Straight Man: I'm going to a masquerade tonight, Chief (Baron, Eddie, Gracie). I'm going as Mahatma Gandhi. *

Comic: Why, Graham (Charlie, Jimmie, George), I'm afraid you'll barely get there.*

Straight Man: Do you mean to tell me you sat in the cage reading, with a lion on either side of you?

Comic: Yes. I was reading between the lions.*

Straight Man: I understand you had an operation at that big hospital just off Riverside Drive. I know a nurse up there. What floor were you on?

Comic: I wasn't on no floor. I was on a table.*

Straight Man: Did your doctor know what you were coming down with?

Comic: He thought I was coming down with seventy-five dollars, but I only came down with fifty.* . . . To-morrow night I'm going to a dance.

Straight Man: Going to a dance, with a newly removed appendix!

Comic: No, sur. I'se gwine with a gentleman friend.**

Sponsor's Spokesman: This is vacation time. Soon you will be enjoying recreation and rest in a strange place. But you won't get much enjoyment if you have stomach disorders.**

Straight Man: Do you mean to tell me you sat in the cage reading, with a lion on either side of you?

Comic: Yes. I was reading between the lions.* (In the case of a gag as good as this, it is all right to use it several times on one program.)

Straight Man: You say you can name a man's profession by looking at him. Would you know that Rubinoff was a violinist before you heard him play?

Comic: No, nor afterwards.**

Straight Man: Why did your brother (father, uncle, cousin) steal forty cents? (It is permissible to joke about any relative except mother, who is still a Sacred Cow, to be used only as a snivel-song heroine, preferably dead.)

Comic: He thought the change would do him good.********

Sponsor's Spokesman: All we ask is that next time you are in doubt, you ask for "Texacos, please!" They're mild because it's dated.**

Straight Man: Well, Bert, did you have a good time on your vacation?

Comic: Did I have a good time? Did I have a good time? Did I have a good time! Did I have a good time!

Straight Man: I'll bet you came home broke.

Comic: No. I met a skunk the last night. So I got here with one scent.**

Straight Man: What is your uncle (brother, cousin, father, nevvoo) doing now?

Comic: Four years.*

Straight Man: I thought your aunt (father, cousin, grandfather) gave him some money to go into business.

Comic: Yes, but he had bad luck. He opened a barber shop and never had a customer.

Straight Man: Where did he open the barber shop?

Comic: In Russia.**

Straight Man: Do you mean to tell me that you sat in the cage reading, with a lion on either side of you?

Comic: Yes, Grahame, and did I mention that when my sister's beau came to call, she made Aunt Julia conceal herself behind the water plug? You see, she wanted to hydrant.

A PERFECT PROGRAM

Out to Lunch, N. Y.

Late last winter the McCann-Erickson advertising agency, handling in behalf of a flock of big oil companies the publicity for what it called the Five Star Theatre, a series of five much better than average radio

programs per week, including Groucho and Chico Marx
and a condensed Aborn light opera, announced that one
of its headliners, Solly Ward, was striving to select and
assemble for his share of the entertainment a layout
which might truly be designated "The Perfect Radio
Program" and would present same to our eager ear-
drums as soon as the minor details of selection and
assemblage had been attended to.

It is my recollection that I was out of touch with radio
for a few weeks subsequent to this announcement, and
inquiry among my operatives has failed to educe evidence that Solly ever tried to follow through. That he
succeeded is beyond belief unless there was a stipulation
that he himself, or McCann-Erickson, or some other individual or very small group should act as sole judge.
To get as many as two people to agree on any radio
program as perfect is impossible, as I shall presently
prove by giving you my own idea of perfection and sug-
gesting that when you have scoffed at it to your heart's
content, you select one yourself and try to find a friend
or acquaintance who will say you haven't made a single
mistake.

There is no doubt in my far from humble mind that
I could win a verdict of unqualified approval if a sponsor were judge. His ideal program would begin with two
minutes of the drawing card—Fanny Brice, or Wynn,
or Cantor, or Jolson; just enough time to prove that the
big name was really there—and then proceed with fifty-
eight minutes of talk by a "good" talker about the
product being "advertised," talk that is always tiresome,
often disgusting, and more often so childishly and mani-
festly untrue that large numbers of the listeners resolve
not to buy the product or, if they have been buying it,
to switch to some other brand. Whenever I am bothered
by the suspicion that my work is not as good as it was a

year ago, I obtain comfort by repeating to myself the word "sponsor" until it becomes almost a cheer.

However, you, not a sponsor, are the judge of my Perfect Program, which you must admit has variety to make up for a lack of thrift:

Announcer: "This is Station WENC and the following program is sponsored by Fleischmann's Antiseptic Cigarette Oil. It comes to you every Saturday night, just an hour before bedtime. The oil is probably as good as any other oil you can buy. We have made no test to prove that statement, but it sounds reasonable because the well we get it from looks almost exactly like all the other oil wells we ever saw, and we have seen our full quota of oil wells. Now our program will open with George Olsen's music and Miss Fanny Brice." (One minute.)

George Olsen's orchestra, without the "railroad effect" theme, plays some new stuff, including a comedy song, dialect if possible, to be sung by Miss Ethel Shutta. Miss Brice, with a straight man, does some comedy dialogue written by someone who can write for Miss Brice. (Four minutes.)

Ohman and Arden, on two pianos, without an orchestra, playing early Gershwin or recent Schwartz or both. (Two minutes.)

Stoopnagle and Budd in dialogue that does not include any reference to Stoopnocracy. (Two minutes.)

Ben Bernie's orchestra, with Ben singing a refrain and making a remark or two. (One minute.)

Jack Pearl and Cliff Hall, doing the kind of stuff they did before they got to doing the kind of stuff they got to doing. (Four minutes.)

The Revelers in a medley of songs intended for quartets. No trick song or comedy song such as What's-his-name playing the rumba on his tuba or any song in which the melody is sung by the bass. (Two minutes.)

Joe Cook, giving directions on how to get to his old home in Evansville from the C. & E. I. station. (Five minutes.)

Bing Crosby in a couple of his specials, with a good orchestra such as Denny's or Goodman's or Lopez's for him to fight it out with. (Four minutes.)

Ed Wynn, with Graham McNamee and Vorhees' band, telling some of those jokes it takes him thirty-one hours per week to write, and trying, as a stunt, not to use his favorite word for 1932-33—"underwear." (Ten minutes.)

Rosa Ponselle, singing an aria from the opera *Norma*. (Two minutes and a half.)

Irvin S. Cobb, waiting for them to stop laughing before he starts his first story. (Half a minute.)

Burns and Allen, with Guy Lombardo's orchestra. We are crowded for time, but Burns and Allen rate as much as Stoopnagle and Budd and shall have it. Miss Gracie, at my request, is doing over twice as much singing as usual. Mr. Lombardo, in the minute allotted to him, will attempt to have his strings and saxophones in tune with his saxophones and strings for at least one encounter. (Five minutes.)

Ruth Etting, queen of the torchers, singing, perhaps, Irving Berlin's old "Remember." (One minute.)

Eddie Cantor and James Wallington in dialogue written by someone who knows how to write for Eddie Cantor. (Two minutes.)

A fellow named Lawrence Tibbett, singing in English a song called "Bendemeer's Stream," or, in Italian, the aria in *Traviata* which Daddy sings to the gal and which is virtually a complete history of France up to the time the United States entered the world War. (Two minutes.)

Fred Allen and Roy Atwell, in dialogue written by Fred Allen for Fred Allen, and something nobody will admit having written for Mr. Atwell. (Two minutes.)

Al Jolson in anything he wants to sing or say. (Two minutes.)

And the remaining eight minutes to the best band in the land, Marse Paul's, who, I hope, will give me all the "Music in the Air" and other recent Kern he can crowd into that all too brief period.

That's my dream program, ladies and gents. If a single one of you agrees with me *in toto*, I will gladly apologize and begin all over.

PARODIES
AND "PLAYS"

THE YOUNG IMMIGRUNTS

BY RING W. LARDNER, JR.

WITH A PREFACE
BY THE FATHER

[The Young Visiters, with preface by Sir James
Barrie, had recently been published. The influence
of the style of that work on "The Young Immigrunts"
will be marked by readers with good memories.—G.S.]

Preface

THE PERSON whose name is signed to this novel was born
on the nineteenth day of August, 1915, and was therefore four years and three months old when the manuscript was found, late in November 1919. The narrative
is substantially true, with the following exceptions:

1. "My Father," the leading character in the work, is
depicted as a man of short temper, whereas the person
from whom the character was drawn is in reality as
pleasant a fellow as one would care to meet and seldom
has a cross word for any one, let alone women and
children.

2. The witty speeches accredited to "My Father"
have, possibly owing to the limitations of a child's
memory, been so garbled and twisted that they do not
look half so good in print as they sounded in the open
air.

3. More stops for gas were made than are mentioned
in the story.

As the original manuscript was written on a typewriter with a rather frayed ribbon, and as certain words were marked out and others handwritten in, I have taken the liberty of copying the entire work with a fresh ribbon and the inclusion of the changes which the author indicated in pencil in the first draft. Otherwise the story is presented to the reader exactly as it was first set down.

THE FATHER.

1. My Parents

My parents are both married and ½ of them are very good looking. The balance is tall and skiny and has a swarty complexion with moles but you hardly ever notice them on account of your gaze being rapped up in his feet which would be funny if brevvity wasnt the soul of wit. Everybody says I have his eyes and I am glad it didnt half to be something else tho Rollie Zeider the ball player calls him owl eyes for a nick name but if I was Rollie Zeider and his nose I wouldnt pick on somebodys else features.

He wears pretty shirts which he bought off of another old ball player Artie Hofman to attrack tension off of his feet and must of payed a big price for them I heard my ant tell my uncle when they thorght I was a sleep down to the lake tho I guess he pays even more for his shoes if they sell them by the frunt foot.

I was born in a hospittle in Chicago 4 years ago and liked it very much and had no idear we were going to move till 1 day last summer I heard my mother arsk our nurse did she think she could get along O. K. with myself and 3 brothers John Jimmie and David for 10 days wilst she and my old man went east to look for a costly home.

Well yes said our nurse barshfully.

I may as well exclaim to the reader that John is 7 and Jimmie is 5 and I am 4 and David is almost nothing as yet you might say and tho I was named for my father they call me Bill thank God.

The conversation amungst my mother and our nurse took place right after my father came back from Toledo where Jack Dempsey knocked Jessie Willard for a gool tho my father liked the big fellow and bet on him.

David was in his bath at the time and my mother and our nurse and myself and 2 elder brothers was standing around admireing him tho I notice that when the rest of the family takes their bath they dont make open house of the occassion.

Well my parents went east and dureing their absents myself and brothers razed hell with David on the night shift but when they come back my mother said to the nurse were they good boys.

Fine replid our nurse lamely and where are you going to live.

Connecticut said my mother.

Our nurse forced a tired smile.

Here we will leave my parents to unpack and end this chapter.

II. Starting Gaily

We spent the rest of the summer on my granmother in Indiana and my father finley went to the worst series to write it up as he has followed sports of all sorts for years and is a expert so he bet on the wite sox and when he come home he acted rarther cross.

Well said my mother simperingly I suppose we can start east now.

We will start east when we get good and ready said my father with a lordly sneeze.

The next thing was how was we going to make the trip as my father had boughten a new car that the cheepest way to get it there was drive it besides carrying a grate deal of our costly bagage but if all of us went in it they would be no room left for our costly bagage and besides 2 of my brothers always acts like devils incarnite when they get in a car so my mother said to our nurse.

If you think you can manage the 2 older boys and David on the train myself and husband will take Bill in the car said my mother to our nurse.

Fine replid our nurse with a gastly look witch my mother did not see.

Myself and parents left Goshen Indiana on a fine Monday morning leaveing our nurse and brothers to come latter in the weak on the railway. Our plans was to reach Detroit that night and stop with my uncle and ant and the next evening take the boat to Buffalo and hence to Connecticut by motor so the first town we past through was Middlebury.

Elmer Flick the old ball player use to live here said my father modestly.

My mother forced a smile and soon we were acrost the Michigan line and my mother made the remark that she was thirsty.

We will stop at Coldwater for lunch said my father with a strate face as he pulls most of his lines without changeing expressions.

Sure enough we puled up to 1 side of the road just after leaveing Coldwater and had our costly viands of frid chicken and doughnuts and milk fernished by my grate ant and of witch I partook freely.

We will stop at Ypsilanti for supper said my father

in calm tones that is where they have the state normal school.

I was glad to hear this and hoped we would get there before dark as I had always wanted to come in contack with normal peaple and see what they are like and just at dusk we entered a large size town and drove past a large size football field.

Heavens said my mother this must be a abnormal school to have such a large football field.

My father wore a qeer look.

This is not Ypsilanti this is Ann Arbor he crid.

But I thorght you said we would go south of Ann Arbor and direct to Ypsilanti said my mother with a smirk.

I did say that but I thorght I would surprise you by comeing into Ann Arbor replid my father with a corse jesture.

Personly I think the surprise was unanimous.

Well now we are here said my mother we might as well look up Bill.

Bill is my uncle Bill so we stoped at the Alfa Delt house and got him and took him down to the hotel for supper and my old man called up Mr. Yost the football coach of the Michigan football team and he come down and visited with us.

What kind of a team have you got coach said my father lamely.

I have got a determined team replid Mr. Yost they are determined to not play football.

At this junction my unlucky mother changed the subjeck to the league of nations and it was 10 o'clock before Mr. Yost come to a semi colon so we could resume our journey and by the time we past through Ypsilanti the peaple was not only subnormal but unconsius. It was nerly midnight when we puled up in frunt of my ants and uncles house in Detroit that had been seting up since 7 expecting us.

Were sorry to be so late said my mother bruskly.

Were awfully glad you could come at all replid my ant with a ill consealed yawn.

We will now leave my relitives to get some sleep and end this chapter.

III. Erie Lake

The boat leaves Detroit every afternoon at 5 oclock and reachs Buffalo the next morning at 9 tho I would better exclaim to my readers that when it is 9 oclock in Buffalo it is only 8 oclock in Goshen for instants as Buffalo peaple are qeer.

Well said my father the next morning at brekfus I wander what time we half to get the car on the board of the boat.

I will find out down town and call up and let you know replid my uncle who is a engineer and digs soors or something.

Sure enough he called up dureing the fornoon and said the car must be on the board of the boat at 3 oclock so my father left the house at 2 oclock and drove down to the worf tho he had never drove a car in Detroit before but has nerves of steal. Latter my uncle come out to his home and took myself and mother and ant down to the worf where my old man was waiting for us haveing put the car on the board.

What have you been doing ever since 3 oclock arsked my mother as it was now nerly 5.

Haveing a high ball my father replid.

I thorght Detroit was dry said my mother shyly.

Did you said my father with a rye smile and as it was now nerly time for the boat to leave we said good by to my uncle and ant and went on the boat. A messenger took our costly bagage and put it away wilst myself and parents went out on the porch and set looking at the peaple on the worf. Suddenly they was a grate hub bub on the worf and a young man and lady started up the gangs plank wilst a big crowd throwed rice and old shoes at them and made a up roar.

Bride and glum going to Niagara Falls said my father who is well traveled and seams to know everything.

Instantly the boat give a blarst on the wistle and I started with suprise.

Did that scare you Bill said my father and seamed to enjoy it and I supose he would of laughed out right had I fell overboard and been drowned in the narsty river water.

Soon we were steeming up the river on the city of Detroit 3.

That is Canada over there is it not said my mother.

What did you think it was the Austrian Tyrol replid my father explodeing a cough. Dureing our progress up the river I noticed sevral funny things flotting in the water with lanterns hanging on them and was wandering what they could be when my mother said they seam to have plenty of boys.

They have got nothing on us replid my father quick as a flarsh.

A little latter who should come out on the porch and set themselfs ner us but the bride and glum.

Oh I said to myself I hope they will talk so as I can hear them as I have always wandered what newlyweds talk about on their way to Niagara Falls and soon my wishs was realized.

Some night said the young glum are you warm enough.

I am perfectly comfertible replid the fare bride tho her looks belid her words what time do we arive in Buffalo.

9 oclock said the lordly glum are you warm enough.

I am perfectly comfertible replid the fare bride what time do we arive in Buffalo.

9 oclock said the lordly glum I am afrade it is too cold for you out here.

Well maybe it is replid the fare bride and without farther adieu they went in the spacius parlers.

I wander will he be arsking her 8 years from now is she warm enough said my mother with a faint grimace.

The weather may change before then replid my father.

Are you warm enough said my father after a slite pause.

No was my mothers catchy reply.

Well said my father we arive in Buffalo at 9 oclock and with that we all went inside as it was now pitch dark and had our supper and retired and when we rose the next morning and drest and had brekfus we puled up to the worf in Buffalo and it was 9 oclock so I will leave the city of Detroit 3 tide to the worf and end this chapter.

IV. Buffalo to Rochester 76.4

As we was leaveing the boat who should I see right along side of us but the fare bride and the lordly glum.

We are right on the dot said the glum looking at his costly watch it is just 9 oclock and so they past out of my life.

We had to wait qite a wile wilst the old man dug up his bill of loading and got the costly moter.

We will half to get some gas he said I wonder where they is a garage.

No sooner had the words fell from his lips when a man with a flagrant Adams apple handed him a card with the name of a garage on it.

Go up Genesee st 5 blks and turn to the left or something said the man with the apple.

Soon we reached the garage and had the gas tank filled with gas it was 27 cents in Buffalo and soon we was on our way to Rochester. Well these are certainly grate roads said my father barshfully.

They have lots better roads in the east than out west replid my mother with a knowing wink.

The roads all through the east are better than out west remarked my father at lenth.

These are wonderfull replid my mother smuggleing me vs her arm.

The time past quickly with my parents in so jocular a mood and all most before I knew it we was on the outer skirts of Batavia.

What town is this quired my mother in a tolerant voice.

Batavia husked my father sloughing down to 15 miles per hour.

Well maybe we would better stop and have lunch here said my mother coyly.

We will have lunch in Rochester replid my father with a loud cough.

My mother forced a smile and it was about ½ past 12 when we arived in Rochester and soon we was on Genesee st and finley stoped in front of a elegant hotel and shared a costly lunch.

v. My Father's Idear

Wilst participateing in the lordly viands my father halled out his map and give it the up and down.

Look at here he said at lenth they seams to be a choice of 2 main roads between here and Syracuse but 1 of them gos way up north to Oswego wilst the other gos way south to Geneva where as Syracuse is strate east from here you might say so it looks to me like we would save both millage and time if we was to drive strate east through Lyons the way the railway gos.

Well I dont want to ride on the ties said my mother with a loud cough.

Well you dont half to because they seams to be a little road that gos strate through replid my father removeing a flys cadaver from the costly farina.

Well you would better stick to the main roads said my mother tacklessly.

Well you would better stick to your own business replid my father with a pungent glance.

Soon my father had payed the check and gave the waiter a lordly bribe and once more we sprang into the machine and was on our way. The lease said about the results of my fathers grate idear the soonest mended in a word it turned out to be a holycost of the first water as after we had covered miles and miles of ribald roads we suddenly come to a abrupt conclusion vs the side of a stagnant freight train that was stone deef to honks. My father set there for nerly ½ a hour reciteing the 4 Horses of the Apoplex in a under tone but finely my mother mustard up her curage and said affectedly why dont we turn around and go back somewheres. I cant spell what my father replid.

At lenth my old man decided that Lyons wouldnt

never come to Mahomet if we set it out on the same lines all winter so we backed up and turned around and retraced 4 miles of shell holes and finely reached our objective by way of Detour.

Puling up in front of a garage my father beckoned to a dirty mechanic.

How do we get to Syracuse from her arsked my father blushing furiously.

Go strate south to Geneva and then east to Syracuse replid the dirty mechanic with a loud cough.

Isnt there no short cut arsked my father.

Go strate south to Geneva and then east to Syracuse replid the dirty mechanic.

You see daddy we go to Geneva after all I said brokenly but luckly for my piece of mind my father dont beleive in corporeal punishment a specially in front of Lyons peaple.

Soon we was on a fine road and nothing more hapened till we puled into Syracuse at 7 that evening and as for the conversation that changed hands in the car between Lyons and Syracuse you could stick it in a day message and send it for 30 cents.

VI. Syracuse to Hudson 183.2

Soon we was on Genesee st in Syracuse but soon turned off a blk or 2 and puled up in front of a hotel that I cant ether spell or pronounce besides witch they must of been a convention of cheese sculpters or something stoping there and any way it took the old man a hour to weedle a parler bed room and bath out of the clerk and put up a cot for me.

Wilst we was enjoying a late and futile supper in the hotel dinning room a man named Duffy reckonized my father and came to our table and arsked him to go to some boxing matchs in Syracuse that night.

Thanks very much said my father with a slite sneeze but you see what I have got on my hands besides witch I have been driveing all day and half to start out again erly in the morning so I guess not.

Between you and I dear reader my old man has been oposed to pugilisms since the 4 of July holycost.

Who is that man arsked my mother when that man had gone away.

Mr. Duffy replid my father shove the ketchup over this way.

Yes I know he is Mr. Duffy but where did you meet him insisted my mother quaintly.

In Boston my father replid where would a person meet a man named Duffy.

When we got up the next morning it was 6 oclock and purring rain but we eat a costly brekfus and my father said we would save time if we would all walk down to the garage where he had horded the car witch he stated was only 2 short blks away from the hotel. Well if it was only 2 short blks why peaple that lives next door to each other in Syracuse are by no means neighbors and when we got there the entire party was soping wet and rarther rabid.

We will all catch our death of cold chuckled my mother.

What of it explained my old man with a dirty look at the sky.

Maybe we would better put up the curtains sugested my mother smirking.

Maybe we wouldn't too said my father cordialy.

Well maybe it will clear up said my mother convulsively.

Maybe it wont too replid my father as he capered into the drivers seat.

My father is charming company wilst driveing on strange roads through a purring rain and even when we past through Oneida and he pronounced it like it was a biscuit neither myself or my mother ventured to correct him but finely we reached Utica when we got to witch we puled up along side the kerb and got out and rang ourselfs out to a small extent when suddenly a closed car sored past us on the left.

Why that was Mrs. Heywood in that car explained my mother with a fierce jesture. By this time it was not raining and we got back into the car and presently over took the closed car witch stoped when they reckonized us.

And witch boy is this quired Mrs. Heywood when the usual compliments had been changed.

This is the third he is named for his father replid my mother forceing a smile.

He has his eyes was the comment.

Bill dont you remember Mrs. Heywood said my mother turning on me she use to live in Riverside and Dr. Heywood tended to you that time you had that slite atack of obesity.

Well yes I replid with a slite accent but did not add how rotten the medicine tasted that time and soon we was on Genesee st on our way out of Utica.

I wander why they dont name some of their sts Genesee in these eastren towns said my father for the sun was now shining but no sooner had we reached Herkimer when the clouds bersed with renude vigger and I think my old man was about to say we will stop here and have lunch when my mother sugested it herself.

No replid my father with a corse jesture we will go on to Little Falls.

It was raining cats and dogs when we arived at Little Falls and my father droped a quaint remark.

If Falls is a verb he said the man that baptized this town was a practicle joker.

We will half to change our close replid my mother steping into a mud peddle in front of the hotel with a informal look.

When we had done so we partook of a meger lunch and as it was now only drooling resumed our jurney.

They soked me 5 for that room said my father but what is a extra sokeing or 2 on a day like this.

I didnt mean for you to get a room said my mother violently.

Where did you want us to change our close on the register said my old man turning pail.

Wasnt it funny that we should happen to see Mrs. Heywood in Utica said my mother at lenth.

They live there dont they my father replid.

Why yes my mother replid.

Well then my father replid the real joke would of been if we had of happened to see her in Auburn.

A little wile latter we past a grate many signs reading dine at the Big Nose Mountain Inn.

Rollie Zeider never told me they had named a mountain after him crid my father and soon we past through Fonda.

Soon we past through Amsterdam and I guess I must of dosed off at lease I cant remember anything between there and Schenectady and I must apologize to my readers for my laps as I am unable to ether describe the scenery or report anything that may of been said between these 2 points but I recall that as we entered

Albany a remark was adrest to me for the first time since lunch.

Bill said my mother with a ½ smirk this is Albany the capital of New York state.

So this is Albany I thorght to myself.

Who is governor of New York now arsked my mother to my father.

Smith replid my father who seams to know everything.

Queer namo said my mother sulkily.

Soon we puled up along side a policeman who my father arsked how do we get acrost the river to the New York road and if Albany pays their policemans by the word I'll say we were in the presents of a rich man and by the time he got through it was dark and still drooling and my old man didn't know the road and under those conditions I will not repete the conversation that transpired between Albany and Hudson but will end my chapter at the city limits of the last named settlemunt.

vII. Hudson

We were turning gaily down the main st of Hudson when a man of 12 years capered out from the side walk and hoped on the runing board.

Do you want a good garage he arsked with a dirty look.

Why yes my good man replid my father tenderly but first where is the best hotel.

I will take you there said the man.

I must be a grate favorite in Hudson my father wispered at my mother.

Soon folling the mans directions we puled up in

front of a hotel but when my father went at the register the clerk said I am full tonight.

Where do you get it around here arsked my father tenderly.

We have no rooms replid the senile clerk paying no tension to my old mans remark but there is a woman acrost the st that takes loggers.

Not to excess I hope replid my father but soon we went acrost the st and the woman agrede to hord us for the night so myself and mother went to our apartmunts wilst my father and the 12 year old besought the garage. When we finley got reunited and went back to the hotel for supper it was past 8 oclock as a person could of told from the viands. Latter in front of our loggings we again met the young man who had welcomed us to Hudson and called my father to 1 side.

There is a sailer going to spend the night here he said in a horse wisper witch has walked all the way from his home Schenectady and he has got to report on his ship in New York tomorrow afternoon and has got no money so if he dont get a free ride he will be up vs it.

He can ride with us replid my father with a hiccup if tomorrow is anything like today a sailer will not feel out of place in my costly moter.

I will tell him replid the man with a corse jesture.

Will you call us at ½ past 5 my mother reqested to our lanlady as we entered our Hudson barracks.

I will if I am awake she replid useing her handkerchief to some extent.

Latter we wandered how anybody could help from being awake in that hot bed of mones and grones and cat calls and caterwauls and gulish screaks of all kinds and tho we had rose erly at Syracuse and had a day of retchedness we was all more than ready to get up when she wraped on our door long ere day brake.

Where is that sailer that stoped here last night quired my father as we was about to make a lordly outburst.

He wouldnt pay his bill and razed hell so I kicked him out replid the lanlady in her bear feet.

Without farther adieu my father payed his bill and we walked into the dismul st so I will end this chapter by leaveing the fare lanlady flaping in the door way in her sredded night gown.

VIII. Hudson to Yonkers 106.5

It was raining a little so my father bad my mother and I stand in the st wilst he went to the garage and retained the costly moter. He returned ½ a hour latter with the story that the garage had been locked and he had to go to the props house and roust him out.

How did you know where he lived quired my mother barshfully.

I used the brains god gave me was my fathers posthumous reply.

Soon we rumpled into Rhinebeck and as it was now day light and the rain had siezed we puled up in front of the Beekman arms for brekfus.

It says this is the oldest hotel in America said my mother reading the programme.

The eggs tastes all right replid my father with a corse jesture.

What is the next town quired my mother when we again set sale.

Pokippsie was my father's reply.

Thats where Vassar is said my mother as my old man stiffled a yawn I wonder if there is a store there that would have a koop for David.

I doubt it they ever heard of him said my father dryly how much do they cost.

Well I dont know.

We entered Pokippsie at lenth and turned to the left up the main st and puled up in front of a big store where myself and mother went in and purchased a koop for my little brother and a kap for me witch only took a ½ hour dureing witch my father lost his temper and when we finley immerged he was barking like a dog and giveing the Vassar yell. 2 men come out of the store with us and tost the koop with the rest of the junk in the back seat and away we went.

Doesnt this look cute on him said my mother in regards to my new kap.

What of it replid my father with a grimace and with that we puled into Garrison.

Isnt this right acrost the river from West Point said my mother with a gastly look.

What of it replid my father tenderly and soon we found ourselfs in Peekskill.

This is where that young girl cousin of mine gos to school said my father from Philadelphia.

What of it said my mother with a loud cough and presently we stoped and bought 15 gals of gas.

I have got a fund of usefull information about every town we come to said my father admireingly for instants this is Harmon where they take off the steem engines and put on the electric bullgines.

My mother looked at him with ill consealed admiration.

And what do you know about this town she arsked as we frisked into Ossining.

Why this is Ossining where they take off the hair and put on the stripes replid my father qick as a flarsh and

the next place is Tarrytown where John D. Rockefeller
has a estate.

What is the name of the estate quired my mother
breathlessly.

Socony I supose was the sires reply.

With that we honked into Yonkers and up the funny
looking main st.

What a funny looking st said my mother and I always thorght it was the home of well to do peaple.

Well yes replid my father it is the home of the ruling
class at lease Bill Klem the umpire and Bill Langford
the referee lives here.

I will end my chapter on that one.

IX. The Bureau of Manhattan

Isn't it about time said my mother as we past Spuyten
Duyvil and entered the Bureau of Manhattan that we
made our plans.

What plans said my father all my plans is all ready
made.

Well then you might make me your confident sugested my mother with a quaint smirk.

Well then heres the dope uttered my father in a vage
tone I am going to drop you at the 125 st station where
you will only half to wait 2 hours and a ½ for the rest
of the family as the train from the west is do at 350 at
125 st in the meen wile I will drive out to Grenitch with
Bill and see if the house is ready and etc and if the other
peaples train is on time you can catch the 4 4 and I an
Bill will meet you at the Grenitch station.

If you have time get a qt of milk for David said my
mother with a pail look.

What kind of milk arsked my dad.

Oh sour milk my mother screened.

As she was now in a pretty bad temper we will leave her to cool off for 2 hours and a ½ in the 125 st station and end this chapter.

x. N. Y. to Grenitch 500.0

The lease said about my and my fathers trip from the Bureau of Manhattan to our new home the soonest mended. In some way ether I or he got balled up on the grand concorpse and next thing you know we was thretning to swoop down on Pittsfield.

Are you lost daddy I arsked tenderly.

Shut up he explained.

At lenth we doubled on our tracks and done much better as we finley hit New Rochelle and puled up along side a policeman with falling archs.

What road do I take for Grenitch Conn quired my father with poping eyes.

Take the Boston post replid the policeman.

I have all ready subscribed to one out of town paper said my father and steped on the gas so we will leave the flat foot gaping after us like a prune fed calf and end this chapter.

xi. How It Ended

True to our promise we were at the station in Grenitch when the costly train puled in from 125 st. Myself and father hoped out of the lordly moter and helped the bulk of the famly off of the train and I aloud our nurse and my 3 brothers to kiss me tho Davids left me rarther moist.

Did you have a hard trip my father arsked to our nurse shyly.

Why no she replid with a slite stager.

She did too said my mother they all acted like little devils.

Did you get Davids milk she said turning on my father.

Why no does he like milk my father replid with a gastly smirk.

We got lost mudder I said brokenly.

We did not screened my father and accidently cracked me in the shins with a stray foot.

To change the subjeck I turned my tensions on my brother Jimmie who is nerest my age.

I've seen our house Jimmie I said brokenly I got here first.

Yes but I slept all night on a train and you didnt replid Jimmie with a dirty look.

Nether did you said my brother John to Jimmie you was awake all night.

Were awake said my mother.

Me and David was awake all night and crid said my brother John.

But I only crid once the whole time said my brother Jimmie.

But I didnt cry at all did I I arsked to my mother.

So she replid with a loud cough Bill was a very very good boy.

So now we will say fare well to the characters in this book.

A FEW PARODIES

A LITERARY DIARY

You don't hardly ever pick up a Sunday paper now days but what some high brow writer has got their dairy in there for the past wk. or in other wds. a record of who they seen and talked to and what they done since the last time we heard from them.

Well naturly they's a good many famous names broughten into these here dairys who the public is interested in reading about them, but the public is also interested in reading about the writers themselfs provided they are famous enough and any way the idear has been suggested that my own dairy for a wk. would make interesting reading even though I don't take lunch very often with men like Babe Ruth, H. G. Wells, and Suzanne Lenglen so any way I am going to write down my journal for Aug. 6-13 inclusive and anybody that is bored by the same can lay it to 1 side and no hard feelings.

Aug. 6

Everybody was cooking their Sunday dinner at once and Great Neck seemed to run out of gas so we had to finnish up the chicken in the coal range and didn't get nothing to eat till after 3 p.m. My sister-in-law Dorothy and husband H. Kitchell and 2 babies come to pay us a visit though they didn't owe us none but at lease they ain't going to stay long. President Harding called up long distants to say hello. The Mrs. talked to him as I was playing with the cat.

Aug. 7

Went to N.Y. city to get a hair cut and was walking along 7th. ave. and seen a man teaseing a musk rat so I went up to the man and busted him in the jaw and knocked him down. A policeman come along and picked the man up and asked him who he was. It turned out that he was Jack Dempsey. I went over to the athletic club and exercised as I ain't been getting none lately.

Aug. 8

Peggy Hopkins called up and wanted we should go for a sail but I had a date to play golf with Sarazen, Hagen, and Barnes. I and Hagan played the other two best ball and added score for a $25.00 nassua but only beat them by about 7 pts. as Hagen wasn't putting good. I had 12 eagles but only managed to get a couple of ones. When I got home Sousa was there and we played some Brahms and Grieg with me at the piano and him at one end of a cornet. "How well you play Lardy," was Sousa's remark. Brahms called up in the evening and him and his wife come over and played rummy.

Aug. 9

David Wark Griffith drove up to the house in his Ford so silently that he caught me setting on the porch before the butler could tell him I was out. He says he was getting up a new picture based on the story of *The Prisoner of Zenda,* and it laid between Jack Barrymore, Richard Barthelmess, and I which one of us should play the lead. "It is yours if you want it," he said to me. "I am sorry, Dave," I says, "but I promised the little woman to not work this summer." "I am sorry, too, Lardy," he said, and drove off. Took a ride on the Long Island R.R. to study human nature. They was a man quarreling with the conductor and the conductor seemed to be getting the worst of it so I throwed the man off of the train. Found out afterwards it was Stan- islaus Zbyszko. Felt bored and sleepy so went home.

Aug. 10

Went to the Follies but a lot of people seen me come in and begun hollering author, author, till it become so embarrassing I had to duck. Had lunch with Beethoven and Bach, and they wanted to know what I was doing in the evening. "Well, boys," I said. "I am at your dis- posal." They acted tickled to death and we spent the evening in the Lambs playing trios. Amongst other pieces we tried out Bach's new sonata for 2 pianos and a cuspidor.

Aug. 11

Had breakfast with Mayor Hylan and Senator Lodge. After breakfast the senator says "Lardy tear us off some Chopin." After I had played them a few pieces I drove the boys down town and I went to the club and played billiards with Willie Hoppe and had a narrow escape from him beating me as I was off my game. "Well," he said when it was over, "I come pretty near beating you that time Lardy." "Yes you did, Willie," I told him with a smile. Went to dinner with Wm. M. Thackeray a English author and he suggested that we should eat crow's knuckles meuniere which I hadn't never tried but it tasted O.K. and reminded a good deal like pelican's finger nails a la creole. "How do you like it Lardy," asked my host. "All right Thack," was my smiling reply. Went home and played some Rubenstein on the black keys.

Aug. 12

This was Saturday and the banks close at noon on Saturdays so I visited them all dureing the forenoon and found everything lovely. Everywhere I went it was hello Lardy how is everything Lardy. Played 4 or 5 rounds of Beethoven and had lunch with Gatti-Casazza and Gen. Pershing. Went home to practice on my harp and the phone rung and it was Madame Jeritska who wanted I should take her to dinner but I pretended like I was busy. Scotti and Gerry Farrar called up in the evening and wanted a game of bridge but I and the Mrs. was invited over to Luccini's to try out their new piano. "Well Lardy we will half to make it some other time," said Gerry. "You said a mouthfull Gerry" was my smileing reply.

YOUR BROADWAY, BEAU, AND YOU CAN HAVE IT

New York. . . . Guiseppe Verdi (Joe Green, as a Frank Adams contrib tagged him) seems to have penned another smash in *Aida*, George Gershwin is Sullivan-Gilberting with his own brother, Ira.

Mrs. Palmer is anticipating a quadruply blessed event (the Marx Brothers). . . . Cal Coolidge is sealed to Grace Goodhue, a Burlington brunette.

A. Lincoln and Gen. McClellan are on the verge . . . Jimmy Madison and Dolly Payne Todd are THAT WAY. (Ed: This is the absolute Choynskie.)

Aleck Hamilton and Aaron Burr have phfft. . . . . . . The Geo. Washingtons (she was Martha Lorber of the Follies) have moved into their Valley Forge snuggery for the Old Man Shiver Days.

Naps Bonaparte has suggested Reno-vation to his femme, Josie . . . They say Jerry Kern was forced by the Society of Composers and Authors to auction his li-ber-ary, the other boys fearing it would smirch the industry's good name to have a song-writer own a book.

What writer on what paper is taking whose golf clubs to what Bahamas?......Arthur Brisbane has signed up to do a daily colyum for William ("Randolph") Hearst.

An Exchange Place investment firm is recommending stock in a company that will convert hootch from liquid to solid form and thus be able to peddle it legally, perhaps as sandwiches. . . . . . You can order me a Scotch on rye.

Recommended to diversion seekers: The Florida East Coast R.R. timetable. . . . . The Lynn Fontannes. . . . . Iodine as a nose gargle to pfffend off the phffflu. . . . . A Madison Square Garden phfffight decision. . . . . A motor trip on Eighth Ave.

F. P. A. has quit the evemaily and is running a swell colyum on the World...... Heywood Broun and the last-named rag have phfft. . . . . The subway is going to install automat turnstiles which you can go through by dropping Anne Nichols in the slot.

Danny Deever is halter bound. . . . . What subscriber to the N.Y. telephone directory has got a cold? .....

ODD'S BODKINS

Author's Note:
Each morn when the neighbors are through with our papers
And stealthily slide them beneath our front door,
I grab the *American,* knowing that there I can
Find O. O. McIntyre's column of lore.
You ask what it's like? I've no copy right here,
But p'rhaps I can give you some sort of idear.

Diary of a Modern New Yorker: Up and out five hours before dawn, and by scooter to the Hermitage Hotel, where the big Seminole Indian Chef, Gwladys, cooked me a flagon of my favorite breakfast dish, beet root and wrestler's knees. Hallooed to Lily Langtry and we fell to arguing over the origin of the word "breakfast," she contending that it was a combination of "break" and "fast," derived from a horse's instructions to a starter in a six-furlong race, and I maintaining that it was five furlongs. We decided to leave it to Percy Hammond, the philatelist, but his nurse told us he was out shoplifting.

Home for a moment to slit my mail and found invitations from Mussolini, Joan Blondell, Joan Crawford, Joan of Arc, President Buchanan, Joe Walcott, and Louisa M. Alcott. Then answered a pleasant long-distance call from Gwladys, the little French chef in the Café des Trois Outfielders in Sydney, her voice as plain as if she were in Melbourne. She had heard I had a cold, she said, and was worried. It was gratifying to hear her whimpers of relief when I assured her the crisis was past.

Breaking bread in the evening at the office of J. P. Morgan & Company and sat between Bernie Shaw, H. J. Wells, Charlie Dickens, Lizzie Barrett, Will Thackeray, Lottie Brontë, Paul Whiteman, and Bill

Klem. Chatted for a moment after dinner with *Who's Who* and, finding a heavy rainstorm outside, dismissed my driver, Gwladys, and pirouetted to the lower West Side, where I sat on the New York Central tracks till dawn, watching the operations of a switch engine. I have always been a sucker for a New York Central switch engine in a heavy rainstorm.

Thingumabobs: I once motored around Vienna for two weeks thinking it was Vienna. When I chided the native jehu, Gwladys, he chirped: "Why, Massa, Ah done thought you knowed it was Vienna all de time." . . . If they did not wear identical hats, Jack Dempsey and Connie Bennett could easily pass for sisters. . . . Ellsworth Vines, the golf pro, is a dead ringer for Frank Crowninshield. . . . One-word description of Franklin Delano Roosevelt—President. . . . Otto Kahn always wears a union suit at first nights. . . . There is something about the name Babe Ruth that suggests rare old Dresden filigree work. . . . Mayor O'Brien is the image of Joan Crawford. . . . One of my favorite people— Senator Long. . . . Tallulah Bankhead and Jimmy Durante have profiles exactly alike. . . . Few ladies with as little money can act as grampous as Bernie Baruch. . . . Two of my favorite people—Senator Long.

Thoughts while strolling: Damon Runyan's feet. Kate Smith, a small-town girl who became nation-wide in a big city. Rosamond Pinchot and Theodore Dreiser could pass for twins. How did I get to thinking about "The Song of the Shirt"? Oh, yes; it started at tea when Fannie Hurst brought up Arthur Brisbane's quaint method of writing. His syndicated column averages close to 130,000 words a day, yet he writes it all in longhand on his shirt bosom, then forgets it and sends his shirt to the laundry. Damon Runyon's feet.

Mention of the name Rex Cole invariably reminds me of the Mother Goose rhyme, "Old King Cole," etc., and I never can figure out why. The surnames of two successful *Saturday Evening Post* writers, Samuel Blythe and Charles Francis Coe, begin with the second and third letters of the alphabet. Damon Runyon's feet. Personal nomination for the most thrilling of the summer's detective yarns—*Dracula*. If you saw only the left side of Theodore Dreiser's face you would swear it was the right side of Ruth Etting's. Rube Goldberg, cover-designer for *Spalding's Base Ball Guide*, never wears a hat to bed. Damon Runyan's feet. One-word description of the Vice-President—Garner.

Insomniacs: While writing a novel "Red" (Socker) Lewis never eats anything but alphabet soup. . . . Irvin S. Cobb cannot eat before, during, or after 5 a.m. . . . Theodore Dreiser always dresses according to the time of day he happens to be writing about. Thus, if an incident in one of his novels takes place in the morning, he puts on a morning coat; if at noon, a noon coat, etc. . . . There is a striking resemblance between Damon Runyan's feet and Ethel Merman. . . . Theodore Dreiser often arises at 2 a.m. and walks for two hours steadily. I once knew a fellow in Gallipolis who often arose at 6 p.m., and at 2 a.m. walked for two hours unsteadily. No dog as cunning as the Cubanola Glide.

DANTE AND ——

Three times daily a trusted employee of Pol Roger, Inc., calls at her apartment to measure her for a new suit or gown. It is her modest boast that she is never seen in the same costume twice and generally not even once. She is known in the fashion magazines as "Little Poker Face," but to her friends she is just Beatrice Kaufman.

Twenty-eight years ago, before there were steamboats, the Gaelic sloop *Glennamaddie* docked at Hoboken, and from their hiding place in the fo'cas'le boom, two stowaways, Pat and Velma Lahey, tip-toed to the rail, slid down the mizzen hawser and alighted on the free soil of New Jersey. They rented a humble cottage in South Orange, next door to the home of the Marx Brothers' grandfather, Baddo Marx, so called by his teachers in school. It was here, two years later, that the girl baby was born, and christened Beatrice, after the Bison City Quartette.

Pat Lahey soon found employment as a steeplejack, and one day, when little Beatrice was delivering her father's dinner pail, she caught her first glimpse of New York City.

"Oh, mumsey (mother)," she said that night to Mrs. Lahey, "please take me to New York so I can marry a Kaufman."

"A wee bairn like ye to be spakin' of marriage!" scolded her mother. "If ye must have a beau, go out and sit ye by the soide of the road and flirt with the judes that rides by in their automobiles."

"I have looked them all over," said the papoose. "There's not a Kaufman in a carload."

The turning point in Beatrice's life came when she was twenty years old. She made the acquaintance of a Lackawanna conductor, and it was through his wiles that she obtained a free ride to the city of her dreams.

As luck would have it, the first person she met when she emerged from the Hudson Tubes was George S.

Kaufman. It could have been S. Jay, as both of them were at that time Hudson Tube "Johnnies."

George often says that Beatrice won his heart through his sense of humor. As they were walking up Broadway together, he spied a small eft on the curb and made as if to scrunch it.

"Don't step on him!" cried Beatrice. "It might be Mary Pickford and her mother."

Kaufman was then at work on the play *Dulcy*, and Beatrice collaborated with him under the name of Marc Connelly. (It has always been one of her foibles to use noms de plume. For a long while she signed herself Beatrice Fairfax in a newspaper column of advice to boys and girls; she assumed the name Beatrice Lillie when she appeared in the *Charlot Revue*; she has written many plays under the sobriquet of Owen Davis, and in 1926 she won the women's national tennis championship as Mrs. Bjurstedt, the former May Bundy.) *Dulcy* was a hit and George proposed.

After an engagement marked by considerable venom on one side and another, Beatrice became Mrs. Kaufman and was enabled to devote more time to her hobbies— taxidermy and the teasing of blooded sheep. The Kaufman apartment on Canal Street is a Mecca for stuffed animals—oxen, beagles, caribou, cygnet, vermin of all kinds. And every morning between five and six, you will find her at the sheepery in Central Park, poking fun at the sheep, coaxing them toward her with a side of beef for bait and then burning their noses with a lighted cigarette; or giving them cross-town transfers that are a month old.

In spite of these activities, Mrs. Kaufman finds time for domesticity and social intrigue. She has adopted a daughter against the latter's better judgment. She is always on hand when George's pens need sharpening and remains near by till he has sharpened them. She is an expert contract-bridge player and lately was honored by an invitation to act as a fifth in a game with Milton C. Work. She can dance a Charleston or a Black Bottom in a manner worthy of Frank McIntyre. And her negro dialect stories have kept many a drawing-room in a state of stoicism.

Mrs. Kaufman is the perfect hostess. If a guest expresses a taste for Kirman rugs, the next time he enters her apartment he will trip over one of them. If he raves about Gobelin tapestries, Mrs. Kaufman will have some hung in a conspicuous spot on the occasion of his second visit. If he is crazy about Rembrandts, the walls will be reeking with them when he comes again. This, I should say, is the *ne plus ultra* of hospitality, and not so expensive as one might suppose, since very few people visit the place twice.

The bulk of Mrs. Kaufman's income derives, of course, from her hotels. She controls the Ritz, the Hermitage, the Mills, and the Navarre, and though capable deputies are in personal charge of all her holdings, it is her habit of dropping in on each one every day she is in town that has won her the nickname of "Little Boniface."

The Kaufmans have a summer camp in the Adirondacks, near Lake Placid. It was formerly owned by Boss Tweed, who built it entirely of knot-holes. When the real-estate man was showing it to Beatrice, she exclaimed:

"Why, I wouldn't think of buying a place so full of holes!"

"They are knot-holes," said the real-estate man.

"Well, they certainly look like it to me," retorted Beatrice.

However, the price was so reasonable that she made the purchase and has never regretted it. What the house lacked—sides, floors, partitions, and a roof—has been added on gradually until now it is one of the show places of the neighborhood, and when sightseers ask who lives there and are told "The George S. Kaufmans," they begin acting silly and playing all kinds of games.

Mrs. Kaufman belongs to the Junior League, the Union League, the American League, the Cotton States League, the Pacific Coast League, and the League of American Wheelmen. She has shaken hands with Presidents Pierce, Hayes, Taft, and Coolidge and some woman she met in front of the Algonquin, but there was a truck going by and she didn't catch her name; something like Cromwell or Dromwell.

She never forgets a face and George thinks she would have made a great politician.

"Don't you think your wife would have made a great politician?" he was asked not long ago.

"How about it, Bee?" he said jokingly, nudging her elbow.

Mrs. Kaufman is a great reader and idolizes the men and women who write books. The little girl, Ann, is named after her mother's favorite author, Nan Britton.

Your reporter, grudgingly ending a recent interview with her (not Nan Britton), remarked: "You ought to be a mighty proud woman, Mrs. Kaufman, when you think what you have made of yourself."

"Hush yo' foolin', big boy!" she replied. "I ain't nevah claim' to of made nuffin of mahse'f nohow. I owes evahthing to Hearn's an' I been mahty lucky."

Lucky! So was Lindy lucky, then, and Bobby Jones and Gene Tunney. And a man named Avery. Luck smiles on the worthy and it has smiled its sweetest on the worthiest of them all, Mrs. Peter Vischer.

SHORT PLAYS

THOMPSON'S VACATION

PLAY IN TWO ACTS

CHARACTERS

THOMPSON, *a plain citizen.*
HAINES, *another.*
DILLON, *another.*

ACT I

August 28. The smoking car of a city-bound suburban train. THOMPSON *is sitting alone.* HAINES *comes in, recognizes him and takes the seat beside him.*

HAINES: Hello there, Thompson.
THOMPSON: Hello, Mr. Haines.
HAINES: What's the good word?
THOMPSON: Well—
HAINES: How's business?
THOMPSON: I don't know. I've been on a vacation for two weeks.
HAINES: Where was you?
THOMPSON: Atlantic City.
HAINES: Where did you stop?
THOMPSON: At the Edgar.

718

HAINES: The Edgar! Who steered you to that joint?

THOMPSON: I liked it all right.

HAINES: Why didn't you go to the Wallace? Same prices and everything up to date. How did you happen to pick out a dirty old joint like the Edgar?

THOMPSON: I thought it was all right.

HAINES: What did you do to kill time down there?

THOMPSON: Oh, I swam and went to a couple of shows and laid around

HAINES: Didn't you go up in the air?

THOMPSON: No.

HAINES: That's the only thing they is to do in Atlantic City, is go up in the air. If you didn't do that, you didn't do nothing.

THOMPSON: I never been up.

HAINES: That's all they is to do down there, especially in August, when it's so hot.

THOMPSON: They was generally always a breeze.

HAINES: Yes, I know what that breeze is in August. It's like a blast out of a furnace. Did you go in any of them cabarets?

THOMPSON: Yes, I was in the Mecca and the Garden.

HAINES: Wasn't you in the La Marne?

THOMPSON: No.

HAINES: If you wasn't in the La Marne, you didn't see nothing.

THOMPSON: I had some real beer in the Mecca.

HAINES: Say, that stuff they give you in the Mecca is dishwater. They's only one place in Atlantic City to get real beer. That's the Wonderland. Didn't you make the Wonderland?

THOMPSON: No.

HAINES: Then you didn't have no real beer. Did you meet many dames?

THOMPSON: Only a couple of them. But they was pips!

HAINES: Pips! You don't see no real pips down there in August. The time to catch the pips down there is— well, June, July, September, May, or any time in the fall or winter or spring. You don't see them there in August. Did you go fishing?

THOMPSON: No.

HAINES: Oh, they's great fishing around there! If you didn't go fishing, you didn't do nothing.

THOMPSON (*rising*): Well, here we are.

HAINES: I think you're a sucker to pick out August for a vacation. May or June or September, that's the time for a vacation.

THOMPSON: Well, see you again.

ACT II

Four minutes later. A downtown subway express.
  THOMPSON *is hanging on a strap.* DILLON *enters and hangs on the next strap.*

DILLON: Hello there, Thompson.

THOMPSON: Hello.

DILLON: How's everything?

THOMPSON: All right, I guess.

DILLON: Ain't you been on a vacation?

THOMPSON: Yeah.

DILLON: What kind of a time did you have?

THOMPSON: Rotten.

DILLON: Where was you?

THOMPSON: Nowhere.

CURTAIN

THE BULL PEN

CAST OF CHARACTERS[1]

BILL CARNEY, *a pitcher, played by Al Ochs*
CY WALTERS, *a pitcher, played by Will Rogers*
JOE WEBB, *a Busher, played by Andy Toombes*

SCENE—*"Bull Pen" at the Polo Grounds during a game between the Yankees and Cleveland.* BILL *and* CY *are seated on empty boxes.*

JOE: What innings is it?

CY: Third.

JOE: What's the score?

CY: One and one. And in case you don't know who's playing, it's us and Cleveland. And you're in the American League.

JOE: I know what league I'm in and I know what league I wisht I was in. I wisht I was back in the Central League.

CY: Looks to me like you was going to get your wish.

JOE: They'll keep me longer than they will you.

CY: Well, I've got a good start on you. You only been here part of one season and I was here all last year besides.

JOE: Yes, but how many games did you pitch?

CY: Well, I pitched 154 games last year and about fifty so far this year. And I pitched 'em all right here where we're standing. Some guys gets all swelled up over pitching one no-hit game. Well, the Yankees has played over 200 games since I been with them and nobody's got a hit off me yet.

---

[1] As played in the *Ziegfeld Follies* of 1922.

JOE: I wisht I was where they paid some attention to a man.

CY: That's what I wished the first part of last season. But the last part of the season, I wished they'd ignore me entirely. I used to make ugly faces at Huggins in hopes he'd get mad and quit speaking to me. But just before every game he'd say, "Go down to the Bull Pen and warm up." *WARM UP!* Say, there may be better pitchers than me in this league, but there ain't none that's hotter.

BILL (*commenting on game*): Bob was lucky to get by that inning! Did you see that one Scotty grabbed off Speaker?

JOE: Them guys don't know how to pitch to Speaker.

CY (*gives him a look*): No? How would *you* pitch to him?

JOE: First I'd give him my fast one—

CY: Hold on! Now you're pitching to the next batter. Speaker's on third base.

JOE: How would he get to third base?

CY: He'd slide.

JOE: You ain't seen my fast one when I'm right. It goes zooy! (*Makes motion with hands.*)

CY: Yes, and after it bounced off Speaker's bat, it'd go zeet! (*Makes similar motion.*) Especially this ball they're using these days with a raisin in it.

BILL: The Babe's up. (*Without raising his voice.*) Come on, Babe! Bust one!

JOE: He wouldn't bust one if I was pitching!

CY: How would you pitch to *him*?

JOE: High and on the outside.

CY: And that's just where it'd go.

BILL: No, he popped up.

JOE: Just the same, I bet Ruth's glad I ain't with some other club.

Cy: He don't know you ain't.

Joe: I bet he don't break no home run record this year.

Cy: Look how long he was out!

Joe: Well, it was his own fault. I bet if I'd went barnstorming, Landis wouldn't of dast suspend *me* that long!

Cy: He wouldn't of suspended you at all. He wouldn't of never heard about it.

Bill: Coveleskie must *have* something in there. He made Baker pop up!

Joe: I wisht I could go in there to the bench.

Cy: What for?

Joe (*with a self-conscious smile*): Well, do you remember before the game, when I was up there throwing to Schang? Well, they was a swell dame come in and set down right behind our bench. She looked like a Follies dame. And she give me *some* smile!

Cy: She done well to keep from laughing outright.

Joe: She was trying to make me.

Cy: She was trying to make you out.

Joe: I bet if Huggins had of left me stay on the bench, I'd be all set by now.

Cy: Yes, and that's why Huggins don't let you stay on the bench. He told me the other day, he says, "Cy, old pal, I hope it won't bother you to have this gargoyle down there warming up with you all the time. But it's against the rules to have gals on the bench, and if he was there I simply couldn't keep them off." He says, "I've got a hard enough bunch to manage without adding Peggy Hopkins."

Joe: How do *you* know that's her name?

Cy: Oh, I seen her looking at you and I asked one of the ushers.

Joe: Peggy Hopkins! Do you know if she's married?

Cy: I can't keep track.

Joe: Do you s'pose her name's in the book?

Cy: Well, seems like I've seen it in print *somewheres*.

Joe (*as if to memorize it*): Peggy Hopkins.

Bill: Bob's wild. It's three and nothing on Sewell.

Cy (*to* Joe): You better cut loose a little, kid. This may be our day.

Joe: Not both of us.

Cy: Sure, providing he picks you first. (*Slight pause.*) But, listen, kid, if I was you I'd leave the dames alone. Wait till you've made good.

Joe: I ain't after no dames. But I can't help the looks they give me.

Cy: No more than you can help the looks *God* give you. And he certainly didn't spread himself.

Bill: He's walked Sewell.

Joe: The *gals* seem to think I look O. K.

Cy: How do you know?

Joe: The way they act. Do you remember that poor little kid in New Orleans?

Cy: What kid?

Joe: The telephone gal in the hotel. She was down to the depot when we went away. But I ducked her. And that dame in Philadelphia.

Cy: What do you owe *her*?

Joe: I don't owe you nothin', but she was out to the game every day, tryin' to flirt.

Cy: Oh, *that* woman!

Joe: What woman?

Cy: That's the woman that goes to the games in Philadelphia. You know those Philadelphia fans? Well, she's their sister.

Joe: I don't know who she is, but she certainly made eyes at me.

Cy: She don't mean to make eyes. That's a nervous disease. She's been looking at the Athletics for six years. But you want to quit thinking about the dames and pay attention to your work.

Joe: *I* pay attention to my work!

Cy: Well, at that, I can see you've made quite a study of the batters. You know how to pitch to Speaker and Ruth.

Joe: Yes, and some of them other high monkey monks.

Cy: Well, how would you go to work on George Sisler?

Joe: Say, that guy won't never get a hit off me.

Cy: I guess you're right. He told me one day that when he was through in the big league, he was through.

Bill: There goes Gardner. Another base on balls.

Joe: But there's one guy I *could* fool, is Sisler!

Cy: Oh, anybody could *fool* him.

Joe: Well, how would *you* fool him?

Cy: I'd say, "Hit this one, George." And then I'd throw him an orange. Then there's another way I bet I could fool him. I could say, "George, come out to the house to dinner to-night. My wife's a great cook. We live at 450 Riverside Drive." When he got there, he'd find out I don't live at that address, and besides, I ain't married.

Joe: Well, I'd like to get a chance at him. And another guy I'd like to pitch against is Cobb.

Cy: Irvin?

Joe: That ain't his name is it?

Cy: You mean the man that writes the outfield for Detroit. That's Irvin.

Joe: That's right, Irvin.

BILL: He hit O'Neill in the arm. The bases is choked, boys.

CY (*to* JOE): Put something on her, kid! If he can just get Coveleskie! (*Warming up at top speed.*) Listen, kid, if you get in, don't be scared to cut loose! You got nothing to lose.

JOE: Do you think it'll be me?

CY: Well, it's one of us.

BILL (*with feeling*): Damn! Damn! And he had a double play right in front of him. Cy! He's waving to you!

CY (*jumps up and tears off his sweater*): Get out of the way, boy! He wants me in there! (JOE, *dazed, gets out of his way and mournfully goes to the bench and sits down.* CY *throws one ball.*)

CY: I'm ready. (*He picks up his sweater and goes off-stage, carrying it on his arm.*)

JOE: A fine manager we're workin' for!

CURTAIN

QUADROON

A PLAY IN FOUR PELTS WHICH MAY ALL BE ATTENDED IN ONE DAY OR MISSED IN A GROUP

(AUTHOR'S NOTE: The characters were all born synonymously; that is, in the "S'uth," they are known as half-castes. The only time the play, or series of plays, was performed with a whole cast, it was stopped by a swarm of little black flies, which don't bite, but are annoying. One time, in Charlotte, Utah, I forget what did happen.

HIC

Part One of *The Quadroon*

CAST
(In Order to Confuse)

CHRISTINE, *his sister, played by Alla Nazimova*
LAVINIA, *her daughter, played by Alice Brady*
CASEY JONES, *a midwife, played by William A. Brady*

SCENE: *A Park Avenue Push-Wagon, Armistice Day, 1860.*

Luncheon Intermission of Half an Hour

The Roth Lunch

127 West Fifty-second Street

November 22, 1931

Special Luncheon, 65 Cents.

Chopped Tenderloin Steak
or Calves' Liver and Bacon.
Carrots Shoestring Potatoes String Beans
Choice of Desserts
Rice Pudding   Strawberry Tart
Tea, Coffee or Milk.

HAEC

Part Two of *The Quadroon*

CAST

CHRISTINE, *his sister, played by Alice Brady*
LAVINIA, *her daughter, played by Alla Nazimova*
FRANKIE AND JOHNNIE, *played by A. H. Woods*

SCENE: *Department of Plant and Structures. An evening in 1850.*

[CHRISTINE *and* LAVINIA *meet off-stage, dancing.*]

LAVINIA: Did you-all evah see me-all in *Hedda Gabler*?

CHRISTINE: Does yo'all mean *Hedda Gabler* by William Anthony McGuire?

LAVINIA: Yo'all done said zac'ly wot Ah'm drivin' at. How did yo'all lak me?

CHRISTINE: Well, Ah seen Mrs. Fiske.

FRANKIE AND JOHNNIE: Let's you and I run up to Elizabeth Arden's and free ourselves from fatigue with an Ardena Bath.

Dinner Intermission of One Hour and a Half[2]
Typical Dinner, $1.50

———

Medaillon of lobster au caviar
Grapefruit
Supreme of fresh fruit, Maraschino

---

[2] It will doubtless promote good fellowship and good service if, when entering the hotel's dining-room, you say to the man in charge: "Hello, Maître d'Hôtel."

Blue Point oyster cocktail
Fresh shrimp cocktail
or
Cream of lettuce, Parmentier
Clear green turtle, Amontillado
(*Choice*)
Filet of sole, Farci Isabella
Broiled Boston scrod, Maitre d'Hôtel
Tartelette of Fresh mushrooms,
Lucullus
Country sausages, apple sauce
Breaded spring lamb chop
with Bacon, tomato sauce
Chicken hash au Gratin
Roast sugar cured ham, cider sauce
Omelette Glacé aux Confitures
Cold—Fresh calf's tongue
with chow chow

———

Stewed celery or fresh string beans
Mashed or French fried potatoes

———

(*Choice*)
Pudding Creole   Coffee éclair
Assorted cakes
Vanilla, raspberry or chocolate
ice cream and cake

———

Delicious apple   Apple pie
French pastry   Coffee, Tea or Milk

*Make the Plaza Central
your New York Home During the
Entire Performance. Ask Arnold.*

HOC

Part Three of *The Quadroon*

CAST

LYNN FONTANNE, *a Mrs. Lunt, played by Grace George*
CASEY JONES, *a midwife, played by Bert Lahr*
FRANK CASE, *proprietor of the Algonquin, played by Alice Brady*

SCENE: *Jimmy Walker's Wardrobe Trunk.*

[THE MAYOR *and the* PRINCE OF WALES *meet outside the stage door, dancing.*]

THE MAYOR: New York is the richest market in the world.

THE PRINCE: Not only that, but the New York Theatre Market is an unrivalled concentration of spending power.

THE MAYOR: The New York Magazine Program reaches that market exclusively.

FRANK CASE: Pardon me, Officer, but can either of you boys play a cellophane?

Passengers will Please not Linger in Washrooms until Other Passengers Have Completed Their Toilets.

HUJUS

Part Four of *The Quadroon*

CAST

CHRISTINE, *her sister, played by Alla Nazimova*
LAVINIA, *their little one, played by Alice Brady*
FRED ASTAIRE, *a hoofer, played by Morris Gest*

SCENE: *An Ambuscade in the Astor Lobby.*

[FRED *and* LAVINIA *dance.*]
LAVINIA: The minute you try Pebeco Tooth Paste you know by its "bitey" tang that here is a tooth paste that really "gets somewheres."
FRED: Will you love me always?
LAVINIA: As long as you keep kissable.
[*She kills her with an oyster fork.*]

(*Leave your ticket check with an usher and your car will come right to your seat.*)

DINNER BRIDGE

CHARACTERS

CROWLEY, *the foreman*
AMOROSI, *an Italian laborer*
TAYLOR, *a Negro laborer*
CHAMALES, *a Greek laborer*
HANSEN, *a Scandinavian laborer*

LLANUZA, *a Mexican laborer*
THE INQUISITIVE WAITER
THE DUMB WAITER

PROGRAM NOTE

This playlet is an adaptation from the Wallachian of Willie Stevens. For a great many years, Long Islanders and Manhattanites have been wondering why the Fifty-ninth Street Bridge was always torn up at one or more points. Mr. Stevens heard the following legend: that Alexander Woollcott, chief engineer in charge of the construction of the bridge, was something of a practical joker; that on the day preceding the completion of the bridge, he was invited to dinner by his wife's brother; that he bought a loaded cigar to give his brother-in-law after the meal, and that the cigar dropped out of his pocket and rolled under the unfinished surface planking. Ever since, gangs of men have been ripping up the surface of the bridge in search of the cigar, but an article the shape of a cigar is apt to roll in any and all directions. This is what has made it so difficult to find the lost article, and the (so far) vain search is the theme of Mr. Stevens' playlet.—*Adapter.*

SCENE: *An area under repair on the Fifty-ninth Street Bridge. Part of the surface has been torn up, and, at the curtain's rise, three of the men are tearing up the rest of it with picks. Shovels, axes, and other tools are scattered around the scene. Two men are fussing with a concrete mixer. Crowley is bossing the job. Crowley and the laborers are dressed in dirty working clothes. In the foreground is a flat-topped truck or wagon. The two waiters, dressed in waiters' jackets, dickies, etc., enter the scene, one of them carrying a tray with cocktails and the other a tray with caviar, etc. The laborers cease their work and consume these appetizers. The noon whistle blows. The waiters bring in a white table cloth and spread it over the truck or wagon. They also distribute six place cards and six chairs, or camp stools, around the truck, but the "table" is left bare of eating implements.*

FIRST WAITER, *to* CROWLEY: Dinner is served.

(CROWLEY *and the laborers move toward the table.*)

TAYLOR, *to* AMOROSI: I believe I am to take you in.

(AMOROSI *gives* TAYLOR *his arm and* TAYLOR *escorts him to the table. The laborers all pick up the place cards to find out where they are to sit.*)

CROWLEY, *to* AMOROSI: Here is your place, Mr. Amorosi. And Taylor is right beside you.

(*Note to producer: Inasmuch as* TAYLOR *and* AMOROSI *do most of the talking, they ought to face the audience. In spite of their nationalities, the laborers are to talk in correct Crowninshield dinner English, except that occasionally, say every fourth or fifth speech, whoever is talking suddenly bursts into dialect, either his own or Jewish or Chinese or what you will.*

All find their places and sit down. The two waiters now re-enter, each carrying one dinner pail. One serves CROWLEY *and the other serves* AMOROSI. *The serving is done by the waiter's removing the cover of the pail and holding it in front of the diner. The latter looks into the pail and takes out some viand with his fingers. First he takes out, say, a sandwich. The waiter then replaces the cover on the pail and exits with it. All the laborers are served in this manner, two at a time, from their own dinner pails. As soon as one of them has completed the sandwich course, the waiter brings him the pail again and he helps himself to a piece of pie or an apple or orange. But the contents of all the pails should be dif-*

*ferent, according to the diner's taste. The serving goes
on all through the scene, toward the end of which everyone is served with coffee from the cups on top of the
pails.*)

CROWLEY (*to* AMOROSI): Well, Mr. Amorosi, welcome to the Fifty-ninth Street Bridge.

AMOROSI: Thank you, I really feel as if this was
where I belonged.

HANSEN (*politely*): How is that?

AMOROSI: On account of my father. He was among
the pioneer Fifty-ninth Street Bridge destroyers. He had
the sobriquet of Giacomo "Rip-Up-the-Bridge" Amorosi.

TAYLOR (*sotto voce, aside to* HANSEN): This fellow
seems to be quite a card!

LLANUZA: I wonder if you could tell me the approxi-
mate date when your father worked here.

AMOROSI: Why, yes. The bridge was completed on
the fifth day of August, 1909. So that would make it the
sixth day of August, 1909, when father started ripping
it up.

TAYLOR (*aside to* HANSEN, *in marked Negro dialect*):
I repeats my assertation that this baby is quite a card!

AMOROSI (*in Jewish dialect*): But I guess it must be a
lot more fun nowadays, with so much motor traffic to
pester.

TAYLOR: And all the funerals. I sure does have fun
with the funerals.

CROWLEY (*in Irish brogue*): Taylor has a great time
with the funerals.

HANSEN, CHAMALES, *and* LLANUZA (*in unison*):
Taylor has a great time with the funerals.

AMOROSI (*to* TAYLOR): How do you do it?

TAYLOR (*in dialect*): Well, you see, I'm flagman for
this outfit. When I get out and wave my flag, whatever
is coming, it's got to stop. When I see a funeral coming,

I let the hearse go by and stop the rest of the parade. Then when I see another funeral coming, I stop their hearse and let the rest of *their* procession go on. I keep doing this all morning to different funerals and by the time they get to Forest Hills, the wrong set of mourners is following the wrong hearse. It generally always winds up with the friends and relatives of the late Mr. Cohen attending the final obsequies of Mrs. Levinsky.

CROWLEY, HANSEN, CHAMALES, *and* LLANUZA (*in unison*): Taylor has a great time with the funerals.

AMOROSI: I'm a *trumpet* medium myself.

TAYLOR (*aside to* HANSEN): This boy will turn out to be quite a card!

LLANUZA: Why do you always have to keep repairing it?

CROWLEY: What do you mean, what's the matter?

LLANUZA: Why do they always have to keep repairing it?

AMOROSI: Perhaps Mr. Crowley has the repairian rights.

TAYLOR (*guffawing and slapping* HANSEN *or* CHAMALES *on the back*): What did I tell you?

LLANUZA (*in dialect*): But down in Mexico, where I come from, they don't keep repairing the same bridge.

AMOROSI (*to* LLANUZA): If you'll pardon a newcomer. Mr. —, I don't believe I got your name.

LLANUZA: Llanuza.

AMOROSI: If you'll pardon a newcomer, Mr. Keeler, I want to say that if the United States isn't good enough for you, I'd be glad to start a subscription to send you back to where you came from.

LLANUZA: I was beginning to like you, Mr. Amorosi.

AMOROSI: You get that right out of your mind, Mr. Barrows. I'm married; been married twice. My first wife died.

HANSEN: How long were you married to her?

AMOROSI: Right up to the time she died.

CHAMALES (*interrupting*): Mr. Amorosi, you said you had been married twice.

AMOROSI: Yes, sir. My second wife is a Swiss girl.

HANSEN: Is she here with you?

AMOROSI: No, she's in Switzerland, in jail. She turned out to be a murderer.

CROWLEY: When it's a woman, you call her a murderess.

TAYLOR: And when it's a Swiss woman, you call her a Swiss-ess.

(*One of the waiters is now engaged in serving AMOROSI with his dinner pail.*)

WAITER, *to* AMOROSI: Whom did she murder?

(*WAITER exits hurriedly without seeming to care to hear the answer.*)

AMOROSI (*after looking wonderingly at the disappearing WAITER*): What's the matter with *him?*

TAYLOR: He's been that way for years—a born questioner but he hates answers.

CROWLEY: Just the same, the rest of us would like to know whom your wife murdered.

TAYLOR, HANSEN, CHAMALES, *and* LLANUZA (*to* CROWLEY): Speak for yourself. We don't want to know.

CROWLEY: Remember, boys, I'm foreman of this outfit. (*Aside to* AMOROSI.) Who was it?

AMOROSI: (*Whispers name in his ear.*)

CROWLEY: I don't believe I knew him.

AMOROSI: Neither did my wife.

CROWLEY: Why did she kill him?

AMOROSI: Well, you see, over in Italy and Switzerland, it's different from, say, Chicago. When they find a man murdered over in those places, they generally try to learn who it is and put his name in the papers. So my wife was curious about this fellow's identity and she figured that the easiest way to get the information was to pop him.

TAYLOR: I'm a *trumpet* medium myself.

(WAITER *enters and serves one of the laborers from his dinner pail.*)

WAITER: How long is she in for?

(WAITER *exits hurriedly without waiting for the answer.* AMOROSI *again looks after him wonderingly.*)

HANSEN (*to* AMOROSI): Did you quarrel much?

AMOROSI: Only when we were together.

TAYLOR: I was a newspaper man once myself.

LLANUZA (*skeptically*): You! What paper did you work on?

TAYLOR: It was a tabloid—The Porno-graphic.

(WAITER *enters to serve somebody.*)

WAITER, *to* TAYLOR: Newspaper men must have lots of interesting experiences. (*Exits without waiting for a response.*)

AMOROSI: I suppose you've all heard this story—

THE OTHER LARORERS (*in unison*): Is it a golf story?

AMOROSI: No.

THE OTHERS (*resignedly*): Tell it.

AMOROSI (*in dialect*): It seems there was a woman went into a photographer's and asked the photographer if he took pictures of children.

(WAITER *enters to serve somebody.*)

WAITER: How does it end? (WAITER *exits hurriedly.*)

AMOROSI: She asked the photographer if he took pictures of children. "Why, yes, madam," replied the photographer—

TAYLOR: He called her "madam."

AMOROSI: The photographer told her yes, that he did take pictures of children. "And how much do you charge?" inquired the madam, and the photographer replied, "Three dollars a dozen." "Well," said the woman, "I guess I'll have to come back later. I've only got eleven."

(*The other laborers act just as if no story had been told.*)

LLANUZA: Down in Mexico, where I come from, they don't keep repairing the same bridge.

TAYLOR (*to* HANSEN): Can you imitate birds?

HANSEN: No.

TAYLOR, *to* CHAMALES: Can you imitate birds?

CHAMALES: No.

TAYLOR: Can anybody here imitate birds?

THE OTHER LABORERS (*in unison*): No.

TAYLOR: *I* can do it. Long before I got a job on this bridge, while I was helping tear up the crosstown streets, I used to entertain the boys all day, imitating birds.

AMOROSI: What kind of birds can you imitate?

TAYLOR: All kinds.

AMOROSI: Well, what do you say we play some other game?

CROWLEY (*rising*): Gentlemen, we are drawing near to the end of this dinner and I feel we should not leave the table until some one has spoken a few words of welcome to our newcomer, Mr. Amorosi. Myself, I am not much of a talker. (*Pauses for a denial.*)

TAYLOR: You said a full quart.

CROWLEY: Therefore, I will call on the man who is second to me in length of service on the Fifty-ninth Street Bridge, Mr. Harvey Taylor. (*Sits down.*)

TAYLOR (*rising amid a dead silence*): Mr. Foreman, Mr. Amorosi, and gentlemen: Welcoming Mr. Amorosi to our little group recalls vividly to my mind an experience of my own on the levee at New Orleans before Prohibition. (*He bursts suddenly into Negro dialect, mingled with Jewish.*) In those days my job was to load and unload those great big bales of cotton and my old mammy used to always be there at the dock to take me in her lap and croon me to sleep.

(WAITER *enters, serves somebody with coffee.*)

WAITER: What was the experience you was going to tell? (*Exits hurriedly.*)

TAYLOR: It was in those days that I studied bird life and learned to imitate the different bird calls. (*Before they can stop him, he gives a bird call.*) The finch. (*The others pay no attention. He gives another call.*) A Dowager. (TAYLOR *is pushed forcibly into his seat.*)

AMOROSI (*rising to respond*): Mr. Foreman and gentlemen: I judge from Mr. Taylor's performance that the practice of imitating birds is quite popular in America. Over where I come from, we often engage in the pastime of mimicking public buildings. For example (*he gives a cry*). The American Express Company's office at Rome. (*He gives another cry.*) The Vatican. (*He gives another cry.*) Hotel McAlpin. (*A whistle blows, denoting that the dinner hour is over.*)

CROWLEY (*rising*): Shall we join the ladies?

(*All rise and resume the work of tearing up the bridge. The waiters enter to remove the table cloth and chairs.*)

WAITER (*the more talkative one*): How many Mack trucks would you guess had crossed this bridge in the last half hour? (*He exits without waiting for a reply.*)

CURTAIN

CORA, OR FUN AT A SPA

AN EXPRESSIONIST DRAMA OF LOVE AND DEATH AND SEX—
IN THREE ACTS

CHARACTERS

(In the order in which I admire them.)

A FRIEND OF THE PRESIDENT.
PLAGUE BENNETT, *an embryo steeplejack.*
ELSA, *their ward.*
MANAGER OF THE PUMP ROOM.
A MAN WHO LOOKS A GOOD DEAL LIKE HEYWOOD
      BROUN.
MRS. TYLER.[1]
CORA.
POULTRY, GAME IN SEASON, ETC.

ACT I

A Pharmacy at a Spa. The Proprietor is at present out of the city and Mrs. Tyler is taking his place. She is a woman who seems to have been obliged to leave school while in the eighth grade. Plague Bennett enters. His mother named him Plague as tribute to her husband, who died of it. As Plague enters, Mrs. Tyler is seen replacing a small vial in a case behind the counter.

PLAGUE: Well Mrs. T.

MRS. TYLER: "Mrs. T." indeed! I see you're still the same old Plague!

---

[1] Mrs. Tyler appears only when one of the other characters is out of the city.

PLAGUE: What are you doing?

MRS. TYLER: What do I look like I was doing, spearing eels? I'm just putting this bottle of germs back in its place. The little fellows were trying to escape. They said they didn't like it here. I said, "Don't bacilli!"

(A FRIEND OF THE PRESIDENT enters.)

PLAGUE: Hello, Doctor.

(He calls him Doctor.)

FRIEND OF THE PRESIDENT (as if to himself): That old devil sea!

PLAGUE: Well, Doctor, I'm going to Washington tomorrow.

(He repeatedly calls him Doctor.)

FRIEND OF THE PRESIDENT: What of it?

PLAGUE: Well, they tell me you and the President are pretty close.

FRIEND OF THE PRESIDENT: He is.

END OF FIRST ACT

ACT II

A poultry yard at a Spa. The chairs and tables are in disarray as if a blotter salesman had been making his rounds. THE MANAGER OF THE PUMP ROOM is out of the city and the poultry are being fed by MRS. TYLER. A DEAD RINGER FOR DAVID BELASCO enters, crosses stage.

MRS. TYLER: You old master you! (Aside.) I can never tell whether he's in first speed or reverse.

(DEAD RINGER FOR DAVID BELASCO exits. MANAGER OF THE PUMP ROOM returns to the city unexpectedly and MRS. TYLER goes into pictures. MANAGER OF THE PUMP

Room *stands in center stage as if he had been everywhere.*)

Manager of the Pump Room (*Aside*): I wonder what is keeping Elsa. (*Looks right.*) Ah! There she comes now, dancing as usual!

(Elsa *enters left, fooling him completely. She is not even dancing. She looks as if she had taken a bath.*)

Elsa: Well——

Manager of the Pump Room (*turns and sees her*): Elsa! I was just thinking about you. I was wondering what was keeping you.

Elsa: I presume you mean who.

(*The curtain is lowered and raised to see if it will work.*)

Manager of the Pump Room: What's the difference between that curtain and Ziegfeld?

Elsa: It works. And that reminds me that I just met a man who looks something like Heywood Broun. Here he comes now, dancing as usual.

(A Man Who Looks A Good Deal Like Heywood Broun *enters.*)

Manager of the Pump Room (*aside*): I'll say so!

Man Who Looks A Good Deal Like Heywood Broun: What's that?

Manager of the Pump Room: Why, this young lady was just saying she thought you looked something like Heywood Broun.

Man Who Etc. (*throwing confetti in all directions*): She's conservative.

END OF SECOND ACT

ACT III

A Mixed Grill at a Spa. Two MILCH COWS sit at a table in one corner, playing draughts. In another corner is seated a gigantic ZEBU.

FIRST MILCH COW: Don't you feel a draught?

SECOND MILCH COW: No. But we'd better be going. That gigantic zebu is trying to make us.

FIRST MILCH COW: He thinks he is a cow catcher.

SECOND MILCH COW (*as they rise*): They say there are still a great many buffaloes in Yellowstone Park.

FIRST MILCH COW: So I herd.

(*The MILCH COWS go out, followed at a distance by the ZEBU. CORA enters. She is dressed in the cat's pajamas. She looks as if she had once gone on an excursion to the Delaware Water Gap.*)

CORA (*aside*): I wonder if it could be!

(*PLAGUE BENNETT and A FRIEND OF THE PRESIDENT enter in time to overhear her remark.*)

PLAGUE (*to FRIEND OF THE PRESIDENT*): Go on without me, Doctor. (*He still calls him Doctor. FRIEND OF THE PRESIDENT exits and PLAGUE turns to CORA.*) You wonder if it could be who?

CORA: Why, I just met a man who looks a little like Heywood Broun. Here he comes now, dancing as usual.

(*A MAN WHO LOOKS A GOOD DEAL LIKE HEYWOOD BROUN enters.*)

PLAGUE (*aside*): He does, at that!

MAN WHO ETC.: At what?

PLAGUE: This little lady was just saying she thought you looked a little like Heywood Broun.

MAN WHO ETC.: A little! She's putting it mildly!

(*Finds he is out of confetti and exits. A poisoned rat dashes into the open air, seeking water.*)

PLAGUE: That rat acts like he was poisoned.

CORA: God! You ought to saw me last night!

END OF THIRD ACT

ABEND DI ANNI NOUVEAU

A PLAY IN FIVE ACTS

CHARACTERS

ST. JOHN ERVINE, *an immigrant.*

WALTER WINCHELL, *a nun.*

HEYWOOD BROUN, *an usher at Roxy's.*

DOROTHY THOMPSON, *a tackle.*

THEODORE DREISER, *a former Follies girl.*

H. L. MENCKEN, *a kleagle in the Moose.*

MABEL WILLEBRANDT, *secretary of the League of American Wheelman.*

BEN HECHT, *a taxi starter.*

JOHN ROACH STRATON, *a tap dancer.*

CARL LAEMMLE, *toys and games, sporting goods, outing flannels.*

ANNE NICHOLS, *a six-day bicyclist.*

ACT I

A hired hall. It is twenty-five minutes of nine on New Year's Eve. A party, to which all the members of the cast were invited, is supposed to have begun at thirty-four minutes after eight. A WAITER enters on a horse and finds all the guests dead, their bodies riddled with bullets and frightfully garbled. He goes to the telephone.

WAITER *(telephoning)*: I want a policeman. I want to report a fire. I want an ambulance.

(He tethers his mount and lies down on the hors d'oeuvres. The curtain is lowered and partially destroyed to denote the passage of four days. Two POLICEMEN *enter, neither having had any idea that the other would come. They find the* WAITER *asleep and shake him. He wakes and smilingly points at the havoc.)*

WAITER: Look at the havoc.

FIRST POLICEMAN: This is the first time I ever seen a havoc.

SECOND POLICEMAN: It's an inside job, I think.

FIRST POLICEMAN: You WHAT?

WAITER: The trouble now is that we'll have to recast the entire play. Every member of the cast is dead.

FIRST POLICEMAN: Is that unusual?

SECOND POLICEMAN: When did it happen?

WAITER: When did what happen?

SECOND POLICEMAN: I've forgotten.

END OF ACT I

ACT II

The interior of an ambulance. Three men named LOUIE BREESE *are playing bridge with an* INTERNE. *The* INTERNE *is* LOUIE BREESE'S *partner.* LOUIE *leads a club. The* INTERNE *trumps it.*

BREESE: Kindly play interne.

INTERNE: I get you men confused.

Breese: I'm not confused.

The Other Two Breeses: Neither of us is confused.

(*They throw the* Interne *onto Seventh Avenue. An East Side* Gangster, *who was being used as a card table, gets up and stretches.*)

Gangster: Where are we at?

Breese: Was you the stretcher we was playing on?

Gangster: Yes.

Breese: There's only three of us now. Will you make a fourt'?

Gangster: There's no snow.

END OF ACT II

ACTS III, IV, AND V

A *one-way street in Jeopardy. Two* Snail-Gunders *enter from the right, riding a tricycle. They shout their wares.*

First Snail-Gunder: Wares! Wares!

A Newsboy: Wares who?

First Snail-Gunder: Anybody. That is, anybody who wants their snails gunded.

(*Three men suddenly begin to giggle. It is a secret, but they give the impression that one of them's mother runs a waffle parlor. They go off the stage still giggling. Two Broadway theatrical* Producers, *riding pelicans, enter almost nude.*)

First Producer: Have you got a dime?

Second Producer: What do you think I am, a stage hand?

First Producer: Have you seen my new farce?

Second Producer: No. I was out of town that night.

END OF ACTS III, IV, AND V

CLEMO UTI—"THE WATER LILIES"

CHARACTERS

PADRE, *a Priest.*
SETHSO
GETHSO } *both twins.*
WAYSHATTEN, *a shepherd's boy.*
TWO CAPITALISTS.[1]
WAMA TAMMISCH, *her daughter.*
KLEMA, *a janitor's third daughter.*
KEVELA, *their mother, afterwards their aunt.*

[TRANSLATOR'S NOTE: *This show was written as if people were there to see it.*]

ACT I

The Outskirts of a Parchesi Board. People are wondering what has become of the discs. They quit wondering and sit up and sing the following song.

CHORUS:
> What has become of the discs?
> What has become of the discs?
> We took them at our own risks,
> But what has become of the discs?

(WAMA *enters from an exclusive waffle parlor. She exits as if she had had waffles.*)

ACTS II & III

(*These two acts were thrown out because nothing seemed to happen.*)

---

[1] NOTE: The two Capitalists don't appear in this show.

ACT IV

A silo. Two RATS *have got in there by mistake. One of them seems diseased. The other looks at him. They go out. Both* RATS *come in again and wait for a laugh. They don't get it, and go out.* WAMA *enters from an off-stage barn. She is made up to represent the Homecoming of Casanova. She has a fainting spell. She goes out.*

KEVELA: Where was you born?

PADRE: In Adrian, Michigan.

KEVELA: Yes, but I thought I was confessing to you.

(The Padre goes out on an old-fashioned high-wheel bicycle. He acts as if he had never ridden many of them. He falls off and is brought back. He is in pretty bad shape.)

ACT V

A COUPLE OF SALESMEN *enter. They are trying to sell Portable Houses. The rest of the cast don't want Portable Houses.*

REST OF THE CAST: We don't want Portable Houses.

(The SALESMEN *become hysterical and walk off-stage left.)*

KEVELA: What a man!

WAYSHATTEN *(the Shepherd's Boy)*: Why wasn't you out there this morning to help me look after my sheep?

CHORUS OF ASSISTANT SHEPHERDS:

Why did you lay there asleep
When you should of looked after his sheep?
Why did you send telegrams
When you should of looked after his lambs?

Why did you sleep there, so old,
   When you should of looked after his fold?
SETHSO: Who is our father?
GETHSO: What of it? We're twins, ain't we?
WAMA: Hush, clemo uti (*the Water Lilies*).

(*Two queels enter, overcome with water lilies. They
both make fools of themselves. They don't seem to
have any self-control. They quiver. They want to play
the show over again, but it looks useless.*)

SHADES

I GASPIRI

(*The Upholsterers*)

A DRAMA IN THREE ACTS

Adapted from the Bukovinan of Casper
Redmonda

CHARACTERS

IAN OBRI, *a blotter salesman.*
JOHAN WASPER, *his wife.*
GRETA, *their daughter.*
HERBERT SWOPE, *a nonentity.*
FFENA, *their daughter, later their wife.*
EGSO, *a pencil guster.*
TONO, *a typical wastebasket.*

ACT I

A public street in a bathroom. A man named Tupper has evidently just taken a bath. A man named Brindle is now taking a bath. A man named Newburn comes out of the faucet which has been left running. He exits through the exhaust. Two strangers to each other meet on the bath mat.

FIRST STRANGER: Where was you born?

SECOND STRANGER: Out of wedlock.

FIRST STRANGER: That's a mighty pretty country around there.

SECOND STRANGER: Are you married?

FIRST STRANGER: I don't know. There's a woman living with me, but I can't place her.

(Three outsiders named Klein go across the stage three times. They think they are in a public library. A woman's cough is heard off-stage left.)

A NEW CHARACTER: Who is that cough?

TWO MOORS: That is my cousin. She died a little while ago in a haphazard way.

A GREEK: And what a woman she was!

(The curtain is lowered for seven days to denote the lapse of a week.)

ACT III

The Lincoln Highway. Two bearded glue lifters are seated at one side of the road.

(TRANSLATOR'S NOTE: The principal industry in Phlace is hoarding hay. Peasants sit alongside of a road on which hay wagons are likely to pass. When a hay wagon does pass, the hay hoarders leap from their points

of vantage and help themselves to a wisp of hay. On an average a hay hoarder accumulates a ton of hay every four years. This is called Mah Jong.)

FIRST GLUE LIFTER: Well, my man, how goes it?
SECOND GLUE LIFTER: (*Sings "My Man," to show how it goes.*)
(*Eight realtors cross the stage in a friendly way. They are out of place.*)

CURTAIN

TAXIDEA AMERICANA

A PLAY IN SIX ACTS

Translated from the Mastoid by
Ring W. Lardner

CHARACTERS

FRED RULLMAN, *an acorn huckster.*
OLD CHLOE, *their colored mammy.*
THOMAS GREGORY, *a poltroon.*
MRS. GREGORY, *his mother, afterward his wife.*
PHOEBE, *engaged to* CHLOE.
PROF. SCHWARTZ, *instructor in Swiss at Wisconsin.*
BUDDY, *their daughter.*
STUDENTS, *policemen, members of the faculty, sailors, etc.*
TIME—*The present.*
PLACE—*Madison, Wisconsin.*

ACT I

In front of the library. Two students in the agricultural college creep across the stage with a seed in their hands. They are silent, as they cannot place one another. DURAND and VON TILZER come down the library steps and stand with their backs to the audience as if in a quandary.

DURAND: Any news from home?

(*They go off stage left. SENATOR LAFOLLETTE enters from right and practices sliding to base for a few moments. RUBY BARRON comes down the library steps.*)

RUBY: Hello, Senator. What are you practicing, sliding to base?

(*The SENATOR goes out left. RUBY does some tricks with cards and re-enters the library completely baffled. Two students in the pharmacy college, PAT and MIKE, crawl on stage from left and fill more than one prescription. On the second refrain PAT takes the obbligato.*)

PAT: I certainly feel sorry for people on the ocean tonight.

MIKE: What makes you think so?

PAT: You can call me whatever you like as long as you don't call me down.

(*They laugh.*)

CURTAIN

(NOTE: *Acts II, III, and IV are left out through an oversight.*)

ACT V

Camp Randall. It is just before the annual game between Wisconsin and the Wilmerding School for the Blind. The Wisconsin band has come on the field and the cheer leaders are leading the Wisconsin battle hymn.

CHORUS:

Far above Cayuga's waters with its waves of blue,
On Wisconsin, Minnesota and Bully for old Purdue.
Notre Dame, we yield to thee! Ohio State, hurrah!
We'll drink a cup o' kindness yet in praise of auld
    Nassau!

(The Wilmerding rooters applaud and then sing their own song.)

CHORUS:

We are always there on time!
We are the Wilmerding School for the Blind!
Better backfield, better line!
We are the Wilmerding School for the Blind!
Yea!

(Coach Ryan of Wisconsin appears on the field fully dressed and announces that the game is postponed to permit Referee Birch to take his turn in the barber's chair. The crowd remains seated till the following Tuesday, when there is a general tendency to go home.)

CURTAIN

ACT III

(NOTE: *The coaches suddenly decide to send in Act III in place of Act VI. A livery barn in Stoughton. Slam*

Anderson, a former Wisconsin end, is making faces at the horses and they are laughing themselves sick. Slam goes home. Enter DR. BONIFACE, *the landlord of a switch engine on the Soo lines. From the other direction,* FARMER HOOKLE *enters on a pogo stick.*)

DR. BONIFACE: Hello, there, Hookle! I hear you are specializing in hogs.

HOOKLE: I don't know where you heard it, but it's the absolute truth.

DR. BONIFACE: Well, do you have much luck with your hogs?

HOOKLE: Oh, we never play for money.

CURTAIN

A partial list of other volumes in the
Viking Portable Library
appears on the next two pages.

THE VIKING PORTABLE LIBRARY

1. AS YOU WERE: A PORTABLE LIBRARY OF AMERICAN PROSE AND POETRY. *Edited by Alexander Woollcott.*

2. THE PORTABLE STEINBECK. *Selected by Pascal Covici. Introduction by Lewis Gannett.*

3. THE TRIUMPH OF LIFE: POEMS OF THE SPIRIT. *Edited by Horace Gregory.*

4. THE PORTABLE DOROTHY PARKER. *Introduction by W. Somerset Maugham.*

5. THE PORTABLE WORLD BIBLE. *Edited by Robert O. Ballou.*

6. THE PORTABLE HEMINGWAY. *Edited by Malcolm Cowley.*

7. SIX NOVELS OF THE SUPERNATURAL. *Edited by Edward Wagenknecht.*

8. THE PORTABLE SHAKESPEARE.

9. THE PORTABLE READER'S COMPANION. *Edited by Louis Kronenberger.*

10. THE PORTABLE CARL VAN DOREN.

11. THE PORTABLE WALT WHITMAN. *Edited by Mark Van Doren.*

12. THE PORTABLE POE. *Edited by Philip Van Doren Stern.*

13. THE PORTABLE MURDER BOOK. *Edited by Joseph Henry Jackson.*

14. THE PORTABLE F. SCOTT FITZGERALD. *Chosen by Dorothy Parker. Introduction by John O'Hara.*

15. THE PORTABLE NOVELS OF SCIENCE. *Edited by Donald A. Wollheim.*